Dedication to the Team

My wife, family (immediate and extended), staff, friends, volunteers, and supporters are the real people who make this book happen. No one ever truly succeeds or suffers alone.

ACKNOWLEDGMENTS

To my wife, Dr. Melodie Sterrett, whose sacrifice is immeasurable. Despite demanding schedules, ceaseless travel, and overwhelming pressure, her inspiration and faithfulness is the substance of much of what I live and present.

Bob Smietana proved to be a gift from God. His down-to-earth, easy manner and diligent efforts brought this book into being. He helped me translate horse terminology for the average reader.

Literary agent Janet Kobobel Grant and Editorial Director Tony Collins of Lion Hudson provided the professional experience and confidence to get this story told.

Thanks also to a host of photographers. Charlie Hilton is a photographer above par, and a man of generous spirit. Donnie Rosie was not only resourceful with photos, but believed in this project before I did. Thanks. Photos were also supplied by Caleb Martin, Hannah O'Brien, Summer Poche, and Laura Clawson.

I also owe a deep debt of gratitude to those who have provided horses for this ministry. Warren and Mary Davis continued in the vein of her parents, J.W. and Betty Bailey, of providing quality stock for the ministry. Berry, Spark, and Romeo are among them. Spotlite is from the home of Benham and Louise Stewart, owners of Singing Pines Plantation and breeders of world-champion horses. Thousands of other horses were provided through our Sermon on the Mount hosts throughout the years.

May the men and women who traveled with Sermon on the Mount over the years as my assistants receive an eternal reward for their investment.

Through the years, Ward Studebaker had the most significant impact on my horse training values, starting with my university experience. Countless contributors, including Doug Milholland, John Lyons, and Kathleen Kronk, have had an encouraging influence.

I am grateful for associates who took time out of their busy schedules to read and add their endorsement to this book: Dan T. Cathy, Jane Graham, Bob Kobielush, Les Steckel, Jesse and Stacy Westfall, and Dr. Todd Williams.

There are countless others whose behind-the-scenes sacrifices are noteworthy, but let it be said on behalf of them and of myself that all credit really belongs to God. For apart from a relationship with God through Jesus Christ, we can do nothing.

FOREWORD

This is more than a book about horses, as one might suppose. It is a story about life and hope: hope that prevails in the unknown, hope that prevails in adversity, and hope that prevails even through death itself.

It provokes the question of how hope can prevail and on what basis. Is it possible to have hope, even joy, amidst great trials in life? The essence of this story is to look at some of life's perplexing circumstances through the eyes of a horse. One can only imagine the feelings a horse might have when he is corralled, roped, saddled, harnessed, and ridden or driven for the first time.

In each of our lives, there are circumstances, people, and situations that can and do provoke all of us to fear, dismay, and even rebellion like a horse. It is my hope that you will gain a fresh perspective and be empowered to respond more effectively and successfully to those things which tend to steal away your hope.

As a counselor, I never expect anyone to really make any substantial change unless they can find a sound and trustworthy basis for renewed hope. This also is true in the life of a horse. Yet, like his peers, he is prone to believe that hope comes from escaping the rider, the bridle, or the fence.

The hope of a true and lasting reward is essential in capturing motivation. When we understand these essentials, we discover the keys to confidence, power, and seamless oneness. I trust that the life lessons of this story will result in a new and lasting hope for you.

CHAPTER 1

DO YOU TRUST ME?

IT STARTED OUT as an ordinary trail ride.

In April 2003, I set out with Spotlight, a young Quarter Horse stallion I'd been training, to get some exercise. He'd been in a trailer most of the previous day, as we were on our way from our ranch in Spring Creek, Pennsylvania to Kansas City, Missouri, to take part in an Equus America event, run by the trainer John Lyons. Along the way, we stopped to visit a friend, who'd invited me to speak at a gathering she had organized.

Spotlight was about four at the time, but had only been in training a few months. He's an unusual case. He grew up at the Singing Pines Plantation in Glenwood, Georgia, and I'd first seen him not long after he was born. His parents were both dynamic horses, and much was expected of this young colt. On the day of his birth, Spotlight looked perfect. He had a golden coat, a white mane and tail, and seemed strong and healthy.

But there was one problem. On his side was a large white spot—as if someone had turned a spotlight on him. That discoloration made him, in essence, worthless. The spot disqualified him from being registered as a Quarter Horse, and while he could be registered as a Paint Horse, he would be an unlikely Paint Stallion, because of his Quarter Horse bloodlines.

So for his first three years, Spotlight was left on his own. He was well fed and cared for, but had no training. He wasn't trained to lead or to ride, or shown how to do many of the useful tasks horses can accomplish. He had an even-tempered personality and was well loved, but no one knew exactly what to do with him.

His owners, who were friends of ours, offered to lend Spotlight to me for a Sermon on the Mount program, where I rode him for the first time. They eventually gave him to me, and so he ended up coming to live at our ranch. My other horse, Top Cat, was getting older, and so I decided to train Spotlight to take his place one day. We'd been working together for a few months when I thought he was ready to go out on the road.

After a long day of driving, we finally pulled into my friends' Missouri ranch, and got the horses and crew settled down for the night. The next morning, I took Spotlight out for a ride. My friends live at a ranch nestled on a mountainside, and so we enjoyed taking in the scenery. My thought was to ride for several miles, and then come back and get ready for the presentation.

About halfway through the ride, we left the road and walked across a pasture to a small pond. As we went along, the ground started getting muddy due to heavy rainfall the night before, and I realized if we went much farther, we'd start tearing up the lawn. So we took a shortcut, heading through some woods and making our way back to the road. Already my thoughts were turning to the details of the presentation I was to lead.

The retreat was a gathering of homeschoolers, and I wondered, with the heavy rains, if enough people were going to show up to make it worth the effort. I also knew we had to get back on the road not long after the presentation to get to Kansas City on time.

Just then, Spotlight came to a stop. He'd not done that before, and I thought he'd gotten distracted or lost track of what he was supposed to be doing. So I told him to move— we were on a tight schedule and didn't have time for him to fool around. But he would not move.

There were times, earlier in my horse-training experience, when I might have assumed that Spotlight was being obstinate, and pushed him to obey, just as a boss or parent might do. Many of us have that reaction, when someone seems to resist our authority. Still, I knew that Spotlight was a good horse, trustworthy and hardworking, always eager to please. I decided to take time to listen to him first. When I looked down, my heart nearly stopped.

There, across his forearm, was a strand of barbed wire. We had run into a fallen-down barbed-wire fence, which can prove disastrous for a horse. When a horse gets caught up in barbed wire, he doesn't think, he only reacts. The result is catastrophic, if not fatal, with the horse suffering lacerations down to the bone. Even if the horse recovers, he is often scarred for life. Barbed-wire wounds are also prone to infection, and the healing process is long and tedious.

I thought we were fortunate that Spotlight had halted in time to avoid being entangled in the fence. So I picked up the reins and turned to go right, but he would not move. That was not a good sign. Stepping off of Spotlight, I took a closer look. Both his rear legs were also caught in barbed wire. The wire, hidden by underbrush, had encircled his legs in a figure eight. In the middle of a quiet, ordinary trail ride, Spotlight had become trapped. One false move, and he—and I—could face a gruesome death.

If you know anything about horses, you know that when a horse is trapped, he panics. He goes ballistic and does not quit. He does not stop and think, he just reacts and tries to run as fast as he can. It's a survival instinct that keeps him alive in the wild.

But wrapped up in barbed wire, panicking was the absolute worst thing Spotlight could do. Any movement would draw the barbed wire even tighter around his legs, causing him to panic more. I could see it all unfolding in my mind's eye. If Spotlight bolted now, he wouldn't quit. He would wrap both of us in barbed wire and we could both die. The more he struggled, the tighter the wire would wrap around him, and with each desperate movement, his flesh would be torn from his body.

If I tried to free Spotlight, he could kill me as well. The chances were high that I'd get caught in the wire and Spotlight would kick and tear me to death as well.

For the first time in years, I was absolutely terrified. I had no wire-cutters to free Spotlight. I had no cell phone to call for help. There seemed no way out. I've seen horses panic and beat themselves to death against the side of a trailer, or kill themselves by getting tangled up in a fence. I once saw a horse panic and throw herself to the ground so hard that it killed her. The wise thing to do, as cruel as it sounds, would have been to turn and walk away and at least save myself.

But I didn't have the heart to leave Spotlight. To stay was stupid. To leave was terrible and heartless. I felt ashamed and angry. Here I was, a trainer with decades of experience, and I was helpless to save this horse who had put his trust in me. Seeing no solution, I cried out, "Oh God, help me."

Chances are you've uttered that prayer at least once in your life. Maybe it was in a doctor's office, where you or someone you loved first heard the word "cancer." Or perhaps it was a phone call in the middle of the day, saying your child was in the principal's office, or at the police station, or had been in a car wreck. It could have been the time when you were summoned to the boss's office and told that your services were no longer required, or when a foreclosure notice came from the bank. Maybe your spouse said she didn't love you anymore. And you knew that one false move, one wrong word spoken in anger, could ruin everything.

Most of the crises in our lives come like that, out of the blue. "The real troubles in your life," Mary Schmich, a columnist from the *Chicago Tribune* once wrote, "are apt to be things that never crossed your worried mind; the kind that blindside you at 4 p.m. on some idle Tuesday." We worry all the time, and still we never see life-shattering events coming.

We live in a world full of pitfalls and crises. And how we react to them will determine the course of our lives. Just like Spotlight, the smallest thing, one wrong step, can ruin us.

In the moment of my prayer for help with Spotlight, a thought popped into my mind. A week earlier, another trainer had shown me a technique for getting a horse to raise its feet. If I tried to reach back and grab Spotlight's rear leg, I'd throw him off balance, and that would pull the wire tighter and spook him. But if I could reach back and squeeze his hock—which is a joint higher up on the rear leg—Spotlight would lift his foot, and step out of danger.

After taking a deep breath and whispering another

prayer, I reached back and squeezed Spotlight's hock. He lifted his rear foot, and slipped it out of the snare, causing the tension on the barbed wire to ease a bit.

One leg down, three more to go. Another breath and another prayer, and I reached back and squeezed the other hock. Rather than kick and fight, Spotlight lifted his leg right out of the snare, and set it down beside the wire.

We were halfway there. Still, the danger remained. If he bolted now, with both front legs still entangled, Spotlight's skin would be torn to the bone. But in our previous training, I'd taught Spotlight another trick. I would tie a rope around his front feet and teach him not to react or try to free his feet. Instead of resisting when I pulled on the rope, Spotlight learned to yield and follow.

So I put my hand around his left front foot and lifted it up—and rather then resist, Spotlight trusted me, and allowed me to gently pull him out of danger. The right foot soon followed, and he was free. I stepped over the barbed wire, which now lay loose on the ground, and led Spotlight safely back to the road.

I'd like to take credit for saving Spotlight's life; to say that the reason he made it free of the barbed wire without a scratch was because I'm a miracle-working, horse-whispering genius. But that wouldn't be the truth. The real hero in this story is

Spotlight, who overcame his fear, and put his faith and trust in me. His courage and faith in that moment of crisis made all the difference.

Trust remains the building block of every human relationship: between parents and children; between workers and their boss; between a husband and a wife; between people and God. Most of us know this. But it's one thing to know that trust is important, and it's another to take active steps, day by day, to build that trust.

I learned that lesson the hard way, from a horse named Nava Rose.

I first met Nava Rose when I was twenty and working for a local horse breeder. At that time, I thought I was hot stuff. After beginning 4-H when I was eight years old, I'd won three national titles and had a room packed with trophies. More than anything, I loved the praise that came with winning. My horses, when they did what I told them, made me look good and earned me the praise of veteran trainers. That was important to me.

My Dad died when I was five, and though my Mom later remarried, his absence loomed large over my life. I grew up thinking that I didn't matter much and was constantly looking for someone to fill the void in my life. So the older horse trainers and leaders became surrogate father figures. Pleasing them took away some of the pain and grief I felt from missing Dad. My very identity and self-worth were on the line every time I worked with a horse. And failure was not an option.

One summer, my boss entrusted me with Nava Rose, a three-year-old mare with the potential to be a national champion show horse. She'd already mastered the basics, and it was my job to push her to learn more complex tasks. I took her out to the back 40, and started work on a particularly difficult maneuver. I placed a tire on the ground and asked her to place her front feet in the center of it. Then I climbed in the saddle and asked her to turn in a circle, while keeping both front legs in the tire and rotating her back legs.

The longer we worked, the more it became clear that Nava Rose just wasn't getting it.

She'd start circling and then panic and lose her focus. First she started stepping forward out of the tire, ruining the maneuver. Once I cured her of that, she started backing up instead.

I'd not had a lot of experience with failure up to that point, and Nava Rose's struggle with the tire started my anger boiling. A smarter or more experienced trainer would have taken a break or tried a different approach. But I was a young horse-training prodigy, and no stubborn three-year-old mare would spoil my reputation.

So I pushed her harder. All I was asking her to do was keep her front legs in the tire. How hard could that be? So I yelled, kicked, and jerked on her. After all, that's what I'd seen other trainers do. They saw training as a test of will and would do whatever it took to conquer a horse and force it to obey.

But despite my yelling and insistence that Nava Rose do things my way, she didn't get it. Finally, I lost it. She started circling and then got her feet caught up in the tire and backed up. I was so frustrated and angry that I stepped off of her and grabbed her by her head and threw her on the ground.

I was a little shocked because she weighed 1,000 pounds, and horses don't throw down easily. Nava Rose lay on the ground, bewildered and shaking. I sat down on the tire and wept. I have just ruined everything I have invested in her, I thought.

Thankfully, Nava Rose was stunned but not injured. She got up right away, and after a few minutes I went over to her and apologized. I hugged her and told her I was sorry; I had no idea if she understood any of that. Then I told God that I was an idiot—that I was impatient and angry and had acted like a fool.

That day was a breakthrough for me. Nava Rose didn't have a problem. I had a problem. I'd asked her to do too much, too fast, and punished her when she couldn't keep up. That's a problem many of us face—when someone won't do what we say, we try to force them to comply. Nava Rose made me look bad, and I couldn't handle it.

At our ranch we think of horses in two categories: "want to" and "have to." The "have to" horses are perfectly good workers. They are safe to ride and do what they are told, most of the time. But the "want to" horses are the ones who excel. What we try to do in training—for both horses and the young guests who come and stay with us—is to capture their "want to." Every trainer is looking for a "want to" horse, just like every parent wants a child who is eager to listen and learn.

Nava Rose helped me learn how to capture the "want to." I had to re-earn her trust and rebuild her confidence. She was afraid to fail because she knew that if she failed, I would punish her. So I stopped trying to lead by fear and intimidation, and looked for ways to build her confidence.

We reached this goal by making the task bite-sized. First, I stood beside her as we walked through the process. I had her place her front feet in the tire and then take one step over. Once she mastered that, I praised her, and gave her a break. Then she did two steps in the tire and stopped. Again I praised her for getting a little bit closer to the goal. Before long, she had enough confidence to circle the tire without stumbling or stepping out. And she trusted me enough to know that if she failed, I would not punish her. Only then did I climb in the saddle and lead her through the process.

The most important lesson I learned was how to listen to what Nava Rose needed. I had to understand her needs first, not just command her to obey me. Once I understood, she had a greater ability and desire to obey.

John Wooden, the famed basketball coach from UCLA, used to tell his teams, "Run but don't hurry." That's another lesson Nava Rose taught me. I wasted days trying to get her to master the tire maneuver all in one bite. Once I broke it into small pieces, the training went quickly. Being deliberate, and taking enough time to listen, ended up being both more efficient and more effective.

Nava Rose and I went on to win a national championship. But her story didn't end well, and that's one last lesson she taught me. Not long after we won the championship, she was sent to work with another trainer. I was headed to Penn State University that fall and wouldn't be able to work her. I went along with her to the new trainer for a month, to ease the transition.

That new trainer did something to Nava Rose that I have never forgotten. To get a smooth ride on a horse, it's best if the horse learns how to keep its head down. So this trainer had poured a block of cement out in a pasture, and set a ring in the center of the cement. He took a short rope, and tied one end to Nava Rose's head, and the other end to the ring, and left her there for a couple of weeks, so that she would never want to lift her head again. When I saw that, it broke my heart. Here was a champion horse, and they took the spirit right out of her. She went on to win more awards, but was never the same. She was broken inside.

Top Cat was broken inside as well, when I first met him. I was in my forties by then, and for almost three decades had been building on the lessons Nava Rose taught me. One day I received a call from a woman who had a horse she wanted me to train. I don't usually train for the general public—usually I work for friends or colleagues that I've known for a long time. But this woman was persistent, so I asked her to tell me a bit about the horse.

"He's a bit explosive," she said.

"Can you expand on that?" I asked. "What exactly does he do?"

"Well," she said, "when you saddle him, he tries to throw himself backward, and when you tie him, he pulls back and goes out of control."

A group of teenagers was coming up to the ranch for a weeklong retreat, and I knew that a horse like that would grab their attention. So I said to Top Cat's owner, "You can bring him up on three conditions. One is that you come and stay the week and see how he is being trained. Two is that I make no promises. And three is that I'll train him in front of an audience."

She agreed and brought him up for the retreat. Over that week, Top Cat and I got to know each other very well. He was a Quarter Horse, with a red coat and brown mane and tail, built more like a racehorse than a cow-working horse. He'd been put on the fast track during his training, and in the beginning did quite well. But the training went too quickly, with no time for him to build the trust or emotional stability needed for long-term success. As a result, he was wound up tight on the inside.

When I entered the training arena, Top Cat panicked anytime I got near him. He spooked easily and ran from me, and his whole body shook with pent-up emotion. His main problem was fear. In his early training, Top Cat learned that any failure led to punishment. If he didn't live up to his trainer's expectations, he was tied up and forced to obey. His only option was to fight back.

"What he needs," I told the crowd of teenagers watching us, "is to learn how to handle his fear, how to deal with his pain, and how to have hope."

That sounded great in theory, but it's not easy for a horse, or a person, to do. The pains and disappointments of the past leave deep scars. Those scars can't be overcome by wishful thinking or platitudes.

One of the lines I heard over and over in churches while growing up was "Let go, and let God." The idea was, that when faced with a conflict or crisis, the best course of action was to quit worrying and ask God to sort things out. That sounds all well and good, but no one ever explained exactly how to let go of my troubles.

With Top Cat, I started very slowly. I put a long rope on him, and pulled on it gently to make him move. My goal was to entice him to give in to the pressure and come to me. If he panicked and bolted, I eased up on the rope, and let him run.

Once he calmed down, I started over.

One small step at a time, he learned to trust again. Once he was able to respond to pressure on the rope and come to me, we went a little bit further. I wrapped the rope around him, pulled it gently, and rewarded Top Cat when he came to me and then stood still. Eventually, I could spook him and though Top Cat would want to run, he moved his feet but didn't flee. Step by step, he learned how to respond to fear, rather than panicking from fear. When he failed, I waited patiently and didn't punish him.

After several days of training, I brought out a saddle. As soon as Top Cat saw it, he tensed up, holding his breath and preparing to blow up his sides so he would be hard to saddle. When I gently placed the saddle on his back, he had enough faith in me to stand his ground. As I brought the girth of the saddle up to his belly, he tensed up and held his breath, ready to explode. Instead of tightening the girth, however, I released it. I did this again and again, holding the girth against his belly until Top Cat breathed a sigh of relief. Then I'd reward that small step of faith by letting up on the pressure. It got so that I could saddle and girth him and Top Cat would stay still. I could almost hear the thoughts inside his head: *I don't have to panic—he is not going to punish me.*

In the end, I even taught him to lie down. That was a struggle. For three hours he fought with me until we were both wringing wet. Again, I didn't force him, or punish him, or strike out in anger. Instead, I put firm and steady pressure on him until he gave in and discovered the release of pressure.

When he lay down, Top Cat groaned and groaned. "They treated me so miserably," he seemed to say. "My life is so terrible." As we worked that through, I won his confidence, and he learned to exhale those emotions of anger and hurt.

At the end of the week, Top Cat's owner did something that stunned me. "This horse needs to be yours," she said. Afterwards she turned Top Cat over to me. In return, I gave her one of my "want to" horses, a quiet, gentle creature who was a pleasure to ride. Top Cat, who came to us as a frightened, damaged horse, became a faithful companion. He and I worked together for years, traveling across the country giving Sermon on the Mount demonstrations.

He became, to me at least, a walking miracle. His life was transformed, not in the blinking of an eye, but by a series of small steps of faith—everyday miracles.

That's what we hope to accomplish with Sermon on the Mount. We travel the country planting the seeds for miracles— teaching people how their lives can be transformed, one step at a time. And I'd like to invite you to come along with us. Whether you are a parent or a preacher, a boss or an employee; whether you are a person of faith or someone who doubts that God exists, there's something here for everyone.

We'll go on a journey, learning how to sow faith and trust step by step, so that when a storm comes, or you get caught in a barbed-wire fence, you'll have everything you need to find the way out.

So come along for the ride.

Chapter 2

Learning the Craft

WHEN I WAS SEVEN years old, my mother got remarried.

And that, more than anything else, is how I ended up as a horse trainer.

In fact, if life had worked out the way my parents planned, I'd have spent most of my life as a dairy farmer, not a horse trainer. But life, as most of us are too well aware, never quite works out the way we planned.

I was born in 1952, and grew up on the Fruitful Manor, our family's dairy farm in Carlisle, Pennsylvania, just outside of Harrisburg. My grandfather had started the farm, and passed it to my dad. We had about 100 cows, housed on the ground floor of an old white bank-style barn, with a hayloft above, along with pigs and chickens in out-buildings.

I was the youngest of five children. Kathleen was the

oldest, followed by Bob, Priscilla, and David. And from early on, we helped out with milking and feeding and mucking out and the dozens of other jobs it takes to keep a farm going.

Our farm was a small but growing operation. Robert Sterrett, my dad, who also taught agriculture at the local high school, had great dreams for the farm. He kept meticulous records, and was always on the look-out for the latest innovations to make the farm more productive.

Like today, there wasn't a lot of money in farming, so with five growing children to feed, my dad supplemented our dairy production by raising all kinds of fruits. We grew apricots, blackberries, cherries, raspberries, plums, apples, and grapes on the farm, and there was always work to be done.

I loved being on the farm, even from an early age. At the center of everything was my dad. And not just on our farm.

He was a pillar in the community as well. Most of our neighbors also had small farms, so none of them could afford to hire help to harvest crops in the fall. So they all worked together in the fields at harvest time. Afterwards, our neighbors often ended up back at our house for a dinner of barbecued chicken and lemonade and potato salad and laughter. We had a number of relatives who also seemed to find their way to the farm.

Most of what I know about my dad comes from talking with my mother, my brothers and sisters, and other relatives, or is gleaned from looking through his files and old family photo albums.

I know he had a great sense of humor. He and his brothers and their dad were always playing tricks on one another.

He was also a diabetic. This was in the days when treatment for diabetes was less sophisticated than it is today. He had to give himself regular shots of insulin, like people do nowadays. But he didn't have the modern testing equipment of today to keep a close eye on his blood sugar.

When his blood sugar went down, my dad was liable to do all sorts of funny things. Like the time he left my grandfather by the side of the road.

They had gone out on a road trip, and my dad hadn't been careful about what he was eating. And sure enough, his blood sugar got out of whack. Unfortunately, my dad was driving at the time. So to my grandfather's horror, my dad started weaving in and out of his line, as if he were drunk. Thankfully, there was little traffic, so he didn't crash into any oncoming vehicles.

My grandfather knew what was happening, and he kept his head.

"Bob," he said, keeping a calm tone to his voice, "I think you had better let me drive."

"All right," said my dad, and pulled over.

But when my grandfather opened his door and got out of the car, my dad slammed on the accelerator and took off down the road.

He stopped a ways down the road, and sat there, with the

engine idling, as my grandfather hurried after him. As soon as my grandfather got within a few feet of the car, off my dad went again, leaving him huffing and puffing in the dust.

This went on for about a mile, with my dad cackling with laughter every time he took off. Finally my grandfather caught up to him long enough to give my dad a candy bar, and he came to his senses.

At that point, I think my grandfather probably wanted to leave him by the side of the road.

But he didn't.

He climbed in the car, they had a good laugh together, and that was the end of that. That was the kind of humor they had. Always pulling stunts like that on each other.

I treasure those stories about my dad, probably because my own memories of him are so few. Mostly I have bits and pieces, impressions or images of being with him, not complete memories. Like sitting on his lap when he drove our Ford tractor on the farm. Or of him carrying me around when I was just three or four, as he visited with neighbors during one of those chicken barbecues.

One fall day in 1957, my dad took the Ford tractor over to our neighbors, Ruth and Craig Fulton, to help with a corn harvest. It was a tricycle-style tractor—two big wheels in the back, set wide apart, and two small wheels in front, right next to each other. That made it very maneuverable and versatile, but also easy to tip over.

To help with the harvest, my dad planned to attach the tractor to a corn picker, a heavy piece of farm equipment. As he backed up to the picker, something went terribly wrong. No one really knows what happened. Maybe my dad was in a hurry, or was distracted, or just made one wrong move.

All we know is that the tractor flipped over and landed on my dad, crushing his chest and pinning him to the ground.

There were two other men around, and somehow they managed to lever the tractor off of him. But it was too late. Today, with the advances in medicine, and with emergency paramedics who fly in helicopters, maybe he would have been saved.

In 1957, however, there was no hope. First they had to find a phone to call for help—there were no cell phones— and then wait for almost an hour for an ambulance to arrive, followed by the long ride back to the hospital, where he was pronounced dead.

What I remember most in the days following my dad's death was a profound sense of loss, of being adrift or shipwrecked, tossed overboard in a storm.

Because my dad was at the center of everything, when he was gone, things fell apart quickly. My mother was an intelligent, capable woman, but she'd always deferred to my dad. He ran the family business, and she took care of the family home. With five kids, that was a tall order.

But it meant that when my dad was gone, my mother

couldn't manage the farm on her own. So we auctioned off our dairy cows and rented out the fields. My mother brought in chickens that she could raise and sell, so we'd at least have some income.

Our neighbors, who had loved my dad, watched out for us. One of them. a grocer, would keep his eyes out for good deals, and set them aside for my mother. Another helped my mother with the auction, and made sure she got a good deal.

Still, without dad's teaching salary, and with little money coming in from the farm, it was a struggle for my mother to make ends meet.

Sometimes at night I sat at the top of the stairs and listened to my mother weeping as she sat in her chair reading her Bible. She wept for my dad, and for herself, and her children. I knew she worried about money all the time. Once, when the sound of her tears woke me, I broke open my piggy bank and brought her down the few dollars I had, so that she could stop worrying, at least for one night.

The British writer, C. S. Lewis, who married late in life, only to lose his wife to cancer, talked about the hopelessness that comes in grief. "No one ever told me that grief felt so like fear," he wrote.

I think that's what my mother felt. She was afraid and alone, and overwhelmed with all that life had thrown at her.

So feeling trapped and fearful, my mother did what a lot of grieving people do. She looked for a lifeline, a way out of the depths of pain and loneliness.

That's why she turned to the man who would become my stepdad. He was a school teacher, like my dad had been. And he was also grieving, left to raise four children alone when his wife died.

And so two years after my dad died, my mother remarried.

What seemed like a reasonable solution was not an easy match. They were both still on the rebound, and so had unrealistic expectations, hoping this new relationship would compensate for the sorrow and loss they felt. Grief was not a strong foundation on which to build their new marriage.

To top it off, there were now nine children in the house. Blending two large families worked in films like *Yours, Mine, and Ours*, or on television, like in *The Brady Bunch*. But it did not work for the Sterrett-Berrys.

We'd had a big family up till that point, but now it was huge. I had three new brothers—Jim, David, and Ken—and a new baby sister, Jeannie. In my biological family, I'd been the youngest, and the apple of my mother's eye, but when Jeannie came on the scene, all of a sudden she was the baby of the family, and I lost my place in the sun.

Bringing three new boys in the house brought more tension as well. We didn't get along, which was to be expected, given all the change in our lives. But rather than helping us work through those difficulties, and learn to get along, the parents took sides. My mother was on our side; my stepdad took the side of his children.

The main problem was this: our stepdad could never fill my dad's shoes. They were two different people—while my dad had been an extrovert, an energetic man who loved people and loved working outdoors, my stepdad was more passive and bookish, and often withdrawn.

He'd come home and want to grade papers, and then read and relax; whereas my dad had been in constant motion, coming home from work and launching himself into farm chores.

My stepdad and I never got along when I was growing up. I don't think I could forgive him for not being my dad. As far as I could tell, we were a mystery to him. He didn't know how to connect with these new children he'd inherited, and so he withdrew.

People get angry when they run out of answers, when the problems they face seem overwhelming. That's what happened to my stepfather. He withdrew, and tried to ignore the troubles in the house, hoping they would go away. But if we kids got into fights, or were disobedient, he'd either become very passive and hide or explode in rage. I just don't think he knew what to do with us.

My mother was sad and lonely, even after the marriage. I remember that at times, when it was so hard to keep peace in the house with the children, and hard to make the finances work, and to have hope that things would get better, I'd still find my mother sitting in the living-room, reading her Bible, and weeping in the middle of the night.

The one thing that kept me going was that I had a great tenderness in my heart toward my mother. She always tried to stand up for us, and reward us when we did well. When we disobeyed, she tried to be firm and fair. When I deserved it, she spanked me, and sent me to my room. But she didn't leave me there for too long.

Whenever I was sent to my room, all the anger and disappointment would stir up inside me. Every child is angry and cries when they are punished, and feels as if they have been treated unfairly. For me, those feelings were intensified by the disappointment and anger that were always hanging in the air. I didn't know what to do with these feelings.

So after I cried for a while, my mother would come and see me. She didn't say anything. Instead, she'd sit on a chair or at the end of my bed, and before long my heart would melt, and I'd let all those emotions out. I wouldn't be the man I am today without my mother's persistent care for me. She never let me get bitter, and always reminded me that even though she didn't always like what I did, she loved me.

Around this time, my parents made another decision that changed my life.

They decided to take us on a family outing to the South Mountain Fair in Arendtsville, about twenty miles from our home.

The idea of spending the whole day pretending that we were having a good time had no appeal for me. Not even the promise of a chicken dinner at the end of the fair held any appeal.

After wandering around seeing the prize pigs and cows, we made our way to the horse arena. A local 4-H drill team was putting on a show that afternoon. As we sat there on the bleachers, in came this brilliantly colored drill team, all dressed in green and white, and riding in perfect unison.

They looked like they were having the time of their lives, riding their horses in pinwheels and spirals and crossing patterns, keeping time to the music.

When the music sped up, the team sped up, cantering and galloping through their maneuvers, to the delight of the crowd. As soon as they finished, I said to my mother, "I want to be a part of that."

Although we lived on a farm, I'd spent very little time around horses. My sister had a big white horse, but I'd never showed much interest. But seeing that team perform together captured my imagination. I wanted to be part of something like that.

So at the beginning, my interest in horses had nothing to do with horses. That changed later on, as I came to love my horses, and invest my life in them. What I wanted was a relationship and connection.

That's an important point to make. There's this mystique that surrounds trainers who work with troubled horses, or who use the methods known as horse whispering. The name itself is misleading—I don't whisper to horses, I listen to them more than anything.

But there's the idea that being a horse whisperer is a kind of mystical gift some trainers are born with. It's as if we have this ability to connect with horses on a spiritual level that other trainers don't have.

Now some trainers do have an innate ability to work with horses. I got my first paying job as a horse trainer when I was fourteen, working with a pony named Colonel Ted, so I had some natural talent as a trainer.

But the techniques I use didn't come from some mystical source. I learned them because I wanted to know what makes a horse tick. First for selfish reasons—I wanted to be part of a drill team, to perform and win medals, to build up my self-esteem and create a sense of belonging. And later, because I wanted to be partners with a horse, so we would both benefit. When I stopped looking at my own needs and began to think about his, things really took off.

But it was never easy. In fact, my first attempt to train a horse ended in disaster.

Not long after coming home from the South Mountain Fair, I purchased a black pony by the name of Scotty. He was old and stubborn, but he was mine, so from the first time we put him in a pasture at our house, I started dreaming of being a champion 4-H rider.

There was just one problem. Riding in a 4-H drill squad is about teamwork, with each horse and rider working in unison. I suppose it's a lot like the marching bands you see at college football games during half time, where dozens of musicians march in perfect unison and create intricate patterns, all in perfect step. It only works if everyone does his job, and is in the right place at the right time.

Scotty, however, had no interest in working as a team. He was a little older, and had developed some bad habits. Whenever I would climb into the saddle, he'd want to take off towards the fence, and then race along the fence-posts, ignoring the directions I gave with the reins. I held on tight until he'd had his fun, and then he was willing to listen.

At eight, I didn't have the strength or experience to know how to guide Scotty. He never tried to hurt me, so I am grateful for that, but trying to join the 4-H team with Scotty would have been a lost cause.

Scotty was too clever for his own good.

We didn't chain the gate of his pen at night. One night, about a year after I had gotten him, Scotty started playing with the latch which held the gate closed. Before too long he had gotten the gate open. He bolted, taking my sister's white horse Topper along with him. It was late at night, with no street lights out in the country along the road that ran by our farm.

Scotty and my sister's horse ran down the farm lane and

across the highway, where a milk truck was passing by. The driver saw the white horse, who was faster than Scotty and took the lead as they ran. In the pitch dark, however, he didn't see Scotty, and hit him, killing him instantly.

My dream of being a champion rider was turning into a nightmare.

One thing you learn early on the farm is that death is a normal part of life. As an eight-year-old, no one blamed me for the accident, although we did learn to latch and chain our gates from that point on.

A few months later, I was climbing into the cab of a box van truck, headed to my first 4-H meeting. In the trailer behind the truck was a sixteen-hand, red-and-white Paint Horse named Cochise. He was part Draft Horse, so he was huge. But he was quiet and gentle, and easy to ride, much easier than Scotty had ever been. Because I was so short, getting in the saddle was a challenge. I had to get a stool and climb him like I was climbing a tree.

I was literally the peanut riding the elephant—that's how I looked when I rode off to join the drill team. The other riders had a good laugh when I started, but Cochise worked well, and soon we were a valid part of the team.

We call an older, well-trained horse like Cochise a babysitter. You can put a small child on him, and if they fall off, the horse will just stand there with his foot up until the child can crawl away—he will not step on that child. He won't mind being climbed on, and he will wait patiently, until the child shimmies up on his back, no matter how long it takes.

Sitting in the cab, with Cochise, I was riding into a whole new world.

CHAPTER 3

ANYTHING WORTH DOING IS WORTH DOING POORLY

SUCCESS IN LIFE IS A GIFT, says bestselling author Malcolm Gladwell, in his book *Outliers*.

It takes lots of hard work, but that's only part of the picture. The other part is having the opportunities that make the hard work pay off. We can only succeed, he argues, with the help of other people, who create the circumstances that allow us to grow and develop.

Take someone like Bill Gates, one of the founders of Microsoft. Now one of the richest men in the world, he spent thousands of hours as a school kid learning how to program computers. That hard work gave him the skills he needed to become a brilliant programmer and innovator.

But Gates was also given opportunities. In the late 1960s,

he attended Lakeside School in Seattle, one of the first schools in America to have access to a computer network. The only reason the school had access to computers was that parents at the school raised enough money to pay for it. In other words, those parents made space for Gates to succeed.

I'm not a genius like Bill Gates, just an honest cowboy. But I know that any success I have in life, I owe to the many people who invested their lives in me when I was growing up. I stand on their shoulders.

As we get older, it's difficult to remember this. The temptation is to think that we are somehow like the Lone Ranger, or Clint Eastwood, or any one of the dozens of heroes of old cowboy movies or modern-day action films, where the lone hero saves the day.

Because of this, we get impatient with other people, when they fail to live up to our expectations. Maybe it's a child who just can't seem to figure out how to get the right answers in his math homework, or a clerk in the store who's having trouble with the cash register, or an employee who keeps messing things up, no matter how many times we lecture him on the right way to do things.

I've had some success in my life. As a teenager, I won several national 4-H titles as a rider and trainer, and by the time I'd graduated from high school I had a room full of trophies and ribbons I'd won. While I was a student at Penn State University, I was elected president of the Block and

Bridle Club, one of the largest student groups on campus, and also as the student representative to the faculty senate for the school of agriculture. My professors offered me a job on campus and allowed me to bring horses to train on my own while I studied. After I finished my bachelor's degree, schools like Ohio State, Colorado State, and Florida State offered me assistantships, so I could go on and earn a master's degree. (I turned them down, but that's a story for a little later on.)

When I was just out of college, one of the largest horse breed associations in the country offered to bring me in as the successor to their president, so he could train me in his job and then I could take over when he retired. Today, I run a well-respected camp and youth training program, and am invited to speak all over the country.

I don't say all of this to brag, but to make a point. It's easy to forget where I came from. It's easy to forget that when I started out, I was an eight-year-old kid, desperate to hang onto the saddle, with no clue what I was doing. I was no one special, just an ordinary farm kid.

Thankfully, when I showed up to join the 4-H drill team, no one laughed me off the rodeo grounds. Despite my looking like a peanut riding on an elephant's back, the rest of the team accepted me. So did the adult leaders of 4-H, who spent countless hours driving us to events, leading our meetings, investing untold hours of their time with us.

One of the first leaders was a woman named Mrs. Dubs, a neighbor who was a widow. Mrs. Dubs was a chain smoker and was considered rough around the edges. That was quite a change for me, as I grew up in a strict Christian household, where my mother was like white on rice about going to church and avoiding any vices. But my parents knew that Mrs. Dubs and the other 4-H leaders cared about me, and so they trusted them enough to let me spend time with them.

At one point, I was elected to become the news reporter for our club. That meant putting together an end of year report on all our accomplishments. Instead of simply typing up a report, I wanted to do something special. So I designed a scrapbook in the shape of a clover-leaf, the symbol of 4-H. Mrs. Dubs offered to help me complete the project.

Before long I realized that there is a reason most scrapbooks are square. Making one in the shape a clover-leaf meant that every page had to fit that pattern. I spent three solid days at Mrs. Dubs' house working on that project. She fed me and put me up and stayed up until the long hours of the night. She offered suggestions, and encouraged me to keep going when I wanted to give up.

Now a scrapbook, I admit, sounds like a small thing. And the easy thing for Mrs. Dubs to do would have been to tell me that a clover-leaf scrapbook was impractical and not worth three days of effort. Instead she stuck with me. She made me feel important; that my ideas mattered.

That scrapbook got me noticed by people in the 4-H organization. It won an award, because the 4-H officials realized it wasn't a run-of-the-mill report, and it opened up doors for me to do other projects in the future.

Then there was George Zimmerman, a local businessman who had a lot of horses. He gave me my first real job as a trainer, when I was still a teenager. Not only did he give me a job, but he bought horses costing many thousands of dollars for me to work and believed that I could train them well enough to increase their value. Once, he and I flew from Pennsylvania all the way out to Albuquerque, New Mexico, to see one of the horses we'd trained run in a race.

Jim Gallagher, an extension specialist for Penn State, took an early interest in me because I was from his county. He opened the door for me to take some of the horses I was working with to the Penn State campus, to train them while I was going to school. He even found a job for me in the horse barn, which took care of my room and board.

The point is this: I didn't get to where I am today on my own, simply by my own skills and effort. I got there because people believed in me, and offered me a chance, even when I was young and unskilled, and made mistakes. Without their help, without their belief in me, I wouldn't be where I am today.

I also owe a great deal to Cochise. He was the perfect horse for me to start with.

He was well trained and responsive; what I call a "want to" horse. That is, he wanted to do what his rider asked him to do. He wanted to be cooperative, and was easy-going, and was responsive to a rider's cues.

So as I started practicing with the drill team, being on Cochise made things very easy. Though I had a lot to learn, I knew that I could trust Cochise to do whatever I asked of him. When I wanted him to speed up, he sped up. When I wanted him to go right, he went right. That put my mind at ease, and while I was on the saddle, my mind could be totally focused on learning the patterns and intricate teamwork required in the drills.

Horses aren't dumb, and Cochise knew that there was no way I could force him to do what I wanted. I didn't have the strength to control him if he wanted to ride off and ignore my directions.

Because he was part work horse, I didn't expect him to be so nimble and athletic. But he made me feel like a champion in the saddle, because we worked flawlessly together.

Scotty, my first horse, had been the exact opposite. He was a "have to" horse, who did what he was asked only when a rider was experienced or strong enough to force him to obey. If I'd taken him to the drill team, it would have been a train-wreck of a disaster. I could force him to do what I wanted, if I concentrated. But it was always a battle.

The same thing would have been true of Skeeter, another horse I trained early on. She was a better horse than Cochise, when it came to her physical attributes. A dark bay Quarter Horse with a black mane and tail, she looked very pretty. She'd been raised out West and had been a ranch horse before I worked with her. I thought she was a real cowboy's horse, and I looked great riding on her in the arena.

That is, until she bucked me off.

Almost every time I rode her, Skeeter would eventually throw me out of the saddle. The problem was this—she was talented but flighty and insecure. She'd been rushed in her early training and as a result was fearful and reactionary. I didn't know how to conquer her fear and so I suffered the consequences.

I stuck with Skeeter for a while, in part because I was too stupid to help her and too stubborn to quit. More than that, I wanted to figure her out.

These two horses, Skeeter and Scotty, perplexed me. They were athletic and talented horses, and so should have been able to run circles around a horse like Cochise. They were small enough that I could force them to do what I wanted, but it was always a struggle.

Cochise, on the other hand, a horse who I could not control by force, was a willing partner. It was Cochise who first taught me the possibilities of working as a team, where the rider and horse are in perfect sync. Even as I moved on to some faster and more athletic horses as I grew, that first partnership with Cochise remained the model I strived for.

I took those lessons from Cochise into my first training job. When I was about fourteen, and still very rough around the edges, some of my neighbors hired me to train a horse named Colonel Ted.

A little roan pony, he'd been kept in a fenced-in field by his owners, and treated well, but had never been ridden. His owners wanted him halter-broken, which means that I needed to civilize him. He was a friendly horse, with a good nature, but had never learned the basics. Imagine a person who'd never learned how to eat with a knife and fork, or other table manners. That's the kind of thing I had to teach Colonel Ted.

His owners wanted him to be able to take a bridle and saddle without resistance; to learn how to stand still and not run off when a rider was climbing in the saddle; to learn how to walk, canter, and trot. Mostly it was about teaching Colonel Ted to be patient, calm, and confident, so that he wouldn't react or buck or rear when something spooked him, or he saw something unusual.

Put yourself in a horse's shoes for a moment. Imagine you are Colonel Ted, and that for most of your life, you've had it pretty easy. You spend most of the time outside in the sunshine, running around and playing, grazing on sweet grass, and being petted and pampered when your masters come to see you. It's a pretty good life.

Only now, a stranger comes into your happy home and starts bossing you around. And he starts tying all kinds of ropes on you, and pulling you around, and maybe even tries to climb on your back. Even worse, he leads you out of the pasture and toward a trailer. The ramp leading up it is metal and it clanks and makes strange noises when you step on it. And as far as you can see, there's no escape route. I don't know about you, but I'd be pretty nervous the first time that happened. Like most of us, he was scared of change.

Remember too that in the wild, horses are prey animals. And God made them fast, with a flight mechanism, so that when they are startled, their first instinct is to run away as fast as they can. That instinct, honed over millennia, is engrained in the heart of any horse.

So it's no surprise that the first time I approached Colonel Ted's enclosure with a rope in my hand, he took off running, trying to put as much distance between him and myself as possible.

I had two choices when I started working with Colonel Ted. I could have cornered him, clipped on the lead rope and tried to force him to do what I wanted. Since Colonel Ted was pretty good natured, he might not have put up too much of a fight. For some of the trainers I met growing up, that kind of domineering approach was the preferred method. You had to let the horse know who was boss from the beginning.

Even as a teenager, that kind of approach didn't appeal to me. Instead, I set out to win Colonel Ted's trust. That meant going over several times and building enough of a friendship with him so that he would trust me enough to let me get close to him and handle him.

The first thing I did was get close to him, approaching him with a slow, gentle manner, so he wasn't spooked. As I walked toward him, I talked in a quiet voice, so that he allowed me to get close enough to pet him. I spent a few hours with him on my first visit, just getting to know Colonel Ted.

When I came back a second time, I wasn't a stranger. He came to me now, when I walked into the corral. And after an hour or so of talking to him, he was at ease enough for me to put a halter on him, and lead him out of his corral and into our horse trailer, so we could take him to our farm. The plan was for me to work with him there for several months, and once he'd been trained on the basics, his owners would come and get him.

When we got back to our farm, I led Colonel Ted out of our trailer and into the corral, where we could work together. I'd come home from school, and spend the rest of the afternoon working with Colonel Ted. In those afternoons together I taught him all the basics, and eventually was able to put a saddle and blanket on him and ride him.

When he went home to be with his owners, I felt the

satisfaction of a job well done. I was still a teenager, and it felt good to have been paid to train a horse. To my knowledge, he always worked out well for his owners.

Some of the lessons from that first training experience have stuck with me over the years. Most importantly perhaps is this: I learned the power of small successes. That's something many of us forget as we grow older.

Rather than focusing on the result I wanted—having Colonel Ted be a well-trained horse—I had to start with a simple step that was right in front of me, then take one step at a time until we reached the goal.

So step one was getting Colonel Ted used to me, so he wasn't nervous being around me. Then I had to get him to let me pet and handle him, especially around his face, so he wouldn't bolt when I put a halter on him. Then it was asking him to do a simple task, like letting me attach a rope to the halter, and following me as I led him.

We took each task, one at a time, and I praised him at every encounter, so that one success built on top of another. It really was like climbing a set of stairs one step at a time, until after a few months Colonel Ted became a well-trained and useful horse.

As I travel the country talking to people about leadership, and how to be seen as an effective, trustworthy leader—whether it's with horses or people—I constantly try to remember the power that small successes have.

When we have something that's working well, like a perfect touchdown pass thrown in a football game, or a horse performing well in the show ring, or an orchestra playing in perfect harmony, it captures our imagination. We want to be like that player on the field, or the rider, or the musician, who seems to be performing perfectly, almost without struggle or effort.

What we don't see is all the practice and struggle that made the performance possible. When we see the finished product, it captures our attention because it is so fluid and seamless, and in harmony. It has power and rhythm and oneness.

Or we see a great marriage, a couple who love each other dearly and work well together, whose children are well behaved and happy, and we say, "I want that."

Unfortunately, that marriage or those great performances seem out of reach. I get frustrated at times when I see something that I aspire to, something that is good and honorable, but I realize I am absolutely clueless about how to get there.

Take, for example, the great Olympic skaters, with their triple axles, and graceful skating that makes it look like they are dancing on ice. It's breathtaking to watch them.

But what happens when I get on the ice? I fall a lot more than I ever stand up, and quickly become disappointed and angry. I am disillusioned quickly, because the process of learning to skate in a straight line, without falling, is frustrating and time-consuming. Before long, I give up. Or I get angry and take it out on the people around me.

Success in anything—real, lasting, long-term success—takes hard work, and a lot of frustration. It's worth it in the end, when we reach the goal, but the irony is that we reach the future goal by focusing on doing what's right in front of us today.

Malcolm Gladwell, who wrote about people who are considered geniuses in his book *Outliers*, describes something he calls "the rule of 10,000 hours"—that is, to be great in any field takes about 10,000 hours of practice. He uses the examples of musicians like Mozart and the Beatles, musical prodigies who achieved enormous success at very young ages. Most people attribute their skill in creating music to sheer talent.

In the play and film *Amadeus*, an older musician named Antonio Salieri is haunted by Mozart's gifts, which seem almost supernatural. He wonders why God would give such talent to Mozart, who lived, by most accounts, an undisciplined life, filled with women and parties, and not Salieri, with his nose-to-the-grindstone approach.

That's not exactly true, Gladwell says. While Mozart had great talent, Gladwell admits, he also reportedly began practicing three hours a day from the time he was three years old. That kind of intensive practice—of scales and learning to play musical compositions note by note, day by day—gave him the skills necessary to bring his musical genius to life.

And the Beatles? Most of us remember them as mop-topped youths, taking America by storm, and causing young women to scream with joy at their mere appearance.

But before they became overnight sensations in the US in the 1960s, the Beatles spent several years playing in Berlin. They played marathon concerts in small clubs, sometimes playing as much as ten hours per night. In those marathon performance sessions, they honed their talent, and learned the skills that later on would allow them to be great. In some ways, the old saying that "practice makes perfect" has some validity.

Take, for example, the professional football player Junior Seau. In December 2008, the New England Patriots football team was decimated by injuries. Five of their linebackers were placed on the team's injured reserve list, meaning they were out for the season. In desperation, they placed a call to Junior Seau, a former star who had retired at the end of the previous season, intending to spend his time surfing and playing with his kids. When he left the game, Seau, who was nearly forty, was one of the most celebrated football players ever, credited with more tackles than any other player in the league's history.

A few weeks after he rejoined the team, a television program visited the Patriots and filmed their practice. There in the middle of the field was Seau, running the same drills as the greenest rookie player.

"You see this," the coach said, pointing to Seau. "All-time leader in the history of football, doing tackling drills."

Not everyone who practices 10,000 hours will become a superstar. But to become successful at anything requires painstaking effort, doing the little things over and over again until they become second nature.

That's not the recipe for a get-rich scheme or a pain-free road to an easy life. That kind of work transforms your life, and can allow you to achieve things you only dreamed about.

Forgetting those lessons, and trying to take short cuts, eventually leads to frustration. That's why my two horses, named Seaweed Sue and Nava Rose, are engrained in my mind.

I bought Seaweed Sue when I was a teenager, spending all my savings to pay for her. A Quarter Horse, she was the most beautiful horse I'd ever seen at that point, dappled gray and well conformed, a huge contrast to Cochise. He was a work horse, she was a racer. He was steady and dependable, she was full of energy and excitement.

By that time, I was a more experienced rider, ready for more speed and more excitement. So we were well matched.

Because she was fast, Seaweed Sue and I could do more complex athletic events, like barrel racing and pole bending. In barrel racing, the horse and rider gallop round a series of barrels, patterned in the arena. You race in at full speed, circle a barrel, race to the next barrel, circle it and then hurry to the next. When you've successfully run around each barrel, the horse and rider race to the end point, trying to finish the course in the least amount of time, without upsetting any barrels.

Pole bending, on the other hand, resembles slalom skiing, where each contestant weaves in and out between a series of stripped poles, trying to navigate the course as fast as possible.

Seaweed Sue excelled at both contests, and the more we won, the harder and faster I pushed her. That got me the results I wanted, but in the end it wasn't in her best interest.

In fact, the more we won, the more obnoxious she became. The only reason I had any control over her at all was because I rode like a monkey—I just hung on to the saddle as hard as I could while she raced and jumped all over the place, doing a jig and sometimes rearing up on her hind legs as she waited for the race to begin. I controlled her by force, and when I let go of the reins, Seaweed Sue was off and running and I was hanging on for dear life.

What I should have done was stop racing her for a while, and gone back to the basics. Because Seaweed Sue was talented, her training was rushed, so she never built up the maturity and self-confidence of a well-trained horse. Instead, like her previous owners, I put up with her difficult personality because she won, and that's all that mattered to me.

I wanted her to be a champion, and I didn't know what it would take to get there. So while we achieved success, we both learned a series of bad habits along with way. If we'd gone back to the beginning, and built up Seaweed Sue's confidence, she might have achieved even more success. Instead, she taught me how to be a bad trainer, who got his way by force. When she gave me trouble, I yanked her back into line.

That approach, as we saw in Chapter One, didn't work

with Nava Rose. I was trying to teach her a complex task—how to spin in a circle while keeping her feet in a tire—and she just didn't get it. She made me look bad, and it upset me. In response, I threw her to the ground.

The focus was on me. In essence, I was telling Nava Rose, "If you do what I say, that will make me look like a better person. If you don't do what I say, that makes me look bad, so I am going punish you."

In order to teach Nava Rose, I had to forget about me for a while. What she was telling me was, "I'm confused and overwhelmed. Help!"

The worst thing to do in that kind of situation is to freak out, and over react by yelling, or in the case of Nava Rose, getting angry and shoving her. Believe me, people have been trying this from the beginning of time, and yelling at a confused person, or horse, only makes things worse.

If I'd been a better listener, I could have avoided that blowup with Nava Rose. Earlier we talked about the importance of practice, and I believe in the power of practice and hard work.

But it's not just the repetition involved in practice. To make practice effective, you've got to always be observant and listen. The idea is this: to take an honest look at your performance in practice, identify where things are going wrong, and then take small steps to improve.

It wasn't that Nava Rose wasn't practicing hard enough.

The problem we had was that I was focused too much on the end goal—of having her be able to spin in a circle—and not enough on the steps needed to reach that goal.

With Seaweed Sue, the goal had been enough. I was strong enough and stubborn enough to muscle past her flare-ups, and hang on to complete our races.

With Nava Rose, who was learning more difficult tasks, strength and determination were not enough. I had to become smarter.

Sometimes the response is to back off, and break things down into more manageable tasks. More often, the answer is to watch and wait, and trust that practice can make perfect.

Just ask Javier, one of my former students.

I met Javier in the 1970s, when I was teaching at a college in California. He was in his early thirties then, and was going back to school to learn the horse industry. Part of that training included learning to ride horses for the very first time.

I liked Javier. He was quiet and unassuming, but underneath that façade was the best pool player I'd ever met. He would make a bet with you, like you were two friends hanging out, and then bang!—he'd knock in every ball and you'd be forced to admit you'd been suckered. But he was far from horse savvy, and had very little experience. It would have been easy to look at him and conclude that he would never be a horseman.

I spent a year teaching Javier to ride, and watching him

was painful. He would sit rigidly and upright, and despite every attempt to get him to relax, he rode at a trot, bouncing up and down, going *bang, bang, bang, bang, bang* in the saddle.

The key to riding a horse is learning how to relax and flow with the horse. New riders are tempted to grip hard with their knees and hang on the reins, as if they are handlebars on a bike. A good rider instead will relax and breathe, and concentrate on moving in time with the horse.

Unfortunately, Javier was caught in a vicious cycle. He was afraid, and so he hung on as tight as he could and gripped the horse with his knees. But the harder he gripped, the more uncomfortable the horse became, and so the horse moved faster, making Javier more insecure, and so he gripped even tighter.

And the more I tried to force him or yell at him, the worse the cycle got. The best way you can help a person like that is to get their focus on something else, to get them to breathe and relax, and to take small steps of success, until they find their rhythm.

So he'd been riding for a year, and still Javier was bouncing all over the place like a sack of potatoes. It would be easy to lose hope in someone like that and become frustrated and angry with them or yell at them.

For a teacher, a student like that is embarrassing. I started thinking that I'd wasted a whole year working with him, and was tempted to believe there was no use putting any more effort into him.

Then one day, he got it.

We were out in the training arena. All of a sudden, I heard this screaming. At first I thought there had been an accident, and someone had been hurt.

As I looked to see where the screaming came from, Javier rode by, yelling at the top of his lungs, "I got it! I got it! I got it!"

Chapter Four

Getting Past No

FROM THE MOMENT I SAW the trucks pull up, I knew I was in trouble.

We were at a fairground in Georgia, where I was scheduled to do a Sermon on the Mount presentation. A large crowd had gathered, including some influential businessmen, so I was eager to make a good first impression.

The organizers had arranged for several local owners to loan me their horses for the evening. What I'm usually looking for are horses who have never been trained or ridden before, or horses who have had some training, but have run into trouble in the process.

Usually I end up working with horses who have been cared for physically—that is, their owners have kept them well fed and healthy, and sometimes even doted on them with love and affection. But somewhere along the way their training has been neglected, and so the horses haven't reached their full potential.

Sometimes their owners have been too busy, or have felt overwhelmed in the training process. And sometimes life has just gotten in the way, and while the owners had good intentions, things haven't worked out.

When I talked to the organizers ahead of time, everything seemed set. But when I arrived, the arrangements had fallen through, and I had no local horses to work with. The organizers apologized, but I told them not to worry.

"Just get me some horses and I'll make it work," I said, trying to assure them.

A little while later, I went outside of the horse arena to get a little fresh air. All of a sudden, two trucks rolled onto the fairground, one pulling a horse trailer behind it. Emblazoned on the sides of the trucks were the letters "PRCA", which stand for the Professional Rodeo Cowboys Association. Inside the trailer were two big and ornery-looking horses.

I started to get a bad feeling in the pit of my stomach. *I am in for it now,* I thought.

The drivers got out of their trucks, and when they saw me, walked over.

"We're looking for Lew Sterrett," one of them said. "Do you know him?"

My first thought was to say, "Never heard of him." Instead, I replied, "That's me."

"We've got some horses for you," he said, with a smile.

A few minutes later they'd unloaded two professional

bucking horses, who were veterans of the rodeo circuit. These horses, sometimes known as broncos, are often especially bred for bucking. They are strong and athletic, usually with great endurance, able to send their back legs flying and twisting their body in the air over and over again, in hopes of dislodging their rider.

As the riders unloaded the horses and led them into a corral, I did a little bit of advance scouting. The first horse was a twelve-year-old rodeo veteran. He was a big-boned, coarse-haired, jug-headed, red roan bronc.

"Has he ever been ridden?" I asked, trying to sound nonchalant.

"Not for more than eight seconds, a couple of times," one of the drivers said, with a smile. (That's how long a professional bronc rider has to hang on in the rodeo.)

This horse was so long gone from relationships with people that he didn't have a name, just a number. I decided to nickname him "the Widowmaker." A little grim, perhaps, but it seemed to fit his personality.

The other horse was lighter in build, and only three years old, but he was ugly and mean, kind of like a seasoned gang member, covered in tattoos and bad attitude.

Because he was younger, I thought he would be easier to work with, and not have as many bad habits. I decided to call him "the Kid." After the Widowmaker, he'd be a piece of cake. So I decided to work with the older one first.

Plus, I thought—only partly tongue in check—if the Widowmaker killed me, I wouldn't have to worry about this younger horse.

The rest of my afternoon was filled with making preparations. Having the right boundaries in place was step one. The organizers set up a round pen in the middle of the arena, about sixty feet in diameter, and I walked around it, making sure everything was in place.

Whenever I do a presentation, I make sure it is in a controlled environment. This is for my benefit, and for the benefit of the horses. The pen gives the horses space to run, but does not let them get too far away. And it gives me space as well.

In this case, I didn't want to be too close to an explosive bucking horse. If he felt crowded, he'd become afraid and strike out in fear. Getting a hoof upside the head from a bucking horse is not my idea of a good time.

Most people have never been in an enclosed space with a volatile and potentially dangerous animal. But most of us have been in similarly tense situations, with a co-worker, or a spouse, or a business associate, where one false word or wrong move can cause everything to go up in flames.

Maybe you have a co-worker who's talented but bad tempered, and you've got to confront him about a missed deadline, or a project that's gone wrong. Or maybe there's a dispute at home, over finances, or any one of dozens of other tensions that families face these days. Perhaps you've got a neighbor who's hard to get along with, and you've just about hit the wall. Or you're a parent, with a teenager staring you in the face, and saying "No" and daring you to do something about it.

If you've had any of those experiences, then you can imagine how I felt when I walked into the round pen with that bucking horse.

I had an agenda in mind. I had to earn the Widowmaker's trust, and get close enough to ride him, and not just for eight seconds. I had to get him to stand still long enough for me to climb in the saddle, and then ride around the arena without trying to buck me off.

All this on a horse who'd been trained for years to buck off anyone who got close to him! It felt like asking a Hell's Angel to come over and teach Sunday school.

To add to the tension, about 700 or 800 people were watching, and so I also felt vulnerable as I stepped through the gate. My reputation was on the line. A failure could be embarrassing. What would people think if I made an idiot of myself?

Still, I had some advantages over the Widowmaker. Like I said before, we'd be working together in a round pen, so there were definite boundaries. No matter how this horse wanted to ignore me, he couldn't get away. So he was in a place of my choosing, and had to work with me on my terms, not his.

At the same time, there was enough space for both of us to be safe. He could run away if he wanted, by circling around the perimeter of the pen, giving him some sense of control and security. I, on the other hand, could get close enough to make my presence known, using a rope or a flag to motivate him, but not close enough that he could reach me with his hind legs. Having those kinds of safe, firm boundaries has become one of the foundations of my training.

On occasion I've had to work in a smaller pen with a bucking horse like Widowmaker, or in a pen that wasn't strong enough or tall enough to keep him in. In settings like that, the results are never good.

Like the time I showed up to do a one-day presentation, and found that the organizers had set up a pen with panels that were relatively short, and placed several unruly horses inside.

"Are you sure you can keep those horses under control?" I asked, with some doubt in my voice.

"Sure we can," they said.

About an hour later, however, I found myself going with a truck and trailer over to a nearby Wal-Mart parking lot, trying to round up those very horses, before they got into trouble, or got themselves or someone else hurt.

Like many horses, these two runaways had been clever. It hadn't taken them very long to figure out that the panels were on the short side, and a few minutes after being placed in the pen, they jumped the fence and ran off to Wal-Mart. Luckily, we rounded them up without incident, and the program went on with only a slight delay.

There was no chance for my friend the bucking horse to escape this time. The panels were high enough and strong enough to keep him safe and secure, without feeling threatened. Even if he put up a struggle there was little chance of him getting loose.

I had one other advantage when I went to work with the Widowmaker. I had a plan. If I'd gone in and tried to force him to my way of thinking, it would have been a lost cause. He was too strong and too ingrained in his ways for me to do that. Besides, I didn't want to change his behavior.

Instead, I was after something much bigger—his trust and his loyalty. As my mentor Ward Studebaker taught me, with trust and loyalty, I could get a horse to do just about anything.

I first met Ward when I was about nineteen, and newly arrived on the campus of Penn State University. He looked like he'd stepped off the set of a John Wayne movie. Tall and handsome, with an easy smile and an outdoorsman's physique, Ward was every inch a cowboy. Originally a farm boy from Southern Illinois, he'd won a number of awards as a horse trainer before coming to Penn State to manage the university's horse herd. Very quietly, and without a lot of show, he'd become one of the state's most respected horsemen.

There's a story that's told about Ward's early days at Penn State. The university's equine program has long had a reputation for excellence, but the barn operation was out of sorts when he first arrived on campus. The previous horse manager had left a few months early, and in the interim, some things had been let go.

Ward began getting things in order, but before he'd gotten established, he was asked to represent the university at a national competition, using one of their prized horses. Without proper time to prepare, Ward realized it was a bad idea, but his boss insisted, and so he agreed.

As he predicted, the competition was a mess. He finished in last place in his class, embarrassing both himself and the school. When he returned to campus, his boss told him to forget about training, and stick to getting the barn operation running smoothly.

He followed his boss's instructions, and before too long the barn was in order. On the side, however, he took one horse, and began working with it little by little to be ready for the next year.

You can guess what happened at the next year's competition. With time to prepare, Ward won his competition class, besting a national champion in the process. He never boasted about his prowess as a trainer, and seldom competed, but when he did, he almost always won.

By the time I arrived at Penn State, I was full of myself.

My room back home was filled with ribbons and trophies, attesting to my supposed skills as a teenage rider and trainer. I'd also been training horses professionally for several years, and through a special dispensation from Dr. Tom Merritt, head of Penn State's equine program, had gotten permission to bring some Appaloosa horses with me to campus, so I could continue to train them while going to school.

The Appaloosas belonged to my boss, George Zimmerman, who had first hired me when I was around sixteen. George was no saint—definitely not the Sunday school teacher role model that my mother would have hoped for.

But George and I had much in common. We were both hungry to win, to prove ourselves as good horsemen. George would buy expensive horses, in hopes that the more we won in competitions, the more the horses would soar in value.

George owned Appaloosa horses, which is the breed I trained and rode to win my national title. Appaloosas are light horses, usually with spotted skin, white around the eye, and colored coat patterns. They were originally bred by the Nez Perce Indians, and were prized for their speed and endurance.

Because I was talented, but relatively inexperienced, George brought in another trainer, an older man from Texas, to mentor me. This older trainer knew how to win, having trained several champions.

But he was aggressive towards our horses, and sometimes even abusive. He used a large bit and a heavy hand on the horses, as a way of imposing his will. Now there's nothing wrong with a bridle and bit per se; they are effective tools to help guide a horse. But this trainer, like others of his generation, used the bit to coerce horses into doing what he wanted. He'd win competitions, but would leave the horse worse for wear.

At first, I looked up to this trainer, and tried to model myself on him. I was never brutal with horses, but I did always want to show them I was the boss. This led me to focusing on the horse's face when I was training instead of their source of power and drive—the hip.

Training horses is a little bit like teaching a gymnast or ballet dancer. They are tremendous athletes, with God-given strength and agility. But an untrained horse can be clumsy, and won't reach his full potential unless he is trained how to balance and control his body.

The best way to do that is not by jerking him around by the reins. That treatment, in the end, leaves him out of balance. To truly train a horse, the trainer needs to have control of the horse's hips. Once that happens, the horse can gain the same kind of grace that a ballet dancer or gymnast has. A well-trained horse is always under control, never reactionary.

Not long after the new trainer came on the scene, I noticed a change in the behavior of George's horses. They seemed stressed, and ill behaved. One horse in particular really struck me. He was a young horse, whose name I've now forgotten. I'd trained him from an early age, and always found him to be an easygoing horse, who was eager to please.

As his training progressed, however, a change came over him. He was always on edge, as if he were afraid to make a mistake and be punished. There was always a tension in the air around him, and this once easygoing horse turned aggressive, biting other horses, and becoming hard for people to handle.

George and I both knew something was wrong. And before too long, our new trainer decided he'd be happier somewhere else.

I brought his bad habits with me to the horse barn at Penn State. That, and my over-confidence from my earlier successes, made me cocky and arrogant, sure that I knew what I was doing.

Ward decided that I needed to be taken down a notch. He didn't do it in an angry or rude way. Instead he teased me, nicknaming my Appaloosa horses the "happy losers," and wondering out loud if they'd ever amount to anything.

He really did more to put water on my over-confidence than anybody else. Sometimes he'd say things like, "I don't know why you want to stay with those happy losers. You ought to just get out of the horse business entirely. You ought to do something worthwhile with your life. After all, who wants to be a trainer all their life?"

I did, of course. I wanted to be like Ward.

He got more out of his horses than any other trainer I'd ever seen, with far less effort. It was Ward who first taught me the importance of training a horse's hip. That's where all the control is.

It's a bit like this: Picture a ship at sea. Not an ordinary boat, but a battleship or aircraft carrier, or perhaps a luxury cruise ship. The captain controls the ship's direction by spinning the wheel, up on the bridge.

But the wheel doesn't turn the ship. The ship will only turn and respond if the wheel is attached to the rudder at the back of the boat. If the rudder is in good working order, the ship will navigate smoothly. If the rudder is out of order, then it doesn't matter how hard you pull on the wheel. Maybe in a small boat, you can pull the wheel hard enough to move the rudder. But you can't do that on a battleship or an ocean liner.

Ward was trying to teach me that force or intimidation might work on a smaller or less talented horse. But if I really wanted to be a great trainer, and to work with the most talented animals, I needed to learn how to capture a horse's "want to."

Ward did this by rewarding his horses for their successes, and then constantly pushing them to get better. He offered a real partnership, that allowed them to do far more than they could have done on their own. He turned raw, untrained horses into prizewinning athletes.

When I got to Penn State, I thought I knew what I was doing. So the first thing Ward had to do was to show me I wasn't so hot. Then he had to break some of my bad habits, by showing me a better way. Like I said, it took me years to understand what he was up to.

Do you remember the television show called *This Old House*? It documented the renovation of an older property that had fallen into disrepair. (It was the old-school version of modern shows like *Flip This House*.)

The first step in renovating a house is the demolition phase. You've got to tear down the walls and get underneath the surface to look at the framework and foundation. If that's solid and level, then the renovation can continue. Usually, however, when you open up a wall, you find trouble.

For example, take the case of a window that won't open right. The problem might be the window, and you can hammer on the window frame and try to force things back into place. The real problem is more likely to be in the wall, where there may be some rotten boards or studs that have gotten out of place. Or maybe the foundation's not level, and that's thrown everything out of square.

To fix things right, you've got to take care of the problems below the surface. Once those are fixed, you can make progress with the renovation.

That's what Ward did for me. I looked good on the outside, but I didn't have the proper foundation of training habits so I'd never reach my full potential unless he took me down a few notches, until I was ready to learn. Then he showed me a better way, with a firm but gentle hand. I wanted to be a better trainer, and I wanted to do things Ward's way, because he got the results I was after.

I thought of Ward when I got into the round pen with the Widowmaker. He too thought he was hot stuff, and didn't need to pay attention to me. So gently, I began to tear down his defenses.

Being in the round pen was a good start. He couldn't get away from me, nor could he annoy me. The first step was getting him to acknowledge my presence and my authority, that I was someone worth paying attention to. So I sent him around the pen, using a flag on the end of a flexible rod to direct him. I never struck him—instead, by waving the flag in front of him, I got him to change directions.

After we'd done that for a while, I asked him to look at me. I didn't do that with words—I'm not Dr. Doolittle and I can't talk to animals. Instead, I stood patiently hissing to him, and waited for him to turn his head towards me, instead of turning his back on me. As soon as he did that, I turned away, giving him a release.

I should explain a bit here. By standing and looking at him or by waving a flag at the Widowmaker, I was putting very subtle pressure on him. What I wanted was for him to respond to that pressure by looking to me for direction.

Once he did what I asked, once he showed the slightest sign that he was paying attention, I backed off the pressure. A few minutes later, I came back to him, with a little bit more pressure. This time I wanted him to follow me. So I began walking away from him. Doing that piqued his curiosity, and before too long, he was following me around. Again, once he did that, I released the pressure, giving him a reward.

Next was getting him to stand still long enough for me to rub his face and neck. That's a sign of affection among horses, but not a usual activity for bucking broncs.

And so we went on, step by step, for the next two hours.

Not everything went smoothly. Before putting a saddle on him, I wrapped a rope several times around his belly, to simulate the feeling of a saddle and girth. Once I pulled that rope, he began to buck all over the place. But that was no surprise. It's what he'd been trained to do for years.

If I'd given up at that point, and said, "Look, he'll never change. You can't teach an old dog—or horse—new tricks," I'd have missed out on what came next.

But I knew that progress is slow, when you are trying to win the heart of a horse—or a person. You've got to do it one step at a time, and it's often two steps forward and one step back. Sometimes it's even one step forward and two steps back.

Once the Widowmaker got the bucking out of his system, and turned towards me, as if to say, "What do you want me to do?", we moved on. He got used to the ropes and not long afterwards, I had a blanket, and then a saddle on him.

Then I rode him, not for eight seconds, but for at least eight minutes. I could have ridden him for hours if I'd had the time. Not because I'd forced him to do what I wanted—that would have been a lost cause. He'd started out defiant and angry, but when I offered him a relationship, the chance to do something new, he jumped at it.

And what happened to the Kid, the young horse I thought would be a piece of cake? I worked with him the same way for two hours, but he never gave in. He bucked and kicked and seethed at me for two hours.

Now I've worked with several thousand unbroken horses—those who have never been saddled and ridden before. There have been all kinds. Stallions, mares, and geldings. Grizzled broncs, and even mustangs who've been right off the western plains. On a handful of occasions, I've not been able to ride one in the short time of a presentation. This night was one of those times. After two hours of tense, hard work, I told the audience it was time to stop.

"I could work with him for another thirty minutes but thirty minutes, or thirty hours, won't do him any good right now," I said.

The Kid was not ready to change. Most likely, if I'd pushed him, one of us would get hurt. I was tired and so was he. But he wasn't ready for a relationship, wasn't ready to change. And that's all right too. Maybe we'll meet up in the future and have another go round.

Even so, my time with the Kid wasn't wasted. A few days after the event was over, I heard from one of the organizers who told me that there were some teenaged girls in the audience who'd been going through a rough time with their parents.

Being a teenager, especially a teenaged girl, is hard. Halfway between being girls and being women, and filled with emotions they don't always understand, they can be hard to live with. And their relationships with their parents get easily frayed.

Sometimes those emotions get out of hand, and turn into disrespect towards parents, or mean and cruel behavior towards other teens.

That night, as the girls watched the Widowmaker and the Kid, something changed in them. They saw one horse overcome its fear and its difficulties, and start to build a new relationship and new patterns of living. They saw another horse refuse to give up its angry ways and end up alone.

And some of them decided they'd rather be like the Widowmaker than the Kid. They'd rather have positive relationships with their parents and friends than be in conflict all the time. They had what we sometimes call an epiphany—a moment of insight when they saw a new way of doing things.

Neither those girls nor the Widowmaker changed overnight. It's not like I waved a magic wand and turned them into perfect angels. But they started on a different path that night, one filled with possibilities.

CHAPTER 5

GOD AND A GIRL

I THOUGHT I WAS DOING God a favor.

I had no idea that God—and a girl—were going to turn my life upside down.

It was just after my junior year of college, and I'd been trying to figure out what to do with the summer. I had one last semester at Penn State and planned on graduating in the December of 1974.

Grad school would come after that, and I was already working on applications for assistantships. I had planned to stay around the university for the summer, but the job I'd lined up fell through. Now I needed a Plan B.

About a year earlier, I'd started going to church again. I grew up Presbyterian, and had gone to church as a youngster, but had dropped out once I got to high school. At Penn State, however, my faith became real and personal. I started going to church, and eventually was baptized.

Not long afterwards, I began to spend a lot of time with

a young lady from the church. She was a real sweet gal. I began to date her, and started wondering, maybe this gal will be my wife someday.

She started telling me about this camp outside of Erie, called Miracle Mountain Ranch. She'd grown up going to the camp, and later volunteered there. Knowing my interest in horses, she thought that working at the camp might make the perfect summer job for me.

I'd been to church camp when I was young, and hadn't liked it much but I thought I'd give the ranch a try. Besides, I thought jokingly, I would be doing it to earn some points with God. After all, how bad could it be?

About a month before camp started, I went there. My girlfriend, Debbie, and I decided to drive up to the camp for the weekend to meet some of the staff and to see about lining up a summer job for me.

My first impressions were, to be honest, underwhelming. For one thing, the camp was in the middle of nowhere, about an hour south of Erie, and a few miles outside of the small town of Corry, Pennsylvania.

And at first glance, the camp facilities left much to be desired as well. A long drive up a steep mountain road, past a pasture full of grazing cattle, led to the main camp grounds. The camp was modeled after an Old West ranch, with bunkhouses, corrals, a horse barn, a dining hall and an indoor rodeo arena. Along with horses for the campers to ride, there was also a herd of sixty Hereford cattle. All of that gave the camp a real cowboy-like feel.

Still, I was unimpressed. The camp buildings had a worn feel to them, and many were in need of renovations. They were rustic bunkhouses, sided only with red roofing paper.

Then there were the horses. By this time, I'd become somewhat a snob when it came to horses. I was used to training championship Quarter Horses and Appaloosas with expensive bloodlines, who'd cost thousands and who'd been bred for the show ring. They were great athletes, born with style and power, who had the God-given talent to be champions.

Since the camp didn't cater for show horses, it was easy to overlook the quality of the horses that were at the camp. I didn't want to work with dull horses, and Miracle Mountain Ranch had plenty of what I first thought of as average horses.

I was suffering for the Lord, as they say. So if I could bring my talent to the camp and improve some less-than-championship horses, I'd consider it a good deed. Little did I realize that the roles were about to be reversed, and that I was about to learn some life lessons from the horses I'd looked down my nose at.

I spent the first day meeting and greeting the staff, and putting a good face on. But inside, I was miserable and cranky. I wanted to get in my car and go. That first night I lay in bed, restless and unable to sleep.

I'll admit it, I was pretty selfish at this point of my life.

I didn't think about anyone else but myself most of the time, and what I wanted.

Despite arriving with a chip on my shoulder, I was soon disarmed by the warmth of the camp staff, in particular the director Dale Linebaugh, and his wife, Opal. The more I learned about the staff, the more impressed by them I became.

For one thing, they were all volunteers, which meant that not only did they have to work full-time, but they also had to raise their own salaries, through donations from friends and family and churches. The reason they were willing to make that commitment was that they believed in the work the camp was doing. By investing their time and energy in the kids who went to camp, they were doing their part to make the world a better place. For the first time, I began to wonder if there were more important things in life than horses.

And then, there was the camp director's daughter, Melodie. She was tall, dark haired, dark eyed, and beautiful, with a disarming smile. Not only that, she'd grown up riding horses, even before she could walk, and was a talented rider and performer. Maybe this camp wasn't so bad after all!

When I left the camp, I had an offer for a summer job to work in the ranch's horsemanship program. If nothing else, I'd get to see more of Melodie. I naively mentioned that to my girlfriend on the way back to the Penn State campus.

"That Melodie is really something, isn't she?" I told her on the ride home.

As you might guess, our relationship didn't last much longer.

Finally summer rolled around and I was back at the ranch. This was a pretty good deal, I thought. Once I got past my initial snobbery, I realized the camp's horses weren't all that bad. And the job was good. I'd be around horses all day long, and get to work with a great team of people.

I secretly hoped that Melodie would be there as well—but she was working at a camp eight hours away. Despite the distance, a romance blossomed between us.

By the end of that summer, I was hooked and realized that Melodie was the woman I wanted to spend the rest of my life with. Besides her physical attractiveness, we were well matched. We shared a love of God and a love of horses, and our personalities complemented each other.

She was vivacious and bold with her love of God and others, while I was more reserved, happy to be in the barn with the horses all day. My easygoing manner was a good complement to her intensity.

She was also strong enough to stand up to me and tell me when I was wrong. Not by yelling at me or by withdrawing, but by looking me right in the eye and giving me a straightforward, honest response.

There were other reasons to love her as well. As a kid coming from a broken home, I was transfixed by her parents. Now that we've been married for more than thirty years, sometimes Melodie accuses me of marrying her for her dad as much as for her.

Dale and Opal Linebaugh, Melodie's parents, had started the camp in 1963, and by the time I arrived, they were drawing over 1,000 kids during the summer season. Dale was a tall and handsome man, equally at home on the back of a horse as he was preaching in a pulpit. He was the kind of leader who naturally attracted people to him, with a likeable and generous spirit. He was like the dad I'd never known.

Dale was surprisingly affectionate as well. He was then—and remains even today—a hugger, greeting friends and family with warm affection. The first time he hugged me, it startled me. I wasn't used to being hugged and so responded by becoming stiff as a board. Dale kept hugging me, and as the weeks at camp wore on, my stiff exterior began to melt.

Even if we don't like to admit it, most of us crave that kind of physical affection and affirmation. That goes even for cowboys, despite our gruff ways.

It was Dale who began to show me that there were more important things to life than winning in the show ring. Watching him work with guests and staff, and later with volunteers and supporters of the camp, I realized he was beloved and highly respected.

Like Ward Studebaker, he didn't lead with an iron fist. Instead, Dale inspired and empowered people, which made them want to follow. He was a master at finding people's "want to."

I wanted to be like him. Which is why, three years later, I found myself sitting in his office and trying desperately to fill his shoes.

Life was a blur in the weeks and months after I'd met Melodie. At the end of summer, I went back to Penn State, and finished my last semester of studies. But things had changed. Instead of applying to graduate school in equine studies, I was planning to go to seminary and prepare for a life in ministry.

It was a huge, life-altering change. Many of my friends and mentors thought I'd lost my mind. They'd invested time and energy in grooming me to go to graduate school because they believed I had a great future in the horse business. It seemed like I was throwing it all away for a girl.

They were partly right, I suppose. It did seem like I was throwing everything away. And in the weeks and months that followed, I second-guessed myself dozens of times. But in the end, I knew I had made the right choice.

First, my entire identity had been built around horses, and winning in the show ring. That's all I lived for. That's a pretty shaky foundation to build a life on.

But Ward Studebaker had taught me that winning, in the end, didn't matter as much as I thought it did. When he competed, Ward won. But he rarely entered shows, and wasn't all that impressed with himself when he did win.

Ward understood something I was just coming to grips

with. Winning is not everything. In fact, the process of training was more important than the actual competition. The journey is more important than the destination.

Now, if that sounds like motivational speaker mumbo-jumbo, consider this: When I trained horses, we won, but only by running myself and the horses ragged. We would do anything and everything to look good for the few minutes we were before the judges. All we got in the end was a trophy or a blue ribbon, but nothing of lasting value. Sometimes we ended up worse off, because we were exhausted and ill-tempered by the pursuit of winning.

Ward, on the other hand, focused on the process of teaching his horses, building one success on another. Slowly but surely, he was molding them into better horses—stronger, more confident, and more capable. Competitions were like mile markers, to show how far they had progressed. But the goal of training was to make them into better horses, not just to win awards.

He never lost perspective on what he was doing. And his sense of self-worth didn't depend on how well he did in the show ring. I needed to learn that, and the only way for me to do it was to walk away from the show ring for a while.

Secondly, Dale was teaching me the connection between the principles I was learning as a horse trainer and the ability to lead people. I began to realize that horses would shed light on human relationships. That the same dynamics of trust that enabled a horse and trainer to work together applied to people as well.

Though mesmerized by Dale, I knew the ranch was no utopia and I would later learn that all was not well. Running a nonprofit youth camp, relying on small donors, always trying to stretch every penny, can take a toll. But despite the difficulties in the camp, Dale and Opal always responded with grace. I wanted to be that kind of person; the kind who could face difficult times without cracking.

Thirdly, I'd always worked with top-quality horses, and I'd started to believe that they were the only horses worth working with. Over the next decade, while working at the ranch, I learned that even the plainest horses—and the most ordinary of people—are capable of great things.

It would have been easier to stay on the for-profit side of the horse business. It meant making good money, having a nice house, and having the respect of my teachers and mentors.

Working at a ranch meant a lot of heartache and hard times. It meant being poor for many years. There were times when I thought we'd have to close the doors and give up. But there's been great joy as well. Amazingly, we stayed solvent.

Melodie and I also gained something money couldn't buy—a solid foundation for our marriage.

Though I had received much from my family and was loved much, our struggles growing up had left me longing for a sense of stability. My mom's remarriage had been a disaster, and she and my stepdad had long since split up. The rest of the family had splintered as well. My brothers and sisters grew up and went their own way, with extreme values ranging from conservative to liberal.

One sister went off to become a Methodist minister; another married a guy who became a drug dealer. My oldest stepbrother published New Age books and ran New Age and sacred sexuality conferences around the country, while another brother would eventually come to work for me on the ranch.

Marrying Melodie meant I had to establish my own family and values and a solid foundation for my life. If that meant marrying into the family business, well, that was all right with me. My relationship with her and her family meant more than any success I ever had in the show ring.

And the ride has been worth every minute.

Of course, I didn't always feel that way. Many mornings, during my early years at the ranch, I'd wake up and wonder, *What have I gotten myself into?*

The first thing I figured out was how much I needed to learn. I knew about horses, but not much about leading people or about the Bible. So I went off to New York for a year, to study at Nyack Bible College, while Melodie went to work as a nurse at Bryan College in Dayton, Tennessee. We married a year later.

It would prove to be a busy year, with her starting a new job and preparing for a wedding, and me studying for my master's degree.

During the week I'd be in class; on the weekends I'd go to downtown NYC, and hang out in the coffee houses and on street corners, talking to drug addicts and derelicts. I was about as far from horses as a country boy could get.

Once I was done at Nyack, and we were married, I spent two years at a horsemanship college out in California, where I developed a whole new perspective for the future. It was there that I met my friend Javier.

While in California, I worked for a man who was very inconsistent in his leadership style. He would often change his mind midstream, and so the staff never knew what to expect from him. We rarely had a sense of momentum in our program, because as soon as we made any progress, our goals and priorities changed. It gave me practice in following someone who was hard to work for, and taught me what kind of boss I didn't want to be.

By 1977, Dale and Opal had decided to leave the ranch, so Dale could go back to school. He wanted to finish his PhD, which had been a long-term dream.

Once Dale and Opal departed, the board began to rethink the ranch's future. Eventually, they decided that the best course of action was to sell the ranch. Though it looked like the sale would go through, the board could never finalize a deal.

The next two years proved difficult. My brother-in-law served as the interim director once Dale left, but it was a thankless job. Because the board were hoping to sell, they didn't want to invest a great deal of money in improvements to the buildings and the staff were left in limbo, unable to make many changes until the new ownership was in place.

It was a time of confusion and uncertainty, which caused a great deal of stress and resentment to build up among staff members. They soldiered on, keeping the camp programs running at a high level but they were becoming stressed and disillusioned.

When the sale fell through, the board asked Melodie and me to come back and assume the leadership of the camp. I was twenty-four, and in way over my head. Most of the staff had already served for decades. I was a bit intimidated about coming on board and making changes.

To make matters worse, the camp's finances were in bad shape. Just a few years earlier, Dale had fallen out with his original partner in the ministry. It was a difficult separation that resulted in the loss of community support. Before the split, the ranch had drawn over 1,000 campers a summer. Over the next few years, the numbers began to steadily drop. By the time I'd been on the scene for three years, that number had dropped to around 300.

Turning things around required drastic measures, including cutting expenses to the bone. We didn't even have enough money to make a long-distance phone call. Most of the camp buildings were heated by wood, so the staff and I, along with their kids, cut our own firewood from the forests on the campgrounds. I can remember many days in the cold and rain, cutting and splitting logs so we'd have enough wood to keep the buildings heated.

It was miserable. But it turned out to be a good team-building time, and it would lay a foundation for the deeper healing that was needed.

At the same time, we didn't want to wring our hands, and watch the camp continue to decline. Most of the bunkhouses needed renovations and we didn't have the cash to pay for material. Given our financial state, I was hesitant to take a loan to make repairs. The donor base was very small, so there was little possibility of adding more donations in the short run.

Faced with an overwhelming task, I drew a lesson from my early days with Nava Rose. What I needed was to cut the project down into small pieces, and solve those small problems one at a time. Since we needed construction materials, I began to look for buildings, like old barns that needed to be torn down, and ask if we could salvage some of the materials. Sometimes I'd be driving down the road and see people working on an old barn, and I'd pull the truck over, hop out and ask right then and there if we could have the old boards. Soon the staff team was actively involved in the salvage business.

I had no shame, really. But I did have a vision. What the camp needed was a facelift. The buildings were sturdy enough, but they looked too similar to each other. Since we were a horse ranch, I wanted the grounds to have more of an Old West town image, as if you'd just walked on to the set of a John Wayne movie.

Since we couldn't afford to rebuild the bunkhouses, we took a cue from those old movies and put false fronts on the buildings, with front porches. Those old, gray, weathered barn boards gave the feeling of authenticity, like they'd really come from the Old West. We removed the old nails, pounded them out flat, and reused them to attach the boards.

Those boards were usually so old and dirty that our faces and arms would turn completely black in the process. We worked our tails off for three years, trying to create something worthwhile out of a pile of junk boards and rusty, bent nails.

While the camp was getting a face-lift on the outside, the staff were being reworked from the inside out. They were dedicated, hard-working people, who loved the ranch and spent years there, often at great personal cost. Over those years, however, small hurts had been allowed to fester under the surface unresolved. And there were some unfinished loose ends from the years of transition.

On the outside, people were warm and friendly, but that happy exterior hid jealousy, bitterness, and wounded spirits. Nobody can pretend as well as professional Christians. Behind every "bless your heart" were hurt feelings that no one wanted to or knew how to talk about.

Lew's favorite tool for life illustrations: a horse. Desired Spark is a 1997 Quarter Horse stallion.

Life from the view of a...

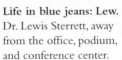

A Horseman – Skip 'N the Spotlite: a 1999 palomino stallion. He is registered both as a Quarter and Paint horse, and is ridden dressage and western seat. His specialty: being a gentleman!

Life in blue jeans: Lew. Dr. Lewis Sterrett, away from the office, podium, and conference center.

A Cowboy – Out for a gallop in Texas on Spark. His specialty: ponying youngsters!

A Trainer – Working with a guest horse on leading and loading. First order of business: building healthy boundaries.

A Man of God – Lew praying with (left to right) Randy Coleman and Charlie Simmons (some of our host crew) before a Plant City, Florida presentation.

Coliseums – State and city-wide campaigns are often hosted in major coliseums. A round pen session at the Will Rogers Coliseum in Ft. Worth, Texas.

All-Terrain – Lew and Rooster's Shalom, a 2004 buckskin Quarter Horse stallion (commonly known as Romeo) discover a small patch of sand.

Indoors is always best, but rain or shine we have gone on since 1981. A leadership training seminar at the Oklahoma State Fairgrounds.

Open lots – An open air forum typically hosted by a group of community organizations in rural settings. Lew on Spark.

On the trail – On the Ranch headquarters in Pennsylvania with guests or students, Lew often takes a break from the arena to teach on the trail.

International travel – Since 2002, this rig has annually traversed a majority of states and provinces in the United States and Canada, making an average of 150 presentations per year.

Training in small steps

Putting protective leg gear on an unhandled horse is a two person job that can prove risky. How they are handled sets the stage for trust or distrust.

Seeing the untrained, fearful horse choose to follow the trainer, rather than avoid him, is a delightful moment for the audience, trainer, and horse.

First saddlings are often met with this reaction. Only a very few buck when Lew mounts a few moments later.

Lew helps a problem horse own and resolve his attitude before he mounts. Graduation presentation at French Camp, Mississippi.

The same horse with 'response-able' training. Everybody wins – the horse, the trainer, and the next generation!

Spark at his best, bridleless and 'mentoring' a young horse for the first saddling and ride.

Lew testing the 'green broke' horse before riding. Featuring Measures of Maturity for a family conference in Big Sandy, Texas.

Results with fruitful outcomes

Discernment – Spark walking through debris of varying natures, obeying Lew's instructions to "come."

Confidence – Romeo being covered by a tarp. The topic – blind faith, or confident trust.

Humility –
Romeo at rest
and seated at the
feet of his master.

Courage –
Romeo's first
walk over a teeter-
totter.

Enjoying "the boys"

Lew with his three stallions (left to right): Spotlite, Romeo, and Spark. Presenting at a men's conference in Colorado on the topic of brotherhood.

Horses love to get out and run, and Spark is no exception. During a photo session, Lew and Spark go for a gallop.

Enjoying some down time on Romeo. Lew has ridden almost every section of the U.S., from the tips of Alaska to Florida.

Training on a brisk winter morning in Texas. Lew saves time by working two horses at once: he rides Romeo to the training corral and returns on Spark.

Time for reflection

Down time is necessary for the horses, too. Fresh grass is always a treat.

Riding together with Melodie has become more of an exception than a rule, but always enjoyed. She grew up riding and training horses on their ranches in New York and Pennsylvania.

After a few months, I realized that someone had to address these conflicts, and since I was the boss, it had to be me. After thinking it over, I decided we'd have a weekly staff morale meeting, every Tuesday morning.

These Tuesday morning meetings became infamous among the staff. First of all, they started out as morning meetings, but soon turned into marathon, all-day sessions.

Not all the problems were caused at the ranch. Some of the staff had come from difficult family backgrounds, and had brought those past hurts with them to the ranch. Those staff members had never developed the skills or confidence to face their hurts and find resolutions.

Some of the time it was like pulling teeth, because no one wanted to be honest. They wanted to put a good face on and pretend things were fine, at least in public.

In the church world, there's this myth that if a leader isn't miserable or living in poverty, then they really aren't spiritual. Ministers and youth workers and camp directors often sacrifice everything for their work—their families, their health, sometimes even their own faith. There's lots of thankless work and little reward, at least on the material side of things.

The ranch staff had somehow come to believe that being poor and depressed was the expected norm. A subtle philosophy had come to be accepted—that the ministry and the camp's programs came first. As long as they were running well, nothing else mattered. So if the staff were bickering behind the scenes, it was all right, as long as they put on fun programs for the campers—as if no one would notice that the staff weren't successful at resolving their own conflicts. But a happy face and a message of God's love don't always cover disharmony and division.

In those Tuesday morning meetings, we began to develop the skills to resolve those conflicts and come to peace.

My father-in-law is a great man, who had the best of intentions. But between the partnership split and living twelve hours away, he was unable to bring about the needed healing. It was my job to make it happen now.

Again, borrowing a page from Nava Rose, I started small. I couldn't start to mend fences with the staff unless they were honest with me. So little by little, as I was honest with them, I began to tease their stories out of them. Much of the time it was not easy to hear or apply these truths about relationships, but they worked.

Paul and Marcia Carlstrom owned a family farm before coming to Miracle Mountain Ranch. They sold their farm and donated most of their equipment to the ranch. They had sacrificed diligently to get the horse-and-cattle program on its feet.

During the transition, it was implied that Paul might eventually be named Director. In order for us to work together, we needed to get past this point.

The Carlstroms lived in an old farmhouse on the camp

grounds, with a cracked foundation that made the house sag in the middle. They'd been promised better housing, but it had never materialized. It would take time for me to make good on those promises.

Another couple lived with their three young children in a travel trailer that had been parked on the grounds. Over the years a small addition had been added on, with a bathroom and living-room, all suspended on wooden posts. But it was no place to raise a family, especially in the bitter Pennsylvania winters. They needed a new place to live.

Once the problems were out in the open, I could go to work on solving them. Part of that process was apologizing to the staff for my own shortcomings, and for anything I'd done which had made matters worse. Then I began to sit down, one on one, to figure out what promises had been made, and what I had to do to make those unfulfilled promises right.

It took years to do that. Some of the staff had decided to leave by then. But some remained and are still with us.

One thing I promised was that I'd always be straightforward with the staff. Once I got a better handle on the housing, I began making plans to do what I could to correct the situations.

"I can't fix this right away," I told the staff. Surprisingly, they weren't angry with my responses. Disappointed, yes, and some decided to leave. But with that straightforward response, I began to earn their trust and respect.

Being a leader often involves disappointing people. It goes with the territory. But honest disappointment beats false hope any day.

While things didn't change overnight, we started to see slow and steady improvement. I knew that I needed to earn their trust.

Sometimes I am asked why I didn't make a clean sweep of things, and start all over with new staff. Making a fresh start might have been easier, given the tension and disrespect that plagued the staff when I arrived.

But it was a shortcut, and I knew it. I could bring in a whole new staff, but unless I changed the way the ranch was run, it was only a matter of time before the new staff were burned out and miserable.

There's an idea floating around Christian leadership circles, borrowed from the corporate world. It goes something like this: Running a business, a church, or a Christian nonprofit organization is like driving a bus. The key to success, according to this approach, is to get the right people on the bus, and toss the wrong people off the bus. Once all the right people are on the bus, everything will run smoothly.

While that is a valid point, it's not the whole answer. I've come to understand that a leader should adapt his methods to the people on his staff. If the people on the bus are miserable, maybe it's time for the leader to change the circumstances. For starters, maybe the bus driver should ask people why they are miserable before giving them the heave-ho. It could be that the bus is the problem, not the people.

Besides, firing people wholesale would have been unethical. These folks had invested their lives in the camp and they deserved a chance to turn things around. And to be honest, it's not like people were beating down the doors to join the staff. If the ranch was to have a future, I needed them as much as they needed me.

Out of this process came the most pivotal decision of my life. I was faced with a fork in the road, and had two clear choices. I could either set my energies, focus, and vision on making the ministry successful, even if it meant burning out the staff in the meantime. Or, I could work to make my staff successful. I could make their success and development my priority, and trust that the results would follow. One is a programmatic model and the other is a relational model. I chose the latter. I had no stomach for burning people out in order to further the ministry.

This philosophy began to change the way I worked with horses as well. Instead of demanding that they conformed to my methods, I began to adapt to their needs and limitations.

What kept me going, even in the difficult days, was the vision I had for the staff. I didn't want a happy staff of people who'd do whatever I said, who'd follow my every direction, and do things just the way I wanted. Instead, I wanted a staff that I could trust.

That vision is a lot like the way I see horses. There's a difference between an obedient horse and a trustworthy horse. An obedient horse will do what you tell them, as long as you are paying attention. But if you lose focus for a moment, or a crisis moment comes up, the horse won't know what to do.

A trustworthy horse will have enough training and experience to know what the right thing to do is, even in a difficult time or crisis.

It's the same with people. I wanted a staff that I could trust and partner with.

It's easier to say, if a horse fails, that it's their fault, and the solution is to get a better horse. And if the staff fail, it's their fault, and the solution is to get a better staff.

Helping a horse or a staff member overcome their failures is hard work. In those early years there were a lot of tears, a lot of loneliness, a lot of sleepless nights. But as the weeks and months went by, I could sense that change was coming.

The funny thing is, we almost didn't make it.

By 1980, three years after I'd become the director, we hit the wall. Our numbers were down, and the stress of trying to turn things around was taking its toll on Melodie and me. Our board of directors could see we had come to the end of our rope and encouraged us to sell. Sitting around a table at a board meeting, they told me it was time to shut down the ranch.

The board wasn't angry with us. If anything, they were disappointed that things were not working out the way they'd hoped. They feared that the stresses of trying to turn the ranch around were starting to fray our marriage.

If the camp shut down, it would be difficult and disappointing. But the board could live with that. What they couldn't live with was the possibility that the camp would come between Melodie and me and ruin our marriage.

"Give me one more year," I said.

I'd been inspired by one of the parables that Jesus told about patience. It's found in the thirteenth chapter of the Gospel of Luke:

> A man had a fig tree, planted in his vineyard, and he went to look for fruit on it, but did not find any.
>
> So he said to the man who took care of the vineyard, 'For three years now I've been coming to look for fruit on this fig tree and haven't found any. Cut it down! Why should it use up the soil?'
>
> 'Sir,' the man replied, 'leave it alone for one more year, and I'll dig around it and fertilize it. If it bears fruit next year, fine! If not, then cut it down.'
>
> (LUKE 13:6–9 NIV)

I'd started to see some improvement in the ranch and wasn't quite ready to quit. The board relented, and said we could stay open one more year. If things didn't get better, they'd shut the camp down and sell off the property.

In some ways, being told the camp was on its last legs sounded like great news to me. It took all the pressure off my back.

For three years, I'd been living with the idea that failure was not an option. I didn't want to let Melodie or her parents down. I was trying to fill her father's shoes, and it was an impossible task. The board lifted that burden off my shoulders. I was free to fail. So we began to take more chances, to try new things, without having to worry about the results.

One of the first things I did was sell off the cattle. Beef prices were up that year, and the profits from the sale would give us some funds to work with and provide much-needed room for the large horse herd. We'd kept the cattle herd mostly because raising cattle had been Dale's dream, and we didn't want to change what he'd started.

As we began to try new ideas, attendance began to rise. Parents would come to us and say the strangest things. "We love to send our kids here, because of your staff," they'd say. "They are so loving and they set a great example for our kids."

I had to stifle a laugh, because on Tuesday mornings we were still fighting. But the conflicts were shorter, and often ended in laughter, because we'd learned to work things through instead of avoiding them.

The outcome that was evident to others was love. Visitors and guests to the camp began to comment on how well the camp staff worked together, and that we seemed to have genuine affection for one another.

I began to make inroads into the community as well. The camp split years earlier had alienated some of our former campers. But with our spruced-up buildings and refreshed staff, campers began to return.

Instead of closing at the end of 1980, we began making plans for the future. Little did we know that all the things we'd been learning would be introduced into a brand-new program that began in 1981. This program would not only involve academics and skill training, but would focus on reaching people's hearts and building the foundation for healthy relationships.

It would also open the door for a new work, called "Sermon on the Mount," which would eventually spread around the world.

CHAPTER 6

OVERCOMING LIMITATIONS

FAST FORWARD SEVEN YEARS. It's now 1987, and by this time, the ranch is experiencing a rebirth. Our summers are full, and we're about to celebrate the ranch's twenty-fifth anniversary. I've also got something new in the works, an idea called "Sermon on the Mount."

When Dale was director of the ranch, he spent nine months of the year on the road, speaking at churches and conferences, trying to raise money to support the ongoing work of the camp. He had a natural gift for speaking to groups of people, and had been trained as a pastor and preacher.

Me, I was a tongue-tied Pennsylvanian Dutchman who was allergic to speaking in front of crowds. I didn't mind talking to guests at the camp, but that was usually as a host where I was welcoming them to the ranch, or making a few housekeeping announcements.

The thought of going out on the road and expecting people to show up at a church meeting or a conference to listen to me speak never crossed my mind in those days. I don't think even I would have shown up to hear me speak.

So imagine my surprise when people were inviting me to be the guest speaker at their events. Only I wasn't going alone. The horses were going with me. And some of the average horses from the ranch, the ones I'd originally thought would never make it, had become the star attractions.

We called the presentations "Sermons on the Mount"—a play on words about Jesus' best-known speech and riding a horse. The idea was pretty straightforward. Working through our difficulties at the camp—along with my horse-training experience—had given me some insight into the way relationships worked, especially the importance of listening and trust. Instead of me standing up for an hour and droning on and on about the principles, my horse would help me bring them to life.

The idea was still ragged around the edges. I used an old Ford pickup and trailer that I'd repainted to take my horses out to do these demonstrations. Neither the rig nor my horses looked like money. But I'd been learning that with horses, like many other areas of life, appearances can be deceiving.

That was one of the first lessons the horses taught me, soon after I arrived at the ranch back in 1974. Since I was in charge of the horsemanship program, I came in a few weeks before the campers arrived for the summer, in order to take stock of the horse herd. There were about seventy of them.

Most of them were older, experienced in being ridden by the campers and relatively safe.

Still, you can never be careful enough with horses. Sometimes a horse that appears to be well trained and responsive can turn explosive and dangerous when startled.

I wanted get a better handle on them, and to sort them by reliability. Before we put our guests on the horses, I wanted to know which were safe for even the youngest of campers, and which ones I needed to keep an eye on, who might cause trouble for inexperienced riders.

In the back of my mind, I was hoping that some of the horses would have the potential for more advanced training. Much to my surprise, I found a number of diamonds in the rough in those first few weeks.

One of the horses that caught my eye was Ribbon, a well-bred Quarter Horse mare with a bright sorrel (reddish-brown) coat. She seemed a better match for the show ring than a summer youth ranch, especially in contrast to some of the other horses.

More typical of the ranch's horses was Peyote, who was, in every sense of the word, an average horse. Average looks, average intelligence, average athleticism, average everything. He was all right for giving riding lessons to young campers but that was about it.

Ribbon was a beautiful horse, with a great deal of talent. If they were in high school, she would have been the prom queen, while Peyote would have been a nobody.

Surely, I thought, Ribbon was capable of doing a lot more than hauling inexperienced campers on trail rides. So as the weeks went by, I began to spend more time with Ribbon, seeing what she was capable of. Despite her talent, however, she was a constant disappointment.

While she was obedient, and would do what I asked her to do, she constantly complained about it. Even when I asked her to do a relatively simple task, she'd pin her ears back or wring her tail—swishing it back and forth in irritation. It was a sign that she was always irritable and unpleasant.

Before too long, it became clear that Ribbon had no interest in being a team player. She did everything with a sour attitude that made her unpleasant to be around. On the outside she was a gorgeous horse, but that beauty was marred by her personality. That attitude kept her from reaching her potential, and instead, limited her to being little better than an easily replaceable and unremarkable lesson horse.

I began to take Ribbon along during our presentations, as she made a great example, especially alongside Peyote. That average horse turned out to be remarkably adept during our training, and he became much more skilled than Ribbon ever was. His attitude, and willingness to be taught, opened the door for his success.

Putting the two together would surprise an audience. They'd see Ribbon and immediately think she was the more accomplished horse, and they'd be surprised by her attitude when I rode her. Her movements were choppy, and she would be constantly complaining. Unlike people, horses are generally transparent with their emotions. When they are ticked off, they'll let you know. And Ribbon—though she would eventually become a reliable horse—was ticked off most of the time.

By contrast, Peyote would ride smoothly and respond to my commands almost without effort. He wasn't great at advanced maneuvers, like a flying lead change—more about that later—but he far exceeded the audience's expectations.

In recent years, the horse-breeding world has begun to catch on to the idea that, when it comes to horses, looks aren't everything. A former student of mine now works for the Waggoner Ranch in Texas, one of the largest horse breeders in the United States.

In the past, they've made most of their money breeding horses for the show ring. But they've discovered an unexpected demand for their ranch horses. Those horses used to be considered less valuable than show horses, mainly based on their physical appearance. The show horses often looked great, but they'd never last a day on a real ranch.

By contrast, some of the less attractive horses know well how to get the job done, a skill that's made them rise in value. In recent years, a whole new market and set of competitions has evolved for the once-underestimated ranch horse.

Working with Ribbon and Peyote, my attitudes about horses began to change as well. When I started at the ranch I was a horse snob, more impressed by a horse's looks and breeding than by their attitude. The more time I spent with the ranch horses, the more I realized that a horse's heart and attitude mattered more than their pedigree and their bloodlines.

The horses also taught me more about myself. On the inside, I wasn't much different than Ribbon. My success in training had given me a big head, and I thought I was too important to work with inferior horses. Only the best would do for me. I was becoming a bit of a prima donna, and treated people and horses based on their abilities and outward appearance.

But in the rustic surroundings of the ranch, I began to wonder if I'd gotten it all wrong. Those early years of running the ranch humbled me. I was no longer the hotshot, horse-training college kid I'd been when I first arrived. Turning the camp around had tested me, and there were many times when I wanted to give up. But we hadn't quit, and now those years of hard work were paying off. There's a Bible verse which says that those who sow in tears will reap in joy someday, and I really felt like that verse was coming to life at the ranch.

Some days, I'd daydream about what I'd left behind. I wondered, now that I was older and a bit wiser, what I might be able to do with a really talented horse, like the ones I used to train for George Zimmerman. But those days were long gone.

Or so I thought.

Despite the headaches of having old equipment, life was good at the ranch. Our numbers were up, and our finances were back on solid footing. I remember early on, we got a letter from a donor who'd offered to give us $100 a month, and we were nearly overcome with joy. In those days $100 meant we could keep the lights on and pay the phone bill.

But by 1987, things were looking up. Since it was the ranch's twenty-fifth anniversary, we decided to throw a party. We invited Dale and Opal to come back, and sent out invitations to donors and former campers alike. On the day of the anniversary celebration, the ranch grounds were packed with old friends. It felt like a giant family reunion.

In the audience that day was J. W. "Squat" Bailey and his wife, Betty. The Baileys were longtime friends of Melodie's parents, who'd come up for the anniversary from their home in Waynesboro, Georgia. The Baileys had a great reputation for raising Palomino horses on their farm and had been longtime supporters.

We wanted to thank them for their help, and honor them for their generous donations to the ministry in the past. It was because of faithful donors like the Baileys that our dreams for the ranch had been made possible.

We'd set up a little platform for the celebration, and I called Squat and Betty up to the microphone, planning on presenting them with a small token of our appreciation. But the Baileys had a surprise in store for me.

Before I could get a word out, Squat pulled out an envelope and handed it to me. Inside were the registration papers for a young stallion foal that had just been born on their farm in Georgia. They called him Paul's Little Red Berry, or Berry for short.

"All you have to do is drive down and get him," Squat said.

I was about to meet the horse who would change my life.

It's hard to put into words what I felt when I first saw Berry.

Before I came to the ranch, I thought training horses would be my life's work. I loved the excitement of competition, and the thrill of seeing thousands of hours of hard work paying off in the show ring, and dreamt of spending my life with great horses.

It wasn't only the prizes. I loved the competition itself, pushing myself and my horses through complicated maneuvers—racing through an arena at full speed and then making a hairpin turn through the slalom course, or coming to a sliding halt and then racing around in a circle, with the horse and rider working in perfect tandem. The joy of being lost in the moment, of having such perfect concentration that nothing else seemed to matter.

I love my horses, being with them and watching them play together. I love it, these days, when I climb into the saddle, without a rein in my hand or a bridle, and know that I can trust them completely. There's a great deal of joy and satisfaction. It's like being a kid all over again, without a care in the world, doing the one thing I love most.

When I became director of the ranch, I lost some of that joy. The work was hard but rewarding and important, and I don't regret my choices, not for one moment. But after a dozen years as an administrator of a nonprofit organization, sitting in an office most of the time, only squeezing in a few minutes to go out to the barn and spend time with my horses, I felt that I had lost something.

Whenever I was at the barn, I felt guilty, like I was wasting my time. Too many cares and worries had robbed me of some of the joy. Though I was proud of our accomplishments, and of how our staff had turned things around, I missed the horses.

Doing the Sermon on the Mount presentations helped. But even then I was always in a rush, hoping the truck wouldn't break down. And the horses were a means to an end, a way to get my point across, rather than true partners.

I'd come to believe that working at the ranch was my calling in life. And though I'd given up my dream of being a horse trainer, what I'd gained in my marriage to Melodie and my relationships with the staff, who'd become closer than family, was worth it. I had love, friends, and meaningful work, and for that I was grateful.

When the Baileys presented me with the papers for Berry, they did more than give me a horse. They gave me my dream back. It was like everything I'd given up was being paid back, with interest.

The weeks following the anniversary went by like a blur. For one thing, I had to make arrangements to go and get Berry. The Baileys lived about sixteen hours away, and bringing a new colt that distance was no simple matter. Seeing that I'd be taking him straight from his mother's side, I really needed to spend a little time with Berry, getting him ready to take such a trip.

And I needed to find the right equipment to bring him back with. I had the trailer I was using for Sermon on the Mount, and that was all right for a trip of a few hundred miles. But this was an 800-mile trip, one way.

Fortunately, some other friends of ours, Bill and Joan Wurst, had been at the anniversary as well, and when they heard about Berry they were delighted. They were taking a trip south anyway, and offered to drive me down to get Berry.

So that's how I found myself standing by a fence on the Baileys' farm, watching a young red Quarter Horse colt romping around his mother. He was beautiful even then, with a red coat so shiny that he literally glistened in the sun, a brilliant white blaze on his face.

Like any colt, he was a bit shy the first time I opened

the gate and walked into the pasture. But his natural curiosity outweighed any shyness he had, and before long he was standing beside me, nuzzling my hand, while I petted his mane and coat and wondered what I'd done to deserve such a gift of grace.

Berry would prove to be a very alert and responsive colt, and it wasn't long before he mastered some of the basics of being halter-broken and following a lead rope.

Like I said, I had given up on the idea that I would ever have the time to invest in training a horse again on a serious level. The camp took too much time, and there was only so much of me to go around. I felt guilty about spending time with the horses when so many other responsibilities—leading the staff, raising money, thinking about the ranch's future—needed my attention.

Accepting the Baileys' gift was much like becoming a parent. I would be responsible for guiding and shaping this young horse. In horse training, like parenting, there's no such thing as "quality time" only. Berry would need several hours of consistent attention and training every day for three or four years to get well established.

It wasn't a task I accepted lightly. It was, however, one I was looking forward to. Though I wouldn't have admitted it at the time, I was spending too much time cooped up in my office, and not enough time out in the barn. I had become, for lack of a better term, a real desk jockey. Getting outside and having daily, hands-on work with Berry was good for my soul.

Over those first two years, Berry's training went better than I could have hoped. A natural people-pleaser, he never gave me a bad day. Unlike Ribbon or some of the other horses I'd trained in the past, he never fought back or complained. Not that he was perfect, or got everything right the first time. But he was a delight to be around.

Before long, I had him out on the road with me for speaking engagements. Even as a colt, audiences would respond to him—people loved to watch him work. He was fast and strong and approached every task with a vigor and joy. He was having the time of his life, and so was I.

Those early days of Sermon on the Mount were a work in progress. Berry and I traveled thousands of miles together, during those early years, going wherever we were invited—schools and conferences and churches, sometimes in front of a few dozen people, other times drawing several hundred people.

Somewhere along the way, the truck would break down along the side of the road. Despite our best attempts to keep the equipment well maintained, some glitch would always come up, and we'd break down again. My team and I became experts at figuring out solutions for difficult situations.

Still, I was having a great time, and looked forward to years of partnership with Berry. Not long after he turned three, however, everything started to go south.

Things started to unravel when Berry and I began working on what's known as flying lead changes, a relatively advanced maneuver.

The idea is to get a horse to change directions while at a canter, which is a bit faster than a trot but not quite a gallop. When the horse goes to the right, their right front foot should look like it leads. When they go to the left, their left front foot should lead.

To master a flying lead change, the horse should switch easily from leading with their right to leading with their left, without slowing down or getting their feet tangled up. Instead, they should move smoothly from one to the other, like a dancer.

Until this point, Berry had mastered everything I'd tried to teach him. Now he struggled. His movements were clumsy and awkward, and no matter what I tried, he couldn't figure out the lead changes. One moment he'd be cantering beautifully, and the next he'd be stumbling and all out of sorts.

I'd never seen a horse respond in that way. He was working hard and willing to try, but the lead changes completely flummoxed him. It's not that Berry didn't want to do the lead changes; it's that he could not get the hang of them.

About this time, my friend John Lyons, the renowned horse trainer, was visiting the ranch. John was traveling the country and his business required an unexpected trip home to Colorado. Since he'd be gone for several weeks, he asked me to look after his horse, Bright Zip.

Zip is a legend among horse trainers. He and John traveled the country for years, giving exhibitions and horsemanship clinics. Later on in life, Zip went blind in both eyes, due to an adverse reaction to medication. Still he and John continued to work together. They were so in tune, and Zip so trusted John, that he could run at a gallop and turn on a dime without being able to see a thing.

When he came back from his trip to Colorado, I asked John to take a look at Berry. I explained the trouble we were having with flying lead changes, and John agreed to work with us for a few days. Even he was at a loss to understand why Berry had hit such a block, and couldn't help us find a way around it.

"I'm sorry, Lew," he said, "but I think you need to find another horse."

Not willing to give up, I called my old friend Ward Studebaker and asked him for advice. Ward offered to come and spend several days working with us. I was hopeful at first, but as the days wore on, that hope began to fade. When he left, he gave me the same advice that John had.

"Find another horse, Lew," Ward said, "He's not going to get it."

I hated to hear those words, because I trusted Ward. He always gave sound, wise advice, and never jumped to conclusions.

When Ward drove off, my heart sank, as if everything Berry and I had worked for was going right down the drain. I'd poured my life into this horse, and loved him, and now I was on the brink of losing all my hopes for him.

Something inside of me wasn't willing to give up. Perhaps it was pure stubbornness, but I felt that there was more I could learn from Berry. If we could overcome this roadblock, both of us would be better off.

Along with my stubbornness, I felt a sense of protectiveness toward Berry, much like a parent. After all this time together, I didn't want him to be defined by his limitations. If he failed in this challenge, it could set a pattern for the rest of his life, of giving up in the face of adversity.

To be honest, I had selfish reasons for not wanting to give up. I felt trapped and disappointed—I'd spent three years working with Berry, and he had such promise. I wasn't ready to walk away from him. Doing that would have left a bitter taste in my mouth for years, and I'd always wonder what might have been.

In the midst of this frustration, Berry taught me one of the most important lessons that a leader can ever learn. He taught me that in order to get past this obstacle, I needed to accept what we could not change, and embrace what we could change. It's not always easy to see the difference between the two.

With Berry, I needed to accept reality. The problem was this: he was not strong enough or flexible enough to master the flying lead changes. With that limitation, he would never master a flying lead change, no matter how many hours we practiced.

In an earlier chapter, we talked about what's called the 10,000 hour rule—to become an expert in any field requires 10,000 hours of practice. It's another version of the old saying that practice makes perfect. Except there is one caveat: you've got to practice the right things. Doing the wrong thing over and over again is pointless.

Since Berry had a physical limitation, I needed to accept that he was not ready to do a flying lead change. In order for him to succeed, we had to go back to the basics. I had to train him with exercises to become stronger and more flexible, until he had the capacity needed to master those maneuvers.

So we went backwards. We put our training on hold, and spent weeks on simple exercises, designed to build strength and flexibility in Berry. We worked on stretching techniques and new ways of warming him up, so when we finally attacked the lead changes again, he was more limber and agile. In the end, we transformed Berry from a willing but clumsy horse into a willing and athletic, capable horse.

Looking back at my time training Berry, I was reminded of a story I'd heard about the great racehorse, Seabiscuit. Though he eventually became one of the most celebrated thoroughbreds of the twentieth century, Seabiscuit's career had a rocky beginning. While he came from great bloodlines—his grandfather was the famed thoroughbred Man o' War—by the time he was two years old, Seabiscuit had lost seventeen races in a row. Things got so bad that his owner put him in a claiming race—the horsing world's equivalent of eBay.

Seabiscuit might have been lost in obscurity, had not a trainer named Tom Smith taken a liking to him. Smith convinced his boss, a man named Charles Howard, to take a chance on the horse. Howard, it seems, had a weakness for lost causes.

Smith teamed up Seabiscuit with a jockey named Red Pollard, and after a rocky start, the two clicked, and Seabiscuit started winning. And winning. And winning.

Eventually Seabiscuit would square off against War Admiral, who'd won the Triple Crown in 1937 and who was considered by many to be the greatest horse of his time.

That is, until November 1, 1938, when Seabiscuit beat War Admiral in a one-on-one match race at Pimlico racetrack outside of Baltimore. An estimated 40 million people listened to the radio broadcast of that race.

It was then, when Seabiscuit had his greatest triumph, that disaster struck. Not long afterward, he ruptured the suspensory ligament in his front left leg while preparing to run the Santa Anita Handicap, which was nicknamed the "hundred grander" for its $100,000 purse.

Smith and Howard feared he would never race again. A few months earlier, Seabiscuit's jockey, Red Pollard, had been nearly killed when a horse he was riding for a friend bolted. Pollard's leg was shattered and he was hospitalized for months. He was already blind in one eye, and his career seemed over as well.

But neither Pollard nor Seabiscuit were ready to give up. He and the horse convalesced together on Howard's farm. They walked for hours together, and little by little, rebuilt their injury-shattered bodies.

Despite their limitations, Seabiscuit and Pollard eventually began to race again. And on March 2, 1940, they won the Santa Anita, posting the fastest time in the history of that race, and ending Seabiscuit's career in a blaze of glory.

It would have been easy for Pollard and Seabiscuit to have given up, to have let their injuries and limitations define their lives. Likewise, it would have been easier for Smith to have overlooked a seventeen-time loser like Seabiscuit.

Berry and I have never won a race like the Santa Anita. Despite my great affection for him and my pride in his accomplishments, he's not Seabiscuit.

In his own way, Berry's story is almost as remarkable. After spending several months building his strength and flexibility, Berry and I tackled the flying lead changes again. This time, with his newfound athleticism, and his perseverance, he mastered them.

Over the next eight years, Berry and I would travel thousand of miles, giving presentations at small schools and churches tucked into the hollows of West Virginia and other Southern states, and later at larger events. Everywhere we went, Berry delighted the crowds who came to see him.

Flying lead changes were only the beginning for Berry. He eventually mastered even more difficult riding techniques. By the time he was six, I'd taught him how to ride without reins or bridle while blindfolded. With no means of seeing the way ahead of him, and without a rein to guide him, he learned to gallop and spin on a dime, and dozens of other intricate patterns, with only the slightest nudge or word from me to point the way.

There's a postscript to this story. When Berry was ten, he began to develop some problems breathing while galloping, which made doing Sermon on the Mount presentations harder for him. He didn't have the wind or endurance he'd once had. He'd also developed some soreness in his legs.

Worst of all, I began to suspect that he was going blind in one eye. That actually took me a while to discover, because he was so responsive to my instructions and we worked so closely together. In the end, he didn't need to see to know where he was going.

Berry and I took one last trip together, this time to a hospital, where veterinarians put him through a battery of tests. They confirmed my suspicions, that Berry was losing sight in one eye and that he had a chest condition that would permanently diminish his endurance. He'd be able to handle less strenuous workouts, but the Sermon on the Mount was too much for him. No amount of exercise or training could compensate for his condition.

After the examination, Berry's doctors showed me a pair of curious X-rays they'd taken. Berry, it turns out, had been born with some abnormal bone structure in his left rear hock and his right front hoof. Both of those areas are used when a horse makes a diagonal movement like a lead change.

Those bone abnormalities meant that movements like a lead change would be difficult for Berry. They wouldn't be painful, and there was no danger of permanent injury—instead he'd be naturally clumsy in those kinds of movements. They wouldn't hurt, but they'd be awkward.

If I'd seen those X-rays early on, I'd have thrown in the towel with Berry, and never seen the way through our struggles. I never would have seen what he could have become.

Not long after we returned home from the hospital, Berry retired from Sermon on the Mount. In the years that followed, he helped me train some of my students to overcome their weaknesses. Whenever a student would complain or say, "I can't do this," I introduced them to Berry.

And this one-eye-blind horse would show them the way.

CHAPTER 7

FIGHT OR FLIGHT

THE VOICE ON THE PHONE was desperate.

"You'd better get up here and get this horse," she said. "Get up here before my husband does, or he'll kill him."

The caller was a friend from a nearby farm, and her voice trembled as she spoke. For a year, I'd been giving her advice on how to deal with Winter, her Paint Stallion. Now something had gone wrong and it had scared the wits out of her.

"I'll be right there," I said.

Soon, I was pulling into the driveway of my friend's farm, towing a horse trailer behind the ranch's Ford pickup. As we walked out toward the horse barn, my friend relayed that afternoon's events.

For several years, my friend had been at a loss on how to deal with Winter, a stallion she'd raised. Winter was a beautiful horse, with a white coat with black spots on his backside. A strong and athletic horse, Winter had great potential, but had one drawback—a surly and aggressive attitude with women. Around a male rider or trainer he did all right, but with women, he become haughty and snotty, displaying an aggressive, macho attitude. He'd rear up on his hind legs and strike, refusing to comply with their instructions, and trying to intimidate them.

When she first came to see me, I gave my friend some pointers on how to establish firm boundaries with Winter and how to earn his respect as well as his trust. Winter was too clever for my friend, or any trainer, to simply manhandle. No one was going to force that horse to do anything he didn't want to do. He got his way by aggressiveness and intimidation, even around other horses.

Unless Winter could learn to control his impulses and to respect boundaries, he'd never progress in his training. He needed to learn how to rein in his aggression, before he or someone else got hurt or before my friend finally decided he was useless and had him put down.

As a last resort, I advised her to have him gelded— while that would ruin Winter as a stud horse by neutering him, it would cut off the testosterone that fueled his aggression. Better to have a sterile horse than an aggressive and unmanageable one.

When every other tactic had failed, my friend gave in and had Winter gelded. Even that didn't solve the problem completely. He was less aggressive, but never cooperative.

When I arrived at the farm, my friend was still trembling

from her encounter with him. She'd been mucking out Winter's stable and gotten careless just for a moment. She turned her back on him, and bent down to pick something up from the floor of the stable. In that split second he pounced on her, grabbing her with his teeth in the middle of her back and throwing her around the stable.

I'd known of other horses who'd turned on their owners like this, and it's never pretty, and sometimes fatal. Another friend of mine had bought a horse with similar tendencies at an auction several years earlier.

When she bought him, the horse seemed well trained and responsive. Once she got him home, though, he began to act out, pinning his ears back and swishing his tail in an agitated manner. At first, she thought he was out of sorts from being in a new environment, and thought he'd get over it soon enough and calm down.

Like Winter's owner, she turned her back on the horse, and in a split second he was after her. Instead of grabbing her in the middle of the back, this horse grabbed his owner by the neck and bit her savagely. Then he knocked her to the ground and began to stomp on her.

She escaped by playing dead, lying perfectly still despite the blows from the horse's hooves raining down on her. When the horse gave up and broke off the attack, he threw his head back and whinnied, as if gloating that he'd killed her.

By sheer luck, someone stopped by her home and

happened to walk into the barn. He saw my friend curled up on the ground and chased the horse away, before pulling her to safety. She was a terrible sight after the attack. That horse had gone psychotic and had to be destroyed.

Luckily for Winter's owner, Winter hadn't lost his mind. He wasn't bent on killing her; he only wanted to frighten and intimidate her.

My friend was saved by her choice of wardrobe. Working out in the barn, she was wearing a lightweight shirt with thin sleeves. As Winter tossed her around, the fabric tore. He lost his grip, and she went flying. She tumbled to the ground and rolled out of the stall, and was out of harm's way. She was shaken up, but not injured seriously.

She called me right afterwards and asked me to take him away. She didn't really care what I did with him—she wanted him gone before her husband got home and shot the horse right there and then.

I get calls about horses like Winter every once in a while, lost causes or reprobates, as we sometimes call them at the ranch, whose owners have lost all hope. On occasion, I've even worked with a horse that's killed someone, though it's usually been an accident, rather than a deliberate act.

Sometimes a horse is beyond help. If a horse is mentally ill, unstable, or dangerous, I won't work with it. But Winter wasn't psychotic—he was a bully that had finally gone too far. He needed a sharp lesson in reality. And he needed someone to show him a better way than aggression and intimidation to get what he wanted out of life.

One of the keys to being a good trainer—or any kind of leader—is to focus on needs, not behavior. Oftentimes we get so focused on someone's negative behavior that we don't stop to evaluate what is causing the person to act or to react in that manner.

I'm not talking about some touchy-feely, why-can't-we-all-get-along approach. Winter had deliberately harmed his trainer, and that was unacceptable. The easy solution would have been to put him down, to say that he wasn't worth saving. But Winter wasn't at that point yet.

What I had to figure out was, why had he attacked my friend? What had gone wrong in his life to cause such a reaction? Why was this horse filled with such anger?

His behavior was only a symptom. I needed to figure out what was causing the behavior.

One cause became clear after I'd talked with Winter's owner. Because he was in training, she'd been giving him a high-powered horse feed. That feed gave him plenty of energy, but he wasn't working enough of that energy off and it kept him going at a frantic pace, as if he'd been on a steady diet of Red Bull or some other high-caffeine, high-sugar energy drink. Taking him off the high-powered feed would help Winter clear his head, and allow him to think straight.

When he arrived at the ranch, I put Winter out to pasture

with a group of older geldings, and let them go to work on him. Horses are herd animals by nature, with a pecking order that puts every horse in its place. Winter had been ruling the roost at his owner's farm, and had gotten a big head.

These older geldings weren't going to be impressed by a young punk with an over-inflated ego. In a few weeks, they'd reminded him that he was a horse, and not a particularly special one at that.

In his book, *A Horse and His Boy*, C. S. Lewis writes about a proud warhorse named Bree, who spends most of his time boasting about how brave and accomplished he is. The boy in the story is a poor fisherman's son named Shasta, who turns out to be more than meets the eye. At a crisis point in the story Bree and Shasta, along with their traveling companions—a girl named Aravis and her mare Hwin—are attacked by a lion. Bree flees for his life in a panic, while Shasta faces the lion, and fights him off.

Afterward, Bree is ashamed and humbled by his behavior, and realizes that he's not quite the brave warhorse he believed he was. With that perspective, Bree becomes a better and happier horse.

Winter was a bit like Bree, too full of himself for his own good. The geldings made a start of bringing him back to reality. They also took the edge off Winter's anger.

When I work with a horse, one of my main training tools is pressure. Since horses can't talk—aside from in C. S. Lewis's

Narnia books—they rely on the nonverbal communication of body language and pressure to communicate. I use pressure—with a rope, or by waving a flag, or by getting close to a horse, to get my message across.

With an angry horse, like an angry person, pressure is counterproductive. There was too much noise from the emotions inside Winter, and he could not hear me. I needed to ratchet Winter's emotions down so he was able to listen and respond. Once Winter had gotten back to some semblance of a normal life, and wasn't seething with anger, I began working with him.

I set up a round pen where there were enough boundaries to keep him honest, and got after him. At first, he acted all haughty and snotty, but that died down when he realized it wasn't doing him any good. Instead of reacting to his behavior, I put steady pressure on him, asking him to comply without complaining. Every time he did, he got a reward of released pressure.

Eventually, Winter began to see that by cooperating with a trainer, his life would get better. That gave him a sense of hope, and he began to progress. Since he'd had such a hard time with women riders, I asked some of our women staff to ride him—once he'd calm down—and rewarded his good behavior.

At the end of my retraining, Winter was a different horse. Once a menace who delighted in temper tantrums, he became one of the most beloved horses on the ranch.

In the end, Winter's problem wasn't so much his behavior. His problem was an attitude of disrespect. Without clear boundaries and consistent authority, he became insecure and took control.

Without hope, without a sense that life can get better, horses—like people—can easily fall into a sense of despair. Winter had no reason to believe that cooperating with his trainer would make his life better. Without hope, he had no incentive to change.

To fix Winter, I didn't need to change his behavior. I needed to change his beliefs—to get him to put his faith in me, and not in his own aggressive control.

Winter had learned that by being aggressive and using intimidation, he could get what he wanted. For a while it worked. He was well fed, had a comfortable stable, and had his trainer doing things his way, not her way.

That eventually fell apart, when he pushed things too far. Once that happened, Winter had no clue about how to put his life back together.

When I train a horse, it's a constant balancing act. If the training is too easy, a horse will lose interest and become bored and sloppy. If the training is too hard, and I ask too much, my horse will either lose hope or become defiant.

When a challenge or training problem is too big, a horse can get overwhelmed and react in anger. In those cases, the first response is fight or flight. The horse either runs away and tries to ignore the problem, or they put up a stink and refuse to comply with the trainer's request, in hopes that the trainer will give up, believing the training is too much of a hassle.

Sound familiar? Anyone who's been a parent has seen these responses. If we're honest, we might admit that we have tried the fight or flight response with a boss or a parent or a spouse. If things go on too long, fight or flight can turn into anger and despair, and a sense of hopelessness for people, or for horses.

When I first met the Smiths, they knew something about hopelessness.

They were both surgeons, who'd passed up prestigious big-city residencies to practice in small-town Pennsylvania, in hope of finding a good quality of life for their family.

For years things went well for the Smiths. They were blessed with four beautiful and talented children, and built up successful medical practices. They had everything going for them.

But as time went by, the pressures of running those practices and maintaining a busy family life took a toll on their marriage. Over the years small hurts and misunderstandings got glossed over, and the pressures of life began to crack their relationship.

Finally it broke. By the time I met Dr. Beth, they'd been separated for several years, and things looked hopeless.

I didn't learn all this the first time I met Dr. Beth. In fact it took quite a while before she told me much about her story. If I'd pried into her background at the beginning, things would probably not have turned out well at all.

We met Dr. Beth through my mother. In her later years, my mother had come to live with us at the ranch, and she'd developed some stomach problems. Dr. Beth was treating her, and one day my mother introduced me to Dr. Beth while I was visiting her at the hospital.

My mother was always interested in people, and it wasn't too long before she'd befriended Dr. Beth. At that time she was raising the four kids on her own, and was about at her wits' end, especially in dealing with her teenaged boys.

Mother invited her out to the ranch to see a Sermon on the Mount presentation, and to her surprise, Dr. Beth agreed. She and the kids came out to the ranch, and something about the presentation resonated with them. Before long, they were regular visitors, and Dr. Beth's son Ben would eventually come and spend the summer with us at the camp.

Once we'd become friends and she trusted us, Dr. Beth told us the story of her marriage, and of the unresolved conflict. At this point, they'd been separated for nine years, with no resolution in sight. But they'd experienced enough pain and hurt to know things couldn't continue on the same path.

There's a preacher named Ed Stetzer who likes to say that people won't change until the pain of remaining the same becomes overwhelming. That's a bit how the Smiths felt. Anything had to be better than their present reality.

So Dr. Beth asked Melodie and me if there was any chance her marriage could be saved. I didn't know at the time but we offered to meet with them, to find out if there was any hope left for them. Before we knew it, they had come in for counseling.

Melodie and I do a lot of marital counseling. We've both earned degrees in that area—as well as having learned from the ups and downs of our own marriage—and have built up a reputation for helping people.

By the time married couples get to us, they are usually at the end of their rope. They have read the books, seen the videos, gone to the conferences, and none of it has worked.

It's only the desperate people who come to us—they have exhausted all their options. The rumor is that we are straightforward and don't sugar-coat things. We don't fix marriages but we can help people who are ready to change.

The first time we met, you could cut the tension in the air with a knife. They sat at opposite ends of the couch, scarcely willing to look at each other. They were sensitive, afraid, and ready to bolt. It seemed there was little hope of recovery.

Like many people stuck in difficult circumstances, they'd come to believe that the only way things would get better was if the other person changed. It's like that at work—if only my boss were more understanding, or I had better co-workers, things would be different. It's like that at church—if only the preacher weren't so boring, my life would be better. And it's like that in marriage. If only my spouse would understand me, I could be happy.

Nobody ever changes unless they see some evidence of hope. Something to put their trust in—something that allows them to set down their defenses and try something new.

People who have lost hope need a stable point of reference, something to put their faith in. They need to put their faith in something or someone who is trustworthy.

In those counseling sessions, the Smiths found enough hope to start over. It wasn't easy. There was a lot of anger, disappointment, rejection, and loneliness to work through. But they created a safe place in that counseling that gave them hope that their relationship could be healed. Over several months they rebuilt their marriage and renewed their vows, putting their family back together.

The kids didn't believe them at first, and put the Smiths through the wringer, testing them to make sure this renewed marriage would last. In recent years, their boys have gotten married themselves, and they've put the lessons their parents learned to good use.

A marriage that was brittle and could have easily ended was saved.

When I first met Rowdy, I knew I was in for it.

Rowdy was a middle-aged gelding, who was full of himself, and who wasn't going to let anyone tell him what to do. So much so, that when his owner brought him into the corral, she led him with a chain, not a rope. That chain, and the cue stick in her hand, were the only things that kept him in line.

When I do a Sermon on the Mount presentation, I often ask for a horse who has had trouble getting along with a rider or trainer, and Rowdy fitted that profile to a tee. Rowdy was no dummy. He knew that he was stronger than any trainer, and understood that if he reared up on his hind legs, he had the advantage over his handler.

He also knew about the power of his head. Earlier, we talked about how, when I was young, I misunderstood horses. I believed that the key to controlling a horse was to control their head, by yanking on their reins or lead rope. But a horse's true power comes from his hips, not his head.

Rowdy knew that, and so he kept the focus on his head. So he'd pull back on the reins or lead rope, or bear his teeth and face the trainer. The trainer could easily get sucked into a power struggle with Rowdy, and never get anywhere with him. It's like a pair of kids stuck in a game of one upmanship. A complete waste of time.

My response was to focus on his hips, not his face. I gave Rowdy a length of rope, and asked him to move. I gave him enough space that he didn't feel crowded, but not so much that he could run away. All the while I watched his response.

If Rowdy was ignoring me, and trying to provoke a fight, he'd yank on the rope and pull it tight. I didn't yank back but I kept a steady pressure on. When he yielded a bit, and eased on the rope, so would I. That release of pressure acted like a reward for Rowdy. If he gave in, he got what he wanted.

A horse like Rowdy needs hope. He needed an incentive or reward for cooperating. I'm not talking about a bribe to earn a horse's cooperation. Instead, he needs an incentive or reward for doing the right thing first.

In other words, I had to be smarter than the horse.

I call this kind of tactic the soft answer to anger. Not a weak answer, giving in to Rowdy's demands. But a soft answer, that defused and redirected his anger and attention. I wanted to make him think and choose a different response.

There's a great story told about Jesus in the New Testament. In his day, Israel was occupied by the Roman Empire, and for most of the population, Rome was seen as the enemy.

The Romans made all the rules, enforced the law with brutal violence, and made the people pay heavy taxes. They were extremely unpopular, especially with the religious leaders, who prayed that God would send someone to rescue them.

Jesus also ran afoul of the religious leaders of his day, because he challenged their authority. Understandably, this made them angry and so some leaders conspired to find ways to get rid of him.

At one point, someone asked Jesus a question about paying taxes to Rome. It was a loaded question. If Jesus said yes, they should pay taxes to Rome, he'd look like a Roman sympathizer and that would turn people against him. If he said no they shouldn't, then Jesus would be a rabble-rouser and in trouble with the law. People who didn't pay taxes to Rome didn't live long.

Instead, Jesus asked a question. "Show me the coin used to pay taxes," he said.

His questioners fished out a coin, which had a portrait of Caesar, the Roman emperor, engraved on it.

"Whose portrait is this?" Jesus asked.

"Caesar's," someone replied.

"Give to Caesar what is Caesar's, and to God what is God's," Jesus said.

That's a perfect soft answer. Rather than taking sides in a debate on taxes, he turned the question back on his opponents. They had to figure out how to respond next.

There's another soft answer in the Bible, found in the Old Testament. Most of us are familiar with the story of David and Bathsheba. David, who was the king, saw Bathsheba, a beautiful woman, bathing naked on her rooftop. She was married but her husband was always away fighting for the king.

David wanted her, and so being king, summoned

Bathsheba to his bedroom, and we all can guess what happened next.

A few months later, though, Bathsheba sent word that she was pregnant. Since her husband had been away, the pregnancy was proof that she and the king had been having an affair.

David summoned her husband back from the war, hoping that he'd sleep with Bathsheba—so that when he discovered she was pregnant, her husband would think the child was his. But her husband, an honorable man, refused to sleep with his wife while his men were out in the field, fighting for the king.

Desperate to cover up the affair, David ordered Bathsheba's husband back to the war. He told another officer to put him at the front line, and then to fall back, abandoning him to the enemy. He was killed, and after a brief period of mourning, Bathsheba married King David.

Now news of something like this never stays hidden. Everyone knew what the king had done, and were appalled by it. No one wanted to confront David to his face—at least no one who valued his head.

But a prophet named Nathan had a better idea. He came to David with a tale of woe. A terrible injustice had taken place in the kingdom, Nathan said.

In a certain village lived a poor man and a rich man. The rich man had much property and many sheep, and was wealthy beyond compare. The poor man had very little. His prized possession was one sheep, whom he kept as a pet for his children.

But one night the rich man had a guest. And instead of slaughtering one of his own sheep and feeding it to the guest, he stole the poor man's pet, killed it, and had it roasted as dinner for his guest.

David, as you can imagine, was livid and vowed to punish the rich man. "Who is this man?" he asked.

Bingo!

Nathan said, "You are."

In that soft answer, David realized that Nathan knew about Bathsheba. He also realized the horror of what he'd done.

David did all the work. He changed and tried to make amends for his crime, not because Nathan angrily confronted him, but because he was ashamed on the inside of what he'd done.

Not long ago, I was asked to travel to Utah, to give a Sermon on the Mount presentation in a small desert town. Some Baptists had invited me in, hoping to foster peace in their town. Typical of Utah, most of the people who lived in the town were Mormons. But some Baptists had also settled there, and the two groups were at odds.

No one remembered who had started the conflict, but there were plenty of hard feelings to go around. The two groups lived separate lives. They lived apart, socialized apart, and shunned each other's company. Neither group trusted the other.

As you can guess, this made life pretty miserable. The one thing the Baptists and the Mormons shared in common was a love for horses. So the Baptists invited me in the hope that I could break the ice between the two groups.

It was rough going. A large crowd had gathered but they were segregated, with the Baptists on one side and the Mormons on the other. I began to work with a mustang who had been run in right off the desert.

He was a strong and healthy colt, who'd never spent any time with people. His mane and tail were knotted and twisted, and he had some bite marks on him from tussling with other horses. We spent several hours together.

As I worked, I noticed one man on the Mormon side come down from the crowd and stand by the fence. We started talking as I worked, and it was clear he knew his way around horses.

Getting a wild mustang settled down takes a while. Usually I can calm a horse down pretty quickly so I can put a bridle on it, but in this case, I needed to take a different approach. I asked the man who'd been observing me to lend a hand.

I'm a terrible roper. I've worked with horses for years, and it's one of the skills that has always eluded me. I can usually rope a horse that's been running around, but not until the horse, and anyone watching, has had a good laugh.

This time, I asked my observer if he'd mind roping the horse. "Sure," he said, and made his way over to the gate of the round pen. Within a few minutes, he had the horse lassoed and handed the rope over to me.

As the program went along, I talked to the audience about the inner battle this mustang was facing. He could keep running and wear himself out. Or he could give in a bit, and trust me.

At some point in the program, I noticed that the man who was watching me had begun to cry.

Eventually the mustang gave in enough to let me get close, and after an hour and a half, he let me put a saddle on him and ride. It was quite a transformation for this wild mustang.

After I was done, the man who'd been watching me came up and we talked. For most of his life, he'd been estranged from his family, and it made him miserable and angry. Watching that mustang had been like seeing himself in the mirror. And he didn't like what he saw and wanted to change.

That conversation and my visit to the town didn't change that community overnight. But it did break open a little space for hope for that man, and for the audience.

Afterward I could see a few of the Baptists and Mormons talking to one another, if not in friendly tones, at least in civil ones. For one night, they didn't see each other as enemies.

If I'd come in and given a leadership seminar about how we all have to get along, and about diversity and about respecting different people's viewpoints, the audience would have applauded nicely and gone home. They might not even have shown up in the first place.

But I gave them a soft answer instead. I made some space for them to set aside their anger and hostility, and to think about what they had in common. That's a start. There was room for more movement in the right direction.

CHAPTER 8

READY FOR A CRISIS

THEY CALLED IT THE MIRACLE on the Hudson.

At about 3:30 in the afternoon on January 15, 2009, US Airways Flight 1549 took off from runaway number 4 at LaGuardia Airport in New York, with 155 passengers on board, headed for Charlotte, on the first leg of a cross-country journey. It was a clear, cold, New York afternoon—a perfect day for flying.

Not long after take-off, however, something went drastically wrong. As the plane banked over the Hudson River, it encountered a flock of Canadian geese. Though those geese weigh less than ten pounds, they can wreak havoc with a plane's engines. Several were sucked into the engines, causing both to go out, sending the aircraft plummeting toward the icy Hudson.

Like all flight crews, the pilots and flight attendants aboard Flight 1549 had trained for emergency landing and before this flight, the flight attendants had instructed their passengers what to do "in the unlikely event of a water landing." Most of those passengers, especially the experienced ones, had likely tuned out the familiar words.

Now that unlikely event was a reality.

By all accounts, the crew acted heroically, putting their years of training into practice. The pilot, Chesley B. "Sully" Sullenberger III, kept the plane level as it crashed into the river. Despite the understandable panic among the passengers, the flight attendants kept their heads. When a group of passengers rushed to the rear of the plane, hoping to get out the back door, the captain and crew convinced them to stop before their added weight forced the tail to sink. While some passengers grabbed for their luggage or struggled from their seats, the flight attendants kept them calm and orderly, getting everyone out of the plane and on the wings.

It must have been a terrifying experience, standing on those wings in twenty-degree temperatures, a few inches above the frigid waters of the Hudson. Anyone who fell in the water would likely die of hypothermia in minutes. There was no hope of swimming to shore. Some passengers had to wade out into knee-deep water to reach the edge of the wings, in order to make space for everyone to get off the plane. And all the while the passengers knew that the plane could go down at any minute.

A few of them were old enough to remember the last time something like this had happened. Back in 1982, an Air

Florida 737 plunged into the Potomac River in Washington, D.C., in the middle of winter. Of the eighty-three people on board, only five survived.

This time, the outcome was happier. Thanks to the fast action of the crew and some local ferry-boat captains, along with rescue crews, everyone was saved. In fact, by the time the news of the crash reached the airwaves, the crisis was over, and all the passengers were ashore, and being treated by paramedics. No wonder people across the country called it a miracle.

I don't know what part divine intervention played on that frozen January afternoon, but one thing I can say for sure: Things would have turned out much differently if the crew hadn't been prepared for a crisis. Without the right training and preparation, they would have failed their greatest test.

Thankfully, most of us will never have to face a crisis of this magnitude. But all of us will face tests of some kind. And our success or failure will largely depend on the kinds of habits, skills, and character we've developed ahead of time.

When I work with a horse, I have one ultimate goal in mind—to develop them into a dependable and trustworthy horse. No matter how talented they are physically, if I can't trust a horse, then they are of no use.

Dr. Martin Luther King Jr. once dreamed that his children would be judged by "the content of their character," not the color of their skin or any external factor.

That's what I am after. It's easy to judge a horse by

external factors but I want to build up the content of their character. We do that in steps.

The first step, as we talked about earlier, is to change the horse's beliefs. Most horses, like most people, are naturally independent and self-sufficient. They look out for number one, as the old saying goes.

As we've seen, that selfishness limits a horse's—or a person's—potential. If a horse, like my mare Ribbon, refuses to cooperate and to work hard, they'll never reach their full potential. They'll never overcome the obstacles they face in life.

On the other hand, even a horse with limitations—like Berry or even Peyote—can overcome those limits. It starts by changing their beliefs, teaching them to focus on the trainer and not on their own needs or limitations.

The second step is making choices. My horses choose every day whether to partner with me and give their all, or to remain inwardly focused.

There's a parallel here to the human world. The crew of Flight 1549 chose to be trained in how to respond in an emergency. Some of the training was likely boring and tedious, with constant repetition until they got it right. It was likely hard work, and I'm sure sometimes they wondered what the point was. They must have gotten tired of reading out those emergency instructions, knowing that many of the passengers weren't listening anyway.

With repetition, choices become habits. I reward my

horses every time they make the right choice, and over time, those choices build good habits of listening and perseverance.

Those habits build character, in the same way that constant training helps a runner build the endurance needed to run a marathon. There are no shortcuts to training for a marathon. You can't prepare your body to run more than twenty-six miles without stopping in a few days or weeks. It takes months of running, day in and day out, to build the muscle strength and endurance a marathon requires.

In the same way, it took Berry months of exercise and stretching to build the strength and flexibility he needed to do flying lead changes and overcome his physical limitations.

The problem with a crisis or a test is this—we never know when it is coming.

For my Quarter Horse Stallion Spark, one of his first tests arrived the day he met the Tennessee Walking Horse.

We were doing a Sermon on the Mount presentation, and Spark was helping me saddle-break a three-year-old horse who'd never been ridden before.

Mostly, when I'm doing presentation, I work one on one with the horse in a sixty-foot-wide round pen. But there's another way to go about this. On the day we met the Tennessee Walking Horse, Spark was assisting me, acting as a mentor or guide for the younger horse.

We call this approach "ponying," and it's helpful on two levels. First, the older horse often has a calming effect on a young, unbroken horse, especially if that horse hasn't spent much time around people. The older horse acts as a mentor, a reassuring presence to build the younger horse's confidence. Since horses have a pecking order, the young horse will often defer to the older horse, and be more willing to pay attention.

Second, the younger horse can mimic the behavior and attitude of the older horse and so can learn by example. That's the message I wanted to get across in this session—to show how the values and character traits Spark had learned could be passed on to a younger, less experienced colt.

Spark and I had come a long way since the first day we met, when he was a little less than a year old. He'd been raised on the Crow Creek division of the C.S. Ranch in New Mexico by my friends Warren and Mary Davis, and I'd driven out west to pick him up.

The ranch utilizes over 300,000 acres in a beautiful mountain setting, with nothing but wide open spaces for miles around. Bordered by the Sangre de Cristo mountains, it boasts some of the most beautiful sunsets in the nation. Spark had spent most of his first year wandering those open ranges with minimal human contact, and was relatively independent.

He is excitable by nature—so much so that the first time I took off his halter, he reacted by jumping up against me and stomping his front legs, cracking three of my ribs. For a stallion, he's sensitive as well. He doesn't like to be hit or crowded by another horse or touched on his nose. As a young colt, he reacted whenever I brought a lead rope near him. To Spark, it looked like a snake on the ground, and he'd like nothing better than to stomp it.

He was particular irritated by sounds, like the snap of a rein being slapped against the side of a horse, or the sound of hoofs walking across a metal surface. So I had to a lot of work to do with Spark in the early days.

He's calmed down significantly, and has become an expert at ignoring outside distractions and being completely focused on listening to my directions, even when that means ignoring the things that would otherwise irritate him. Spark is so responsive to my commands, that I'll often ride him bridleless, using nothing but the pressure of my legs or a spoken word to guide him. His focus makes him well suited for ponying. Oftentimes I'll ride him with another horse's lead rope dallied to the horn of my saddle.

The Tennessee Walking Horse colt seemed like a good candidate for ponying. Like many young horses I work with, the colt had been well fed and cared for but his training had been neglected. As far as I knew, he didn't have any behavior problems, aside from being a bit spoiled.

Still, Walking Horses are known for being even-tempered and easygoing, and while the colt was barely halter broken, he seemed agreeable enough. Until I grabbed hold of his lead rope.

The second I dallied the rope around the saddle horn, the Walking Horse began showing his true colors. He leaned over and snapped at Spark, trying to sink his teeth into my horse's side, and then kicked at Spark.

As a stallion, Spark's natural reaction was to retaliate. But that's not how I had trained him, and so despite the abuse of this spoiled brat of a colt, Spark stood his ground.

I asked Spark to move forward, hoping to put a little distance between him and the colt, while at the same time distracting the colt from lashing out at Spark.

As soon as Spark moved, the colt bolted. Before I knew it, the two horses were at full gallop, barreling around the rodeo arena. Like most arenas, it had a wide dirt floor surrounded by a steel fence that separated the performing area from the bleachers where the spectators sat. A gasp rose up from the crowds as they realized I was stuck on the back of one of the two runaway horses with no bridle to guide Spark back under control.

By this point, I could tell Spark was ticked. If he'd wanted to retaliate against the colt, I wouldn't have blamed him. As the two horses raced around the arena, it would have been easy for him to ignore me and to focus on his new found rival.

Despite his irritation and the excitement of the chase, Spark never lost his head. He knew that no matter what was going on around him, he could look to me for guidance. As we galloped, I cued him to turn, directing him towards one of the steel fences.

As he approached the wall, Spark did what I had trained him to do—he dug in his back feet and slid us to a stop. Seeing the fence in front of him, the colt did the same.

Whew, I thought. *That was a close one.*

As soon as we turned away from the fence, the colt bolted again, and once more we were off on a merry chase. When I turned Spark toward the fence, the colt, who was still dallied to us, showed no sign of stopping. *This is going to hurt,* I thought.

Looking back, it seems funny now—the thought of racing around that arena with the two horses, with no reins to guide Spark. More than anything, it reminds me of a scene from an old movie, where the driver and passenger of a car are arguing about which turn to take, and both grab onto the wheel as the car races down the highway. As they both yank on the steering wheel, it comes loose, and now the car is out of control, with no way to steer.

There was real danger in that moment. Crashing into a steel-pipe fence while attached to 2,000 pounds of horseflesh would have been ugly. Several years ago, I saw a young colt who'd gotten so excited that he tried to leap a fence and ended up impaled on one of the posts. He survived, but was permanently impaired because of the torn muscles in his chest.

And I've known of riders who've been seriously injured after being thrown from a horse. Ralph, who is my right-hand man at the ranch, fell from a horse back in 2008, and suffered such a severe concussion that we feared he had irreparable brain damage. For months, he couldn't concentrate and would forget where he was.

Once, while at a church service, he got so confused that he sat down next to a woman in one of the pews, thinking he was sitting next to his wife. Then he looked up and realized he didn't know who she was. "You're not my wife, are you?" he said, with a sheepish grin on his face. Ralph did eventually make a full recovery, but he had us worried for a while.

As we approached the fence for a second go round, time seemed to slow down, like the pause just before a train wreck, when you can see it coming but are helpless to stop it. For a fleeting moment, I thought, *This horse is not going to stop.*

Just shy of the fence, Spark put on the brakes and he and the colt skidded to a halt once more.

By this time, the colt had run out of steam. While he wasn't quite ready to give me his full attention, he wasn't about to bolt again. Within about half an hour, he'd begun to listen, and allowed me to saddle and ride him, leaving us with a relatively happy ending. All's well that ends well, as Shakespeare said.

If Spark had been a different horse and hadn't been able to hear my voice when that colt bolted, it would have been a different story. Like the crew of Flight 1549, Spark and I started our training long before we ever faced a crisis.

As I mentioned, he was pretty wound up and excitable as a young colt. Once I had got him to stop wanting to stomp on his lead rope as if it were a snake, we went to work in earnest. My first goal was to grab Spark's attention, so that no matter what was going on around him, he'd always look to me, and focus on my directions, not on his circumstances.

When dealing with a horse that's excitable or easily distracted, the natural reaction is to try to desensitize him. That's an approach police departments often use while training their mounted patrols. Because of the nature of their work, police horses are often in loud, dangerous situations. One of their most common responsibilities is crowd control, which is uncomfortable for horses. They don't like crowds of people, or the sound of yelling or sirens, and strange people touching their faces or manes and tails. All of that can happen in a crowd.

To compensate for this, police horses are often trained to ignore any distractions around them. If a horse gets used to a siren going off around him, then he won't panic when a police car pulls up, with its siren wailing. Likewise, if the horse is taught to ignore groups of strangers, then he's less likely to react when he is stuck in the middle of a crowd.

The downside to all this is the horses can become so desensitized that they even ignore the officers riding on their backs. In a crowd of people, or a crisis situation, it can be a recipe for disaster.

That's what the St. Paul, Minnesota police department was worried about in the summer of 2007. The following year, the city would be hosting the Republican National Convention. Along with the delegates, this was likely to attract thousands of protesters, some of them very angry about the direction in which the country was going.

Angry protesters and horses don't mix very well. The department had heard horror stories about protesters throwing broken glass on the sidewalk in front of horses, hoping to cut their feet; or protesters yanking on the reins of horses or crowding around them, trying to spook them.

The last thing the department wanted was for that to happen and for one of their horses to overreact, resulting in injury. So they asked me to come in and work with some of their mounted patrol officers.

The officers were great to work with—highly dedicated and eager to improve their skills. To be honest, however, their training had been inconsistent. Most were riding their own horses, so there were a variety of breeds in the patrol, with varied skill levels. Some officers were highly trained, others were not.

One horse in particular caught my eye. A huge Draft Horse I nicknamed "Dozer," as in bulldozer, because of his massive size—he was well over 2,000 pounds. Dozer was a perfect example of a desensitized horse.

He had an easy nature and nothing seemed to faze him—including his rider. That made Dozer the department's greatest asset for crowd control, and its biggest liability. Standing 16 to 17 hands high and backed by 2,000 pounds of muscle, Dozer could bust up any crowd. Unfortunately, once he got started, there was no stopping him. He'd learned his lessons too well.

So I put Dozer through some training exercises and began to focus him on learning to listen. In some ways, it was like giving a set of hearing aids to someone who'd gone deaf. Then I had the officers from the patrol work their horses, in the same way, so that when something startled them or made them feel uncomfortable, they'd tune out everything but their rider's voice and directions.

I also told them about my own experiences with Spark. When Spark was two, he and I took a trip to Ohio, where I was scheduled to do a Sermon on the Mount presentation. It was a relatively short trip so I didn't have all my equipment with me, and the church that was hosting us wasn't able to come up with a round pen for me to use.

So we improvised. The church set up seating on the front lawn, which faced a state highway. I parked my rig and trailer on the church's lawn, between the building and the highway, so we'd at least have a barrier between where I was working and the road.

On one side was the audience; on the other was my

trailer, with Spark and myself between them. There were no side barriers, but I wasn't too concerned. We weren't going to be racing around the lawn too much, so I felt we were relatively safe.

After showing the audience some basic tricks that Spark had learned, I got to the main event. The focus that night was on trust, and how to have inner confidence and peace, no matter what our circumstances. To demonstrate that principle, I'd set up an obstacle course on the lawn. Spark and I had been working on similar courses back home at the ranch.

Because they are prey animals, horses are cautious by nature. When they are running on familiar surfaces—grass, dirt, gravel—horses run comfortably, without any concerns. When they see something unusual, say a tarp or a board or something else out of the ordinary, they hesitate and prepare to run from it.

So I set up a load of debris on the lawn, with some of my gear and a few items borrowed from the church. I started with some crates and a ladder, followed by a saddle rack from the truck, and covered it all with a blue tarp. In between the debris I made a narrow path for Spark to make his way through.

I stood on one side, in front of the audience, and Spark stood by the trailer. Then I called him to me.

When he heard me, he looked up and started walking forward. As he approached the debris, he paused and reached out one of his feet to test and see where it was safe for him to walk. All the while I called to him, and so despite his uncertainty about the debris, he started walking towards me.

Part way through, Spark took a misstep. I'd laid the tarp over the saddle rack, and on that rack there was one small gap, just wide enough for a horse's foot to get through. We'd been working with racks and tarps and other obstacles for months, and Spark never had a problem.

This time, however, he put his foot in precisely the wrong spot, and it slipped through the rungs at the bottom of the saddle rack. When he pulled his foot back, the whole pile collapsed, trapping his leg in the debris.

Suddenly, I was scared. Here was a three-year-old colt, reactionary by nature, with his leg trapped in a pile of debris and a tarp fluttering right in his face. Worse yet, I wasn't anywhere near him, so I couldn't hold him in place long enough to get his leg clear. And there was no perimeter fence to protect him from running off or dragging the debris madly through the audience. Every instinct in Spark's body was telling him to bolt, which was the absolute worst thing he could have done.

As Spark began to lift his foot and try to tug it clear, I called out to him. "Spark," I said. "Stay."

Though he was only three years old, Spark knew that he could trust me. So despite the rising panic in his chest, he held his foot still. Calmly I walked over to him, and asked for a few volunteers. Three men from the audience stood up and within a few minutes, they'd cleared the debris and Spark was free.

The audience, most of whom had no idea how bad things could have gotten, broke out in applause. But Spark didn't panic, and because he trusted me, we were able to cope with the crisis and come through unscathed.

I don't know about you, but there have been many times in my life when I've felt trapped, like Spark did, and all I wanted to do was run away. Even though I knew it was the wrong thing to do in the long run, the temptation to flee in hard times is almost overwhelming.

As I write these words, our country is going through a difficult time. People have lost their jobs or their retirement savings and wonder how they are going to make ends meet in the future. Those who haven't lost their jobs wonder if they'll be next. At times like this, it's easy to get overwhelmed by fear and uncertainty.

Like Spark, we need to find something or someone to hold onto in days like these. For me, it's my faith, the belief that God is with me even in the hardest time.

That doesn't mean that life is easy or without pain. But even in the most difficult times, I know I'm not alone. That faith, that assurance, helps me to keep walking even when I can't see the way ahead.

That moment on the lawn in Ohio became a turning point for Spark and me. He knew he could trust me to keep him safe, and I knew that I had his full attention. We've become true partners in the months and years that have followed.

We've become so in tune that when we are out on a ride, I have been known to ride him bridleless, with a coffee cup in one hand and my laptop in the other, while I'm searching for a wi-fi Internet signal.

Not long ago, we were in Joshua, Texas, to give a presentation at a cowboy church. The church has invited me to speak to them several times, and every visit, it seems the church is bigger. The first time I went to this church, there were only thirty or so people, and I set up my round pen right in the middle of the congregation.

The next time I came back, there were 400 people there. The time after that, there were 1,200 and they'd moved to a larger building—a barn-style building with a dirt floor and folding chairs all around.

Each time I spoke, because the crowds were bigger, my round pen started getting smaller. Before too long, it seemed like the horse and I were right on top of each other, which made both of us nervous. The horse felt crowded and wanted to bolt over the fence.

Finally I told the church that though I loved to come and speak to them, this setup wasn't working. So the next time they invited me, the church rented an indoor arena that seated 2,500 for the weekend.

I'd been assured by the church that this setting would be perfect, with plenty of room for my sixty-foot-wide round pen. Because there were bleachers in the arena, the congregation would get a better view as well.

When I pulled up to the arena, however, things weren't exactly perfect. Signs for a motocross event—acrobatic racing on motorcycles—were plastered all over the place. The arena's owners had trucked in tons of dirt, and had bulldozed it into hills and moguls for motocross.

There was even less room for my round pen than there had been back in the church. In fact, there wasn't a flat piece of ground to be found anywhere on the floor of that arena.

"Don't worry," my friend from the church said. "The owners promised to bulldoze everything flat by Sunday morning."

As you can probably guess, when we arrived on Sunday morning, there was still hardly a flat piece of ground in that arena. In desperation, I jerry-rigged my round-pen panels into a rectangular pen between two of the hills. That proved to be less than ideal, and though we soldiered on, I could tell the crowd was disappointed.

I need to do something to catch their attention, I thought. *And I've got just the thing for it.*

Slipping out the gate of the pen, Spark and I rode right up the stairs of the bleachers, and into the second level, where we rode from side to side. Bleachers are not exactly a horse's idea of a great place to ride. They don't like the echoes of their hooves on the metal surfaces, or being that close to a crowd of people. And they certainly don't like to walk up and down stairs.

But nothing fazes Spark these days. The last time he was startled by anything came when we rode through the ballroom at the Hilton Hotel and Convention Center in New Orleans. As we rode up on stage, a camera focused on Spark and projected his image on the big screen in the convention center. Spark was startled for a minute, seeing himself on a big screen. Then he turned and walked nonchalantly away.

As we rode through the arena and down from the bleachers, a cheer rose up from the crowd. *That'll give them something to remember,* I thought, as Spark and I rode into the sunset.

Chapter 9

Overcoming Past Failures

THIS PAST CHRISTMAS I went to jail to see my son.

It wasn't exactly the kind of holiday experience that gets pictured on a Hallmark greeting card. There were no festive lights and laughter, no happy family gathered around the Christmas tree, opening presents and singing carols. But that's the way life is for our family right now.

Not long ago, Jeremiah was sentenced to nine years in prison, and is currently serving his time at the Coxsackie Correction Facility in Coxsackie, New York. Since he could not come home for Christmas—obviously—Melodie and I, along with our other son, Daniel, went to see him.

Again, it wasn't a Hallmark moment. But we were glad for the chance to be together. Daniel, who was just back from a tour of duty in Iraq, hadn't seen his brother for several years, and they had a bittersweet reunion—glad to see each other, but saddened by the circumstances that led to Jeremiah being in jail. It's not the way life is supposed to turn out. But then again, it's the way life is for the Sterretts.

Like any couple who have been married for more than a few years, our lives haven't been perfect. While most people are able to keep their difficulties behind closed doors—keeping their skeletons in the closet—that's not been our experience.

When your child goes to jail, you have two choices. You can cut off contact completely and erase any trace of them from your life. Or you can choose to love your child, no matter what.

The first choice is understandable. We've shed a lot of tears over the years for Jeremiah and watched him go through a great deal of heartache. I'm on the road most of the time these days, speaking at churches and conferences, and I often speak to married couples or groups of fathers and sons. Sometimes I wonder what I'm doing—if my own family isn't perfect, what right do I have to stand up and speak?

There have been times when I wanted to withdraw, shut down, and never speak to a group again. And there have been many times when I have wished my life was different.

But God hasn't allowed me to wallow in that kind of self-pity, no matter how tempting that is. Instead, every time I've wanted to quit, God's given me just enough prompting and spurring to keep going.

I mentioned earlier that couples often come to see

Melodie and me when they are at their wits' end; when every other attempt to save their marriage has failed. Sometimes I think we should hang a sign up that says, "If you are desperate, we can help."

Not that we are experts at marriage. Sometimes when we speak, people introduce us as relationships experts, as if we've discovered some hidden secret about marriage, and if a couple will only follow our advice, they'll live happily ever after and never have a problem again.

By now you've guessed that's not true. But what we have learned is how to pick up the pieces of life that fall apart. We bring hope to people because we have been through difficult times and have come through them stronger. I don't want people to learn how to survive those hard times. I want them to find enough hope that they can thrive as a result of those hard times. If we had not struggled, we'd have no hope to offer people.

That's what brought us to prison this past Christmas. We're hoping for a miracle, that Jeremiah's life can be healed. But miracles and redemption don't come when we sit around waiting for them. They come when we get up and begin taking small steps toward redemption.

There's a story told in the New Testament about the time that Jesus fed 5,000 people, who'd come out to the wilderness to hear him speak. The story is a familiar one but there's one aspect that always strikes me.

At one point in the story, the disciples come to Jesus and ask him to send the crowds away. After all, it's getting late and people are hungry. The disciples want Jesus to call a dinner break, and send the crowds to forage for food on their own. Instead, Jesus tells the disciples to serve a meal to the crowd.

Feeding a group of 5,000 people is a major undertaking. At the ranch, if we were preparing a meal for that many people, it'd take weeks of planning ahead, of ordering extra food, and putting up tents and renting extra kitchen equipment, and bringing in added help to get the meal prepared. It's not like whipping up a meal for a few dinner guests.

While the disciples wander around, complaining about how unfair Jesus is being to them, and how he's asked them to do the impossible, a little boy steps forward. In his hand are five loaves and two fish, and he offers them to Jesus.

That one small act opens up the space for Jesus to do something remarkable. By the time the meal is over, all 5,000 people have been fed, and there are twelve baskets full of fish and bread left over.

I've never seen 5,000 people fed with five loaves and two fish. What I have seen, though, are remarkable turnarounds that started with very small steps, like the ones taken by that little boy, almost 2,000 years ago.

Just before he died, Mike Yaconelli gave an interview, where he talked about the power of what he called small acts of grace. Yaconelli had written a book called *Messy*

Spirituality, where he talked about the struggles that most people, even those with deep faith, face. And he talked about the way that our modern secular society can squash the faith out of people.

"Our secular pagan culture doesn't make us get drunk, it makes us dull," he said. "It robs us of our creativity. We don't sit around thinking, how can I redeem this situation? We have lost the power of the tiny, of the small, of the little thoughtful things that we can do for each other that will make all the difference in the world. That's what happens in a pagan culture. It's not that we run around doing these horrible sins. It's that we don't run around doing these little acts of grace that we ought to be doing."

Of course, none of this means that life will turn around in an instant. In some ways, repairing or redeeming the life of a horse or a human being is harder than feeding 5,000 people. Often it takes thousands of tiny steps of faith and years of setbacks and stumbling, when you are tempted to throw in the towel, before a single life can be turned around.

Jeremiah has made major progress towards healing, towards putting his life back together. If we shunned him, that journey would be a great deal longer and a great deal more difficult.

No matter what, we won't do that. Not because we are great parents, but because Jeremiah and his brother Daniel have taught us the power of unconditional love.

Learning to love the boys wasn't easy. Not because of anything they had done, but because of how Melodie and I met them. Like most newlywed couples, we'd started out with dreams for having children and starting a family. Within a few years, it became clear that something was wrong. No matter how hard we tried, Melodie wasn't getting pregnant.

We eventually visited several doctors, who told us that we were infertile. A surprising number of people have trouble getting pregnant, and for them infertility is an emotional roller coaster. Each month begins with hope and ends with sorrow.

The Bible often refers to couples who don't have children as being barren, and the word fits. These days, doctors prefer the term "infertility," but that word lacks the punch and emotional heartache conveyed in the word "barren."

Because we were in ministry and had literally thousands of people coming through the ranch, word of our circumstances got around. Several people came forward, wondering if we'd be open to adopting a child. They knew of young women facing an unplanned pregnancy, who weren't able to care for a baby and wanted to place their child in a good home.

During those years, on several occasions we had opportunities offered to us, to adopt infants. So we did what all expecting parents do. We bought baby clothes and furniture, painted the nursery, and made space in our home for this new life.

At the last minute, these offers fell through. The first

time that happened, it was like a body blow, with all of our hopes being dashed. But we still held on to hope that the next time would be different. By the last time, we were wrung out emotionally, and wondered what we'd done to deserve this pain. Those were not easy years.

In our outreach to children, we worked with several foster agencies. Through that process we met Daniel and Jeremiah and felt clearly led to adopt them. They were half brothers, with the same mom but different dads, and both had had traumatic upbringings. I won't go into all the details—that's their story to tell, not mine.

As a result of their early struggles, life was hard for Daniel and Jeremiah. They had a lot of damage to undo. It took us years to realize how much they'd suffered before we knew them.

When you become a parent, it's a life long commitment. Before Daniel and Jeremiah came on the scene, I thought I knew what love was. I was wrong.

Over the last twenty years those boys have broken my heart. They have filled my life with joy. They stretched me beyond my limits many times. And they taught me that love is a choice. I love my sons, not because of their accomplishments, but because they are my sons.

Several years ago, I wrote them both a letter. For years, I realized, I'd projected my expectations on them. Most of those expectations were good—I want my boys to be honest, caring, strong men of character. Others weren't so good.

In some ways I wanted them to succeed in order to validate my status as their father. When they failed, though I never said it out loud, they could sense my disappointment, like a weight hanging over them.

Knowing that, I wrote them each a letter, telling them that I loved them, and releasing them from having to live up to my expectations. I blessed them, and told them that no matter what, I would always be grateful to be their father. They taught me how to love, and how to be a father, and I wanted them to know I was thankful.

Those letters, and our subsequent conversations, have changed our relationship. They don't have to worry about disappointing me any more. I still have hopes and dreams for them, but I want them to know that they are loved simply for who they are, and not for their accomplishments.

The inspiration for that letter came from an unlikely source—my stepfather. For years we'd been estranged, and I'd lost touch with him after he and my mother divorced. I hated him when I was younger, and went out of my way to point that out whenever I could. I'd ignore my stepfather, or disrespect him, or even provoke him as a teenager, refusing to give him any respect. He was not my father and I went out of my way to make that point any time I had the chance. In time I learned how to push his buttons, adding tension to our already stress-filled home. He and my mother had a rocky relationship already, and my behavior only made matters worse.

By the time I'd reached my twenties, regret began to sink in over the way I'd treated my stepdad. I like to say that God got a hold of me, and pointed out that I'd been a jerk. One of the Ten Commandments is to honor your mother and father, and I'd broken that one on a number of occasions.

Whatever my stepfather's shortcomings, he didn't deserve the kind of treatment I gave him. I didn't even show him the kind of common courtesy I showed to strangers. In short, I'd been a jerk. In my twenties, I began to realize that I had a lot to apologize for.

After tracking down my stepfather's address, I wrote out a letter, telling him how sorry I was for the way I'd acted, and how much I regretted it. Sometimes you write a letter like that, and then lose the courage to send it. Instead it ends up in the trash or in a drawer somewhere.

I was so convicted about my actions, and so desperate to take responsibility for them, that I dropped it in the mailbox, with more than a little bit of fear and trembling. Then I waited for a response. It never came, so I summoned up the courage to call him.

To my surprise, he was glad to hear from me. He accepted my apology, and said he'd regretted the distance that had come between us. He wished that we had been closer when I was growing up and that things could have been different between us.

That wasn't all he said. "I forgive you," he told me. "And I give you my blessing."

He had every right to withhold that forgiveness. My mother and he had long been divorced, and he didn't owe me anything. I don't even know if we were technically related anymore. None of that seemed to matter to my stepdad.

His words released me from the guilt and regret I'd carried for years. Now I wanted to pass that same kind of grace on to my sons.

The writer of the Old Testament book Isaiah knew something about that kind of grace as well. The prophet was speaking to people who were exiled—at this time, the Babylonians had conquered Israel, and driven the people far from their homes. Some were slaves, and some were refugees, with little hope that life could ever get better. Isaiah wrote:

> The Spirit of the Lord GOD is upon me, because the LORD hath anointed me to preach good tidings unto the meek; he hath sent me to bind up the brokenhearted, to proclaim liberty to the captives, and the opening of the prison to them that are bound; To proclaim the acceptable year of the LORD, and the day of vengeance of our God; to comfort all that mourn; To appoint unto them that mourn in Zion, to give unto them beauty for ashes, the oil of joy for mourning, the garment of praise for the spirit of heaviness; that they might be called trees

of righteousness, the planting of the LORD, that he might be glorified.

(ISAIAH 61:1–3)

That phrase, "beauty for ashes" has always struck me. Most of the things that matter in my life began as ashes and were turned into something beautiful. The ranch, my family, my work with horses, even becoming a father, all began with heartache and struggle. Over the years, they've been transformed and rebuilt into something great.

It's a bit like the way pearls are made. They begin when a parasite or some other irritant invades the mouth of an oyster. That invader irritates the sensitive parts of the oyster, and in response, the oyster begins to cover the intruder with layers of minerals. In this process, the oyster creates a pearl of great price.

I should not have been surprised at the irony that my broken relationship with my stepfather Earl Berry, and the difficulty that I had to work through with my horse Berry, would prove to be irritants that would result in pearls of wisdom.

I got the first glimpse of what that phrase—ashes to beauty—meant almost forty years ago, when I first began working with horses.

Our neighbors, the Fultons, spent many weekends at

horse shows and competitions, and they often invited me to go along. They'd load up their horses in the back of a horse van, fill the cab with kids, and off we'd go.

One of the regulars at the local horse shows was a woman whose name I have forgotten, who rode a dark bay gelding named Tweedy. Without fail, the two of them were among the best teams in the local shows. They rode in perfect unison, and seem to win while hardly breaking a sweat. There was something effortless about their performances.

At the time, I assumed that Tweedy was a ringer. This lady only had one horse, and didn't have a reputation as a great trainer, so I assumed she'd gone out and bought an expensive, fancy, well-trained horse, and that's why he rode so well.

It was then that I learned the truth. Tweedy wasn't a fancy horse at all. In fact, this woman had bought him at a horse auction, where his former owners were dumping him for pennies on the dollar. Tweedy was hardly more than skin and bones when she brought him home, and he'd been malnourished and neglected for some time.

Tweedy had hit rock bottom and been thrown on the trash heap. That's where his rider had found him. I don't know why she bought him—whether it was out of pity or compassion or if he was the only horse she could afford. But much like the great thoroughbred Seabiscuit, who'd been lingering in low-level claiming races before being rescued by his trainer, Tom Smith, there was more to Tweedy than met the eye.

His new owner put Tweedy on a healthy diet, fattened him up, and began to rebuild him with care and love and lots of exercise. Then she trained him.

Here's what struck me about Tweedy: He didn't just survive under her care, he blossomed. He gained confidence and always seemed eager to please. Together, they had a great partnership for many years.

The horse world can be a bit funny. We think that a horse is in its prime when it is young, between the ages of two and seven—that's when they are the strongest, fastest, and the most capable. But they spend relatively few years in that prime of life.

If a horse is in good shape when they are seven, they'll likely be active for another fifteen to twenty years. The quality of those years is based on how their training went in the early years. If they have a good foundation, they'll become a great horse for kids or grandkids, or amateur riders. Their best years become the decades they spend training young riders.

When I start training a horse, I'm not only thinking about the task at hand, or even what I'm going to teach six months down the road; I want the horse to learn the habits that will last for a lifetime, and then to be able to pass them on.

We call that mentoring, and I often use Spark to demonstrate how it works. It's not always easy. Spark's a stallion, and if you've spent any time around stallions, you'll know that they are territorial by nature. More than anything, they are really big boys who don't like to share. In the wild, and often in captivity, stallions will mark their territory and defend it fiercely from any horse who infringes on their space.

If there is a mare around, then as the saying goes, boys will be boys. Think of a stallion as a teenaged boy on steroids, and you'll get the idea.

When I train a stallion like Spark or Spotlight or my youngest horse, Romeo, I want them to set aside their aggression, their territoriality, and even their hormones, and focus all of their attention on me. That may sound selfish on my part, but it's not. In the end, I have their best interests at heart.

As long as a stallion is ruled by his emotions, he'll never reach his full potential, or be able to think clearly in a crisis, or when another horse is losing its mind. Once they have control of their emotions and can look to me—that's a different story.

Of course, even I have trouble reining in my emotions sometimes. Like the time I was flying through the air and about to land in an audience member's lap.

Spark and I were training an unbroken gelding, and things were not going quite as I planned. Most times when I pony another horse to Spark, by dallying their lead rope to my saddle horn, things go well. The untrained horse will mimic Spark's actions, shortening the training process as it learns by doing.

When things don't go well, that's when I have come to rely on Spark. With this gelding, things were not going well. I've had unbroken horses kick out at Spark or try and bite him, but that is par for the course. In fact, I usually put special pads on his legs to protect him from any kind of permanent injury.

We were in Washington State, doing a Sermon on the Mount presentation, when this gelding did something I'd not thought possible. We were by the edge of the arena, and suddenly he lurched towards Spark, throwing all of his weight against him, and knocking my stallion clear off his feet. I went flying over the fence and into the lap of a startled audience member.

Luckily I kept my head and didn't express my true feelings into the wireless microphone I wore. "Well, folks," I said, "things don't always go this well."

Then I jumped over the fence and got back at it. Spark had regained his feet by this time, and glanced at the gelding with a wary eye. But it takes more than that to deter Spark and myself. In a few minutes, we were leading the gelding back in the arena, with a little less slack on the lead rope so he couldn't pick up steam. Once he realized that we weren't impressed by his antics, the gelding calmed down and got with the program.

A similar thing happened in North Carolina, where I was working with a Trakehner mare, who'd never been ridden.

Trakehners are European warmblood horses, bred for their strength and athleticism, and are one of the larger breeds of horses. They're called warmbloods because they are descended from both "hot-blooded horses," like Arabians, who are known for their speed and high-strung personalities, and "cold-blooded horses," like draft horses, who are usually strong and steady.

This mare, who was heavily muscled, was at least a foot taller than Spark and outweighed him by several hundred pounds. She had no interest in cooperating with us, and resented being led by a smaller and lighter horse. So the mare launched a mini protest, right in the middle of the arena.

Without warning, she threw herself on the ground, laid out flat, and refused to move. If you're a parent, this may sound familiar, as two-year-olds often try this technique. It's meant to wear down a parent's or authority figure's patience. The idea is to become such a pain that the parent will give up, thinking that fighting with the child is not worth the effort.

I've been at this too long to fall for a trick like that, so I gently flicked a rope across her nose and the mare popped back to her feet. It was just enough to let her know that I wasn't impressed.

A few other things are worth noting. When I pony another horse, Spark is usually without a bridle. That's to make a point. When Spark is bridleless, he's under no compulsion to follow my lead. He follows my instructions because he wants to, not because he has to. Also, I don't have to worry about the other horse getting tangled in my reins.

On the other hand, at times the untrained horse won't do what they are told, even though I've got a lead rope tied to them. No matter what the other horse does, Spark ignores their bad behavior. He also controls his own hormones. Like I said, Stallions are like teenaged boys on steroids, and they usually find a mare irresistible. I've seen mares literally throw themselves at Spark, and he won't respond to their advances.

This particular mare, however, had no interest in anyone but herself. Within a few minutes of getting back on her feet, she tried the flopping act again. This second time, she refused to get up, even after I flicked her with a rope.

Undaunted, I hopped off and took a hold of her nose, and gave it a gentle squeeze. Not enough to hurt but enough to get her attention, because it cut off a little of her breathe. Once again, she hopped to her feet. The audience was impressed by the response, and by Spark's steadfastness, despite her antics.

One of the keys to our success in the Sermon on the Mount is that, for the most part, we've lost any fear of being embarrassed, and so we aren't ashamed to fail. I've got a saying: Anything worth doing, is worth doing poorly.

It's not that I don't believe that excellence matters. Quite the opposite. The only way to do something with excellence is to start out doing things poorly, and then learn from your mistakes.

A number of years ago, the owners of the Singing Pines Plantation in Glenwood, Georgia, asked to me to come down and work with some of their young colts. We were doing a round pen session, and they brought in a three-year-old for me to work with. He was a beautiful sorrel colt with a chiseled face, a powerful physique, and a mahogany red coat. The owners were planning on selling him, and thought his session with me might attract a buyer.

That first session didn't go very well. This particular colt had been left on his own most of the time, and so he wasn't domesticated enough for me to get close to him. He had a long reach with his front feet and had become quite accomplished at striking out with them. Every horse has its preferred method of defense. Some buck, some bite, some kick out with their hind legs, while others strike out with their front.

I'd not worked with this bloodline of Quarter Horse much before, and this colt was giving me a crash course. At first, his owners were miffed—they thought I was making their horse look bad. His aggressive behavior reflected poorly on them, and made a poor advertisement for this colt.

But as I worked the colt, I began to understand what made him tick. We got him settled down, and I put the lessons I learned with him to use with the next colt I worked with. Things went so well after that, that they'd invite me down every year to break in that year's group of colts.

It would have been easy to give up after the first day at the Singing Pines. I've got no interest in being kicked by a horse, or in upsetting the good people who'd invited me into their ranch.

By seeing it as a learning experience, and by not being afraid to fail, that first day at Singing Pines became the basis for a long-time friendship. Eventually the owners would give me Spotlight.

There's a bit of ironic twist to the story. Spotlight is a Quarter Horse, and on the day he was born, the president of one of the Quarter Horse clubs happened to be visiting Singing Pines. Even on that first day, Spotlight was a stunning colt, with a perfect physique and a golden coat, that made him seem a perfect specimen. The club president was so taken with Spotlight that he offered to buy him right then and there.

"He's not for sale," the owners said, but the president insisted. He pulled out his checkbook, tore off a check, signed it, handed the blank check to the owners of Singing Pines, and said, "You fill in the amount."

As he said that, Spotlight turned around, and the president's jaw dropped. On one side, Spotlight had a perfect golden coat. On the other side, however, he had a large white spot—as if someone had turned a spotlight on him. At the time, that discoloration made him worthless. He was disqualified from being registered as a Quarter Horse, and while he could be registered as a Paint Horse, he would be an unlikely Paint Stallion, because of his Quarter Horse bloodlines.

My friends who owned the Singing Pines handed the check back to the horse club president with a knowing smile. They were disappointed as well, knowing that this colt who they'd had such high hopes for had an uncertain future.

Things turned out all right in the end. Spotlight came to Miracle Mountain Ranch and began his training. Meanwhile, my friends at the Singing Pines suggested I should not give up hope for Spotlight's future. The Quarter Horse Association was considering changing its rules to allow Paint Horses to be cross-registered as Quarter Horses. When that happened this once worthless horse became a rarity—a Quarter Horse and a Paint Stallion, and worth far more than the average Quarter Horse.

There is one other reason that I've learned to never give up hope. That's because I've lived long enough to know that in life, anything can happen. Just ask my friend Ralph.

For more than thirty years, Ralph has been my right-hand man at the ranch. He runs the summer camp, works with our apprentices, and specializes in working with difficult campers—those who don't think the rules apply to them. Ralph's an expert with those kinds of kids, because he used to be one.

Ralph first came to Miracle Mountain Ranch more than

forty years ago, as an eight- or nine-year-old boy. By that time, he'd already been thrown out of three other camps, and—after arriving at the ranch—tried to make it four.

If not for Dale Linebaugh, Ralph might have succeeded. But Dale had a way with boys like Ralph, and as Ralph's mother drove off, Dale put his firm but gentle hand on the back of his neck, gave a squeeze, and said, "We're going to get along just fine." And they did, though Ralph gave Dale a run for his money. (Little did Ralph know that he'd spend most of the rest of his life at the ranch.)

Years later, Ralph repaid Dale's investment as he sat with an eight-year-old named Jeremiah Beize at the dining-room table while the other campers had gone, insisting that Jeremiah could leave as soon as he finished his dinner.

No matter how Jeremiah fumed or screamed, "Help, they are killing me!", Ralph sat without reacting, as if he had all the time in the world. Ralph knew that on the inside, Jeremiah wasn't a bad kid. But he was angry at his abusive parents and the foster-care system. One year later, Jeremiah would become Dale's grandson and our son.

Ralph's parents' divorce had driven a wedge between Ralph and his mom as well. Though she cared for him, and made sure he always had enough to eat and had clothes on his back, she withheld any words of love or appreciation.

By the time he'd arrived at the ranch, Ralph had also been suspended several times from school for fighting. He and his mom moved often when he was growing up, and he was often a target for bullies as the new kid in town.

But Ralph was strong and tough for his size. So whenever he moved to a new school, he figured out who the biggest bully was, and picked a fight with that kid. Most of the time Ralph won the fights, ensuring that other bullies would leave him alone. If there was going to be a fight, Ralph made sure he got the first punch in.

Ralph came to the ranch with that chip on his shoulder, daring the other campers or anyone in authority to knock it off. But Dale knew that Ralph's attitude was mostly an act. Once you got past that outer shell, there was a boy who missed his father and didn't know what to do with that anger. His gentle but firm response eventually defused Ralph's anger, and began to turn his life around. When I became the ranch's director, Ralph was one of the first people I hired.

Despite all his success at the camp, there was one thing still missing from his life. It could be summed up in three simple words that Ralph's mother had never spoken to him in his nearly fifty years of life. Just three simple words: "I love you."

Every time he talked to his mother, Ralph made a point of telling her that he loved her. At first she ignored him. Then, when they were talking on the phone, she'd pause after saying goodbye, waiting for him to say, "I love you."

After two years, she was finally able to say, "Um hum,"

after he told her that he loved her. But still, she couldn't say the words.

Finally, after three years, she ended a phone call by saying, "I love you."

Some things are worth waiting for, even if it takes fifty years.

CHAPTER 10

A RESPONSIBLE CHOICE

WHEN I WAS SEVENTEEN, God snuck up on me.

My family was Presbyterian, and when it came to going to church, my mother didn't mess around. She often spent her night reading the Bible into the wee hours of the morning, and she made sure we were found every Sunday sitting in the pews of our home church, until I was teenager.

When I joined 4-H, however, my mother began to ease up. Many of the horse shows and other 4-H events were scheduled on Sundays, and reluctantly, she let me skip out on services.

After a couple of years, I became an expert on getting out of church. If it wasn't a 4-H event, then I'd say that I had some chores to do at the neighbors' farms, or some work to do on my horses. I always had some kind of excuse handy.

My mother wasn't pleased, but as long as I promised to read my Bible to make up for missing church, she'd give in. This infuriated my stepfather, but my mother would always cover for me. Things were already tense enough at home, and she wanted to avoid making church one more battleground. She was working diligently to hang on to me.

In 1970, I won the statewide veterinary science and horse project competitions for 4-H, which meant a trip to Chicago, Illinois, for the national conference. That year marked the fiftieth anniversary of 4-H, and among the celebrities making an appearance at the event was then-President Richard Nixon. The Ford Motor Company was one of the main sponsors, and the convention promised to be quite a show.

I was glad to be away from home, and was looking forward to having a good time, far away from my mother's watchful eye. I wasn't a bad kid or a troublemaker back then, but I'd started rebelling against my mother's strict rules about drinking and smoking, or spending too much time hanging out with girls.

We arrived at the hotel in downtown Chicago on Saturday, and had Sunday morning free. Some of the kids I was hanging out with wanted to go over to the Moody Bible Church, a Chicago institution founded by the famed evangelist Dwight L. Moody. I thought, *Oh, stink! Not church!*

Then again, there was this pretty girl in the group. She was Miss Rodeo Washington State, and I thought, *I'd like to have some of her attention.* When we talked, she mentioned that she was going to church the next morning, and hoped I was going too. Since she was going to church, I was willing to go.

As far as Miss Rodeo Washington State went, church was a lousy investment—she soon lost interest in me. I even tried writing to her once the convention was over, but after an initial response, she eventually stopped replying. I should have slept in or gone down to the pool instead.

Still, that Sunday's service wasn't a complete waste of time. I'd heard lots of sermons growing up, and most had gone in one ear and out the other. For some reason, the sermon in that Chicago service got through. The preacher's name has escaped me, but the Bible passage he used that morning still echoes in my mind. It was from the Gospel of Matthew, where Jesus talked about what really matters in life. Jesus said:

> If anyone would come after me, he must deny himself
> and take up his cross and follow me. For whoever
> wants to save his life will lose it, but whoever loses
> his life for me will find it. What good will it be for a
> man if he gains the whole world, yet forfeits his soul?
> Or what can a man give in exchange for his soul?
>
> (MATTHEW 16:24–26 NIV)

That question lingered in my mind as I made my way back to the hotel. What good is it to gain the whole world—money, success, fame—if it costs you your soul?

Winning a 4-H national championship is not the kind of thing that people sell their soul for. I'd won three of those, and had started to see that winning didn't make me feel any better about myself, at least not in the long run.

The desire to win was making me push my horses harder and harder, without much concern beyond the next trophy. While it worked in the short run, even then I knew I was on shaky ground. The harder I pushed them, the more likely one of the horses was going to crack, and not be able to handle the pressure. In the back of my mind, I knew that pushing them so hard wasn't good for them in the long run.

There were also temptations in the horse show world. There was a lot of money at stake for a trainer who could consistently produce winners. That money added to the pressure to succeed in the show ring. Even then, I knew that money alone wasn't going to make me happy.

Though I wouldn't have admitted it at the time, I didn't like the person I was becoming. I had the reputation for being a straight-laced kid, and so I played that up in public. When I was with my friends, I'd swear and drink and chase girls, but when I was at shows or 4-H events, I put on the face of a good Christian boy.

That act got me in good with a girl named Cindy Biel. She was sixteen, and her dad was a prominent horse dealer in a neighboring county. He sold horses and tack, and all the other paraphernalia from the horse show world.

Cindy was a sweet girl, and she was into 4-H, so we ended up spending a lot of time together. Later on, she invited me to spend time with her family, and I hit it off with them as well. I began to think that this was the kind of family I'd really like to be a part of.

Almost ten years after his death, the loss of my father still felt like a heavy weight on my chest. So much had changed since then. We'd lost the farm, our family had splintered, and the grief over an absent dad was always there in the background.

Much like a horse who'd been separated from the herd and run in off the range, I felt corralled, wishing there was some way I could hop the fence and find some release from my painful loneliness.

Cindy's dad, Mr. Biel, was the kind of father figure I craved. If I could find another family to be a part of, I told myself that I could be happy. I liked Cindy, and I liked her family, and I thought if things worked, this is the kind of family I'd always wanted to be a part of. I was still a kid then, so I wasn't thinking seriously about marriage, but the thought of a future with Cindy and her family crossed my mind more than a few times.

My wife, Melodie, sometimes kids me that I married her for her dad, and she's more than a little bit right. In Mr. Biel, I saw some of the same characteristics that would later draw me to Dale Linebaugh.

One night, some of my friends and I decided to hang out at the sale barn. The barn was filled with teens and adults, hanging out while the sale went on in the background.

While I was walking around the outside, suddenly,

someone came up from behind and grabbed me. They put their hands over my eyes, so I couldn't see who it was. I figured it was one of my friends, playing a trick on me, so in order to impress my friends, I responded in a coarse and arrogant manner.

Then I heard the deep voice of Mr. Biel ring in my ears. "Well, if that's the way you feel about it," he said. He let go of me, and walked off into the dark. I could have slid under the lowest door-sill; I felt that embarrassed and that small. This man had seen right through me.

Mr. Biel taught me a valuable lesson that night. To really know someone, watch their reactions, not their actions. I realized that I am never the man of my actions—I'm always the man of my reactions. I've never forgotten that lesson.

That night I saw myself painfully clear, and the view wasn't pleasant. The vulgar words weren't the main problem. In essence, I'd become two-faced, putting on a good show when it was to my advantage, but hiding what I was really like on the inside.

I use that lesson often while training horses. On the surface, a horse can seem perfectly well mannered and trustworthy. But you never know what a horse is capable of until you push them out of their comfort zone.

Some of the owners who come to me, asking for help with their horses, have been riding time bombs, and they never knew it. Push a horse a bit too far and they'll react, showing their true personality.

Before I ever saddle a horse, I wrap a rope around his body, following the same pattern that the saddle girth will take. I want to see how the horse will respond when those girths are tightened.

I don't do it quickly—I prepare the horse by putting the rope over his head and laying a blanket on his back, and rewarding him for remaining calm. I use the rope to make sure he is ready. The last thing I want is to be on a horse's back and have him lower the hammer on me.

That's exactly what happened to a friend of mine. She'd been training dressage horses for years, and finally had acquired the horse of her dreams. Dressage is sometimes called a ballet for horses, where athleticism and agility are highly prized.

My friend had found the perfect horse for the event from a breeder in Holland. The horse was a Hanoverian, the perfect combination of agility and strength for dressage. Even before the horse arrived at her farm, she imagined them becoming champions.

Because he was a costly investment, my friend had a thirty-day grace period before the final payment was due. That first month was like being on a honeymoon. The horse was everything my friend had hoped for. Not only was he talented and capable as a performer, but he was also responsive and enthusiastic as a training partner. He did what she asked him to do, without a moment's hesitation or complaining.

But as most of us know, the honeymoon has to end someday. No sooner had my friend signed the contract and sent the final payment, than this new horse showed his true colors.

My friend went out to work with her horse, as she'd done for a month, and he turned on her. As she climbed in the saddle, he bolted and sent her flying. She ended up lying flat on her face in the dirt, while her dream horse ambled off, as if nothing was out of the ordinary.

By the time she called me, my friend had been dumped five or six times, and was in a panic. The horse had cost her tens of thousands of dollars, and now she wondered if she'd flushed that money down the toilet and was left with a worthless horse.

I wasn't quite as bad as that Hanoverian. But I'm not sure any one could really trust me. Push me too far, and there was no telling what I might do.

When I got to Penn State, there were more tests. On the outside, I was still Mr. Clean Cut. On the inside—well, that was another story.

Here was my problem in a nutshell: I couldn't change myself.

We see the same problem in a horse. A wild horse, or a horse who has grown up on a ranch or farm can't train itself. To reach his full potential, every horse needs to learn how to partner with his trainer or owner, and how to follow his direction. The horse needs someone to show the way.

My stepfather did that for me, when I wrote to him, asking for forgiveness. There was nothing I could do to make our relationship right. I could tell him I was sorry, and ask for forgiveness, but I could not make things right between us. Only my stepfather could do that. Once he forgave me, then relationship was restored.

It was the same, later on, with the staff at Miracle Mountain Ranch. They'd been hurt and felt taken advantage off, so they reacted in fear and mistrust when I took over the ranch. I could reach out my hand in friendship and ask them to follow, but I could not compel them to do it.

They had to take, in essence, a leap of faith, and put their trust in me. Or they could leave, and go someplace that better suited them. Unless they could set aside those hurts and trust me, they'd never be happy at the ranch.

At Penn State, I found a mentor in my friend and teacher, Ward Studebaker. Not only did he teach me about horses and character, but he taught me about God.

Like I said, I'd heard many sermons, but very few had ever gotten through to me. Ward did, however, in a very low-key and simple way.

When we were done with classes, I'd often talk with Ward about some of my struggles with drinking or other temptations on campus. He'd never tell me what to do. Instead, he'd say something like this: "I don't know, Lew, but the Bible says…" I don't even recall what verses in the Bible he pointed out. The thing that convicted me was that he had a foundation to stand on. When he needed to make a decision, he had a reliable source of wisdom to draw on, outside of his own feelings. Somehow the Bible and God were real to him.

That intrigued me. I thought, *I have no lighthouse, no guidepost, no standard to live by.* I didn't have the kind of confidence that Ward had.

Still, I wasn't much interested in God, no matter how much he was trying to get my attention. I wanted to enjoy my life, to have a good time, and I didn't want any God spoiling my plans. When I was old, then I'd have time for God.

I was really like a mustang, who'd been perfectly happy living out in the desert plains, and who now had been run into a corral and had to deal with a trainer who wanted to mess with his life.

There's a misperception about God in our culture, one that I used to fully embrace. God, so the conventional wisdom goes, wants to ruin your life. To know or follow God, I thought, meant giving up all of life's pleasures and becoming a shriveled prune of a puritan, afraid that someone, somewhere is having a good time. I thought being a Christian meant being miserable. I was mistaken.

More than anything, I was like that wild mustang, who'd rather stand by the edge of the round pen and look for a way to jump the fence and get back on the prairie, than turn to the trainer in the arena.

I came to understand that God didn't want to ruin my life. He wanted to offer me something better than wandering around the prairie on my own for the rest of my life. He wanted to give me a family and friends and a chance to do great things.

More than that, he wanted to forgive me, and help me take off the mask that I'd been wearing, and to take the burden of grief and anger from my father's death off my shoulders.

"Come to me, all you who are weary and burdened, and I will give you rest," Jesus once said. "Take my yoke upon you and learn from me, for I am gentle and humble in heart, and you will find rest for your souls. For my yoke is easy and my burden is light" (Matthew 11:28–30 NIV).

I had a need and I couldn't meet it, and so I needed help, just like a horse who can't do it on his own. I realized that Jesus came into my arena, like a trainer coming in to work with a horse, so that I would come to know and trust him. He didn't make me come to him, and require that I clean myself up and make myself worthy of his attention. He came into my life, as messy and unruly as it was, and embraced me just as I was. Just as I want a horse to take the initiative and move towards me, God wanted me to move towards him, and trust him.

In many ways I was like Spotlight, caught in the barbed wire on that Missouri mountainside. If I tried to wrench myself free, I'd only pull the wire tighter. I needed someone to come and cut the wire and show me the way to walk. And I needed to have enough trust in my Heavenly Trainer to overcome my natural inclination to run.

I needed help getting out of that snare. And help came in the form of Jesus, and of letting go of my past, and deciding to follow him.

It didn't all happen in an instant. God didn't ask me to take a leap of faith. Instead, he asked me to take one small step at a time. As those steps built one upon another, the course of my life began to change—acknowledging my desperate need, turning to the one God had sent, and asking God both to forgive me and to be the boss of my life.

The first step was found in chapter 10 of the New Testament book of Romans, which says that, "If you confess with your mouth, 'Jesus is Lord,' and believe in your heart that God raised him from the dead, you will be saved. For it is with your heart that you believe and are justified, and it is with your mouth that you confess and are saved" (verses 9–10 NIV).

That one small step of faith was the biggest step I would ever take, as it changed my life forever.

CHAPTER 11

FRUIT OF THE SPIRIT

EARLIER IN THIS BOOK, I made a confession: Though I've been a cowboy for nearly fifty years now, I still can't rope for beans.

If you've got a wild horse that's never been ridden, and you need someone to take him in a round pen and tame him, I'm your man. If you've got to have someone ride circles around breakfast tables in a hotel banquet hall on horseback, I've been there and done that.

Ask me to rope a horse—and things get ugly.

That's why I got up early one morning this past summer to take lessons from a teenager. We had a Sermon on the Mount presentation scheduled at the camp that day, and as part of that presentation, I planned to rope an untrained horse before ponying with Spark.

Roping is not my strong point at the best of times, so I decided a little practice was in order. That way I wouldn't completely embarrass myself in front of the crowd later on that evening.

With a target set up in the middle of the outdoor arena at the ranch, I got to work. Whirling the rope several times around my head, I took aim at the target, and let the rope fly.

Missed. The lasso sailed over the target, and landed in the sand.

Undaunted, I tried again. Whirl the rope, aim, toss the rope.

Missed. Deep breath. Whirl, aim, toss the rope.

Missed again. Another deep breath. Whirl, aim toss.

Got it!

This pattern went on for another hour. I was successful about 20 per cent of the time, or one out of every five throws, on a stationary target. It was going to be a long night.

About this time, Johnston Williams, one of our apprentices, happened by the arena. He'd grown up on a ranch, and had been roping cattle and horses from the time he could walk. He settled down on the fence to watch me practice, adding to my anxiety.

I was the supposed horsemanship expert, and he was spending two years as an apprentice at the ranch to learn from me and our staff. And now Johnston was going to see that I was struggling with a task he'd mastered as a kid. This was the last thing I needed. Or maybe it was just the thing I needed.

"Mind giving me some pointers here?" I asked, in a hopeful voice.

For more than thirty years, I've been preaching and practicing what's known as servant leadership. Rather than barking orders and expecting people to jump at my commands, I try to understand the needs of my staff first. Knowing their needs and personalities allows me to better serve them.

That doesn't mean that I'm always best buddies with my staff. The ranch isn't a democracy—I'm the boss. Still, I want my staff to be self-motivated, to see when something needs to be done, and do it, without waiting for instructions from me, and I also want them to function as a team.

It's the same way with my horses. I want them to be trustworthy and confident, to know how to react during a crisis, or when facing an obstacle.

Building confidence doesn't happen overnight. And it doesn't happen by me telling the staff, "Be confident," or holding motivational meetings. Confidence comes with practice.

I needed some pointers on roping. Johnston was the expert. The smart thing to do was to ask for his help. In my book, the leader always does the smart thing, rather than the thing that makes him look good.

For the next hour or so, I got a lesson in roping 101, and made subtle changes to my technique. By the end, I was hitting on four out of five throws—a vast improvement.

That night, my apprentice-turned-instructor sat on the fence and watched as I roped a wild horse on the first try.

Johnston smiled and raised his hands in a cheer, proud of my accomplishment and of his first success as a teacher.

I learned this approach to leadership the hard way. After graduating from Penn State, I spent a year in New York, studying at Nyack Bible College. Once I was done there, Melodie and I got married, and then started looking for the next step.

I had planned to go on to graduate school and work in the horse industry, but my new-found faith, and new marriage, got me thinking of more eternal values. Marrying Melodie did not make joining the family ministry a requirement, but it did open a wide door of opportunity.

For years, I'd built my identity around being a trainer, working with championship-caliber horses. As a result, I'd become a horse snob, thinking that only expensive horses were worth my time.

It wasn't that working with horses was wrong for me. But I had built my identity and my worth around the horse industry and what I could accomplish. I suddenly realized I was trusting more in that than what the Lord had for me. So I walked away from it. In the process, I got a lesson in humility.

In the summer of 1975, I got a call from the president of the Appaloosa Horse Club. They'd sponsored me when I was in college, and now the president wanted to offer me a job. I'd be his assistant, with the idea that he'd train me to succeed him when he retired.

This sounded like my dream job, and I was sorely tempted by the opportunity. In fact, I accepted the job just before Melodie and I got married, but didn't tell anyone about it, especially not her parents. There was no reason to ruin our wedding with the news. Dale and Opal hoped that we'd follow in their footsteps of serving the Lord, and taking this job would mean going in a different direction.

Around the same time, I heard about an opening at the Rawhide Vocational College in California. The school combined horse training with Christian ministry, so that young people would learn the horse business while growing in their faith. This job paled in comparison to the one I'd been offered at the Appaloosa Horse Club—a national breed association—so I put it out of my mind.

"I won't even talk to them unless someone else pays for the long-distance call," I told Melodie one day, as we were talking through our options for the future. That's the kind of thing you should never say. Later that night, we were visiting with Melodie's parents when a friend of the family stopped by. He'd heard about this job in California and thought it'd be a perfect place for me to start.

"Tell you what," he said. "Pick up the phone right now, and I'll even pay for the call."

Oh stink, I thought.

A few weeks later, we were on our way to California. It seemed clear that God wanted us to take this job. In fact, when I'd balked at the cost of flying out to California for the interview—this was a non profit camp—another family friend gave us $400 for the plane tickets.

After a few months on the job, I wondered what I'd got myself into. The pay was poor, and though the horses were above average, and some were even world champions, my boss—well, he was a tough man to follow. It's not that he was angry or abusive. Not at all. In fact, he treated Melodie and me well in the two years we spent there. But as a boss, he was a disaster.

The major problem was that he was impulsive by nature, so he was always changing his mind. One day he'd tell you to start working on a project and the next he'd tell you to abandon that and jump on something else. You never knew from one day to the next what he wanted.

He was also rough with the students, believing that shame was the best way to teach them. He had an uncanny ability to push people's buttons, to get them to do what he wanted, or to upset them.

When we arrived, less than a quarter of the students were making it through the two-year program, and staff turnover was even faster. Six months in, I was ready to quit.

Then a friend gave me some wise advice. "There's something you need to learn here," he said. My friend knew about my estranged relationship with my stepfather, and felt like that had left a flaw in my character. I'd never be a leader unless I learned how to be a follower.

Not exactly the advice I wanted to hear. Now, however, I realize he was right on. Like Berry, my horse with the congenital defect in his legs, I had a weakness in my character, and my new boss was like a personal trainer, attacking that character flaw. I needed to learn how to respect authority and how to be a follower.

When I work with an untrained horse, I can usually get them saddle-broken in around an hour and a half, even if they've been run in right off the plains. But that first step is only the beginning. It's a long, hard journey to turn that untrained horse into a trustworthy partner. When I start working a new horse, I know it'll be two or three years until my work pays off in his or her life.

Working at Rawhide, I learned that the same was true in my faith. The New Testament book of Galatians talks about the signs of a mature Christian, calling them the "fruits of the Spirit." Among those fruits are "love, joy, peace, patience, kindness, goodness, faithfulness, gentleness and self-control" (Galatians 5:22–23 NIV).

There's no magic pill you can take to make those character traits instantly appear in your life. You have to learn them over years of practice.

For those two years at Rawhide, I took a notebook with me everywhere I went, and began to write down my ideas about leadership. I wanted to know what motivated people, and discouraged them. In the end, I boiled them down to some simple truths.

Communicate clearly. That was the first and most important lesson. If people don't know what you want, they can't deliver it. This also means showing people how they fit into the bigger picture.

Prepare people for change, don't spring it on them. Over those two years, I learned that people don't mind following, if they believe their leader knows what he or she is doing. They also don't want to waste their time. There's nothing more disheartening than to spend days or weeks toiling on a project, only to find out you've been wasting your time. Before too long, people will slack off, believing that their hard work doesn't matter.

Correct people in private, not in public. Respect is perhaps the most important gift a leader can give. Respect your people, and let them use their talents. If they do something wrong, talk to them in private—don't embarrass them in front of their peers. Everyone wants to save face.

Deal with conflict immediately. If a problem arises, don't sweep it under the table. Deal with it head on, not with force, but with a listening ear. Chances are, if someone on your staff is angry or withdrawn, or upset at you, they've got a reason. Ask for their opinions, and then listen.

These lessons form the basis of my leadership style, with people and with horses.

Respect is a key factor here. When I work with a new horse, I never try to push them too far. I don't expect major leaps of faith. I want small, measurable steps toward success.

So whenever a horse does what I ask him to, I give him a reward, and back off the pressure. I respect that he has the ability to choose to do the right thing of his own volition.

The more you respect a horse, the more he will respect you as a person. When he respects you, and comes to believe that you have his best interests at heart, he'll take the initiative and move towards you.

When I try something new with a horse, I don't expect him to get it right the first time. More than anything, I want to know that he is listening and that he trusts me. When a horse looks at me and tells me, through his body language, that he is afraid or confused, but remains in place rather than following his natural inclination to flee—that means his whole value system has changed.

Those first few months in California, I was angry and disappointed, feeling that God was wasting my time. I had turned down the job of my dreams in order to follow what I thought was God's leading, and what had it gotten me? A miserable job.

Over the two years I worked at Rawhide, my attitude slowly changed. As I put those leadership principles into practice, the students responded. By the time we left, retention was up from less than 25 per cent to more than 90 per cent.

Many of those students remain friends to this day, and when we started Sermon on the Mount, they invited me to come and speak at their churches or camps. If I'd quit, none of those doors would have opened.

A few years after leaving Rawhide and going back to Miracle Mountain Ranch, I went to see the leader of another camp, looking for tips on how to become a better leader. It was a disappointment. He said I was too concerned about respecting the people who worked for me, which made me indecisive in his eyes.

"You'll never amount to much of a leader," he said. "You're too much of a nice guy." He was a bold, winner-take-all kind of leader, who always had to be in charge.

As much as his comments hurt, I didn't want to follow his example. I thought, *I will serve others and see what happens.*

Several years ago, Rich Stearns, a successful corporate CEO, decided to leave behind his corner office—and the Jaguar that came with it—to become director of World Vision, which is the largest Christian relief and development organization in the world. The idea was that Stearns' business acumen would help World Vision become more efficient at doing its job of feeding hungry people, providing clean water, caring for AIDS orphans and other acts of love in the name of Jesus.

During his first year on the job, Stearns didn't make any major changes. In fact, he didn't say much at all. Sometimes, when a business leader like Stearns comes to a nonprofit organization, they bring a chip on their shoulder, believing that the nonprofit world or ministry world is an easier place to work than the corporate world.

In an interview with *Christianity Today* magazine, Stearns said that business leaders often have a bias that goes something like this: "I know all the answers, because I played in the big leagues. This is the way it's going to be, and I'm going to change everything." That attitude is a recipe for failure, Stearns said.

"If I had come to World Vision saying, 'I know all the answers. Watch and learn,' World Vision would have rejected me as a leader like a body would reject a heart transplant as foreign tissue."

Instead, he took this approach: "I don't know the answers, but I think you do, and I want to learn from you. If you can teach me, and I can learn from you, then I hope to get to a place where I can add value to what you're doing."

In my early days of horse training, I spent much of my time at Colonial Acres, the farm owned by my boss, George Zimmerman. Most of the farm was on hillsides, spotted with outcroppings of limestone.

Among other things, that made it a pain to mow the grass that we'd bale to make hay. Being at Colonial Acres made me long to be back at the Fruitful Manor, which had been my family's farm before my dad died.

George eventually hired another trainer, who came from Texas, and he marveled at the hills on George's property. He insisted on exercising our colts on those hills. Before long, we had developed colts whose fitness and muscle tone made them winners.

The limestone in the soil also ensured that our grass was filled with minerals and other nutrients. Again, this new trainer pointed out that the rocky terrain was a benefit to our horses, not a detriment. I wasn't thinking about nutrition at that point—I was too busy complaining about how hard it was to mow those hills.

It was years before I realized that trainer was right. The broad green pastures, bordered by picket fences, look great on a postcard or in a painting hung on the wall. But we need the hills and obstacles in life to make us strong.

One reason that the horses at Colonial won so often, was that they were in better shape than the competition. The daily routine of running up those hills made them strong, and built up their endurance, so that they could train harder and longer than the average horse. More training and better endurance meant a better chance of winning.

Going to work for the Appaloosa Horse Club had been my dream. It's what I wanted. But what I needed and what I wanted were two different things. I needed to learn how to follow and persevere, even in difficult times.

There were times, however, when following what I thought was God's will was really difficult and even painful. I'd be lying if I said that I never wanted to quit. Chances are, if you're honest, most of us have felt that way at one point or another, whether it's in our marriage, or our work, or with our families.

One of the most popular hardcover books in U.S. history is called *The Purpose-Driven Life*. The idea of that book is relatively simple: God has a purpose for your life, and you'll never be truly satisfied until you find that purpose.

But what happens when you find your purpose in life, only to see all of your dreams go off the rails? When everything you hoped for has vanished in a puff of smoke— what do you do then?

I don't know what your life is like, or if you've ever felt like giving up. If it hasn't happened to you before now, praise the Lord. But it's going to happen someday. When that day comes, keep this story in mind.

In the early days of our leadership training seminars, when I was giving a talk about being a servant leader, a man in the front of the audience got up and boldly spoke out. He was a man in his seventies, and was visibly upset by something I'd said. I wasn't sure what to do, as nothing like this had ever happened before.

He stood up and pointed a finger at me and said, "Where

have you been all my life? Why didn't someone tell me this when I was younger, before it was too late?"

He sat down again and I froze for a moment. I had no idea how to respond. How do you answer a question like that? Though he had been faithfully religious all his life, he had suddenly realized the years spent living for himself had resulted in waste and disappointment.

Sometime later, this man called me, late at night, and asked if he and his wife could come in and see me. When they arrived at my office, I knew something was up. They both were irritable and visibly upset.

"We've been married fifty-three years," his wife said, "and I'm done with him."

Over the next few hours, they told me their story. After fifty-three years of marriage, they had quite a tale to tell. There'd been a great deal of betrayal; some of it was out in the open, some of it hidden for years.

"He's been lying to me from the beginning," she said. "Our whole marriage is a lie."

This wasn't quite true. After many years of marriage, there was plenty of blame to go around. Over those decades the fundamental trust that any relationship needs had been broken and crushed into the ground.

When couples come to see us, they are often desperate. In this case, the wife was so forlorn that at night, while her husband was asleep, she'd take out a gun and debate whether or not to shoot him and then end it all. After so many years of misery, this couple really were desperate.

Even in that darkest moment, there was the tiniest shred of hope. Like Spotlight stuck in the barbed wire, they were trapped. If they bolted and divorced, it would shatter their lives and the lives of their children and grandchildren. But they could not stay where they were either. They needed someone to show them the way out.

For Spotlight, that meant putting his fate in someone else's hands. In the end, that's what this couple did. Only they put their fate in the hands of God. Though they had long before heard and responded to the message of salvation, they had never really trusted in God's full control of their lives.

At their crisis point, they got on their knees and asked God for help. Rather than cling to their bitterness and hurt, they let go of their past, and chose to forgive each other.

In the prayer that Jesus taught his disciples, there's a line that fits here: "Forgive us our trespasses, as we forgive those who trespass against us." As they found God's forgiveness, they were able to forgive each other.

Over the next few months, they worked through the pain and disappointments, and began to trust each other once again. It was never easy and they wanted to give up. Like Spotlight, however, they eventually found their way out.

Today, this couple, and their children and grandchildren, are growing in their walks with God and in their marriages.

They sit together in church, filled with love and laughter, rather than the anger and despair that had defined their lives for so long. By any definition, that's a miracle worth believing in.

If God can save this couple when all hope was lost, he can save any hopeless situation. They discovered that true and lasting hope is found when absolute trust is placed in the person and work of Jesus Christ.

Join me on my journey of knowing the greatest trainer of all time—the Lord Jesus Christ.

DRACULA

by

BRAM STOKER

With an Introduction by Leonard Wolf
and an Afterword by Jeffrey Meyers

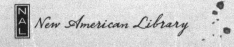

New American Library
Published by New American Library, a division of
Penguin Group (USA) Inc., 375 Hudson Street,
New York, New York 10014, USA
Penguin Group (Canada), 90 Eglinton Avenue East, Suite 700, Toronto,
Ontario M4P 2Y3, Canada (a division of Pearson Penguin Canada Inc.)
Penguin Books Ltd., 80 Strand, London WC2R 0RL, England
Penguin Ireland, 25 St. Stephen's Green, Dublin 2,
Ireland (a division of Penguin Books Ltd.)
Penguin Group (Australia), 250 Camberwell Road, Camberwell, Victoria 3124,
Australia (a division of Pearson Australia Group Pty. Ltd.)
Penguin Books India Pvt. Ltd., 11 Community Centre, Panchsheel Park,
New Delhi - 110 017, India
Penguin Group (NZ), 67 Apollo Drive, Rosedale, North Shore 0632,
New Zealand (a division of Pearson New Zealand Ltd.)
Penguin Books (South Africa) (Pty.) Ltd., 24 Sturdee Avenue,
Rosebank, Johannesburg 2196, South Africa

Penguin Books Ltd., Registered Offices:
80 Strand, London WC2R 0RL, England

Published by New American Library, a division of Penguin Group (USA) Inc. This edition
of *Dracula* was previously published in a Dutton hardcover edition without the Leonard
Wolf introduction and the Jeffrey Meyers afterword.

First New American Library Printing, October 2010
1 3 5 7 9 10 8 6 4 2

Introduction copyright © Leonard Wolf, 1992
Afterword copyright © Jeffrey Meyers, 2002
Letter from Dacre Stoker copyright © Dacre Stoker, 2009
Excerpt from *Dracula the Un-Dead* copyright © Dacre Stoker and Ian Zisholtz, 2009

Set in Adobe Caslon Pro
Designed by Amy Hill

Printed in the United States of America

CONTENTS

INTRODUCTION:
RETURNING TO *DRACULA*

There is a delicious and reassuring excitement to be found in rereading a classical novel for perhaps the thirtieth time. One feels like a child hearing a loved fairy tale he knows by heart. There is the same eager impatience to hear the familiar phrases, the same feeling of reassurance when they come in their remembered places.

When the beloved story is *Dracula*, there is, in addition to the pleasures of recognition, that other delight of fear stalking the pages perpetually on cue, always in the same guise, sending, without fail, the same elegant and icy fingers rippling up and down one's spine.

In 1997 Bram Stoker's novel had been in print for a full one hundred years. The event was celebrated in various parts of the world. In New York City, New York University was the venue for the "Dracula Centennial: Aesthetics of Fear Conference," at which a glittering array of achievers in the arts and sciences—Joyce Carol Oates, Stephen King, Stephen Jay Gould, and Naomi Wolf—had something to say about Dracula. Also in New York City, the Museum of Modern Art's film department sponsored a "CineDracula" retrospective that ran for a full month. There were similar celebrations in Los Angeles and Miami, and in England, France, and Belgium.

What is amazing is that Count Dracula, who is, after all, an invented monster, has become so entrenched in the imagination of the west as to seem a figure that has come down to us from the farthest reaches of antiquity. And yet that is what he is. There is hardly a living man, woman, or child who does not know what he looks like or what his attributes are: He is tall, red-lipped, and pale. He sleeps by day and moves about by night. He has sharp canine incisors. He can shift shapes at will and can become a wolf, a bat, or a puff of smoke. He is immortal, so long as he is able to drink the blood of the living. He has enormous physical power at the same time as he is vulnerable to such homely defences as garlic, wolfsbane, crucifixes, and holy water. What adults know, and children would be surprised to hear, is that Dracula is attractive to women.

Though *Dracula* made its appearance in the late nineteenth century, it is still recognizable as a Gothic novel, a literary genre that made its appearance in England in the middle of the eighteenth century. Characteristically, a Gothic novel has as its protagonist a beautiful and genteel young woman who is pursued by a tall, dark villain who has darkly erotic evil on his mind. The reader follows her flight and his pursuit through a variety of ominous places: ruined castles, noisome caves, prison cells, vaults, sepulchers, monasteries or convents. There are rooms with trapdoors, secret passageways, portraits that leave their walls and walk, animated skeletons, and talking ghosts. Usually, but not always, the heroine is saved from what used to be called a fate worse than death by the heroic efforts of a young, handsome, sexually unthreatening man who, as the novel ends, turns out to be as rich as he is heroic and, coincidentally, to be in need of a wife.

Horace Walpole's *The Castle of Otranto* (1764) is generally credited with being the first English Gothic tale. Walpole gives us the tale of the tyrannical Manfred, Prince of Otranto, who, to avert a prophecy that his dynasty will end, divorces his wife and then tries to force the Princess Isabella of Vincenzas to marry him. Isabella, who had been betrothed to Manfred's now dead son, has her heart set on the handsome and pure-minded Theodore. Theodore, in his turn, longs for Manfred's daughter, Matilda. Isabella flies from Manfred who, pursuing her, inadvertently kills Matilda. Then Manfred, appalled at what he has done, repents. He and his wife assume the life of religion. It is then that we learn that the peasant Theodore is not really a peasant after all. He is, instead, the rightful heir to the throne of Otranto. After a suitable interval, he marries Isabella.

The Castle of Otranto is a book whose style has become extremely dated since it was written. It offers its reader neither psychological truth nor character analysis and has a plot so cumbersome that it crosses the border of the ridiculous. Still, the story can be read for its antiquarian charm and, of course, as the work that established the form and content of Gothic fiction.

Ann Radcliffe's *Mysteries of Udolpho* (1794) is an altogether more engaging work. Radcliffe, perhaps the most accomplished writer of Gothic fiction in the eighteenth century, tells the story of the young and beautiful Emily St. Aubert, whose misfortune it is to be pursued by her aunt's husband, the wicked Montoni. The scenes of flight and pursuit involve ingeniously imagined dreadful situations and places—portraits that move and strange, inexplicable sounds. Always, there is the suggestion that something supernatural is taking place. What often spoils Radcliffe's fictions are the ingenious explanations that prove to the reader that there were no supernatural events at all.

Despite the snail's pace at which her novels move and her self-indulgent descriptions of "sublime" landscapes, Ann Radcliffe's ingenious plots have a way of compelling her readers to read on.

When we turn to Matthew Lewis's *The Monk* (1796) both the plot and the manner we encounter are wild and vivid. Lewis's youthful, perfervid prose is the perfect vehicle for his turbulent tale.

Lewis tells us that he wrote his book in ten weeks and his story has the sense of urgency of a compelled work. His villain, Ambrosio, is a thirty-year-old monk whose austere purity is the talk of Madrid. But when the devil's minion, who has been posing as Rosario, a handsome young novice, reveals himself to be the ravishing Matilda, Ambrosio, forgetting his vows, succumbs to her blandishments and begins his downward slide to damnation. Ambrosio tires of Matilda just in time to be overwhelmed by lust for the fifteen-year-old, beautiful, and pure

Antonia. Except for an intrusive subplot that takes up many, many pages, in which we get the famous Bleeding Nun episode and an interminable story involving Raymond de las Cisternas and his beloved Agnes, we return once again to the foreground story of Ambrosio and Antonia. Ambrosio's pursuit of Antonia leads him finally from lust to blasphemy, from blasphemy to matricide, and from thence to incest, murder, and finally damnation.

Charles Maturin, like Sheridan LeFanu and Bram Stoker, was an Irishman. His *Melmoth the Wanderer* (1820), a novel also focused on the theme of damnation, is a fiction of an altogether higher order of achievement than Lewis's *The Monk*. *Melmoth* is a rich, sober, thoughtful and profoundly ironic study of the way hell begins and ends within the self. Melmoth, Maturin's protagonist, makes a Faustian bargain with the devil for the sake of a one-hundred-fifty-year life span. In a book filled with ingenious horrors, the most overwhelming horror of them all is the knowledge Melmoth comes to that the world in which he has spent his hundred fifty years is hardly different from the hell to which, having bartered his soul, he is condemned.

One needs, finally, to notice the three nineteenth-century vampire fictions that preceded Stoker's *Dracula*: John Polidori's *The Vampyre* (1821), James Malcolm Rymer's *Varney the Vampyre* (1847), and Sheridan LeFanu's *Carmilla* (1872).

John Polidori, who was Byron's physician, was, along with Mary and Percy Shelley, in that small company of friends who were gathered on a famous rainy night in June 1816, at Byron's Villa Diodati in Geneva. Byron, to amuse his guests, proposed a task: "We will each write a ghost story." Byron began a tale part of which found its way into his poem "Mazzeppa." Percy Shelley, after a perfunctory try, abandoned the project. Mary Shelley began, and eventually finished, *Frankenstein* (1816). Polidori, who, like Mary Shelley, took up Byron's challenge, produced *The Vampyre* (1821) which, though it is a weak novel, has the distinction that it introduces the vampire to English literature.

James Malcolm Rymer's *Varney the Vampyre* (1847) is an ebullient potboiler which has as its protagonist the most enthusiastic vampire in literature. Rymer's Varney is salacious, swift, inventive, superficial and, long before the word "camp" was invented, amused (and continues to amuse) its readers with its self-parodying, hyperventilating prose.

Sheridan LeFanu's *Carmilla* (1872) is an authentic work of literature in which LeFanu uses Central European folklore as the armature on which to construct a subtle tale of vampirism that is at once physical and psychological. *Carmilla*, with its female vampire and her female victim, also has the virtue of high seriousness as it deals with what still feels like a very contemporary theme, "the rapture of that cruelty which yet is love."

The story's protagonist, young Laura, tells us that she is the daughter of an Englishman who, having served in the Austrian army, has retired to a castle in Styria, a province in eastern Austria, where "a small income . . . goes a long way." LeFanu emphasizes how isolated and lonely life is for Laura. The nearest neighbor is General Spielsdorf, whose castle is twenty miles away.

One night, Laura is visited by a strange and frightening apparition, a young woman who "caressed me with her hands, and lay down beside me on the bed, and drew me towards her, smiling."

Twelve years later Laura and her father hear about the death, in suspicious circumstances, of General Spielsdorf's niece. At the same time, Laura and her father harbor a young woman named Carmilla whose mother leaves her in their charge after her coach has broken down. Laura, enchanted to have a visitor, welcomes Carmilla warmly, only to be betrayed by her vampire friend.

Of the vampire tales written in England in the nineteenth century, only *Carmilla* can be said to have had any direct influence on Stoker when he came to write *Dracula*. James L. Campbell, Sr., writing in *Supernatural Fiction Writers* (edited by E. F. Bleiler), says:

> All of the rituals and set pieces common to the modern formula [for a vampire fiction] appear in *Carmilla*, beginning with its three-part formal design—attack, death-resuscitation, and hunt-destruction. Also included are the vampire's seduction of the

victim, the confusion between dream and reality, the vain attempt to explain supernatural events in rational terms, and the folk recipes for recognizing, capturing, and killing vampires. (p. 220)

As we turn to a discussion of the life of Bram Stoker (1847-1912), the Irish-born author of *Dracula*, one needs to note that in 1996, Barbara Belford's carefully researched and responsible biography, *Bram Stoker: A Biography of the Author of Dracula*, was published by Alfred Knopf. Until the appearance of that book, the two Stoker biographies we had were Harry Ludlam's *A Biography of Dracula* (London: W. Foulsham and Co., 1962) and Daniel Farson's *The Man Who Wrote Dracula: a Biography of Bram Stoker* (London: Michael Joseph, 1975). The first was a light once-over treatment, and the second, a mean-spirited equally lightweight work with all the authority of family gossip.

Stoker spent twenty-seven years as a factotum for Sir Henry Irving, England's greatest interpreter of Shakespeare, and as acting manager of Irving's Lyceum Theatre. It was a busy and demanding life and it had its effect on Stoker. For one thing, it made him a facile writer. Stoker tells us that, as Sir Henry Irving's amanuensis, "I think I shall be very well within the mark when I say that during my time of working with Henry Irving I have written in his name nearer half a million than a quarter of a million letters." (*Personal Reminiscences of Henry Irving*, 1906, p. 62) Beyond developing a facile pen, working for Irving gave Stoker a heavy exposure to Shakespeare's rhythms and diction as they were sounded by England's greatest Shakespearean actor.

Busy as Stoker was, he had time to produce short stories and novels. However, Stoker's achievement in the works of fiction that precede and follow *Dracula* (1897) is never more than mediocre. *The Snake's Pass* (1890), *The Jewel of the Seven Stars* (1903), and *The Lair of the White Worm* (1911) are journeymen works which, except for the repulsive peculiarity of *The Lair of the White Worm*, are mostly forgettable.

Not so *Dracula*. Here, in a book with a coherent vision of evil, we get characters who, if they are not deeply imagined, are at least individualized and profoundly tested.

What was that vision? and why, as it is set forth in the pages of *Dracula*, has it intrigued, amazed, frightened, and pleased reading audiences for more than a hundred years? What is it about Stoker's story that makes it so perpetually appealing to filmmakers that there is hardly a decade since the film industry began that has not seen one or several films with the name Dracula in them?

The simplest answer to these questions is that Stoker found in 1897 a theme that made for first-rate storytelling. If we read *Dracula* simply as a Gothic adventure tale, what a rousing story it is. There are the good guys, Quincey Morris, Jonathan Harker, Dr. John Seward, and the Honorable Arthur Holmwood, all of them upright, handsome young men forming, with their wise old leader, Dr. Van Helsing, a sort of heroic posse riding to the rescue of their composite maiden, Lucy Westenra–Mina Harker, who is in the clutches of the dark and foreign vampire who would keep her in thrall.

At that level of narrative alone, there is plenty of Gothic detail to engage a reader: a dark and distant country hidden somewhere in Central Europe; a vast ruined castle; a supernaturally powerful villain who drinks blood; chase scenes, confrontations, surprises and alarums, and plenty of quaint local color in England and abroad.

But Stoker has done more than tell a straightforward Gothic story. He designed *Dracula* to be read as a Christian allegory as well. The struggle is not merely between good guys and a supremely bad man, but between high-minded Christians and a minion of the devil. Dracula (his name, in Romanian, means "dragon") is a creature of the night, cut off from God because he has chosen immortality under the sponsorship of Satan rather than of Christ. Though Dracula has supernatural powers, he is weak in God's daylight; he shrinks from any contact with the cross. Still, he represents a more than mortal danger in his victims because his blood drinking is not simply an act of nourishment. The more the vampire drinks, the greater is the victim's spiritual empoisonment so that, when death finally comes, it brings not release from the shocks that flesh is heir to but the beginning of damnation.

There is even more to the Christian allegory than that. Stoker is at great pains to have us see that his adventure story has in it adumbrations of Armageddon. Renfield, Dr. Seward's mental patient who believes that he is imbibing life as he catches and eats the flies he entices to his room and whose periods of excitement correspond to Dracula's comings and goings, refers to Dracula as his Lord and Master. In language that recalls the temptation of Christ by Satan in the wilderness (Matthew IV, 9) the martyred Renfield describes how Dracula tempted him: "All these lives will I give you, ay, and many more and greater, through countless ages, if you will fall down and worship me!" Lest we miss the point that Dracula represents the Antichrist, the pronouns referring to him in Renfield's dying speech are often capitalized.

Stoker, I think, knew what he was doing when he crafted his adventure tale and overlaid it with Christian content. But if *Dracula* were no more than an elaborated version of the story of St. George and the Dragon it would not be the towering masterpiece of fear that it is. What has become clearer and clearer, particularly in the *fin de siècle* years of the twentieth century, is that the novel's power has its source in the sexual implications of the blood exchange between the vampire and his victims. Those blood exchanges and the extraordinary eroticism that comes off the pages on which they are described are what make *Dracula* such an amazing book.

Dracula has embedded in it a very disturbing psychosexual allegory whose meaning I am not sure Stoker entirely understood: that there is a demonic force at work in the world whose intent is to eroticize women. In *Dracula*, we see how that force transforms Lucy Westenra, a beautiful nineteen-year-old virgin, into a shameless slut. When Lucy dies, after Dracula's many night visits to her, Doctor Van Helsing, Quincey Morris, Arthur Holmwood, and Dr. Seward meet her in the graveyard. The newly vampirized Lucy is carrying a child victim at her breast. She is Lucy Westenra, but as Seward describes her:

> Lucy Westenra, but yet how changed. The sweetness was turned to adamantine, heartless cruelty, and the purity to voluptuous wantonness. . . .

She still advanced, however, and with a languorous, voluptuous grace, said:—
"Come to me, Arthur. Leave these others and come to me. My arms are hungry for you. Come, and we can rest together. Come, my husband, come!"

What the kindly Dr. Van Helsing teaches the three young men who have witnessed her transformation is how to put a stop to such languorous, voluptuous grace by driving a stake that is three feet long and whose tip has been sharpened and hardened in fire into her bosom.

Later in the novel Mina Harker, after her forced blood-union with Dracula, accuses herself of being "Unclean, unclean! I must touch him [her husband, Jonathan] no more." In her account of Dracula's foul love-making what stands out is that, while Dracula pressed her mouth to the bleeding wound in his chest and his lips to her throat, her husband Jonathan was lying beside her sleeping "so soundly that it seemed as if it was he who had taken the sleeping draught, and not I."

The magniloquence of the speech that Dracula makes to her on that occasion is a fine example of how Stoker's style was affected by his long relationship with Sir Henry Irving:

"And so you, like the others, would play your brains against mine. You would help these men to hunt me and frustrate me in my designs! . . . They should have kept their energies for use closer to home. Whilst they played wits against me—against me who commanded nations, and intrigued for them, and fought for them, hundreds of years before they were born—I was countermining them. And you, their best beloved one, are now to me, flesh of my flesh; blood of my blood; kin of my kin; my bountiful wine-press for a while; and shall be later on my companion and my helper . . ."

The movie industry, beginning in Germany with F. W. Murnau's *Nosferatu* (1922), was immediately clearer than Stoker was about the link between blood-scene and love-scene. In that film, subtitled "Eine Symphonie des Grauens" (A Symphony of Horror), the vampire is called Count Orlok, and as Max Schreck played him, he is a fright to behold: tall, slim, round shouldered, pointy-eared, and scuttling, he has more in common with Varney the vampire than with Stoker's aloof and chilling nobleman. In Murnau's version of the story the relationship between Hutter, his wife Nina, and Count Orlok is clearly that of a marriage triangle. Nina, waiting for the vampire to come to her room, manages to appear exalted by self-sacrifice, swollen with lust, and tormented by guilt. When Orlok kneels at her bedside, there is no ambiguity about the nature of the sacrifice she is about to make in order to save Bremen from the plague with which Orlok has infected it.

In 1931, nearly ten years after *Nosferatu*, Universal Pictures released Tod Browning's *Dracula*, in which Bela Lugosi took the title role. The film has become so firmly fixed in the pantheon of classical horror movies that it seems either too late or beside the point to say that it is a pretty poor movie. That does not mean, however, that it is unmemorable. Indeed, Bela Lugosi's wooden performance has come to be the image that first occurs to anyone when the word "Dracula" is mentioned.

There is something in Lugosi's face, something even more in his Hungarian accent, that has sealed him in our memories (and, by now, in the collective unconscious) as the Dracula of record. And, lest a reader think I am scanting Tod Browning's contribution to the film's durability, it should be said that Browning has suffused his film with a brooding atmosphere that is nearly as memorable as Lugosi's presence in it. The long shots of stone stairways, the vampire's hand emerging from a closed coffin, the bizarre and huge spiderwebs that remain undisturbed when Lugosi walks through them and the deliberate pacing of the film are all signs of good judgment, a fine eye, and respect for the medium of film. What is too bad is that Browning used the Balderston-Deane stage play as his model so that there are too many scenes played for laughs.

Still, who will ever forget Lugosi saying, "I am Dracula." Or "I do not drink . . . wine." Or, "Listen to them, children of the night. What music they make."

In 1936, Universal Pictures released *Dracula's Daughter,* starring Gloria Holden and Otto Kruger. To this day, there has been no film on the Dracula theme that is as starkly poignant or as lyric as this one. Directed by Lambert Hillyer, with a screenplay by Garret Fort, the film begins where Tod Browning's *Dracula* ends. As the film opens we see Doctor Van Helsing (played again by Edward Van Sloan) being arrested for having driven a stake through Dracula's heart. Later, the Countess Marya Zaleska, Dracula's daughter, steals her father's body and, in a fine scene of fake/authentic ritual, consigns it to a funeral pyre as she intones a wishful prayer that her father's "body, long undead, find destruction throughout eternity in the name of thy dark unholy master."

The coldly beautiful Countess believes for a while that with her father's death, she has escaped the curse of vampirism, but when she finds that she is mistaken, she consults Geoffrey Garth, whose advice is to meet her problem head on. When the Countess, by now in love with Garth, kidnaps his fiancée and takes her to Transylvania as a way to force him to come to her, Sandor, the Countess's devoted servitor, fumes with a jealousy that leads naturally to the story's disastrous climax.

In 1958, London's Hammer Films made *The Horror of Dracula* directed by Terence Fisher and starring Christopher Lee. Fisher's direction, Lee's performance, and Hammer Films' willing expenditure of money to create lavish sets, plus a startlingly candid eroticism on camera, signaled a whole new approach both to horror films and to the Dracula legend. Lee has described how he understood his role:

With Dracula, certain things are important. You should never see him climbing out of his coffin. If you've noticed, I'm always discovered standing beside it. . . .

I had to make some decisions: first of all, he is a nobleman, so he must be noble in his physical presence; impressive. If he was going to be irresistible to women, he had to be also a superior being . . . superhumanly strong. An unstoppable force. . . .

What I try to convey is his tremendous stillness and the way it combines with his savagery to produce a hypnotic power. And with Dracula there is something else. The loneliness of evil. . . .

(A Dream of Dracula, pp. 176–77)

In 1979 Universal Pictures released John Badham's *Dracula*, starring Frank Langella. The film, marred, like the 1931 Lugosi *Dracula*, by being an adaptation of the Balderston-Deane play, is important nevertheless because it gives us what one may almost call a sunny version of the vampire. Langella plays the role with such dash and humor, with so much straightforward masculine charm that, caught up by the picturesque seductions on screen, one forgets to be frightened.

There have been scores of other Draculas. Some have been so foolish as to be engaging: *Billy the Kid Versus Dracula* (1965) and *The Legend of the Seven Golden Vampires* (1974); or so stolid as to seem foolish: *Dracula* starring Jack Palance (1974); or so beautiful that one forgets that the business of a Dracula film is to frighten its viewers (Werner Herzog's 1979 remake of *Nosferatu*); or just peculiar: *Andy Warhol's Dracula* (1973). And in 1992, the last twentieth-century Dracula film appeared: Francis Ford Coppola's *Bram Stoker's Dracula*.

It would be nice to report that Coppola's film, the most expensive vampire movie ever made, is also the best. What one can say is that it is surely the most spectacular and the most sexually graphic film based on Stoker's novel.

The most notable difference between Coppola's Dracula and all of the others that appeared before it is that screenwriter James V. Hart has inverted the moral meaning of the story. Since 1922 when Murnau's silent *Nosferatu* appeared, every Dracula film has followed Stoker's lead in seeing Dracula as a villainous, satanic creature.

Hart starts his tale in the fifteenth century and directly identifies Dracula as the historical Vlad Tepes, notable for his cruelties. When Vlad Tepes is given the news that his bride-to-be committed suicide when she received the false news of his death in battle, he curses God.

The story then shifts to the nineteenth century. Vlad travels to London, believing that his long-lost love has been reincarnated there as

{ xviii }

Mina Murray, Jonathan Harker's fiancée. From that point on, Dracula, though he is still occasionally given his demonic form, is essentially a romantic hero in quest of true love. It is no accident then that, as the film unwinds, Van Helsing and the young men whom he leads are seen as impediments to love's fulfillment.

The Coppola-Hart story is an extraordinary reinvention of Stoker's *Dracula*, and it tells us a great deal about the distance in the direction of secularization that the western world has traveled since his time.

It is hard to know what Bram Stoker would make of all of this. He thought he was writing a "shilling-shocker." He had neither the ambition nor the belief that he was capable of writing a great work of fiction. The irony is that his book has, for more than a hundred years, continued to shock us. But to our own surprise, it has ended by behaving like a very great work of fiction.

It is a protean work, a tapestry of paradoxes. Its central metaphor, the blood exchange between vampire and victim, is this century's most ambiguous symbol and Stoker's characters, thinly drawn though they are, are nevertheless figures in a psychological allegory whose meaning almost appears to be within our grasp even as, invariably, it eludes us. We sense, more than we know, that some profound mystery is taking place. No wonder that, like Melville, we are reduced to sighing, "Ah, Dracula, ah humanity."

—Leonard Wolf

DRACULA

To My Dear Friend

HOMMY-BEG

How these papers have been placed in sequence will be made manifest in the reading of them. All needless matters have been eliminated, so that a history almost at variance with the possibilities of later-day belief may stand forth as simple fact. There is throughout no statement of past things wherein memory may err, for all the records chosen are exactly contemporary, given from the standpoints and within the range of knowledge of those who made them.

CHAPTER 1.

—◆—

JONATHAN HARKER'S JOURNAL—*(Kept in shorthand.)*

3 May. Bistritz.—Left Munich at 8:35 P.M., on 1st May, arriving at Vienna early next morning; should have arrived at 6:46, but train was an hour late. Buda-Pesth seems a wonderful place, from the glimpse which I got of it from the train and the little I could walk through the streets. I feared to go very far from the station, as we arrived late and would start as near the correct time as possible. The impression I had was that we were leaving the West and entering the East; the most western of splendid bridges over the Danube, which is here of noble width and depth, took us among the traditions of Turkish rule.

We left in pretty good time, and came after nightfall to Klausen-burgh. Here I stopped for the night at the Hotel Royale. I had for dinner, or rather supper, a chicken done up some way with red pepper, which was very good but thirsty. (*Mem.,* get recipe for Mina.) I asked the waiter, and he said it was called "paprika hendl," and that, as it was a national dish, I should be able to get it anywhere along the Carpathians. I found my smattering of German very useful here; indeed, I don't know how I should be able to get on without it.

Having had some time at my disposal when in London, I had visited the British Museum, and made search among the books and maps in the library regarding Transylvania; it had struck me that some foreknowledge of the country could hardly fail to have some importance in dealing with a nobleman of that country. I find that the district he named is in the extreme east of the country, just on the borders of three states, Transylvania, Moldavia and Bukovina, in the midst of the Carpathian mountains; one of the wildest and least known portions of Europe. I was not able to light on any map or work giving the exact locality of the Castle Dracula, as there are no maps of this country as yet to compare with our own Ordnance Survey maps; but I found that Bistritz, the post town named by Count Dracula, is a fairly well-known place. I shall enter here some of my notes, as they may refresh my memory when I talk over my travels with Mina.

In the population of Transylvania there are four distinct nationalities: Saxons in the South, and mixed with them the Wallachs, who are the descendants of the Dacians; Magyars in the West, and Szekelys in the East and North. I am going among the latter, who claim to be descended from Attila and the Huns. This may be so, for when the Magyars conquered the country in the eleventh century they found the Huns settled in it. I read that every known superstition in the world is gathered into the horseshoe of the Carpathians, as if it were the centre of some sort of imaginative whirlpool; if so my stay may be very interesting. (*Mem.*, I must ask the Count all about them.)

I did not sleep well, though my bed was comfortable enough, for I had all sorts of queer dreams. There was a dog howling all night under my window, which may have had something to do with it; or it may have been the paprika, for I had to drink up all the water in my carafe, and was still thirsty. Towards morning I slept and was wakened by the continuous knocking at my door, so I guess I must have been sleeping soundly then. I had for breakfast more paprika, and a sort of porridge of maize flour which they said was "mamaliga," and egg-plant stuffed with forcemeat, a very excellent dish, which they call "impletata." (*Mem.*, get recipe for this also.) I had to hurry breakfast, for the train started a little before eight, or rather it ought to have done so, for after rushing to the station at 7:30 I had to sit in the carriage for more than an hour before we began to move. It seems to me that the further east you go the more unpunctual are the trains. What ought they to be in China?

All day long we seemed to dawdle through a country which was full of beauty of every kind. Sometimes we saw little towns or castles on the top of steep hills such as we see in old missals; sometimes we ran by rivers and streams which seemed from the wide stony margin on each side of them to be subject to great floods. It takes a lot of water, and running strong, to sweep the outside edge of a river clear. At every station there were groups of people, sometimes crowds, and in all sorts of attire. Some of them were just like the peasants at home or those I saw coming through France and Germany, with short jackets and round hats and home-made trousers; but others were very picturesque. The women looked pretty, except when you got near them, but they were very clumsy about the waist. They had all full white sleeves of some kind or other, and the most of them had big belts with a lot of strips of something fluttering from them like the dresses in a ballet, but of course there were petticoats under them. The strangest figures we saw were the Slovaks, who were more barbarian than the rest, with their big cow-boy hats, great baggy dirty-white trousers, white linen shirts, and enormous heavy leather belts, nearly a foot wide, all studded over with brass nails. They wore high boots, with their trousers tucked into them, and had long black hair and heavy black moustaches. They are very picturesque, but do not look prepossessing. On the stage they would be set down at once as some old Oriental band of brigands. They are, however, I am told, very harmless and rather wanting in natural self-assertion.

It was on the dark side of twilight when we got to Bistritz, which is a very interesting old place. Being practically on the frontier—for the Borgo Pass leads from it into Bukovina—it has had a very stormy existence, and it certainly shows marks of it. Fifty years ago a series of great fires took place, which made terrible havoc on five separate occasions. At the very beginning of the seventeenth century it underwent a siege of three weeks and lost 13,000 people, the casualties of war proper being assisted by famine and disease.

Count Dracula had directed me to go to the Golden Krone Hotel, which I found, to my great delight, to be thoroughly old-fashioned, for of course I wanted to see all I could of the ways of the country. I was evidently expected, for when I got near the door I faced a cheery-looking elderly woman in the usual peasant dress—white undergarment with long double apron, front, and back, of coloured stuff fitting almost too tight for modesty. When I came close she bowed and said, "The Herr Englishman?" "Yes," I said, "Jonathan Harker." She smiled, and gave some message to an elderly man in white shirtsleeves, who had followed her to the door. He went, but immediately returned with a letter:—

> "My Friend.—Welcome to the Carpathians. I am anxiously expecting you. Sleep well to-night. At three to-morrow the diligence will start for Bukovina; a place on it is kept for you. At the Borgo Pass my carriage will await you and will bring you to me. I trust that your journey from London has been a happy one, and that you will enjoy your stay in my beautiful land.
>
> > "Your friend,
> > "Dracula."

4 May.—I found that my landlord had got a letter from the Count, directing him to secure the best place on the coach for me; but on making inquiries as to details he seemed somewhat reticent, and pretended that he could not understand my German. This could not be true, because up to then he had understood it perfectly; at least, he answered my questions exactly as if he did. He and his wife, the old lady who had received me, looked at each other in a frightened sort of way. He mumbled out that the money had been sent in a letter, and that was all he knew. When I asked him if he knew Count Dracula, and could tell me anything of his castle, both he and his wife crossed themselves, and, saying that they knew nothing at all, simply refused to speak further. It was so near the time of starting that I had no time to ask any one else, for it was all very mysterious and not by any means comforting.

Just before I was leaving, the old lady came up to my room and said in a very hysterical way:

"Must you go? Oh! young Herr, must you go?" She was in such an excited state that she seemed to have lost her grip of what German she knew, and mixed it all up with some other language which I did not know at all. I was just able to follow her by asking many questions. When I told her that I must go at once, and that I was engaged on important business, she asked again:

"Do you know what day it is?" I answered that it was the fourth of May. She shook her head as she said again:

"Oh, yes! I know that! I know that, but do you know what day it is?" On my saying that I did not understand, she went on:

"It is the eve of St. George's Day. Do you not know that to-night, when the clock strikes midnight, all the evil things in the world will have full sway? Do you know where you are going, and what you are going to?" She was in such evident distress that I tried to comfort her, but without effect. Finally she went down on her knees and implored me not to go; at least to wait a day or two before starting. It was all very ridiculous but I did not feel comfortable. However, there was business to be done, and I could allow nothing to interfere with it. I therefore tried to raise her up, and said, as gravely as I could, that I thanked her, but my duty was imperative, and that I must go. She then rose and dried her eyes, and taking a crucifix from her neck offered it to me. I did not know what to do, for, as an English Churchman, I have been taught to regard such things as in some measure idolatrous, and yet it seemed so ungracious to refuse an old lady meaning so well and in such a state of mind. She saw, I suppose, the doubt in my face, for she put the rosary round my neck, and said, "For your mother's sake," and went out of the room. I am writing up this part of the diary whilst I am waiting for the coach, which is, of course, late; and the crucifix is still round my neck. Whether it is the old lady's fear, or the many ghostly traditions of this place, or the crucifix itself, I do not know, but I am not feeling nearly as easy in my mind as usual. If this book should ever reach Mina before I do, let it bring my good-bye. Here comes the coach!

5 May. The Castle.—The grey of the morning has passed, and the sun is high over the distant horizon, which seems jagged, whether with trees or hills I know not, for it is so far off that big things and little are mixed. I am not sleepy, and, as I am not to be called till I awake, naturally I write till sleep comes. There are many odd things to put down, and, lest who reads them may fancy that I dined too well before I left Bistritz, let me put down my dinner exactly. I dined on what they called "robber steak"—bits of bacon, onion, and beef, seasoned with red pepper, and strung on sticks and roasted over the fire, in the simple style of the London cat's meat! The wine was Golden Mediasch, which produces a queer sting on the tongue, which is, however, not disagreeable. I had only a couple of glasses of this, and nothing else.

When I got on the coach the driver had not taken his seat, and I saw him talking with the landlady. They were evidently talking of me, for every now and then they looked at me, and some of the people who were sitting on the bench outside the door—which they call by a name meaning "word-bearer"—came and listened, and then looked at me, most of them pityingly. I could hear a lot of words often repeated, queer words, for there were many nationalities in the crowd; so I quietly got my polyglot dictionary from my bag and looked them out. I must say they were not cheering to me, for amongst them were "Ordog"—Satan, "pokol"—hell, "stregoica"—witch, "vrolok" and "vlkoslak"—both of which mean the same thing, one being Slovak and the other Servian for something that is either werewolf or vampire. (*Mem.*, I must ask the Count about these superstitions.)

When we started, the crowd round the inn door, which had by this time swelled to a considerable size, all made the sign of the cross and pointed two fingers towards me. With some difficulty I got a fellow-passenger to tell me what they meant; he would not answer at first, but on learning that I was English, he explained that it was a charm or guard against the evil eye. This was not very pleasant for me, just starting for an unknown place to meet an unknown man; but every one seemed so kind-hearted, and so sorrowful, and so sympathetic that I could not but be touched. I shall never forget the last glimpse which I had of the inn-yard and its crowd of picturesque figures, all crossing themselves, as they stood round the wide archway, with its background of rich foliage of oleander and orange trees in green tubs clustered in the centre of the yard. Then our driver, whose wide linen drawers covered the whole front of the box-seat—"gotza" they call them—cracked his big whip over his four small horses, which ran abreast, and we set off on our journey.

I soon lost sight and recollection of ghostly fears in the beauty of the scene as we drove along, although had I known the language, or rather languages, which my fellow-passengers were speaking, I might not have been able to throw them off so easily. Before us lay a green sloping land full of forests and woods, with here and there steep hills, crowned with clumps of trees or with farmhouses, the blank gable end to the road. There was everywhere a bewildering mass of fruit blossom—apple, plum, pear, cherry; and as we drove by I could see the green grass under the trees spangled with the fallen petals. In and out amongst these green hills of what they call here the "Mittel Land" ran the road, losing itself as it swept round the grassy curve, or was shut out by the straggling ends of pine woods, which here and there ran down the hillsides like tongues of flame. The road was rugged, but still we seemed to fly over it with a feverish haste. I could not understand then what the haste meant, but the driver was evidently bent on losing no time in reaching Borgo Prund. I was told that this road is in summertime excellent, but that it had not yet been put in order after the winter snows. In this respect it is different from the general run of roads in the Carpathians, for it is an old tradition that they are not to be kept in too good order. Of old the Hospadars would not repair them, lest the Turk should think that they were preparing to bring in foreign troops, and so hasten the war which was always really at loading point.

Beyond the green swelling hills of the Mittel Land rose mighty slopes of forest up to the lofty steeps of the Carpathians themselves. Right and left of us they towered, with the afternoon sun falling full upon them and bringing out all the glorious colours of this beautiful range, deep blue and purple in the shadows of the peaks, green and brown where grass and rock mingled, and an endless perspective of jagged rock and pointed crags, till these were themselves lost in the distance, where the snowy peaks rose grandly. Here and there seemed mighty rifts in the mountains, through which, as the sun began to sink, we saw now and again the white gleam of falling water. One of my companions touched my arm as we swept round the base of a hill and opened up the lofty, snow-covered peak of a mountain, which seemed, as we wound on our serpentine way, to be right before us:—

"Look! Isten szek!"—"God's seat!"—and he crossed himself reverently.

As we wound on our endless way, and the sun sank lower and lower behind us, the shadows of the evening began to creep round us. This was emphasised by the fact that the snowy mountaintop still held the sunset, and seemed to glow out with a delicate cool pink. Here and there we passed Cszeks and Slovaks, all in picturesque attire, but I noticed that goitre was painfully prevalent. By the roadside were many crosses, and as we swept by, my companions all crossed themselves. Here and there was a peasant man or woman kneeling before a shrine, who did not even turn round as we approached, but seemed in the self-surrender of devotion to have neither eyes nor ears for the outer world. There were many things new to me: for instance, hay-ricks in the trees, and here and there very beautiful masses of weeping birch, their white stems shining like silver through the delicate green of the leaves. Now and again we passed a leiter-wagon—the ordinary peasant's cart—with its long, snake-like vertebra, calculated to suit the inequalities of the road. On this were sure to be seated quite a group of home-coming peasants, the Cszeks with their white, and the Slovaks with their coloured, sheepskins, the latter carrying lance-fashion their long staves, with axe at end. As the evening fell it began to get very cold, and the growing twilight seemed to merge into one dark mistiness the gloom of the trees, oak, beech, and pine, though in the valleys which ran deep between the spurs of the hills, as we ascended through the Pass, the dark firs stood out here and there against the background of late-lying snow. Sometimes, as the road was cut through the pine woods that seemed in the darkness to be closing down upon us, great masses of greyness, which here and there bestrewed the trees, produced a peculiarly weird and solemn effect, which carried on the thoughts and grim fancies engendered earlier in the evening, when the falling sunset threw into strange relief the ghost-like clouds which amongst the Carpathians seem to wind ceaselessly through the valleys. Sometimes the hills were so steep that, despite our driver's haste, the horses could only go slowly. I wished to get down and walk up them, as we do at home, but the driver would not hear of it. "No, no," he said; "you must not walk here; the dogs are too fierce"; and then he added, with what he evidently meant for grim pleasantry—for he looked round to catch the approving smile of the rest—"and you may have enough of such matters before you go to sleep." The only stop he would make was a moment's pause to light his lamps.

When it grew dark there seemed to be some excitement amongst the passengers, and they kept speaking to him, one after the other, as though urging him to further speed. He lashed the horses unmercifully with his long whip, and with wild cries of encouragement urged them on to further exertions. Then through the darkness I could see a sort of patch of grey light ahead of us, as though there were a cleft in the hills. The excitement of the passengers grew greater; the crazy coach rocked on its great leather springs, and swayed like a boat tossed on a stormy sea. I had to hold on. The road grew more level, and we appeared to fly along. Then the mountains seemed to come nearer to us on each side and to frown down upon us; we were entering on the Borgo Pass. One by one several of the passengers offered me gifts, which they pressed upon me with an earnestness which would take no denial; these were certainly of an odd and varied kind, but each was given in simple good faith, with a kindly word, and a blessing, and that strange mixture of fear-meaning movements which I had seen outside the hotel at Bistritz—the sign of the cross and the guard against the evil eye. Then, as we flew along, the driver leaned forward, and on each side the passengers, craning over the edge of the coach, peered eagerly into the darkness. It was evident that

something very exciting was either happening or expected, but though I
asked each passenger, no one would give me the slightest explanation.
This state of excitement kept on for some little time; and at last we saw
before us the Pass opening out on the eastern side. There were dark, rolling clouds overhead, and in the air the heavy, oppressive sense of thunder. It seemed as though the mountain range had separated two
atmospheres, and that now we had got into the thunderous one. I was
now myself looking out for the conveyance which was to take me to the
Count. Each moment I expected to see the glare of lamps through the
blackness; but all was dark. The only light was the flickering rays of our
own lamps, in which the steam from our hard driven horses rose in a
white cloud. We could see now the sandy road lying white before us,
but there was on it no sign of a vehicle. The passengers drew back with
a sigh of gladness, which seemed to mock my own disappointment. I
was already thinking what I had best do, when the driver, looking at his
watch, said to the others something which I could hardly hear, it was
spoken so quietly and in so low a tone; I thought it was "An hour less
than the time." Then turning to me he said in German worse than my
own:—

"There is no carriage here. The Herr is not expected after all. He will
now come on to Bukovina, and return to-morrow or the next day; better
the next day." Whilst he was speaking the horses began to neigh and
snort and plunge wildly, so that the driver had to hold them up. Then,
amongst a chorus of screams from the peasants and a universal crossing
of themselves, a calèche, with four horses, drove up behind us, overtook
us, and drew up beside the coach. I could see from the flash of our
lamps, as the rays fell on them, that the horses were coal-black and
splendid animals. They were driven by a tall man, with a long brown
beard and a great black hat, which seemed to hide his face from us. I
could only see the gleam of a pair of very bright eyes, which seemed red
in the lamplight, as he turned to us. He said to the driver:—

"You are early to-night, my friend." The man stammered in reply:—

"The English Herr was in a hurry," to which the stranger replied:—

"That is why, I suppose, you wished him to go on to Bukovina. You cannot deceive me, my friend; I know too much, and my horses are swift." As he spoke he smiled, and the lamplight fell on a hard-looking mouth, with very red lips and sharp-looking teeth, as white as ivory. One of my companions whispered to another the line from Burger's "Lenore:"—

"Denn die Todten reiten schnell"—
("For the dead travel fast.")

The strange driver evidently heard the words, for he looked up with a gleaming smile. The passenger turned his face away, at the same time putting out his two fingers and crossing himself. "Give me the Herr's luggage," said the driver; and with exceeding alacrity my bags were handed out and put in the calèche. Then I descended from the side of the coach, as the calèche was close alongside, the driver helping me with a hand which caught my arm in a grip of steel; his strength must have been prodigious. Without a word he shook his reins, the horses turned, and we swept into the darkness of the Pass. As I looked back I saw the steam from the horses of the coach by the light of the lamps, and projected against it the figures of my late companions crossing themselves. Then the driver cracked his whip and called to his horses, and off they swept on their way to Bukovina. As they sank into the darkness I felt a strange chill, and a lonely feeling came over me; but a cloak was thrown over my shoulders, and a rug across my knees, and the driver said in excellent German:—

"The night is chill, mein Herr, and my master the Count bade me take all care of you. There is a flask of slivovitz (the plum brandy of the country) underneath the seat, if you should require it." I did not take any, but it was a comfort to know it was there all the same. I felt a little strangely, and not a little frightened. I think had there been any alternative I should have taken it, instead of prosecuting that unknown night journey. The carriage went at a hard pace straight along, then we made a complete turn and went along another straight road. It seemed to me that we were simply going over and over the same ground again; and so I took note of some salient point, and found that this was so. I would have liked to have asked the driver what this all meant, but I really feared to do so, for I thought that, placed as I was, any protest would have had no effect in case there had been an intention to delay. By-and-by, however, as I was curious to know how time was passing, I struck a match, and by its flame looked at my watch; it was within a few minutes of midnight. This gave me a sort of shock, for I suppose the general superstition about midnight was increased by my recent experiences. I waited with a sick feeling of suspense.

Then a dog began to howl somewhere in a farmhouse far down the road—a long, agonised wailing, as if from fear. The sound was taken up by another dog, and then another and another, till, borne on the wind which now sighed softly through the Pass, a wild howling began, which seemed to come from all over the country, as far as the imagination could grasp it through the gloom of the night. At the first howl the horses began to strain and rear, but the driver spoke to them soothingly, and they quieted down, but shivered and sweated as though after a runaway from sudden fright. Then, far off in the distance, from the mountains on each side of us began a louder and a sharper howling—that of wolves—which affected both the horses and myself in the same way—for I was minded to jump from the calèche and run, whilst they reared again and plunged madly, so that the driver had to use all his great strength to keep them from bolting. In a few minutes, however, my own ears got accustomed to the sound, and the horses so far became quiet that the driver was able to descend and to stand before them. He petted and soothed them, and whispered something in their ears, as I have heard of horse-tamers doing, and with extraordinary effect, for under his caresses they became quite manageable again, though they still trembled. The driver again took his seat, and shaking his reins, started off at a great pace. This time, after going to the far side of the Pass, he suddenly turned down a narrow roadway which ran sharply to the right.

Soon we were hemmed in with trees, which in places arched right over the roadway till we passed as through a tunnel; and again great frowning rocks guarded us boldly on either side. Though we were in shelter, we could hear the rising wind, for it moaned and whistled through the rocks, and the branches of the trees crashed together as we swept along. It grew colder and colder still, and fine, powdery snow began to fall, so that soon we and all around us were covered with a white blanket. The keen wind still carried the howling of the dogs, though this grew fainter as we went on our way. The baying of the wolves sounded nearer and nearer, as though they were closing round on us from every side. I grew dreadfully afraid, and the horses shared my fear. The driver, however, was not in the least disturbed; he kept turning his head to left and right, but I could not see anything through the darkness.

Suddenly, away on our left, I saw a faint flickering blue flame. The driver saw it at the same moment; he at once checked the horses, and, jumping to the ground, disappeared into the darkness. I did not know what to do, the less as the howling of the wolves grew closer; but while I wondered the driver suddenly appeared again, and without a word took his seat, and we resumed our journey. I think I must have fallen asleep and kept dreaming of the incident, for it seemed to be repeated endlessly, and now looking back, it is like a sort of awful nightmare. Once the flame appeared so near the road, that even in the darkness around us I could watch the driver's motions. He went rapidly to where the blue flame arose—it must have been very faint, for it did not seem to illumine the place around it at all—and gathering a few stones, formed them into some device. Once there appeared a strange optical effect: when he stood between me and the flame he did not obstruct it, for I could see its ghostly flicker all the same. This startled me, but as the effect was only momentary, I took it that my eyes deceived me straining through the darkness. Then for a time there were no blue flames, and we sped onwards through the gloom, with the howling of the wolves around us, as though they were following in a moving circle.

At last there came a time when the driver went further afield than he had yet gone, and during his absence, the horses began to tremble worse than ever and to snort and scream with fright. I could not see any cause for it, for the howling of the wolves had ceased altogether; but just then the moon, sailing through the black clouds, appeared behind the jagged crest of a beetling, pine-clad rock, and by its light I saw around us a ring of wolves, with white teeth and lolling red tongues, with long, sinewy limbs and shaggy hair. They were a hundred times more terrible in the grim silence which held them than even when they howled. For myself, I felt a sort of paralysis of fear. It is only when a man feels himself face to face with such horrors that he can understand their true import.

All at once the wolves began to howl as though the moonlight had had some peculiar effect on them. The horses jumped about and reared, and looked helplessly round with eyes that rolled in a way painful to see; but the living ring of terror encompassed them on every side; and they had perforce to remain within it. I called to the coachman to come, for it seemed to me that our only chance was to try to break out through the ring and to aid his approach I shouted and beat the side of the calèche, hoping by the noise to scare the wolves from that side, so as to give him a chance of reaching the trap. How he came there, I know not, but I heard his voice raised in a tone of imperious command, and looking towards the sound, saw him stand in the roadway. As he swept his long arms, as though brushing aside some impalpable obstacle, the wolves fell back and back further still. Just then a heavy cloud passed across the face of the moon, so that we were again in darkness.

When I could see again the driver was climbing into the calèche, and the wolves had disappeared. This was all so strange and uncanny that a dreadful fear came upon me, and I was afraid to speak or move. The time seemed interminable as we swept on our way, now in almost complete darkness, for the rolling clouds obscured the moon. We kept on ascending, with occasional periods of quick descent, but in the main always ascending. Suddenly, I became conscious of the fact that the driver was in the act of pulling up the horses in the courtyard of a vast ruined castle, from whose tall black windows came no ray of light, and whose broken battlements showed a jagged line against the moonlit sky.

CHAPTER 2.

———◇———

JONATHAN HARKER'S JOURNAL—*continued.*

5 May.—I must have been asleep, for certainly if I had been fully awake I must have noticed the approach of such a remarkable place. In the gloom the courtyard looked of considerable size, and as several dark ways led from it under great round arches, it perhaps seemed bigger than it really is. I have not yet been able to see it by daylight.

When the calèche stopped, the driver jumped down and held out his hand to assist me to alight. Again I could not but notice his prodigious strength. His hand actually seemed like a steel vice that could have crushed mine if he had chosen. Then he took out my traps, and placed them on the ground beside me as I stood close to a great door, old and studded with large iron nails, and set in a projecting doorway of massive stone. I could see even in the dim light that the stone was massively carved, but that the carving had been much worn by time and weather. As I stood, the driver jumped again into his seat and shook the reins; the horses started forward, and trap and all disappeared down one of the dark openings.

I stood in silence where I was, for I did not know what to do. Of bell or knocker there was no sign; through these frowning walls and dark window openings it was not likely that my voice could penetrate. The time I waited seemed endless, and I felt doubts and fears crowding upon me. What sort of place had I come to, and among what kind of people? What sort of grim adventure was it on which I had embarked? Was this a customary incident in the life of a solicitor's clerk sent out to explain the purchase of a London estate to a foreigner? Solicitor's clerk! Mina would not like that. Solicitor—for just before leaving London I got word that my examination was successful; and I am now a full-blown solicitor! I began to rub my eyes and pinch myself to see if I were awake. It all seemed like a horrible nightmare to me, and I expected that I should suddenly awake, and find myself at home, with the dawn struggling in through the windows, as I had now and again felt in the morning after a day of overwork. But my flesh answered the pinching test, and my eyes were not to be deceived. I was indeed awake and among the Carpathians. All I could do now was to be patient, and to wait the coming of the morning.

Just as I had come to this conclusion I heard a heavy step approaching behind the great door, and saw through the chinks the gleam of a coming light. Then there was the sound of rattling chains and the clanking of massive bolts drawn back. A key was turned with the loud grating noise of long disuse, and the great door swung back.

Within, stood a tall old man, clean shaven save for a long white moustache, and clad in black from head to foot, without a single speck of colour about him anywhere. He held in his hand an antique silver lamp, in which the flame burned without chimney or globe of any kind, throwing long quivering shadows as it flickered in the draught of the open door. The old man motioned me in with his right hand with a courtly gesture, saying in excellent English, but with a strange intonation:—

"Welcome to my house! Enter freely and of your own will!" He made no motion of stepping to meet me, but stood like a statue, as though his gesture of welcome had fixed him into stone. The instant, however, that I had stepped over the threshold, he moved impulsively forward, and holding out his hand grasped mine with a strength which made me wince, an effect which was not lessened by the fact that it seemed as cold as ice—more like the hand of a dead than a living man. Again he said:—

"Welcome to my house. Come freely. Go safely; and leave something of the happiness you bring!" The strength of the handshake was so much akin to that which I had noticed in the driver, whose face I had not seen, that for a moment I doubted if it were not the same person to whom I was speaking; so to make sure, I said interrogatively:—

"Count Dracula?" He bowed in a courtly way as he replied:—

"I am Dracula; and I bid you welcome, Mr. Harker, to my house. Come in; the night air is chill, and you must need to eat and rest." As he was speaking, he put the lamp on a bracket on the wall, and stepping out, took my luggage; he had carried it in before I could forestall him. I protested but he insisted:—

"Nay, sir, you are my guest. It is late, and my people are not available. Let me see to your comfort myself." He insisted on carrying my traps along the passage, and then up a great winding stair, and along another great passage, on whose stone floor our steps rang heavily. At the end of this he threw open a heavy door, and I rejoiced to see within a well-lit room in which a table was spread for supper, and on whose mighty hearth a great fire of logs, freshly replenished, flamed and flared.

The Count halted, putting down my bags, closed the door, and crossing the room, opened another door, which led into a small octagonal room lit by a single lamp, and seemingly without a window of any sort. Passing through this, he opened another door, and motioned me to enter. It was a welcome sight; for here was a great bedroom well lighted and warmed with another log fire,—also added to but lately, for the top logs were fresh—which sent a hollow roar up the wide chimney. The Count himself left my luggage inside and withdrew, saying, before he closed the door:—

"You will need, after your journey, to refresh yourself by making your toilet. I trust you will find all you wish. When you are ready, come into the other room, where you will find your supper prepared."

The light and warmth and the Count's courteous welcome seemed to have dissipated all my doubts and fears. Having then reached my normal state, I discovered that I was half famished with hunger; so making a hasty toilet, I went into the other room.

I found supper already laid out. My host, who stood on one side of the great fireplace, leaning against the stonework, made a graceful wave of his hand to the table, and said:—

"I pray you, be seated and sup how you please. You will, I trust, excuse me that I do not join you; but I have dined already, and I do not sup."

I handed to him the sealed letter which Mr. Hawkins had entrusted to me. He opened it and read it gravely; then, with a charming smile, he handed it to me to read. One passage of it, at least, gave me a thrill of pleasure.

"I must regret that an attack of gout, from which malady I am a constant sufferer, forbids absolutely any travelling on my part for some time to come; but I am happy to say I can send a sufficient substitute, one in whom I have every possible confidence. He is a young man, full of energy and talent in his own way, and of a very faithful disposition. He is discreet and silent, and has grown into manhood in my service. He shall be ready to attend on you when you will during his stay, and shall take your instructions in all matters."

The Count himself came forward and took off the cover of a dish, and I fell to at once on an excellent roast chicken. This, with some cheese and a salad and a bottle of old Tokay, of which I had two glasses, was my supper. During the time I was eating it the Count asked me many questions as to my journey, and I told him by degrees all I had experienced.

By this time I had finished my supper, and by my host's desire had drawn up a chair by the fire and begun to smoke a cigar which he offered me, at the same time excusing himself that he did not smoke. I had now an opportunity of observing him, and found him of a very marked physiognomy.

His face was a strong—a very strong—aquiline, with high bridge of the thin nose and peculiarly arched nostrils; with lofty domed forehead, and hair growing scantily round the temples but profusely elsewhere.

His eyebrows were very massive, almost meeting over the nose, and with bushy hair that seemed to curl in its own profusion. The mouth, so far as I could see it under the heavy moustache, was fixed and rather cruel-looking, with peculiarly sharp white teeth; these protruded over the lips, whose remarkable ruddiness showed astonishing vitality in a man of his years. For the rest, his ears were pale, and at the tops extremely pointed; the chin was broad and strong, and the cheeks firm though thin. The general effect was one of extraordinary pallor.

Hitherto I had noticed the backs of his hands as they lay on his knees in the firelight, and they had seemed rather white and fine; but seeing them now close to me, I could not but notice that they were rather coarse—broad, with squat fingers. Strange to say, there were hairs in the centre of the palm. The nails were long and fine, and cut to a sharp point. As the Count leaned over me and his hands touched me, I could not repress a shudder. It may have been that his breath was rank, but a horrible feeling of nausea came over me, which, do what I would, I could not conceal. The Count, evidently noticing it, drew back; and with a grim sort of smile, which showed more than he had yet done his protuberant teeth, sat himself down again on his own side of the fire-place. We were both silent for a while; and as I looked towards the window I saw the first dim streak of the coming dawn. There seemed a strange stillness over everything; but as I listened I heard as if from down below in the valley the howling of many wolves. The Count's eyes gleamed, and he said:—

"Listen to them—the children of the night. What music they make!" Seeing, I suppose, some expression in my face strange to him, he added:—

"Ah, sir, you dwellers in the city cannot enter into the feelings of the hunter." Then he rose and said:—

"But you must be tired. Your bedroom is all ready, and to-morrow you shall sleep as late as you will. I have to be away till the afternoon; so sleep well and dream well!" With a courteous bow, he opened for me himself the door to the octagonal room, and I entered my bed-room. . . .

I am all in a sea of wonders. I doubt; I fear; I think strange things, which I dare not confess to my own soul. God keep me, if only for the sake of those dear to me!

7 May.—It is again early morning, but I have rested and enjoyed the last twenty-four hours. I slept till late in the day, and awoke of my own accord. When I had dressed myself I went into the room where we had supped, and found a cold breakfast laid out, with coffee kept hot by the pot being placed on the hearth. There was a card on the table, on which was written:—

"I have to be absent for a while. Do not wait for me.—D." I set to and enjoyed a hearty meal. When I had done, I looked for a bell, so that I might let the servants know I had finished but I could not find one. There are certainly odd deficiencies in the house, considering the extraordinary evidences of wealth which are round me. The table service is of gold, and so beautifully wrought that it must be of immense value. The curtains and upholstery of the chairs and sofas and the hangings of my bed are of the costliest and most beautiful fabrics, and must have been of fabulous value when they were made, for they are centuries old, though in excellent order. I saw something like them in Hampton Court, but there they were worn and frayed and moth-eaten. But still in none of the rooms is there a mirror. There is not even a toilet glass on my table, and I had to get the little shaving glass from my bag before I could either shave or brush my hair. I have not yet seen a servant anywhere, or heard a sound near the castle except the howling of wolves. Some time after I had finished my meal—I do not know whether to call it breakfast or dinner, for it was between five and six o'clock when I had it—I looked about for something to read, for I did not like to go about the castle until I had asked the Count's permission. There was absolutely nothing in the room, book, newspaper, or even writing materials; so I opened another door in the room and found a sort of library. The door opposite mine I tried, but found it locked.

In the library I found, to my great delight, a vast number of English books, whole shelves full of them, and bound volumes of magazines and newspapers. A table in the centre was littered with English magazines and newspapers, though none of them were of very recent date. The books were of the most varied kind—history, geography, politics, political economy, botany, geology, law—all relating to England and English life and customs and manners. There were even such books of reference as the London Directory, the "Red" and "Blue" books, Whitaker's Almanac, the Army and Navy Lists, and—it somehow gladdened my heart to see it—the Law List.

Whilst I was looking at the books, the door opened, and the Count entered. He saluted me in a hearty way, and hoped that I had had a good night's rest. Then he went on:—

"I am glad you found your way in here, for I am sure there is much that will interest you. These companions"—and he laid his hand on some of the books—"have been good friends to me, and for some years past, ever since I had the idea of going to London, have given me many, many hours of pleasure. Through them I have come to know your great England; and to know her is to love her. I long to go through the crowded streets of your mighty London, to be in the midst of the whirl and rush of humanity, to share its life, its change, its death, and all that makes it what it is. But alas! as yet I only know your tongue through books. To you, my friend, I look that I know it to speak."

"But, Count," I said, "you know and speak English thoroughly!" He bowed gravely.

"I thank you, my friend, for your all too-flattering estimate, but yet I fear that I am but a little way on the road I would travel. True, I know the grammar and the words, but yet I know not how to speak them."

"Indeed," I said, "you speak excellently."

"Not so," he answered. "Well, I know that, did I move and speak in your London, none there are who would not know me for a stranger. That is not enough for me. Here I am noble; I am *boyar*; the common people know me, and I am master. But a stranger in a strange land, he is no one; men know him not—and to know not is to care not for. I am content if I am like the rest, so that no man stops if he sees me, or pause in his speaking if he hear my words, 'Ha, ha! a stranger!' I have been so long master that I would be master still—or at least that none other should be master of me. You come to me not alone as agent of my friend Peter Hawkins, of Exeter, to tell me all about my new estate in London. You shall, I trust, rest here with me awhile, so that by our talking I may learn the English intonation; and I would that you tell me when I make error, even of the smallest, in my speaking. I am sorry that I had to be away so long to-day; but you will, I know, forgive one who has so many important affairs in hand."

Of course I said all I could about being willing, and asked if I might come into that room when I chose. He answered: "Yes, certainly," and added:—

"You may go anywhere you wish in the castle, except where the doors are locked, where of course you will not wish to go. There is reason that all things are as they are, and did you see with my eyes and know with my knowledge, you would perhaps better understand." I said I was sure of this, and then he went on:—

"We are in Transylvania; and Transylvania is not England. Our ways are not your ways, and there shall be to you many strange things. Nay, from what you have told me of your experiences already, you know something of what strange things there may be."

This led to much conversation; and as it was evident that he wanted to talk, if only for talking's sake, I asked him many questions regarding things that had already happened to me or come within my notice. Sometimes he sheered off the subject, or turned the conversation by pretending not to understand; but generally he answered all I asked most frankly. Then as time went on, and I had got somewhat bolder, I asked him of some of the strange things of the preceding night, as, for instance, why the coachman went to the places where he had seen the blue flames. He then explained to me that it was commonly believed that on a certain night of the year—last night, in fact, when all evil spirits are supposed to have unchecked sway—a blue flame is seen over any place where treasure has been concealed. "That treasure has been hidden," he went on, "in the region through which you came last night, there can be but little doubt; for it was the ground fought over for centuries by the Wallachian, the Saxon, and the Turk. Why, there is hardly a foot of soil in all this region that has not been enriched by the blood of men, patriots or invaders. In old days there were stirring times, when the Austrian and the Hungarian came up in hordes, and the patriots went out to meet them—men and women, the aged and the children too—and waited their coming on the rocks above the passes, that they might sweep destruction on them with their artificial avalanches. When the invader was triumphant he found but little, for whatever there was had been sheltered in the friendly soil."

"But how," said I, "can it have remained so long undiscovered, when there is a sure index to it if men will but take the trouble to look?" The Count smiled, and as his lips ran back over his gums, the long, sharp, canine teeth showed out strangely; he answered:—

"Because your peasant is at heart a coward and a fool! Those flames only appear on one night; and on that night no man of this land will, if he can help it, stir without his doors. And, dear sir, even if he did he would not know what to do. Why, even the peasant that you tell me of who marked the place of the flame would not know where to look in daylight even for his own work. Even you would not, I dare be sworn, be able to find these places again."

"There you are right," I said. "I know no more than the dead where even to look for them." Then we drifted into other matters.

"Come," he said at last, "tell me of London and of the house which you have procured for me." With an apology for my remissness, I went into my own room to get the papers from my bag. Whilst I was placing them in order I heard a rattling of china and silver in the next room, and as I passed through, noticed that the table had been cleared and the lamp lit, for it was by this time deep into the dark. The lamps were also lit in the study or library, and I found the Count lying on the sofa, reading, of all things in the world, an English Bradshaw's Guide. When I came in he cleared the books and papers from the table; and with him I went into plans and deeds and figures of all sorts. He was interested in everything, and asked me myriad questions about the place and its surroundings. He clearly had studied beforehand all he could get on the subject of the neighbourhood, for he evidently at the end knew very much more than I did. When I remarked this, he answered:—

"Well, but, my friend, is it not needful that I should? When I go there I shall be all alone, and my friend Harker Jonathan—nay, pardon me, I fall into my country's habit of putting your patronymic first—my friend Jonathan Harker will not be by my side to correct and aid me. He will be in Exeter, miles away, probably working at papers of the law with my other friend, Peter Hawkins. So!"

We went thoroughly into the business of the purchase of the estate at Purfleet. When I had told him the facts and got his signature to the necessary papers, and had written a letter with them ready to post to Mr. Hawkins, he began to ask me how I had come across so suitable a place. I read to him the notes which I had made at the time, and which I inscribe here:—

"At Purfleet, on a by-road, I came across just such a place as seemed to be required, and where was displayed a dilapidated notice that the place was for sale. It is surrounded by a high wall, of ancient structure, built of heavy stones, and has not been repaired for a large number of years. The closed gates are of heavy old oak and iron, all eaten with rust.

"The estate is called Carfax, no doubt a corruption of the old *Quatre Face*, as the house is four-sided, agreeing with the cardinal points of the compass. It contains in all some twenty acres, quite surrounded by the solid stone wall above mentioned. There are many trees on it, which make it in places gloomy, and there is a deep, dark-looking pond or small lake, evidently fed by some springs, as the water is clear and flows away in a fair-sized stream. The house is very large and of all periods back, I should say, to mediaeval times, for one part is of stone immensely thick, with only a few windows high up and heavily barred with iron. It looks like part of a keep, and is close to an old chapel or church. I could not enter it, as I had not the key of the door leading to it from the house, but I have taken with my kodak views of it from various points. The house has been added to but in a very straggling way, and I can only guess at the amount of ground it covers, which must be very great. There are but few houses close at hand, one being a very large house only recently added to and formed into a private lunatic asylum. It is not, however, visible from the grounds."

When I had finished, he said:—

"I am glad that it is old and big. I myself am of an old family, and to live in a new house would kill me. A house cannot be made habitable in a day; and, after all, how few days go to make up a century. I rejoice also that there is a chapel of old times. We Transylvanian nobles love not to think that our bones may lie amongst the common dead. I seek not gaiety nor mirth, not the bright voluptuousness of much sunshine and sparkling waters which please the young and gay. I am no longer young; and my heart, through weary years of mourning over the dead, is not attuned to mirth. Moreover, the walls of my castle are broken; the shadows are many, and the wind breathes cold through the broken battlements and casements. I love the shade and the shadow, and would be alone with my thoughts when I may." Somehow his words and his look did not seem to accord, or else it was that his cast of face made his smile look malignant and saturnine.

Presently, with an excuse, he left me, asking me to put all my papers together. He was some little time away, and I began to look at some of the books around me. One was an atlas, which I found opened naturally at England, as if that map had been much used. On looking at it I found in certain places little rings marked, and on examining these I noticed that one was near London on the east side, manifestly where his new estate was situated; the other two were Exeter, and Whitby on the Yorkshire coast.

It was the better part of an hour when the Count returned. "Aha!" he said; "still at your books? Good! But you must not work always. Come; I am informed that your supper is ready." He took my arm, and we went into the next room, where I found an excellent supper ready on the table. The Count again excused himself, as he had dined out on his being away from home. But he sat as on the previous night, and chatted whilst I ate. After supper I smoked, as on the last evening, and the Count stayed with me, chatting and asking questions on every conceivable subject, hour after hour. I felt that it was getting very late indeed, but I did not say anything, for I felt under obligation to meet my host's wishes in every way. I was not sleepy, as the long sleep yesterday had fortified me; but I could not help experiencing that chill which comes over one at the coming of the dawn, which is like, in its way, the turn of the tide. They say that people who are near death die generally at the change to the dawn or at the turn of the tide; any one who has when tired, and tied as it were to his post, experienced this change in the atmosphere can well believe it. All at once we heard the crow of a cock coming up with preternatural shrillness through the clear morning air; Count Dracula, jumping to his feet, said:—

"Why, there is the morning again! How remiss I am to let you stay up so long. You must make your conversation regarding my dear new country of England less interesting, so that I may not forget how time flies by us," and, with a courtly bow, he quickly left me.

I went into my own room and drew the curtains, but there was little to notice; my window opened into the courtyard, all I could see was the warm grey of quickening sky. So I pulled the curtains again, and have written of this day.

8 May.—I began to fear as I wrote in this book that I was getting too diffuse; but now I am glad that I went into detail from the first, for there is something so strange about this place and all in it that I cannot but feel uneasy. I wish I were safe out of it, or that I had never come. It may be that this strange night-existence is telling on me; but would that that were all! If there were any one to talk to I could bear it, but there is no one. I have only the Count to speak with, and he!—I fear I am myself the only living soul within the place. Let me be prosaic so far as facts can be; it will help me to bear up, and imagination must not run riot with me. If it does I am lost. Let me say at once how I stand—or seem to.

I only slept a few hours when I went to bed, and feeling that I could not sleep any more, got up. I had hung my shaving glass by the window, and was just beginning to shave. Suddenly I felt a hand on my shoulder, and heard the Count's voice saying to me, "Good morning." I started, for it amazed me that I had not seen him, since the reflection of the glass covered the whole room behind me. In starting I had cut myself slightly, but did not notice it at the moment. Having answered the Count's salutation, I turned to the glass again to see how I had been mistaken. This time there could be no error, for the man was close to me, and I could see him over my shoulder. But there was no reflection of him in the mirror! The whole room behind me was displayed; but there was no sign of a man in it, except myself. This was startling, and, coming on the top of so many strange things, was beginning to increase that vague feeling of uneasiness which I always had when the Count is near; but at the instant I saw that the cut had bled a little, and the blood was trickling over my chin. I laid down the razor, turning as I did so half round to look for some sticking plaster. When the Count saw my face, his eyes blazed with a sort of demoniac fury, and he suddenly made a grab at my throat. I drew away, and his hand touched the string of beads which held the crucifix. It made an instant change in him, for the fury passed so quickly that I could hardly believe that it was ever there.

"Take care," he said, "take care how you cut yourself. It is more dangerous than you think in this country." Then seizing the shaving glass, he went on: "And this is the wretched thing that has done the mischief. It is a foul bauble of man's vanity. Away with it!" and opening the heavy window with one wrench of his terrible hand, he flung out the glass, which was shattered into a thousand pieces on the stones of the courtyard far below. Then he withdrew without a word. It is very annoying, for I do not see how I am to shave, unless in my watch-case or the bottom of the shaving-pot, which is fortunately of metal.

When I went into the dining-room, breakfast was prepared; but I could not find the Count anywhere. So I breakfasted alone. It is strange that as yet I have not seen the Count eat or drink. He must be a very peculiar man! After breakfast I did a little exploring in the castle. I went out on the stairs, and found a room looking towards the South. The view was magnificent, and from where I stood there was every opportunity of seeing it. The castle is on the very edge of a terrible precipice. A stone falling from the window would fall a thousand feet without touching anything! As far as the eye can reach is a sea of green tree tops, with occasionally a deep rift where there is a chasm. Here and there are silver threads where the rivers wind in deep gorges through the forests.

But I am not in heart to describe beauty, for when I had seen the view I explored further; doors, doors, doors everywhere, and all locked and bolted. In no place save from the windows in the castle walls is there an available exit.

The castle is a veritable prison, and I am a prisoner!

CHAPTER 3.

⊶—◇—⊷

JONATHAN HARKER'S JOURNAL—*continued.*

When I found that I was a prisoner a sort of wild feeling came over me. I rushed up and down the stairs, trying every door and peering out of every window I could find; but after a little the conviction of my helplessness overpowered all other feelings. When I look back after a few hours I think I must have been mad for the time, for I behaved much as a rat does in a trap. When, however, the conviction had come to me that I was helpless I sat down quietly—as quietly as I have ever done anything in my life—and began to think over what was best to be done. I am thinking still, and as yet have come to no definite conclusion. Of one thing only am I certain; that it is no use making my ideas known to the Count. He knows well that I am imprisoned; and as he has done it himself, and has doubtless his own motives for it, he would only deceive me if I trusted him fully with the facts. So far as I can see, my only plan will be to keep my knowledge and my fears to myself, and my eyes open. I am, I know, either being deceived, like a baby, by my own fears, or else I am in desperate straits; and if the latter be so, I need, and shall need, all my brains to get through.

I had hardly come to this conclusion when I heard the great door below shut, and knew that the Count had returned. He did not come at once to the library, so I went cautiously to my own room and found him making the bed. This was odd, but only confirmed what I had all along thought—that there were no servants in the house. When later I saw him through the chink of the hinges of the door laying the table in the dining-room, I was assured of it; for if he does himself all these menial offices, surely it is proof that there is no one else to do them. This gave me a fright, for if there is no one else in the castle, it must have been the Count himself who was the driver of the coach that brought me here. This is a terrible thought; for if so, what does it mean that he could control the wolves, as he did, by only holding up his hand in silence? How was it that all the people at Bistritz and on the coach had some terrible fear for me? What meant the giving of the crucifix, of the garlic, of the wild rose, of the mountain ash? Bless that good, good woman who hung the crucifix round my neck! for it is a comfort and a strength to me whenever I touch it. It is odd that a thing which I have been taught to regard with disfavour and as idolatrous should in a time of loneliness and trouble be of help. Is it that there is something in the essence of the thing itself, or that it is a medium, a tangible help, in conveying memories of sympathy and comfort? Some time, if it may be, I must examine this matter and try to make up my mind about it. In the meantime I must find out all I can about Count Dracula, as it may help me to understand. To-night he may talk of himself, if I turn the conversation that way. I must be very careful, however, not to awake his suspicion.

Midnight.—I have had a long talk with the Count. I asked him a few questions on Transylvania history, and he warmed up to the subject wonderfully. In his speaking of things and people, and especially of battles, he spoke as if he had been present at them all. This he afterwards explained by saying that to a *boyar* the pride of his house and name is his own pride, that their glory is his glory, that their fate is his fate. Whenever he spoke of his house he always said, "we," and spoke almost in the plural, like a king speaking. I wish I could put down all he said exactly as he said it, for to me it was most fascinating. It seemed to have in it a whole history of the country. He grew excited as he spoke, and walked about the room pulling his great white moustache and grasping anything on which he laid his hands as though he would crush it by main strength. One thing he said which I shall put down as nearly as I can; for it tells in its way the story of his race:—

"We Szekelys have a right to be proud, for in our veins flows the blood of many brave races who fought as the lion fights, for lordship. Here, in the whirlpool of European races, the Ugric tribe bore down from Iceland the fighting spirit which Thor and Wodin gave them, which their Berserkers displayed to such fell intent on the seaboards of Europe, ay, and of Asia and Africa too, till the peoples thought that the werewolves themselves had come. Here, too, when they came, they found the Huns, whose warlike fury had swept the earth like a living flame, till the dying peoples held that in their veins ran the blood of those old witches, who, expelled from Scythia, had mated with the devils in the desert. Fools, fools! What devil or what witch was ever so great as Attila, whose blood is in these veins?" He held up his arms. "Is it a wonder that we were a conquering race; that we were proud; that when the Magyar, the Lombard, the Avar, the Bulgar, or the Turk poured his thousands on our frontiers, we drove them back? Is it strange that when Arpad and his legions swept through the Hungarian fatherland he found us here when he reached the frontier; that the Honfoglalas was completed there? And when the Hungarian flood swept eastward, the Szekelys were claimed as kindred by the victorious Magyars, and to us for centuries was trusted the guarding of the frontier of Turkey-land; ay, and more than that, endless duty of the frontier guard, for, as the Turks say, 'water sleeps, an enemy is sleepless.' Who more gladly than we throughout the Four Nations received the 'bloody sword,' or at its war-like call flocked quicker to the standard of the King? When was redeemed that great shame of my nation, the shame of Cassova, when the flags of the Wallach and the Magyar went down beneath the Crescent? Who was it but one of my own race who at Voivode crossed the

Danube and beat the Turk on his own ground? This was a Dracula indeed! Woe was it that his own unworthy brother, when he had fallen, sold his people to the Turk and brought the shame of slavery on them! Was it not this Dracula, indeed, who inspired that other of his race who in a later age again and again brought his forces over the great river into Turkey-land; who, when he was beaten back, came again, and again, and again, though he had to come alone from the bloody field where his troops were being slaughtered, since he knew that he alone could ultimately triumph! They said that he thought only of himself. Bah! what good are peasants without a leader? Where ends the war without a brain and heart to conduct it? Again, when, after the battle of Mohács, we threw off the Hungarian yoke, we of the Dracula blood were amongst their leaders, for our spirit would not brook that we were not free. Ah, young sir, the Szekelys—and the Dracula as their heart's blood, their brains, and their swords—can boast a record that mushroom growths like the Hapsburgs and the Romanoffs can never reach. The warlike days are over. Blood is too precious a thing in these days of dishonourable peace; and the glories of the great races are as a tale that is told."

It was by this time close on morning, and we went to bed. (*Mem.*, this diary seems horribly like the beginning of the "Arabian Nights," for everything has to break off at cockcrow—or like the ghost of Hamlet's father.)

12 May.—Let me begin with facts—bare, meagre facts, verified by books and figures, and of which there can be no doubt. I must not confuse them with experiences which will have to rest on my own observation, or my memory of them. Last evening when the Count came from his room he began by asking me questions on legal matters and on the doing of certain kinds of business. I had spent the day wearily over books, and, simply to keep my mind occupied, went over some of the matters I had been examined in at Lincoln's Inn. There was a certain method in the Count's inquiries, so I shall try to put them down in sequence; the knowledge may somehow or some time be useful to me.

First, he asked if a man in England might have two solicitors or more. I told him he might have a dozen if he wished, but that it would not be wise to have more than one solicitor engaged in one transaction, as only one could act at a time, and that to change would be certain to militate against his interest. He seemed thoroughly to understand, and went on to ask if there would be any practical difficulty in having one man to attend, say, to banking, and another to look after shipping, in case local help were needed in a place far from the home of the banking solicitor. I asked him to explain more fully, so that I might not by any chance mislead him, so he said:—

"I shall illustrate. Your friend and mine, Mr. Peter Hawkins, from under the shadow of your beautiful cathedral at Exeter, which is far from London, buys for me through your good self my place at London. Good! Now here let me say frankly, lest you should think it strange that I have sought the services of one so far off from London instead of some one resident there, that my motive was that no local interest might be served save my wish only; and as one of London residence might, perhaps, have some purpose of himself or friend to serve, I went thus afield to seek my agent, whose labours should be only to my interest. Now, suppose I, who have much of affairs, wish to ship goods, say, to Newcastle, or Durham, or Harwich, or Dover, might it not be that it could with more ease be done by consigning to one in these ports?" I answered that certainly it would be most easy, but that we solicitors had a system of agency one for the other, so that local work could be done locally on instruction from any solicitor, so that the client, simply placing himself in the hands of one man, could have his wishes carried out by him without further trouble.

"But," said he, "I could be at liberty to direct myself. Is it not so?"

"Of course," I replied; and "such is often done by men of business, who do not like the whole of their affairs to be known by any one person."

"Good!" he said, and then went on to ask about the means of making consignments and the forms to be gone through, and of all sorts of difficulties which might arise, but by forethought could be guarded against. I explained all these things to him to the best of my ability, and he certainly left me under the impression that he would have made a wonderful solicitor, for there was nothing that he did not think of or foresee.

For a man who was never in the country, and who did not evidently do much in the way of business, his knowledge and acumen were wonderful. When he had satisfied himself on these points of which he had spoken, and I had verified all as well as I could by the books available, he suddenly stood up and said:—

"Have you written since your first letter to our friend Mr. Peter Hawkins, or to any other?" It was with some bitterness in my heart that I answered that I had not, that as yet I had not seen any opportunity of sending letters to anybody.

"Then write now, my young friend," he said, laying a heavy hand on my shoulder: "write to our friend and to any other; and say, if it will please you, that you shall stay with me until a month from now."

"Do you wish me to stay so long?" I asked, for my heart grew cold at the thought.

"I desire it much; nay, I will take no refusal. When your master, employer, what you will, engaged that someone should come on his behalf, it was understood that my needs only were to be consulted. I have not stinted. Is it not so?"

What could I do but bow acceptance? It was Mr. Hawkins's interest, not mine, and I had to think of him, not myself; and besides, while Count Dracula was speaking, there was that in his eyes and in his bearing which made me remember that I was a prisoner, and that if I wished it I could have no choice. The Count saw his victory in my bow, and his mastery in the trouble of my face, for he began at once to use them, but in his own smooth, resistless way:—

"I pray you, my good young friend, that you will not discourse of things other than business in your letters. It will doubtless please your friends to know that you are well, and that you look forward to getting home to them. Is it not so?" As he spoke he handed me three sheets of note-paper and three envelopes. They were all of the thinnest foreign post, and looking at them, then at him, and noticing his quiet smile, with the sharp, canine teeth lying over the red underlip, I understood as well as if he had spoken that I should be careful what I wrote, for he would be able to read it. So I determined to write only formal notes now, but to write fully to Mr. Hawkins in secret, and also to Mina, for to her I could write in shorthand, which would puzzle the Count, if he did see it. When I had written my two letters I sat quiet, reading a book whilst the Count wrote several notes, referring as he wrote them to some books on his table. Then he took up my two and placed them with his own, and put by his writing materials, after which, the instant the door had closed behind him, I leaned over and looked at the letters, which were face down on the table. I felt no compunction in doing so, for under the circumstances I felt that I should protect myself in every way I could.

One of the letters was directed to Samuel F. Billington, No. 7, the Crescent, Whitby, another to Herr Leutner, Varna; the third was to Coutts & Co., London, and the fourth to Herren Klopstock & Billreuth, bankers, Buda-Pesth. The second and fourth were unsealed. I was just about to look at them when I saw the door-handle move. I sank back in my seat, having just had time to replace the letters as they had been and to resume my book before the Count, holding still another letter in his hand, entered the room. He took up the letters on the table and stamped them carefully, and then turning to me, said:—

"I trust you will forgive me, but I have much work to do in private this evening. You will, I hope, find all things as you wish." At the door he turned, and after a moment's pause said:—

"Let me advise you, my dear young friend—nay, let me warn you with all seriousness, that should you leave these rooms you will not by any chance go to sleep in any other part of the castle. It is old, and has many memories, and there are bad dreams for those who sleep unwisely. Be warned! Should sleep now or ever overcome you, or be like to do, then haste to your own chamber or to these rooms, for your rest will then be safe. But if you be not careful in this respect, then"—He finished his speech in a gruesome way, for he motioned with his hands as if he were washing them. I quite understood; my only doubt was as to whether any dream could be more terrible than the unnatural, horrible net of gloom and mystery which seemed closing around me.

Later.—I endorse the last words written, but this time there is no doubt in question. I shall not fear to sleep in any place where he is not. I have placed the crucifix over the head of my bed—I imagine that my rest is thus freer from dreams; and there it shall remain.

When he left me I went to my room. After a little while, not hearing any sound, I came out and went up the stone stair to where I could look out towards the South. There was some sense of freedom in the vast expanse, inaccessible though it was to me, as compared with the narrow darkness of the courtyard. Looking out of this, I felt that I was indeed in prison, and I seemed to want a breath of fresh air, though it were of the night. I am beginning to feel this nocturnal existence tell on me. It is destroying my nerve. I start at my own shadow, and am full of all sorts of horrible imaginings. God knows that there is ground for my terrible fear in this accursed place! I looked out over the beautiful expanse, bathed in soft yellow moonlight till it was almost as light as day. In the soft light the distant hills became melted, and the shadows in the valleys and gorges of velvety blackness. The mere beauty seemed to cheer me; there was peace and comfort in every breath I drew. As I leaned from the window my eye was caught by something moving a storey below me, and somewhat to my left, where I imagined, from the order of the rooms, that the windows of the Count's own room would look out. The window at which I stood was tall and deep, stone-mullioned, and though weatherworn, was still complete; but it was evidently many a day since the case had been there. I drew back behind the stonework, and looked carefully out.

What I saw was the Count's head coming out from the window. I did not see the face, but I knew the man by the neck and the movement of his back and arms. In any case I could not mistake the hands which I had had so many opportunities of studying. I was at first interested and somewhat amused, for it is wonderful how small a matter will interest and amuse a man when he is a prisoner. But my very feelings changed to repulsion and terror when I saw the whole man slowly emerge from the window and begin to crawl down the castle wall over that dreadful abyss, *face down* with his cloak spreading out around him like great wings. At first I could not believe my eyes. I thought it was some trick of the moonlight, some weird effect of shadow; but I kept looking, and it could be no delusion. I saw the fingers and toes grasp the corners of the stones, worn clear of the mortar by the stress of years, and by thus using every projection and inequality move downwards with considerable speed, just as a lizard moves along a wall.

What manner of man is this, or what manner of creature is it in the semblance of man? I feel the dread of this horrible place overpowering me; I am in fear—in awful fear—and there is no escape for me; I am encompassed about with terrors that I dare not think of. . . .

15 May.—Once more have I seen the Count go out in his lizard fashion. He moved downwards in a sidelong way, some hundred feet down, and a good deal to the left. He vanished into some hole or window. When his head had disappeared, I leaned out to try and see more, but without avail—the distance was too great to allow a proper angle of sight. I knew he had left the castle now, and thought to use the opportunity to explore more than I had dared to do as yet. I went back to the room, and taking a lamp, tried all the doors. They were all locked, as I had expected, and the locks were comparatively new; but I went down the stone stairs to the hall where I had entered originally. I found I could pull back the bolts easily enough and unhook the great chains; but the door was locked, and the key was gone! That key must be in the Count's room; I must watch should his door be unlocked, so that I may get it and escape. I went on to make a thorough examination of the various stairs and passages, and to try the doors that opened from them. One or two small rooms near the hall were open, but there was nothing to see in them except old furniture, dusty with age and moth-eaten. At last, however, I found one door at the top of the stairway which, though it seemed to be locked, gave a little under pressure. I tried it harder, and found that it was not really locked, but that the resistance came from the fact that the hinges had fallen somewhat; and the heavy door rested on the floor. Here was an opportunity which I might not have again, so I exerted myself, and with many efforts forced it back so that I could enter. I was now in a wing of the castle further to the right than the rooms I knew and a storey lower down. From the windows I could see that the suite of rooms lay along to the south of the castle, the windows of the end room looking out both west and south. On the latter side, as well as to the former, there was a great precipice. The castle was built on the corner of a great rock, so that on three sides it was quite impregnable, and great windows were placed here where sling, or bow, or culverin could not reach, and consequently light and comfort, impossible to a position which had to be guarded, were secured. To the west was a great valley, and then, rising far away, great jagged mountain fastnesses, rising peak on peak, the sheer rock studded with mountain ash and thorn, whose roots clung in cracks and crevices and crannies of the stone. This was evidently the portion of the castle occupied by the ladies in bygone days, for the furniture had more air of comfort than any I had seen. The windows were curtainless, and the yellow moonlight, flooding in through the diamond panes, enabled one to see even colours; whilst it softened the wealth of dust which lay over all and disguised in some measure the ravages of time and the moth. My lamp seemed to be of little effect in the brilliant moonlight, but I was glad to have it with me, for there was a dread loneliness in the place which chilled my heart and made my nerves tremble. Still, it was better than living alone in the rooms which I had come to hate from the presence of the Count, and after trying a little to school my nerves, I found a soft quietude come over me. Here I am, sitting at a little oak table where in old times possibly some fair lady sat to pen, with much thought and many blushes, her ill-spelt love-letter, and writing in my diary in shorthand all that has happened since I closed it last. It is nineteenth century up-to-date with a vengeance. And yet, unless my senses deceive me, the old centuries had, and have, powers of their own which mere "modernity" cannot kill.

Later: the morning of 16 May.—God preserve my sanity, for to this I am reduced. Safety and the assurance of safety are things of the past. Whilst I live on here there is but one thing to hope for, that I may not go mad, if, indeed, I be not mad already. If I be sane, then surely it is maddening to think that of all the foul things that lurk in this hateful place the Count is the least dreadful to me; that to him alone I can look for safety, even though this be only whilst I can serve his purpose. Great God! merciful God! Let me be calm for out of that way lies madness indeed. I begin to get new lights on certain things which have puzzled me. Up to now I never quite knew what Shakespeare meant when he made Hamlet say:—

"My tablets! quick, my tablets!
'Tis meet that I put it down," etc.,

For now, feeling as though my own brain were unhinged or as if the shock had come which must end in its undoing, I turn to my diary for repose. The habit of entering accurately must help to soothe me.

The Count's mysterious warning frightened me at the time; it frightens me more now when I think of it, for in future he has a fearful hold upon me. I shall fear to doubt what he may say!

When I had written in my diary and had fortunately replaced the book and pen in my pocket I felt sleepy. The Count's warning came into my mind, but I took a pleasure in disobeying it. The sense of sleep was upon me, and with it the obstinacy which sleep brings as outrider. The soft moonlight soothed, and the wide expanse without gave a sense of freedom which refreshed me. I determined not to return to-night to the gloom-haunted rooms, but to sleep here, where, of old, ladies had sat and sung and lived sweet lives whilst their gentle breasts were sad for their menfolk away in the midst of remorseless wars. I drew a great couch out of its place near the corner, so that as I lay, I could look at the lovely view to east and south, and unthinking of and uncaring for the dust, composed myself for sleep. I suppose I must have fallen asleep; I hope so, but I fear, for all that followed was startlingly real—so real that now sitting here in the broad, full sunlight of the morning, I cannot in the least believe that it was all sleep.

I was not alone. The room was the same, unchanged in any way since I came into it; I could see along the floor, in the brilliant moonlight, my own footsteps marked where I had disturbed the long accumulation of dust. In the moonlight opposite me were three young women, ladies by their dress and manner. I thought at the time that I must be dreaming when I saw them, for, though the moonlight was behind them, they threw no shadow on the floor. They came close to me, and looked at me for some time, and then whispered together. Two were dark, and had high aquiline noses, like the Count, and great dark, piercing eyes, that seemed to be almost red when contrasted with the pale yellow moon. The other was fair, as fair as can be, with great wavy masses of golden hair and eyes like pale sapphires. I seemed somehow to know her face, and to know it in connection with some dreamy fear, but I could not recollect at the moment how or where. All three had brilliant white teeth that shone like pearls against the ruby of their voluptuous lips. There was something about them that made me uneasy, some longing and at the same time some deadly fear. I felt in my heart a wicked, burning desire that they would kiss me with those red lips. It is not good to note this down; lest some day it should meet Mina's eyes and cause her pain; but it is the truth. They whispered together, and then they all three laughed—such a silvery, musical laugh, but as hard as though the sound never could have come through the softness of human lips. It was like the intolerable, tingling sweetness of water-glasses when played on by a cunning hand. The fair girl shook her head coquettishly, and the other two urged her on. One said:—

"Go on! You are first, and we shall follow; yours is the right to begin." The other added:—

"He is young and strong; there are kisses for us all." I lay quiet, looking out under my eyelashes in an agony of delightful anticipation. The fair girl advanced and bent over me till I could feel the movement of her breath upon me. Sweet it was in one sense, honey-sweet, and sent the same tingling through the nerves as her voice, but with a bitter underlying the sweet, a bitter offensiveness, as one smells in blood.

I was afraid to raise my eyelids, but looked out and saw perfectly under the lashes. The girl went on her knees, and bent over me, simply gloating. There was a deliberate voluptuousness which was both thrilling and repulsive, and as she arched her neck she actually licked her lips like an animal, till I could see in the moonlight the moisture shining on the scarlet lips and on the red tongue as it lapped the white sharp teeth. Lower and lower went her head as the lips went below the range of my mouth and chin and seemed about to fasten on my throat. Then she paused, and I could hear the churning sound of her tongue as it licked her teeth and lips, and could feel the hot breath on my neck. Then the skin of my throat began to tingle as one's flesh does when the hand that is to tickle it approaches nearer—nearer. I could feel the soft, shivering touch of the lips on the super-sensitive skin of my throat, and the hard dents of two sharp teeth, just touching and pausing there. I closed my eyes in a languorous ecstasy and waited—waited with beating heart.

But at that instant, another sensation swept through me as quick as lightning. I was conscious of the presence of the Count, and of his being as if lapped in a storm of fury. As my eyes opened involuntarily I saw his strong hand grasp the slender neck of the fair woman and with giant's power draw it back, the blue eyes transformed with fury, the white teeth champing with rage, and the fair cheeks blazing with passion. But the Count! Never did I imagine such wrath and fury, even to the demons of the pit. His eyes were positively blazing. The red light in them was lurid, as if the flames of hell-fire blazed behind them. His face was deathly pale, and the lines of it were hard like drawn wires; the thick eyebrows that met over the nose now seemed like a heaving bar of white-hot metal. With a fierce sweep of his arm, he hurled the woman from him, and then motioned to the others, as though he were beating them back; it was the same imperious gesture that I had seen used to the wolves. In a voice which, though low and almost in a whisper, seemed to cut through the air and then ring round the room he said:—

"How dare you touch him, any of you? How dare you cast eyes on him when I had forbidden it? Back, I tell you all! This man belongs to me! Beware how you meddle with him, or you'll have to deal with me."

The fair girl, with a laugh of ribald coquetry, turned to answer him:—

"You yourself never loved; you never love!" On this the other women joined, and such a mirthless, hard, soulless laughter rang through the room that it almost made me faint to hear; it seemed like the pleasure of fiends. Then the Count turned, after looking at my face attentively, and said in a soft whisper:—

"Yes, I too can love; you yourselves can tell it from the past. Is it not so? Well, now I promise you that when I am done with him you shall kiss him at your will. Now go! go! I must awaken him, for there is work to be done."

"Are we to have nothing to-night?" said one of them, with a low laugh, as she pointed to the bag which he had thrown upon the floor, and which moved as though there were some living thing within it. For answer he nodded his head. One of the women jumped forward and opened it. If my ears did not deceive me there was a gasp and a low wail, as of a half-smothered child. The women closed round, whilst I was aghast with horror; but as I looked they disappeared, and with them the dreadful bag. There was no door near them, and they could not have passed me without my noticing. They simply seemed to fade into the rays of the moonlight and pass out through the window, for I could see outside the dim, shadowy forms for a moment before they entirely faded away.

Then the horror overcame me, and I sank down unconscious.

CHAPTER 4.

— ◇ —

JONATHAN HARKER'S JOURNAL—*continued.*

I awoke in my own bed. If it be that I had not dreamt, the Count must have carried me here. I tried to satisfy myself on the subject, but could not arrive at any unquestionable result. To be sure, there were certain small evidences, such as that my clothes were folded and laid by in a manner which was not my habit. My watch was still unwound, and I am rigorously accustomed to wind it the last thing before going to bed, and many such details. But these things are no proof, for they may have been evidences that my mind was not as usual, and, from some cause or another, I had certainly been much upset. I must watch for proof. Of one thing I am glad: if it was that the Count carried me here and undressed me, he must have been hurried in his task, for my pockets are intact. I am sure this diary would have been a mystery to him which he would not have brooked. He would have taken or destroyed it. As I look round this room, although it has been to me so full of fear, it is now a sort of sanctuary; for nothing can be more dreadful than those awful women, who were—who *are*—waiting to suck my blood.

18 May.—I have been down to look at that room again in daylight, for I *must* know the truth. When I got to the doorway at the top of the stairs I found it closed. It had been so forcibly driven against the jamb that part of the woodwork was splintered. I could see that the bolt of the lock had not been shot, but the door is fastened from the inside. I fear it was no dream, and must act on this surmise.

19 May.—I am surely in the toils. Last night the Count asked me in the suavest tones to write three letters, one saying that my work here was nearly done, and that I should start for home within a few days, another that I was starting on the next morning from the time of the letter, and the third that I had left the castle and arrived at Bistritz. I would fain have rebelled, but felt that in the present state of things it would be madness to quarrel openly with the Count whilst I am so absolutely in his power; and to refuse would be to excite his suspicion and to arouse his anger. He knows that I know too much, and that I must not live, lest I be dangerous to him; my only chance is to prolong my opportunities. Something may occur which will give me a chance to escape. I saw in his eyes something of that gathering wrath which was manifest when he hurled that fair woman from him. He explained to me that posts were few and uncertain, and that my writing now would ensure ease of mind to my friends; and he assured me with so much impressiveness that he would countermand the later letters, which would be held over at Bistritz until due time in case chance would admit of my prolonging my stay, that to oppose him would have been to create new suspicion. I therefore pretended to fall in with his views, and asked him what dates I should put on the letters. He calculated a minute, and then said:—

"The first should be June 12, the second June 19, and the third June 29."

I know now the span of my life. God help me!

28 May.—There is a chance of escape, or at any rate of being able to send word home. A band of Szgany have come to the castle, and are encamped in the courtyard. These Szgany are gypsies; I have notes of them in my book. They are peculiar to this part of the world, though allied to the ordinary gypsies all the world over. There are thousands of them in Hungary and Transylvania, who are almost outside all law. They attach themselves as a rule to some great noble or *boyar*, and call themselves by his name. They are fearless and without religion, save superstition, and they talk only their own varieties of the Romany tongue.

I shall write some letters home, and shall try to get them to have them posted. I have already spoken to them through my window to begin acquaintanceship. They took their hats off and made obeisance and many signs, which, however, I could not understand any more than I could their spoken language. . . .

I have written the letters. Mina's is in shorthand, and I simply ask Mr. Hawkins to communicate with her. To her I have explained my situation, but without the horrors which I may only surmise. It would shock and frighten her to death were I to expose my heart to her. Should the letters not carry, then the Count shall not yet know my secret or the extent of my knowledge. . . .

I have given the letters; I threw them through the bars of my window with a gold piece, and made what signs I could to have them posted. The man who took them pressed them to his heart and bowed, and then put them in his cap. I could do no more. I stole back to the study, and began to read. As the Count did not come in, I have written here. . . .

The Count has come. He sat down beside me, and said in his smoothest voice as he opened two letters:—

"The Szgany has given me these, of which, though I know not whence they come, I shall, of course, take care. See!"—he must have looked at it—"one is from you, and to my friend Peter Hawkins; the other"—here he caught sight of the strange symbols as he opened the envelope, and the dark look came into his face, and his eyes blazed wickedly—"the other is a vile thing, an outrage upon friendship and hospitality! It is not signed. Well! so it cannot matter to us." And he calmly held letter and envelope in the flame of the lamp till they were consumed. Then he went on:—

"The letter to Hawkins—that I shall, of course, send on, since it is yours. Your letters are sacred to me. Your pardon, my friend, that unknowingly I did break the seal. Will you not cover it again?" He held out the letter to me, and with a courteous bow handed me a clean envelope. I could only redirect it and hand it to him in silence. When he went out of the room I could hear the key turn softly. A minute later I went over and tried it, and the door was locked.

When, an hour or two after, the Count came quietly into the room, his coming awakened me, for I had gone to sleep on the sofa. He was very courteous and very cheery in his manner, and seeing that I had been sleeping, he said:—

"So, my friend, you are tired? Get to bed. There is the surest rest. I may not have the pleasure to talk to-night, since there are many labours to me; but you will sleep, I pray." I passed to my room and went to bed, and, strange to say, slept without dreaming. Despair has its own calms.

31 May.—This morning when I woke I thought I would provide myself with some paper and envelopes from my bag and keep them in my pocket, so that I might write in case I should get an opportunity, but again a surprise, again a shock!

Every scrap of paper was gone, and with it all my notes, my memoranda, relating to railways and travel, my letter of credit, in fact all that might be useful to me were I once outside the castle. I sat and pondered awhile, and then some thought occurred to me, and I made search of my portmanteau and in the wardrobe where I had placed my clothes.

The suit in which I had travelled was gone, and also my overcoat and rug; I could find no trace of them anywhere. This looked like some new scheme of villainy. . . .

17 June.—This morning, as I was sitting on the edge of my bed cudgelling my brains, I heard without a cracking of whips and pounding and scraping of horses' feet up the rocky path beyond the courtyard. With joy I hurried to the window, and saw drive into the yard two great leiter-wagons, each drawn by eight sturdy horses, and at the head of each pair a Slovak, with his wide hat, great nail-studded belt, dirty sheepskin, and high boots. They had also their long staves in hand. I ran to the door, intending to descend and try and join them through the main hall, as I thought that way might be opened for them. Again a shock: my door was fastened on the outside.

Then I ran to the window and cried to them. They looked up at me stupidly and pointed, but just then the "hetman" of the Szgany came out, and seeing them pointing to my window, said something, at which they laughed. Henceforth no effort of mine, no piteous cry or agonised entreaty, would make them even look at me. They resolutely turned away. The leiter-wagons contained great, square boxes, with handles of thick rope; these were evidently empty by the ease with which the Slovaks handled them, and by their resonance as they were roughly moved. When they were all unloaded and packed in a great heap in one corner of the yard, the Slovaks were given some money by the Szgany, and spitting on it for luck, lazily went each to his horse's head. Shortly afterwards, I heard the cracking of their whips die away in the distance.

24 June, before morning.—Last night the Count left me early, and locked himself into his own room. As soon as I dared I ran up the winding stair, and looked out of the window, which opened south. I thought I would watch for the Count, for there is something going on. The Szgany are quartered somewhere in the castle and are doing work of some kind. I know it, for now and then I hear a faraway muffled sound as of mattock and spade, and, whatever it is, it must be the end of some ruthless villainy.

I had been at the window somewhat less than half an hour, when I saw something coming out of the Count's window. I drew back and watched carefully, and saw the whole man emerge. It was a new shock to me to find that he had on the suit of clothes which I had worn whilst travelling here, and slung over his shoulder the terrible bag which I had seen the women take away. There could be no doubt as to his quest, and in my garb, too! This, then, is his new scheme of evil: that he will allow others to see me, as they think, so that he may both leave evidence that

I have been seen in the towns or villages posting my own letters, and that any wickedness which he may do shall by the local people be attributed to me.

It makes me rage to think that this can go on, and whilst I am shut up here, a veritable prisoner, but without that protection of the law which is even a criminal's right and consolation.

I thought I would watch for the Count's return, and for a long time sat doggedly at the window. Then I began to notice that there were some quaint little specks floating in the rays of the moonlight. They were like the tiniest grains of dust, and they whirled round and gathered in clusters in a nebulous sort of way. I watched them with a sense of soothing, and a sort of calm stole over me. I leaned back in the embrasure in a more comfortable position, so that I could enjoy more fully the äerial gamboling.

Something made me start up, a low, piteous howling of dogs somewhere far below in the valley, which was hidden from my sight. Louder it seemed to ring in my ears, and the floating motes of dust to take new shapes to the sound as they danced in the moonlight. I felt myself struggling to awake to some call of my instincts; nay, my very soul was struggling, and my half-remembered sensibilities were striving to answer the call. I was becoming hypnotised! Quicker and quicker danced the dust; the moonbeams seemed to quiver as they went by me into the mass of gloom beyond. More and more they gathered till they seemed to take dim phantom shapes. And then I started, broad awake and in full possession of my senses, and ran screaming from the place. The phantom shapes, which were becoming gradually materialised from the moonbeams, were those of the three ghostly women to whom I was doomed. I fled, and felt somewhat safer in my own room, where there was no moonlight and where the lamp was burning brightly.

When a couple of hours had passed I heard something stirring in the Count's room, something like a sharp wail quickly suppressed; and then there was silence, deep, awful silence, which chilled me. With a beating heart, I tried the door; but I was locked in my prison, and could do nothing. I sat down and simply cried.

As I sat I heard a sound in the courtyard without—the agonised cry of a woman. I rushed to the window, and throwing it up, peered out between the bars. There, indeed, was a woman with dishevelled hair, holding her hands over her heart as one distressed with running. She was leaning against a corner of the gateway. When she saw my face at the window she threw herself forward, and shouted in a voice laden with menace:—

"Monster, give me my child!"

She threw herself on her knees, and raising up her hands, cried the same words in tones which wrung my heart. Then she tore her hair and beat her breast, and abandoned herself to all the violences of extravagant emotion. Finally, she threw herself forward, and, though I could not see her, I could hear the beating of her naked hands against the door.

Somewhere high overhead, probably on the tower, I heard the voice of the Count calling in his harsh, metallic whisper. His call seemed to be answered from far and wide by the howling of wolves. Before many minutes had passed a pack of them poured, like a pent-up dam when liberated, through the wide entrance into the courtyard.

There was no cry from the woman, and the howling of the wolves was but short. Before long they streamed away singly, licking their lips.

I could not pity her, for I knew now what had become of her child, and she was better dead.

What shall I do? What can I do? How can I escape from this dreadful thing of night and gloom and fear?

25 June, morning.—No man knows till he has suffered from the night how sweet and how dear to his heart and eye the morning can be. When the sun grew so high this morning that it struck the top of the great gateway opposite my window, the high spot which it touched seemed to me as if the dove from the ark had lighted there. My fear fell from me as if it had been a vaporous garment which dissolved in the warmth. I must take action of some sort whilst the courage of the day is upon me. Last night one of my post-dated letters went to post, the first of that fatal series which is to blot out the very traces of my existence from the earth.

Let me not think of it. Action!

It has always been at night-time that I have been molested or threatened, or in some way in danger or in fear. I have not yet seen the Count in the daylight. Can it be that he sleeps when others wake, that he may be awake whilst they sleep? If I could only get into his room! But there is no possible way. The door is always locked, no way for me.

Yes, there is a way, if one dares to take it. Where his body has gone why may not another body go? I have seen him myself crawl from his window. Why should not I imitate him, and go in by his window? The chances are desperate, but my need is more desperate still. I shall risk it. At the worst it can only be death; and a man's death is not a calf's, and the dreaded Hereafter may still be open to me. God help me in my task! Good-bye, Mina, if I fail; good-bye, my faithful friend and second father; good-bye, all, and last of all Mina!

Same day, later.—I have made the effort, and, God helping me, have come safely back to this room. I must put down every detail in order. I went whilst my courage was fresh straight to the window on the south side, and at once got outside on the narrow ledge of stone which runs around the building on this side. The stones are big and roughly cut, and the mortar has by process of time been washed away between them. I took off my boots, and ventured out on the desperate way. I looked down once, so as to make sure that a sudden glimpse of the awful depth would not overcome me, but after that kept my eyes away from it. I knew pretty well the direction and distance of the Count's window, and made for it as well as I could, having regard to the opportunities available. I did not feel dizzy—I suppose I was too excited—and the time seemed ridiculously short till I found myself standing on the window-sill and trying to raise up the sash. I was filled with agitation, however, when I bent down and slid feet foremost in through the window. Then I looked around for the Count, but, with surprise and gladness, made a discovery. The room was empty! It was barely furnished with odd things, which seemed to have never been used; the furniture was something the same style as that in the south rooms, and was covered with dust. I looked for the key, but it was not in the lock, and I could not find it anywhere. The only thing I found was a great heap of gold in one corner—gold of all kinds, Roman, and British, and Austrian, and Hungarian, and Greek and Turkish money, covered with a film of dust, as though it had lain long in the ground. None of it that I noticed was less than three hundred years old. There were also chains and ornaments, some jewelled, but all of them old and stained.

At one corner of the room was a heavy door. I tried it, for, since I could not find the key of the room or the key of the outer door, which was the main object of my search, I must make further examination, or all my efforts would be in vain. It was open, and led through a stone passage to a circular stairway, which went steeply down. I descended, minding carefully where I went, for the stairs were dark, being only lit by loopholes in the heavy masonry. At the bottom there was a dark, tunnel-like passage, through which came a deathly, sickly odour, the odour of old earth newly turned. As I went through the passage the smell grew closer and heavier. At last I pulled open a heavy door which stood ajar, and found myself in an old, ruined chapel, which had evidently been used as a graveyard. The roof was broken, and in two places were steps leading to vaults, but the ground had recently been dug over, and the earth placed in great wooden boxes, manifestly those which had been brought by the Slovaks. There was nobody about, and I made search for any further outlet, but there was none. Then I went over every inch of the ground, so as not to lose a chance. I went down even into the vaults, where the dim light struggled, although to do so was a dread to my very soul. Into two of these I went, but saw nothing except fragments of old coffins and piles of dust; in the third, however, I made a discovery.

There, in one of the great boxes, of which there were fifty in all, on a pile of newly dug earth, lay the Count! He was either dead or asleep, I could not say which—for the eyes were open and stony, but without the glassiness of death—and the cheeks had the warmth of life through all their pallor; the lips were as red as ever. But there was no sign of movement, no pulse, no breath, no beating of the heart. I bent over him, and tried to find any sign of life, but in vain. He could not have lain there long, for the earthy smell would have passed away in a few hours. By the side of the box was its cover, pierced with holes here and there. I thought he might have the keys on him, but when I went to search I saw the dead eyes, and in them, dead though they were, such a look of hate though unconscious of me or my presence, that I fled from the place, and leaving the Count's room by the window, crawled again up the castle wall. Regaining my room, I threw myself panting upon the bed and tried to think. . . .

29 June.—To-day is the date of my last letter, and the Count has taken steps to prove that it was genuine, for again I saw him leave the castle by the same window, and in my clothes. As he went down the wall, lizard fashion, I wished I had a gun or some lethal weapon, that I might destroy him; but I fear that no weapon wrought alone by man's hand would have any effect on him. I dared not wait to see him return, for I feared to see those weird sisters. I came back to the library, and read there till I fell asleep.

I was awakened by the Count, who looked at me as grimly as a man can look as he said:—

"To-morrow, my friend, we must part. You return to your beautiful England, I to some work which may have such an end that we may never meet. Your letter home has been despatched; to-morrow I shall not be here, but all shall be ready for your journey. In the morning come the Szgany, who have some labours of their own here, and also come some Slovaks. When they have gone, my carriage shall come for you, and shall bear you to the Borgo Pass to meet the diligence from Bukovina to Bistritz. But I am in hopes that I shall see more of you at Castle Dracula." I suspected him, and determined to test his sincerity. Sincerity! It seems like a profanation of the word to write it in connection with such a monster, so asked him point-blank:—

"Why may I not go to-night?"

"Because, dear sir, my coachman and horses are away on a mission."

"But I would walk with pleasure. I want to get away at once." He smiled, such a soft, smooth, diabolical smile that I knew there was some trick behind his smoothness. He said:—

"And your baggage?"

"I do not care about it. I can send for it some other time."

The Count stood up, and said, with a sweet courtesy which made me rub my eyes, it seemed so real:—

"You English have a saying which is close to my heart, for its spirit is that which rules our *boyars*: 'Welcome the coming; speed the parting guest.' Come with me, my dear young friend. Not an hour shall you wait in my house against your will, though sad am I at your going, and that you so suddenly desire it. Come!" With a stately gravity, he, with the lamp, preceded me down the stairs and along the hall. Suddenly he stopped.

"Hark!"

Close at hand came the howling of many wolves. It was almost as if the sound sprang up at the rising of his hand, just as the music of a great orchestra seems to leap under the bâton of the conductor. After a pause of a moment, he proceeded, in his stately way, to the door, drew back the ponderous bolts, unhooked the heavy chains, and began to draw it open.

To my intense astonishment I saw that it was unlocked. Suspiciously, I looked all round, but could see no key of any kind.

As the door began to open, the howling of the wolves without grew louder and angrier; their red jaws, with champing teeth, and their blunt-clawed feet as they leaped, came in through the opening door. I knew then that to struggle at the moment against the Count was useless. With such allies as these at his command, I could do nothing. But still the door continued slowly to open, and only the Count's body stood in the gap. Suddenly it struck me that this might be the moment and means of my doom; I was to be given to the wolves, and at my own instigation. There was a diabolical wickedness in the idea great enough for the Count, and as a last chance I cried out:—

"Shut the door; I shall wait till morning!" and covered my face with my hands to hide my tears of bitter disappointment. With one sweep of his powerful arm, the Count threw the door shut, and the great bolts clanged and echoed through the hall as they shot back into their places.

In silence we returned to the library, and after a minute or two I went to my own room. The last I saw of Count Dracula was his kissing his hand to me; with a red light of triumph in his eyes, and with a smile that Judas in hell might be proud of.

When I was in my room and about to lie down, I thought I heard a whispering at my door. I went to it softly and listened. Unless my ears deceived me, I heard the voice of the Count:—

"Back, back, to your own place! Your time is not yet come. Wait! Have patience! To-night is mine. To-morrow night is yours!" There was a low, sweet ripple of laughter, and in a rage I threw open the door, and saw without the three terrible women licking their lips. As I appeared they all joined in a horrible laugh, and ran away.

I came back to my room and threw myself on my knees. It is then so near the end? To-morrow! to-morrow! Lord, help me, and those to whom I am dear!

30 June, morning.—These may be the last words I ever write in this diary. I slept till just before the dawn, and when I woke threw myself on my knees, for I determined that if Death came he should find me ready.

At last I felt that subtle change in the air, and knew that the morning had come. Then came the welcome cockcrow, and I felt that I was safe. With a glad heart, I opened my door and ran down to the hall. I had seen that the door was unlocked, and now escape was before me. With hands that trembled with eagerness, I unhooked the chains and drew back the massive bolts.

But the door would not move. Despair seized me. I pulled, and pulled, at the door, and shook it till, massive as it was, it rattled in its casement. I could see the bolt shot. It had been locked after I left the Count.

Then a wild desire took me to obtain that key at any risk, and I determined then and there to scale the wall again and gain the Count's room. He might kill me, but death now seemed the happier choice of evils. Without a pause I rushed up to the east window, and scrambled down the wall, as before, into the Count's room. It was empty, but that was as I expected. I could not see a key anywhere, but the heap of gold remained. I went through the door in the corner and down the winding stair and along the dark passage to the old chapel. I knew now well enough where to find the monster I sought.

The great box was in the same place, close against the wall, but the lid was laid on it, not fastened down, but with the nails ready in their places to be hammered home. I knew I must reach the body for the key, so I raised the lid, and laid it back against the wall; and then I saw something which filled my very soul with horror. There lay the Count, but looking as if his youth had been half renewed, for the white hair and moustache were changed to dark iron-grey; the cheeks were fuller, and the white skin seemed ruby-red underneath; the mouth was redder than ever, for on the lips were gouts of fresh blood, which trickled from the corners of the mouth and ran over the chin and neck. Even the deep, burning eyes seemed set amongst swollen flesh, for the lids and pouches underneath were bloated. It seemed as if the whole awful creature were simply gorged with blood. He lay like a filthy leech, exhausted with his repletion. I shuddered as I bent over to touch him, and every sense in me revolted at the contact; but I had to search, or I was lost. The coming night might see my own body a banquet in a similar way to those horrid three. I felt all over the body, but no sign could I find of the key. Then I stopped and looked at the Count. There was a mocking smile on the bloated face which seemed to drive me mad. This was the being I was helping to transfer to London, where, perhaps, for centuries to come he might, amongst its teeming millions, satiate his lust for blood, and create a new and ever-widening circle of semi-demons to batten on the helpless. The very thought drove me mad. A terrible desire came upon me to rid the world of such a monster. There was no lethal weapon at hand, but I seized a shovel which the workmen had been using to fill the cases, and lifting it high, struck, with the edge downward, at the hateful face. But as I did so the head turned, and the eyes fell full upon me, with all their blaze of basilisk horror. The sight seemed to paralyse me, and the shovel turned in my hand and glanced from the face, merely making a deep gash above the forehead. The shovel fell from my hand across the box, and as I pulled it away the flange of the blade caught the edge of the lid which fell over again, and hid the horrid thing from my sight. The last glimpse I had was of the bloated face, bloodstained and fixed with a grin of malice which would have held its own in the nethermost hell.

I thought and thought what should be my next move, but my brain seemed on fire, and I waited with a despairing feeling growing over me. As I waited I heard in the distance a gypsy song sung by merry voices coming closer, and through their song the rolling of heavy wheels and the cracking of whips: the Szgany and the Slovaks of whom the Count had spoken were coming. With a last look around and at the box which contained the vile body, I ran from the place and gained the Count's room, determined to rush out at the moment the door should be opened. With strained ears, I listened, and heard downstairs the grinding of the key in the great lock and the falling back of the heavy door. There must have been some other means of entry, or some one had a key for one of the locked doors. Then there came the sound of many feet tramping and dying away in some passage which sent up a clanging echo. I turned to run down again towards the vault, where I might find the new entrance; but at the moment there seemed to come a violent puff of wind, and the door to the winding stair blew to with a shock that set the dust from the lintels flying. When I ran to push it open, I found that it was hopelessly fast. I was again a prisoner, and the net of doom was closing round me more closely.

As I write there is in the passage below a sound of many tramping feet and the crash of weights being set down heavily, doubtless the boxes, with their freight of earth. There is a sound of hammering; it is the box being nailed down. Now I can hear the heavy feet tramping again along the hall, with many other idle feet coming behind them.

The door is shut, and the chains rattle; there is a grinding of the key in the lock; I can hear the key withdrawn: then another door opens and shuts; I hear the creaking of lock and bolt.

Hark! in the courtyard and down the rocky way the roll of heavy wheels, the crack of whips, and the chorus of the Szgany as they pass into the distance.

I am alone in the castle with those awful women. Faugh! Mina is a woman, and there is nought in common. They are devils of the Pit!

I shall not remain alone with them; I shall try to scale the castle wall farther than I have yet attempted. I shall take some of the gold with me, lest I want it later. I may find a way from this dreadful place.

And then away for home! away to the quickest and nearest train! away from this cursed spot, from this cursed land, where the devil and his children still walk with earthly feet!

At least God's mercy is better than that of these monsters, and the precipice is steep and high. At its foot a man may sleep—as a man. Good-bye, all! Mina!

CHAPTER 5.

—◆—

LETTER FROM MISS MINA MURRAY
TO MISS LUCY WESTENRA.

"*9 May.*

"My dearest Lucy,—

"Forgive my long delay in writing, but I have been simply overwhelmed with work. The life of an assistant schoolmistress is sometimes trying. I am longing to be with you, and by the sea, where we can talk together freely and build our castles in the air. I have been working very hard lately, because I want to keep up with Jonathan's studies, and I have been practising shorthand very assiduously. When we are married I shall be able to be useful to Jonathan, and if I can stenograph well enough I can take down what he wants to say in this way and write it out for him on the typewriter, at which also I am practising very hard. He and I sometimes write letters in shorthand, and he is keeping a stenographic journal of his travels abroad. When I am with you I shall keep a diary in the same way. I don't mean one of those two-pages-to-the-week-with-Sunday-squeezed-in-a-corner diaries, but a sort of journal which I can write in whenever I feel inclined. I do not suppose there will be much of interest to other people; but it is not intended for them. I may show it to Jonathan some day if there is in it anything worth sharing, but it is really an exercise book. I shall try to do what I see lady journalists do: interviewing and writing descriptions and trying to remember conversations. I am told that, with a little practice, one can remember all that goes on or that one hears said during a day. However, we shall see. I will tell you of my little plans when we meet. I have just had a few hurried lines from Jonathan from Transylvania. He is well, and will be returning in about a week. I am longing to hear all his news. It must be so nice to see strange countries. I wonder if we—I mean Jonathan and I—shall ever see them together. There is the ten o'clock bell ringing. Good-bye.

"Your loving

"MINA.

"Tell me all the news when you write. You have not told me anything for a long time. I hear rumours, and especially of a tall, handsome, curly-haired man???"

LETTER, LUCY WESTENRA
TO MINA MURRAY.

"*17, Chatham Street,*
"*Wednesday.*

"My dearest Mina,—

"I must say you tax me *very* unfairly with being a bad correspondent. I wrote to you *twice* since we parted, and your last letter was only your *second.* Besides, I have nothing to tell you. There is really nothing to interest you. Town is very pleasant just now, and we go a good deal to picture-galleries and for walks and rides in the park. As to the tall, curly-haired man, I suppose it was the one who was with me at the last Pop. Some one has evidently been telling tales. That was Mr. Holmwood. He often comes to see us, and he and mamma get on very well together; they have so many things to talk about in common. We met some time ago a man that would just *do for you*, if you were not already engaged to Jonathan. He is an excellent *parti*, being handsome, well off, and of good birth. He is a doctor and really clever. Just fancy! He is only nine-and-twenty, and he has an immense lunatic asylum all under his own care. Mr. Holmwood introduced him to me, and he called here to see us, and often comes now. I think he is one of the most resolute men I ever saw, and yet the most calm. He seems absolutely imperturbable. I can fancy what a wonderful power he must have over his patients. He has a curious habit of looking one straight in the face, as if trying to read one's thoughts. He tries this on very much with me, but I flatter myself he has got a tough nut to crack. I know that from my glass. Do you ever try to read your own face? *I do,* and I can tell you it is not a bad study, and gives you more trouble than you can well fancy if you have never tried it. He says that I afford him a curious psychological study, and I humbly think I do. I do not, as you know, take sufficient interest in dress to be able to describe the new fashions. Dress is a bore. That is slang again, but never mind; Arthur says that every day. There, it is all out. Mina, we have told all our secrets to each other since we were *children*; we have slept together and eaten together, and laughed and cried together; and now, though I have spoken, I would like to speak more. Oh, Mina, couldn't you guess? I love him. I am blushing as I write, for although I *think* he loves me, he has not told me so in words. But oh, Mina, I love him; I love him; I love him! There, that does me good. I wish I were with you, dear, sitting by the fire undressing, as we used to sit; and I would try to tell you what I feel. I do not know how I am writing this even to you. I am afraid to stop, or I should tear up the letter, and I don't want to stop, for I *do* so want to tell you all. Let me hear from you *at once*, and tell me all that you think about it. Mina, I must stop. Good-night. Bless me in your prayers; and, Mina, pray for my happiness.

"LUCY.

"P.S.—I need not tell you this is a secret. Good-night again.

"L."

LETTER FROM LUCY WESTENRA TO MINA MURRAY.

"*24 May.*

"My dearest Mina,—

"Thanks, and thanks, and thanks again for your sweet letter. It was so nice to be able to tell you and to have your sympathy.

"My dear, it never rains but it pours. How true the old proverbs are. Here am I, who shall be twenty in September, and yet I never had a proposal till to-day, not a real proposal, and to-day I have had three. Just fancy! THREE proposals in one day! Isn't it awful! I feel sorry, really and truly sorry, for two of the poor fellows. Oh, Mina, I am so happy that I don't know what to do with myself. And three proposals! But, for goodness' sake, don't tell any of the girls, or they would be getting all sorts of extravagant ideas and imagining themselves injured and slighted if in their very first day at home they did not get six at least. Some girls are so vain! You and I, Mina dear, who are engaged and are going to settle down soon soberly into old married women, can despise vanity. Well, I must tell you about the three, but you must keep it a secret, dear, from *every one*, except, of course, Jonathan. You will tell him, because I would, if I were in your place, certainly tell Arthur. A woman ought to tell her husband everything—don't you think so, dear?—and I must be fair. Men like women, certainly their wives, to be quite as fair as they are; and women, I am afraid, are not always quite as fair as they should be. Well, my dear, Number One came just before lunch. I told you of him, Dr. John Seward, the lunatic-asylum man, with the strong jaw and the good forehead. He was very cool outwardly, but was nervous all the same. He had evidently been schooling himself as to all sorts of little things, and remembered them; but he almost managed to sit down on his silk hat, which men don't generally do when they are cool, and then when he wanted to appear at ease he kept playing with a lancet in a way that made me nearly scream. He spoke to me, Mina, very straightfor-wardly. He told me how dear I was to him, though he had known me so little, and what his life would be with me to help and cheer him. He was going to tell me how unhappy he would be if I did not care for him, but when he saw me cry he said that he was a brute and would not add to my present trouble. Then he broke off and asked if I could love him in time; and when I shook my head his hands trembled, and then with some hesitation he asked me if I cared already for any one else. He put it very nicely, saying that he did not want to wring my confidence from me, but only to know, because if a woman's heart was free a man might have hope. And then, Mina, I felt a sort of duty to tell him that there was some one. I only told him that much, and then he stood up, and he looked very strong and very grave as he took both my hands in his and said he hoped I would be happy, and that if I ever wanted a friend I must count him one of my best. Oh, Mina dear, I can't help crying: and you must excuse this letter being all blotted. Being proposed to is all very nice and all that sort of thing, but it isn't at all a happy thing when you have to see a poor fellow, whom you know loves you honestly, going away and looking all broken-hearted, and to know that, no matter what he may say at the moment, you are passing quite out of his life. My dear, I must stop here at present, I feel so miserable, though I am so happy.

"*Evening.*

"Arthur has just gone, and I feel in better spirits than when I left off, so I can go on telling you about the day. Well, my dear, number Two came after lunch. He is such a nice fellow, an American from Texas, and he looks so young and so fresh that it seems almost impossible that he has been to so many places and has had such adventures. I sympathise with poor Desdemona when she had such a dangerous stream poured in her ear, even by a black man. I suppose that we women are such cowards that we think a man will save us from fears, and we marry him. I know now what I would do if I were a man and wanted to make a girl love me. No, I don't, for there was Mr. Morris telling us his stories, and Arthur never told any, and yet—— My dear, I am somewhat previous. Mr. Quincey P. Morris found me alone. It seems that a man always does find a girl alone. No, he doesn't, for Arthur tried twice to *make* a chance, and I helping him all I could; I am not ashamed to say it now. I must tell you beforehand that Mr. Morris doesn't always speak slang—that is to say, he never does so to strangers or before them, for he is really well educated and has exquisite manners—but he found out that it amused me to hear him talk American slang, and whenever I was present, and there was no one to be shocked, he said such funny things. I am afraid, my dear, he has to invent it all, for it fits exactly into whatever else he has to say. But this is a way slang has. I do not know myself if I shall ever speak slang; I do not know if Arthur likes it, as I have never heard him use any as yet. Well, Mr. Morris sat down beside me and looked as happy and jolly as he could, but I could see all the same that he was very nervous. He took my hand in his, and said ever so sweetly:—

"'Miss Lucy, I know I ain't good enough to regulate the fixin's of your little shoes, but I guess if you wait till you find a man that is you will go join them seven young women with the lamps when you quit. Won't you just hitch up alongside of me and let us go down the long road together, driving in double harness?'

"Well, he did look so good-humoured and so jolly that it didn't seem half so hard to refuse him as it did poor Dr. Seward; so I said, as lightly as I could, that I did not know anything of hitching, and that I wasn't broken to harness at all yet. Then he said that he had spoken in a light manner, and he hoped that if he had made a mistake in doing so on so grave, so momentous, an occasion for him, I would forgive him. He really did look serious when he was saying it, and I couldn't help feeling a bit serious too—I know, Mina, you will think me a horrid flirt—though I couldn't help feeling a sort of exultation that he was number two in one day. And then, my dear, before I could say a word he began pouring out a perfect torrent of love-making, laying his very heart and soul at my feet. He looked so earnest over it that I shall never again think that a man must be playful always, and never earnest, because he is merry at times. I suppose he saw something in my face which checked him, for he suddenly stopped, and said with a sort of manly fervour that I could have loved him for if I had been free:—

"'Lucy, you are an honest-hearted girl, I know. I should not be here speaking to you as I am now if I did not believe you clean grit, right through to the very depths of your soul. Tell me, like one good fellow to another, is there any one else that you care for? And if there is I'll never trouble you a hair's breadth again, but will be, if you will let me, a very faithful friend.'

"My dear Mina, why are men so noble when we women are so little worthy of them? Here was I almost making fun of this great-hearted, true gentleman. I burst into tears—I am afraid, my dear, you will think this a very sloppy letter in more ways than one—and I really felt very badly. Why can't they let a girl marry three men, or as many as want her, and save all this trouble? But this is heresy, and I must not say it. I am glad to say that, though I was crying, I was able to look into Mr. Morris's brave eyes, and told him out straight:—

"'Yes, there is some one I love, though he has not told me yet that he even loves me.' I was right to speak to him so frankly, for quite a light came into his face, and he put out both his hands and took mine—I think I put them into his—and said in a hearty way:—

"'That's my brave girl. It's better worth being late for a chance of winning you than being in time for any other girl in the world. Don't cry, my dear. If it's for me, I'm a hard nut to crack; and I take it standing up. If that other fellow doesn't know his happiness, well, he'd better look for it soon, or he'll have to deal with me. Little girl, your honesty and pluck have made me a friend, and that's rarer than a lover; it's more unselfish anyhow. My dear, I'm going to have a pretty lonely walk between this and Kingdom Come. Won't you give me one kiss? It'll be something to keep off the darkness now and then. You can, you know, if you like, for that other good fellow—he must be a good fellow, my dear, and a fine fellow, or you could not love him—hasn't spoken yet.' That quite won me, Mina, for it *was* brave and sweet of him, and noble, too, to a rival—wasn't it?—and he so sad; so I leant over and kissed him. He stood up with my two hands in his, and as he looked down into my face—I am afraid I was blushing very much—he said:—

"'Little girl, I hold your hand, and you've kissed me, and if these things don't make us friends nothing ever will. Thank you for your sweet honesty to me, and good-bye.' He wrung my hand, and taking up his hat, went straight out of the room without looking back, without a tear or a quiver or a pause; and I am crying like a baby. Oh, why must a man like that be made unhappy when there are lots of girls about who would worship the very ground he trod on? I know I would if I were free—only I don't want to be free. My dear, this quite upset me, and I feel I cannot write of happiness just at once, after telling you of it; and I don't wish to tell of the number three until it can be all happy."

"Ever your loving
"LUCY.

"P.S.—Oh, about number Three—I needn't tell you of number Three, need I? Besides, it was all so confused; it seemed only a moment from his coming into the room till both his arms were round me, and he was kissing me. I am very, very happy, and I don't know what I have done to deserve it. I must only try in the future to show that I am not ungrateful to God for all His goodness to me in sending to me such a lover, such a husband, and such a friend.

"Good-bye."

DR. SEWARD'S DIARY. (Kept in phonograph.)

25 May.—Ebb tide in appetite to-day. Cannot eat, cannot rest, so diary instead. Since my rebuff of yesterday I have a sort of empty feeling; nothing in the world seems of sufficient importance to be worth the doing. . . . As I knew that the only cure for this sort of thing was work, I went down amongst the patients. I picked out one who has afforded me a study of much interest. He is so quaint that I am determined to understand him as well as I can. Today I seemed to get nearer than ever before to the heart of his mystery.

I questioned him more fully than I had ever done, with a view to making myself master of the facts of his hallucination. In my manner of doing it there was, I now see, something of cruelty. I seemed to wish to keep him to the point of his madness—a thing which I avoid with the patients as I would the mouth of hell.

(*Mem.*, under what circumstances would I *not* avoid the pit of hell?) *Omnia Romae venalia sunt.* Hell has its price! *verb. sap.* If there be anything behind this instinct it will be valuable to trace it afterwards *accurately*, so I had better commence to do so, therefore—

R. M. Renfield, aetat 59.—Sanguine temperament; great physical strength; morbidly excitable; periods of gloom, ending in some fixed idea which I cannot make out. I presume that the sanguine temperament itself and the disturbing influence end in a mentally-accomplished finish; a possibly dangerous man, probably dangerous if unselfish. In selfish men caution is as secure an armour for their foes as for themselves. What I think of on this point is, when self is the fixed point the centripetal force is balanced with the centrifugal; when duty, a cause, etc., is the fixed point, the latter force is paramount, and only accident or a series of accidents can balance it.

LETTER FROM QUINCEY P. MORRIS TO
THE HONOURABLE ARTHUR HOLMWOOD.

"*25 May.*
"My dear Art,—
"We've told yarns by the camp-fire in the prairies; and dressed one another's wounds after trying a landing at the Marquesas; and drunk healths on the shore of Titicaca. There are more yarns to be told, and other wounds to be healed, and another health to be drunk. Won't you let this be at my camp-fire to-morrow night? I have no hesitation in asking you, as I know a certain lady is engaged to a certain dinner-party, and that you are free. There will only be one other, our old pal at the Korea, Jack Seward. He's coming, too, and we both want to mingle our weeps over the wine-cup, and to drink a health with all our hearts to the happiest man in all the wide world, who has won the noblest heart that God has made and the best worth winning. We promise you a hearty

welcome, and a loving greeting, and a health as true as your own right hand. We shall both swear to leave you at home if you drink too deep to a certain pair of eyes. Come!

"Yours, as ever and always,

"QUINCEY P. MORRIS."

TELEGRAM FROM ARTHUR HOLMWOOD
TO QUINCEY P. MORRIS.

26 May.—Count me in every time. I bear messages which will make both your ears tingle.

CHAPTER 6.

———◇———

MINA MURRAY'S JOURNAL.

24 July. Whitby.—Lucy met me at the station, looking sweeter and love-lier than ever, and we drove up to the house at the Crescent in which they have rooms. This is a lovely place. The little river, the Esk, runs through a deep valley, which broadens out as it comes near the harbour. A great viaduct runs across, with high piers, through which the view seems somehow further away than it really is. The valley is beautifully green, and it is so steep that when you are on the high land on either side you look right across it, unless you are near enough to see down. The houses of the old town—the side away from us—are all red-roofed, and seem piled up one over the other anyhow, like the pictures we see of Nuremberg. Right over the town is the ruin of Whitby Abbey, which was sacked by the Danes, and which is the scene of part of "Marmion," where the girl was built up in the wall. It is a most noble ruin, of immense size, and full of beautiful and romantic bits; there is a legend that a white lady is seen in one of the windows. Between it and the town there is another church, the parish one, round which is a big graveyard, all full of tombstones. This is to my mind the nicest spot in Whitby, for it lies right over the town, and has a full view of the harbour and all up the bay to where the headland called Kettleness stretches out into the sea. It descends so steeply over the harbour that part of the bank has fallen away, and some of the graves have been destroyed. In one place part of the stonework of the graves stretches out over the sandy pathway far below. There are walks, with seats beside them, through the church-yard; and people go and sit there all day long looking at the beautiful view and enjoying the breeze. I shall come and sit here very often myself and work. Indeed, I am writing now with my book on my knee, and listening to the talk of three old men who are sitting beside me. They seem to do nothing all day but sit up here and talk.

The harbour lies below me, with, on the far side, one long granite wall stretching out into the sea, with a curve outwards at the end of it, in the middle of which is a lighthouse. A heavy sea-wall runs along outside of it. On the near side, the sea-wall makes an elbow crooked inversely, and its end too has a lighthouse. Between the two piers there is a narrow opening into the harbour, which then suddenly widens.

It is nice at high water; but when the tide is out it shoals away to nothing, and there is merely the stream of the Esk, running between banks of sand, with rocks here and there. Outside the harbour on this side there rises for about half a mile a great reef, the sharp edge of which runs straight out from behind the south lighthouse. At the end of it is a buoy with a bell, which swings in bad weather, and sends in a mournful sound on the wind. They have a legend here that when a ship is lost bells are heard out at sea. I must ask the old man about this; he is coming this way. . . .

He is a funny old man. He must be awfully old, for his face is all gnarled and twisted like the bark of a tree. He tells me that he is nearly a hundred, and that he was a sailor in the Greenland fishing fleet when Waterloo was fought. He is, I am afraid, a very sceptical person, for when I asked him about the bells at sea and the White Lady at the abbey he said very brusquely:—

"I wouldn't fash masel' about them, miss. Them things be all wore out. Mind, I don't say that they never was, but I do say that they wasn't in my time. They be all very well for comers and trippers, an' the like, but not for a nice young lady like you. Them feet-folks from York and Leeds that be always eatin' cured herrin's an' drinkin' tea an' lookin' out to buy cheap jet would creed aught. I wonder masel' who'd be bothered tellin' lies to them—even the newspapers, which is full of fool-talk." I thought he would be a good person to learn interesting things from, so I asked him if he would mind telling me something about the whale-fishing in the old days. He was just settling himself to begin when the clock struck six, whereupon he laboured to get up, and said:—

"I must gang ageeanwards home now, miss. My granddaughter doesn't like to be kept waitin' when the tea is ready, for it takes me time to crammle aboon the grees, for there be a many of 'em; an', miss, I lack belly-timber sairly by the clock."

He hobbled away, and I could see him hurrying, as well as he could, down the steps. The steps are a great feature on the place. They lead from the town up to the church, there are hundreds of them—I do not know how many—and they wind up in a delicate curve; the slope is so gentle that a horse could easily walk up and down them. I think they must originally have had something to do with the abbey. I shall go home too. Lucy went out visiting with her mother, and as they were only duty calls, I did not go. They will be home by this.

1 August.—I came up here an hour ago with Lucy, and we had a most interesting talk with my old friend and the two others who always come and join him. He is evidently the Sir Oracle of them, and I should think must have been in his time a most dictatorial person. He will not admit anything, and downfaces everybody. If he can't out-argue them he bullies them, and then takes their silence for agreement with his views. Lucy was looking sweetly pretty in her white lawn frock; she has got a beautiful colour since she has been here. I noticed that the old men did not lose any time in coming up and sitting near her when we sat down. She is so sweet with old people; I think they all fell in love with her on the spot. Even my old man succumbed and did not contradict her, but gave me double share instead. I got him on the subject of the legends, and he went off at once into a sort of sermon. I must try to remember it and put it down:—

"It be all fool-talk, lock, stock, and barrel; that's what it be, an' nowt else. These bans an' wafts an' boh-ghosts an' barguests an' bogles an' all anent them is only fit to set bairns an' dizzy women a-belderin'. They be nowt but air-blebs. They, an' all grims an' signs an' warnin's, be all invented by parsons an' illsome beuk-bodies an' railway touters to skeer an' scanner hafflin's, an' to get folks to do somethin' that they don't other incline to. It makes me fretful to think o' them. Why, it's them that, not content with printin' lies on paper an' preachin' them out of pulpits, does want to be cuttin' them on the tombstones. Look here all around you in what airt ye will; all them steans, holdin' up their heads as well as they can out of their pride, is acant—simply tumblin' down with the weight o' the lies wrote on them, 'Here lies the body' or 'Sacred to the memory' wrote on all of them, an' yet in nigh half of them there bean't no bodies at all; an' the memories of them bean't cared a pinch of snuff about, much less sacred. Lies all of them, nothin' but lies of one kind or another! My gog, but it'll be a square scowderment at the Day of Judgment when they come tumblin' up in their death-sarks, all jouped together an' tryin' to drag their tombsteans with them to prove how good they was; some of them trimmlin' and ditherin', with their hands that dozzened an' slippy from lyin' in the sea that they can't even keep their grup o' them."

I could see from the old fellow's self-satisfied air and the way in which he looked round for the approval of his cronies that he was "showing off," so I put in a word to keep him going:—

"Oh, Mr. Swales, you can't be serious. Surely these tombstones are not all wrong?"

"Yabblins! There may be a poorish few not wrong, savin' where they make out the people too good; for there be folk that do think a balm-bowl be like the sea, if only it be their own. The whole thing be only lies. Now look you here; you come here a stranger, an' you see this kirk-garth." I nodded, for I thought it better to assent, though I did not quite understand his dialect. I knew it had something to do with the church.

He went on: "And you consate that all these steans be aboon folk that be happed here, snod an' snog?" I assented again. "Then that be just where the lie comes in. Why, there be scores of these lay-beds that be toom as old Dun's 'bacca-box on Friday night." He nudged one of his companions, and they all laughed. "And my gog! how could they be otherwise? Look at that one, the aftest abaft the bier-bank: read it!" I went over and read:—

"Edward Spencelagh, master mariner, murdered by pirates off the coast of Andres, April, 1854, aet. 30." When I came back Mr. Swales went on:—

"Who brought him home, I wonder, to hap him here? Murdered off the coast of Andres! an' you consated his body lay under! Why, I could name ye a dozen whose bones lie in the Greenland seas above"—he pointed northwards—"or where the currents may have drifted them. There be the steans around ye. Ye can, with your young eyes, read the small-print of the lies from here. This Braithwaite Lowrey—I knew his father, lost in the *Lively* off Greenland in '20; or Andrew Woodhouse, drowned in the same seas in 1777; or John Paxton, drowned off Cape Farewell a year later; or old John Rawlings, whose grandfather sailed with me, drowned in the Gulf of Finland in '50. Do ye think that all these men will have to make a rush to Whitby when the trumpet sounds? I have me antherums aboot it! I tell ye that when they got here they'd be jommlin' an' jostlin' one another that way that it 'ud be a fight up on the ice in the old days, when we'd be at one another from daylight to dark, an' tryin' to tie up our cuts by the light of the aurora borealis." This was evidently local pleasantry, for the old man cackled over it, and his cronies joined in with gusto.

"But," I said, "surely you are not quite correct, for you start on the assumption that all the poor people, or their spirits, will have to take their tombstones with them on the Day of Judgment. Do you think that will be really necessary?"

"Well, what else be they tombstones for? Answer me that, miss!"

"To please their relatives, I suppose."

"To please their relatives, you suppose!" This he said with intense scorn. "How will it pleasure their relatives to know that lies is wrote over them, and that everybody in the place knows that they be lies?" He pointed to a stone at our feet which had been laid down as a slab, on which the seat was rested, close to the edge of the cliff. "Read the lies on that thruff-stean," he said. The letters were upside down to me from where I sat, but Lucy was more opposite to them, so she leant over and read:—

"Sacred to the memory of George Canon, who died, in the hope of a glorious resurrection, on July 29, 1873, falling from the rocks at Kettleness. This tomb was erected by his sorrowing mother to her dearly beloved son. He was the only son of his mother, and she was a widow.— Really, Mr. Swales, I don't see anything very funny in that!" She spoke her comment very gravely and somewhat severely.

"Ye don't see aught funny! Ha! ha! But that's because ye don't gawm the sorrowin' mother was a hell-cat that hated him because he was acrewk'd—a regular lamiter he was—an' he hated her so that he committed suicide in order that she mightn't get an insurance she put on his life. He blew nigh the top of his head off with an old musket that they had for scarin' the crows with. 'Twarn't for crows then, for it brought the clegs and the dowps to him. That's the way he fell off the rocks. And, as to hopes of a glorious resurrection, I've often heard him say masel' that he hoped he'd go to hell, for his mother was so pious that she'd be sure to go to heaven, an' he didn't want to addle where she was. Now isn't that stean at any rate"—he hammered it with his stick as he spoke—"a pack of lies? and won't it make Gabriel keckle when Geordie comes pantin' up the grees with the tombstean balanced on his hump, and asks it to be took as evidence!"

I did not know what to say, but Lucy turned the conversation as she said, rising up:—

"Oh, why did you tell us of this? It is my favourite seat, and I cannot leave it; and now I find I must go on sitting over the grave of a suicide."

"That won't harm ye, my pretty; an' it may make poor Geordie gladsome to have so trim a lass sittin' on his lap. That won't hurt ye. Why,

I've sat here off an' on for nigh twenty years past, an' it hasn't done me no harm. Don't ye fash about them as lies under ye, or that doesn' lie there either! It'll be time for ye to be gettin' scart when ye see the tombsteans all run away with, and the place as bare as a stubble-field. There's the clock, an' I must gang. My service to ye, ladies!" And off he hobbled.

Lucy and I sat awhile, and it was all so beautiful before us that we took hands as we sat; and she told me all over again about Arthur and their coming marriage. That made me just a little heart-sick, for I haven't heard from Jonathan for a whole month.

The same day. I came up here alone, for I am very sad. There was no letter for me. I hope there cannot be anything the matter with Jonathan. The clock has just struck nine. I see the lights scattered all over the town, sometimes in rows where the streets are, and sometimes singly; they run right up the Esk and die away in the curve of the valley. To my left the view is cut off by a black line of roof of the old house next the abbey. The sheep and lambs are bleating in the fields away behind me, and there is a clatter of a donkey's hoofs up the paved road below. The band on the pier is playing a harsh waltz in good time, and further along the quay there is a Salvation Army meeting in a back street. Neither of the bands hears the other, but up here I hear and see them both. I wonder where Jonathan is and if he is thinking of me! I wish he were here.

DR. SEWARD'S DIARY.

5 June.—The case of Renfield grows more interesting the more I get to understand the man. He has certain qualities very largely developed; selfishness, secrecy, and purpose. I wish I could get at what is the object of the latter. He seems to have some settled scheme of his own, but what it is I do not know. His redeeming quality is a love of animals, though, indeed, he has such curious turns in it that I sometimes imagine he is only abnormally cruel. His pets are of odd sorts. Just now his hobby is catching flies. He has at present such a quantity that I have had myself to expostulate. To my astonishment, he did not break out into a fury, as I expected, but took the matter in simple seriousness. He thought for a moment, and then said: "May I have three days? I shall clear them away." Of course, I said that would do. I must watch him.

18 June.—He has turned his mind now to spiders, and has got several very big fellows in a box. He keeps feeding them with his flies, and the number of the latter is becoming sensibly diminished, although he has used half his food in attracting more flies from outside to his room.

1 July.—His spiders are now becoming as great a nuisance as his flies, and to-day I told him that he must get rid of them. He looked very sad at this, so I said that he must clear out some of them, at all events. He cheerfully acquiesced in this, and I gave him the same time as before for reduction. He disgusted me much while with him, for when a horrid blow-fly, bloated with some carrion food, buzzed into the room, he caught it, held it exultantly for a few moments between his finger and thumb, and, before I knew what he was going to do, put it in his mouth and ate it. I scolded him for it, but he argued quietly that it was very good and very wholesome; that it was life, strong life, and gave life to him. This gave me an idea, or the rudiment of one. I must watch how he gets rid of his spiders. He has evidently some deep problem in his mind, for he keeps a little notebook in which he is always jotting down something. Whole pages of it are filled with masses of figures, generally single numbers added up in batches, and then the totals added in batches again, as though he were "focussing" some account, as the auditors put it.

8 July.—There is a method in his madness, and the rudimentary idea in my mind is growing. It will be a whole idea soon, and then, oh, unconscious cerebration! you will have to give the wall to your conscious brother. I kept away from my friend for a few days, so that I might notice if there were any change. Things remain as they were except that he has parted with some of his pets and got a new one. He has managed to get a sparrow, and has already partially tamed it. His means of taming is simple, for already the spiders have diminished. Those that do remain, however, are well fed, for he still brings in the flies by tempting them with his food.

19 July.—We are progressing. My friend has now a whole colony of sparrows, and his flies and spiders are almost obliterated. When I came in he ran to me and said he wanted to ask me a great favour—a very, very great favour; and as he spoke he fawned on me like a dog. I asked him what it was, and he said, with a sort of rapture in his voice and bearing:—

"A kitten, a nice little, sleek playful kitten, that I can play with, and teach, and feed—and feed—and feed!" I was not unprepared for this request, for I had noticed how his pets went on increasing in size and vivacity, but I did not care that his pretty family of tame sparrows should be wiped out in the same manner as the flies and the spiders; so I said I would see about it, and asked him if he would not rather have a cat than a kitten. His eagerness betrayed him as he answered:—

"Oh, yes, I would like a cat! I only asked for a kitten lest you should refuse me a cat. No one would refuse me a kitten, would they?" I shook my head, and said that at present I feared it would not be possible, but that I would see about it. His face fell, and I could see a warning of danger in it, for there was a sudden fierce, sidelong look which meant killing. The man is an undeveloped homicidal maniac. I shall test him with his present craving and see how it will work out; then I shall know more.

10 p.m.—I have visited him again and found him sitting in a corner brooding. When I came in he threw himself on his knees before me and implored me to let him have a cat; that his salvation depended upon it. I was firm, however, and told him that he could not have it, whereupon he went without a word, and sat down, gnawing his fingers, in the corner where I had found him. I shall see him in the morning early.

20 July.—Visited Renfield very early, before the attendant went his rounds. Found him up and humming a tune. He was spreading out his sugar, which he had saved, in the window, and was manifestly beginning his fly-catching again; and beginning it cheerfully and with a good grace. I looked around for his birds, and not seeing them, asked him where they were. He replied, without turning round, that they had all flown away. There were a few feathers about the room and on his pillow a drop of blood. I said nothing, but went and told the keeper to report to me if there were anything odd about him during the day.

11 a.m.—The attendant has just been to me to say that Renfield has been very sick and has disgorged a whole lot of feathers. "My belief is, doctor," he said, "that he has eaten his birds, and that he just took and ate them raw!"

11 p.m.—I gave Renfield a strong opiate to-night, enough to make even him sleep, and took away his pocket-book to look at it. The thought that has been buzzing about my brain lately is complete, and the theory proved. My homicidal maniac is of a peculiar kind. I shall have to invent a new classification for him, and call him a zoöphagous (life-eating) maniac; what he desires is to absorb as many lives as he can, and he has laid himself out to achieve it in a cumulative way. He gave many flies to one spider and many spiders to one bird, and then wanted a cat to eat the many birds. What would have been his later steps? It would almost be worth while to complete the experiment. It might be done if there were only a sufficient cause. Men sneered at vivisection, and yet look at its results to-day! Why not advance science in its most difficult and vital aspect—the knowledge of the brain? Had I even the secret of one such mind—did I hold the key to the fancy of even one lunatic—I might advance my own branch of science to a pitch compared with which Burdon-Sanderson's physiology or Ferrier's brain-knowledge would be as nothing. If only there were a sufficient cause! I must not think too much of this, or I may be tempted; a good cause might turn the scale with me, for may not I too be of an exceptional brain, congenitally?

How well the man reasoned; lunatics always do within their own scope. I wonder at how many lives he values a man, or if at only one. He has closed the account most accurately, and to-day begun a new record. How many of us begin a new record with each day of our lives?

To me it seems only yesterday that my whole life ended with my new hope, and that truly I began a new record. So it will be until the Great Recorder sums me up and closes my ledger account with a balance to profit or loss. Oh, Lucy, Lucy, I cannot be angry with you, nor can I be angry with my friend whose happiness is yours; but I must only wait on hopeless and work. Work! work!

If I only could have as strong a cause as my poor mad friend there— a good, unselfish cause to make me work—that would be indeed happiness.

MINA MURRAY'S JOURNAL.

26 July.—I am anxious, and it soothes me to express myself here; it is like whispering to one's self and listening at the same time. And there is also something about the shorthand symbols that makes it different from writing. I am unhappy about Lucy and about Jonathan. I had not heard from Jonathan for some time, and was very concerned; but yesterday dear Mr. Hawkins, who is always so kind, sent me a letter from him. I had written asking him if he had heard, and he said the enclosed had just been received. It is only a line dated from Castle Dracula, and says that he is just starting for home. That is not like Jonathan; I do not understand it, and it makes me uneasy. Then, too, Lucy, although she is so well, has lately taken to her old habit of walking in her sleep. Her mother has spoken to me about it, and we have decided that I am to lock the door of our room every night. Mrs. Westenra has got an idea that sleep-walkers always go out on roofs of houses and along the edges of cliffs and then get suddenly wakened and fall over with a despairing cry that echoes all over the place. Poor dear, she is naturally anxious about Lucy, and she tells me that her husband, Lucy's father, had the same habit; that he would get up in the night and dress himself and go out, if he were not stopped. Lucy is to be married in the autumn, and she is already planning out her dresses and how her house is to be arranged. I sympathise with her, for I do the same, only Jonathan and I will start in life in a very simple way, and shall have to try to make both ends meet. Mr. Holmwood—he is the Hon. Arthur Holmwood, only son of Lord Godalming—is coming up here very shortly—as soon as he can leave town, for his father is not very well, and I think dear Lucy is counting the moments till he comes. She wants to take him up to the seat on the churchyard cliff and show him the beauty of Whitby. I daresay it is the waiting which disturbs her; she will be all right when he arrives.

27 July.—No news from Jonathan. I am getting quite uneasy about him, though why I should I do not know; but I do wish that he would write, if it were only a single line. Lucy walks more than ever, and each night I am awakened by her moving about the room. Fortunately, the weather is so hot that she cannot get cold; but still the anxiety and the perpetually being wakened is beginning to tell on me, and I am getting nervous and wakeful myself. Thank God, Lucy's health keeps up. Mr. Holmwood has been suddenly called to Ring to see his father, who has been taken seriously ill. Lucy frets at the postponement of seeing him, but it does not touch her looks; she is a trifle stouter, and her cheeks are a lovely rose-pink. She has lost that anaemic look which she had. I pray it will all last.

3 August.—Another week gone, and no news from Jonathan, not even to Mr. Hawkins, from whom I have heard. Oh, I do hope he is not ill. He surely would have written. I look at that last letter of his, but somehow it does not satisfy me. It does not read like him, and yet it is his writing. There is no mistake of that. Lucy has not walked much in her sleep the last week, but there is an odd concentration about her which I do not understand; even in her sleep she seems to be watching me. She tries the door, and finding it locked, goes about the room searching for the key.

6 August.—Another three days, and no news. This suspense is getting dreadful. If I only knew where to write to or where to go to, I should feel easier; but no one has heard a word of Jonathan since that last letter. I must only pray to God for patience. Lucy is more excitable than ever, but is otherwise well. Last night was very threatening, and the fishermen say that we are in for a storm. I must try to watch it and learn the weather signs. To-day is a grey day, and the sun as I write is hidden in thick clouds, high over Kettleness. Everything is grey—except the green grass, which seems like emerald amongst it; grey earthy rock; grey clouds, tinged with the sunburst at the far edge, hang over the grey sea, into which the sand-points stretch like grey fingers. The sea is tumbling in over the shallows and the sandy flats with a roar, muffled in the sea-mists drifting inland. The horizon is lost in a grey mist. All is vastness; the clouds are piled up like giant rocks, and there is a "brool" over the sea that sounds like some presage of doom. Dark figures are on the beach here and there, sometimes half shrouded in the mist, and seem "men like trees walking." The fishing-boats are racing for home, and rise and dip in the ground swell as they sweep into the harbour, bending to the scuppers. Here comes old Mr. Swales. He is making straight for me, and I can see, by the way he lifts his hat, that he wants to talk. . . .

I have been quite touched by the change in the poor old man. When he sat down beside me, he said in a very gentle way:—

"I want to say something to you, miss." I could see he was not at ease, so I took his poor old wrinkled hand in mine and asked him to speak fully; so he said, leaving his hand in mine:—

"I'm afraid, my deary, that I must have shocked you by all the wicked things I've been sayin' about the dead, and such like, for weeks past; but I didn't mean them, and I want ye to remember that when I'm gone. We aud folks that be daffled, and with one foot abaft the krok-hooal, don't altogether like to think of it, and we don't want to feel scart of it; an' that's why I've took to makin' light of it, so that I'd cheer up my own heart a bit. But, Lord love ye, miss, I ain't afraid of dyin', not a bit; only I don't want to die if I can help it. My time must be nigh at hand now, for I be aud, and a hundred years is too much for any man to expect; and I'm so nigh it that the Aud Man is already whettin' his scythe. Ye see, I can't get out o' the habit of caffin' about it all at once; the chafts will wag as they be used to. Some day soon the Angel of Death will sound his trumpet for me. But don't ye dooal an' greet, my deary!"—for he saw that I was crying—"if he should come this very night I'd not refuse to answer his call. For life be, after all, only a waitin' for somethin' else than what we're doin'; and death be all that we can rightly depend on. But I'm content, for it's comin' to me, my deary, and comin' quick. It may be comin' while we be lookin' and wonderin'. May be it's in that wind out over the sea that's bringin' with it loss and wreck, and sore distress, and sad hearts. Look! look!" he cried suddenly. "There's something in that wind and in the hoast beyont that sounds, and looks, and tastes, and smells like death. It's in the air; I feel it comin'. Lord, make me answer cheerful when my call comes!" He held up his arms devoutly, and raised his hat. His mouth moved as though he were praying. After a few minutes' silence, he got up, shook hands with me, and blessed me, and said good-bye, and hobbled off. It all touched me, and upset me very much.

I was glad when the coastguard came along, with his spyglass under his arm. He stopped to talk with me, as he always does, but all the time kept looking at a strange ship.

"I can't make her out," he said; "she's a Russian, by the look of her; but she's knocking about in the queerest way. She doesn't know her mind a bit; she seems to see the storm coming, but can't decide whether to run up north in the open, or to put in here. Look there again! She is steered mighty strangely, for she doesn't mind the hand on the wheel; changes about with every puff of wind. We'll hear more of her before this time to-morrow."

CHAPTER 7.

———◇———

CUTTINGS FROM "THE DAILYGRAPH,"
(*Pasted in Mina Murray's Journal.*)
From a Correspondent.

Whitby, 8 August.
One of the greatest and suddenest storms on record has just been experienced here, with results both strange and unique. The weather had been somewhat sultry, but not to any degree uncommon in the month of August. Saturday evening was as fine as was ever known, and the great body of holiday-makers laid out yesterday for visits to Mulgrave Woods, Robin Hood's Bay, Rig Mill, Runswick, Staithes, and the various trips in the neighbourhood of Whitby. The steamers *Emma* and *Scarborough* made trips up and down the coast, and there was an unusual amount of "tripping" both to and from Whitby. The day was unusually fine till the afternoon, when some of the gossips who frequent the East Cliff churchyard, and from that commanding eminence watch the wide sweep of sea visible to the north and east, called attention to a sudden show of "mares'-tails" high in the sky to the north-west. The wind was then blowing from the south-west in the mild degree which in barometrical language

is ranked "No. 2: light breeze." The coastguard on duty at once made report, and one old fisherman, who for more than half a century has kept watch on weather signs from the East Cliff, foretold in an emphatic manner the coming of a sudden storm. The approach of sunset was so very beautiful, so grand in its masses of splendidly-coloured clouds, that there was quite an assemblage on the walk along the cliff in the old churchyard to enjoy the beauty. Before the sun dipped below the black mass of Kettleness, standing boldly athwart the western sky, its downward way was marked by myriad clouds of every sunset-colour—flame, purple, pink, green, violet, and all the tints of gold; with here and there masses not large, but of seemingly absolute blackness, in all sorts of shapes, as well outlined as colossal silhouettes. The experience was not lost on the painters, and doubtless some of the sketches of the "Prelude to the Great Storm" will grace the R. A. and R.I. walls in May next. More than one captain made up his mind then and there that his "cobble" or his "mule," as they term the different classes of boats, would remain in the harbour till the storm had passed. The wind fell away entirely during the evening, and at midnight there was a dead calm, a sultry heat, and that prevailing intensity which, on the approach of thunder, affects persons of a sensitive nature. There were but few lights in sight at sea, for even the coasting steamers, which usually "hug" the shore so closely, kept well to seaward, and but few fishing-boats were in sight. The only sail noticeable was a foreign schooner with all sails set, which was seemingly going westwards. The foolhardiness or ignorance of her officers was a prolific theme for comment whilst she remained in sight, and efforts were made to signal her to reduce sail in face of her danger. Before the night shut down she was seen with sails idly flapping as she gently rolled on the undulating swell of the sea,

"As idle as a painted ship upon a painted ocean."

Shortly before ten o'clock the stillness of the air grew quite oppressive, and the silence was so marked that the bleating of a sheep inland or the barking of a dog in the town was distinctly heard, and the band on the pier, with its lively French air, was like a discord in the great harmony of nature's silence. A little after midnight came a strange sound from over the sea, and high overhead the air began to carry a strange, faint, hollow booming.

Then without warning the tempest broke. With a rapidity which, at the time, seemed incredible, and even afterwards is impossible to realise, the whole aspect of nature at once became convulsed. The waves rose in growing fury, each overtopping its fellow, till in a very few minutes the lately glassy sea was like a roaring and devouring monster. White-crested waves beat madly on the level sands and rushed up the shelving cliffs; others broke over the piers, and with their spume swept the lanthorns of the lighthouses which rise from the end of either pier of Whitby Harbour. The wind roared like thunder, and blew with such force that it was with difficulty that even strong men kept their feet, or clung with grim clasp to the iron stanchions. It was found necessary to clear the entire piers from the mass of onlookers, or else the fatalities of the night would have been increased manifold. To add to the difficulties and dangers of the time, masses of sea-fog came drifting inland—white, wet clouds, which swept by in ghostly fashion, so dank and damp and cold that it needed but little effort of imagination to think that the spirits of those lost at sea were touching their living brethren with the clammy hands of death, and many a one shuddered as the wreaths of sea-mist swept by. At times the mist cleared, and the sea for some distance could be seen in the glare of the lightning, which now came thick and fast, followed by such sudden peals of thunder that the whole sky overhead seemed trembling under the shock of the footsteps of the storm.

Some of the scenes thus revealed were of immeasurable grandeur and of absorbing interest—the sea, running mountains high, threw skyward with each wave mighty masses of white foam, which the tempest seemed to snatch at and whirl away into space; here and there a fishing-boat, with a rag of sail, running madly for shelter before the blast; now and again the white wings of a storm-tossed sea-bird. On the summit of the East Cliff the new searchlight was ready for experiment, but had not yet

been tried. The officers in charge of it got it into working order, and in
the pauses of the inrushing mist swept with it the surface of the sea.
Once or twice its service was most effective, as when a fishing-boat,
with gunwale under water, rushed into the harbour, able, by the guidance of the sheltering light, to avoid the danger of dashing against the
piers. As each boat achieved the safety of the port there was a shout of
joy from the mass of people on shore, a shout which for a moment
seemed to cleave the gale and was then swept away in its rush.

Before long the searchlight discovered some distance away a schooner with all sails set, apparently the same vessel which had been noticed
earlier in the evening. The wind had by this time backed to the east,
and there was a shudder amongst the watchers on the cliff as they realised the terrible danger in which she now was. Between her and the
port lay the great flat reef on which so many good ships have from time
to time suffered, and, with the wind blowing from its present quarter,
it would be quite impossible that she should fetch the entrance of the
harbour. It was now nearly the hour of high tide, but the waves were so
great that in their troughs the shallows of the shore were almost visible,
and the schooner, with all sails set, was rushing with such speed that,
in the words of one old salt, "she must fetch up somewhere, if it was
only in hell." Then came another rush of sea-fog, greater than any hitherto—a mass of dank mist, which seemed to close on all things like a
grey pall, and left available to men only the organ of hearing, for the
roar of the tempest, and the crash of the thunder, and the booming of
the mighty billows came through the damp oblivion even louder than
before. The rays of the searchlight were kept fixed on the harbour
mouth across the East Pier, where the shock was expected, and men
waited breathless. The wind suddenly shifted to the north-east, and the
remnant of the sea-fog melted in the blast; and then, *mirabile dictu*,
between the piers, leaping from wave to wave as it rushed at headlong
speed, swept the strange schooner before the blast, with all sails set,
and gained the safety of the harbour. The searchlight followed her, and
a shudder ran through all who saw her, for lashed to the helm was a
corpse, with drooping head, which swung horribly to and fro at each

motion of the ship. No other form could be seen on deck at all. A great awe came on all as they realised that the ship, as if by a miracle, had found the harbour, unsteered save by the hand of a dead man! However, all took place more quickly than it takes to write these words. The schooner paused not, but rushing across the harbour, pitched herself on that accumulation of sand and gravel washed by many tides and many storms into the south-east corner of the pier jutting under the East Cliff, known locally as Tate Hill Pier.

There was of course a considerable concussion as the vessel drove up on the sand heap. Every spar, rope, and stay was strained, and some of the "top-hammer" came crashing down. But, strangest of all, the very instant the shore was touched, an immense dog sprang up on deck from below, as if shot up by the concussion, and running forward, jumped from the bow on the sand. Making straight for the steep cliff, where the churchyard hangs over the laneway to the East Pier so steeply that some of the flat tombstones—"thruff-steans" or "through-stones," as they call them in the Whitby vernacular—actually project over where the sustaining cliff has fallen away, it disappeared in the darkness, which seemed intensified just beyond the focus of the searchlight.

It so happened that there was no one at the moment on Tate Hill Pier, as all those whose houses are in close proximity were either in bed or were out on the heights above. Thus the coastguard on duty on the eastern side of the harbour, who at once ran down to the little pier, was the first to climb on board. The men working the searchlight, after scouring the entrance of the harbour without seeing anything, then turned the light on the derelict and kept it there. The coastguard ran aft, and when he came beside the wheel, bent over to examine it, and recoiled at once as though under some sudden emotion. This seemed to pique general curiosity, and quite a number of people began to run. It is a good way round from the West Cliff by the Drawbridge to Tate Hill Pier, but your correspondent is a fairly good runner, and came well ahead of the crowd. When I arrived, however, I found already assembled on the pier a crowd, whom the coastguard and police refused to allow to come onboard. By the courtesy of the chief boatman, I was, as your correspondent, permitted to climb on deck, and was one of a small group who saw the dead seaman whilst actually lashed to the wheel.

It was no wonder that the coastguard was surprised, or even awed, for not often can such a sight have been seen. The man was simply fastened by his hands, tied one over the other, to a spoke of the wheel. Between the inner hand and the wood was a crucifix, the set of beads on which it was fastened being around both wrists and wheel, and all kept fast by the binding cords. The poor fellow may have been seated at one time, but the flapping and buffeting of the sails had worked through the rudder of the wheel and dragged him to and fro, so that the cords with which he was tied had cut the flesh to the bone. Accurate note was made of the state of things, and a doctor—Surgeon J. M. Caffyn, of 33, East Elliot Place—who came immediately after me, declared, after making examination, that the man must have been dead for quite two days. In his pocket was a bottle, carefully corked, empty save for a little roll of paper, which proved to be the addendum to the log. The coastguard said the man must have tied up his own hands, fastening the knots with his teeth. The fact that a coastguard was the first on board may save some complications, later on, in the Admiralty Court; for coastguards cannot claim the salvage which is the right of the first civilian entering on a derelict. Already, however, the legal tongues are wagging, and one young law student is loudly asserting that the rights of the owner are already completely sacrificed, his property being held in contravention of the statutes of mortmain, since the tiller, as emblemship, if not proof, of delegated possession, is held in a *dead hand*. It is needless to say that the dead steersman has been reverently removed from the place where he held his honourable watch and ward till death—a steadfastness as noble as that of the young Casabianca—and placed in the mortuary to await inquest.

Already the sudden storm is passing, and its fierceness is abating; crowds are scattering homeward, and the sky is beginning to redden over the Yorkshire wolds. I shall send, in time for your next issue, further details of the derelict ship which found her way so miraculously into harbour in the storm.

Whitby, 9 August.

The sequel to the strange arrival of the derelict in the storm last night is almost more startling than the thing itself. It turns out that the schooner is a Russian from Varna, and is called the *Demeter*. She is almost entirely in ballast of silver sand, with only a small amount of cargo—a number of great wooden boxes filled with mould. This cargo was consigned to a Whitby solicitor, Mr. S. F. Billington, of 7, The Crescent, who this morning went aboard and formally took possession of the goods consigned to him. The Russian consul, too, acting for the charter-party, took formal possession of the ship, and paid all harbour dues, etc. Nothing is talked about here to-day except the strange coincidence; the officials of the Board of Trade have been most exacting in seeing that every compliance has been made with existing regulations. As the matter is to be a "nine days' wonder," they are evidently determined that there shall be no cause of after complaint. A good deal of interest was abroad concerning the dog which landed when the ship struck, and more than a few of the members of the S.P.C.A., which is very strong in Whitby, have tried to befriend the animal. To the general disappointment, however, it was not to be found; it seems to have disappeared entirely from the town. It may be that it was frightened and made its way on to the moors, where it is still hiding in terror. There are some who look with dread on such a possibility, lest later on it should in itself become a danger, for it is evidently a fierce brute. Early this morning a large dog, a half-bred mastiff belonging to a coal merchant close to Tate Hill Pier, was found dead in the roadway opposite to its master's yard. It had been fighting, and manifestly had had a savage opponent, for its throat was torn away, and its belly was slit open as if with a savage claw.

Later.—By the kindness of the Board of Trade inspector, I have been permitted to look over the log-book of the *Demeter*, which was in order up to within three days, but contained nothing of special interest except as to facts of missing men. The greatest interest, however, is with regard to the paper found in the bottle, which was to-day produced at the inquest; and a more strange narrative than the two between them unfold it has not been my lot to come across. As there is no motive for conceal-ment, I am permitted to use them, and accordingly send you a rescript, simply omitting technical details of seamanship and supercargo. It almost seems as though the captain had been seized with some kind of mania before he had got well into blue water, and that this had devel-oped persistently throughout the voyage. Of course my statement must be taken *cum grano*, since I am writing from the dictation of a clerk of the Russian consul, who kindly translated for me, time being short.

LOG OF THE "DEMETER." *Varna to Whitby.*

Written 18 July, things so strange happening, that I shall keep accurate note henceforth till we land.

On 6 July we finished taking in cargo, silver sand and boxes of earth. At noon set sail. East wind, fresh. Crew, five hands . . . two mates, cook, and myself (captain).

On 11 July at dawn entered Bosphorus. Boarded by Turkish Customs officers. Backsheesh. All correct. Under way at 4 p.m.

On 12 July through Dardanelles. More Customs officers and flagboat of guarding squadron. Backsheesh again. Work of officers thorough, but quick. Want us off soon. At dark passed into Archipelago.

On 13 July passed Cape Matapan. Crew dissatisfied about something. Seemed scared, but would not speak out.

On 14 July was somewhat anxious about crew. Men all steady fel-lows, who sailed with me before. Mate could not make out what was wrong; they only told him there was *something*, and crossed themselves. Mate lost temper with one of them that day and struck him. Expected fierce quarrel, but all was quiet.

On 16 July mate reported in the morning that one of crew, Petrofsky, was missing. Could not account for it. Took larboard watch eight bells last night; was relieved by Abramoff, but did not go to bunk. Men more downcast than ever. All said they expected something of the kind, but would not say more than there was *something* aboard. Mate getting very impatient with them; feared some trouble ahead.

On 17 July, yesterday, one of the men, Olgaren, came to my cabin, and in an awestruck way confided to me that he thought there was a strange man aboard the ship. He said that in his watch he had been sheltering behind the deckhouse, as there was a rain-storm, when he saw a tall, thin man, who was not like any of the crew, come up the companionway, and go along the deck forward, and disappear. He followed cautiously, but when he got to bows found no one, and the hatchways were all closed. He was in a panic of superstitious fear, and I am afraid the panic may spread. To allay it, I shall to-day search entire ship carefully from stem to stern.

Later in the day I got together the whole crew, and told them, as they evidently thought there was some one in the ship, we would search from stem to stern. First mate angry; said it was folly, and to yield to such foolish ideas would demoralise the men; said he would engage to keep them out of trouble with a handspike. I let him take the helm, while the rest began thorough search, all keeping abreast, with lanterns: we left no corner unsearched. As there were only the big wooden boxes, there were no odd corners where a man could hide. Men much relieved when search over, and went back to work cheerfully. First mate scowled, but said nothing.

22 July.—Rough weather last three days, and all hands busy with sails—no time to be frightened. Men seem to have forgotten their dread. Mate cheerful again, and all on good terms. Praised men for work in bad weather. Passed Gibraltar and out through Straits. All well.

24 July.—There seems some doom over this ship. Already a hand short, and entering on the Bay of Biscay with wild weather ahead, and yet last night another man lost—disappeared. Like the first, he came off his watch and was not seen again. Men all in a panic of fear; sent a round robin, asking to have double watch, as they fear to be alone. Mate angry. Fear there will be some trouble, as either he or the men will do some violence.

28 July.—Four days in hell, knocking about in a sort of maelstrom, and the wind of a tempest. No sleep for any one. Men all worn out. Hardly know how to set a watch, since no one fit to go on. Second mate volunteered to steer and watch, and let men snatch a few hours' sleep. Wind abating; seas still terrific, but feel them less, as ship is steadier.

29 July.—Another tragedy. Had single watch to-night, as crew too tired to double. When morning watch came on deck could find no one except steersman. Raised outcry, and all came on deck. Thorough search, but no one found. Are now without second mate, and crew in a panic. Mate and I agreed to go armed henceforth and wait for any sign of cause.

30 July.—Last night. Rejoiced we are nearing England. Weather fine, all sails set. Retired worn out; slept soundly; awaked by mate telling me that both man of watch and steersman missing. Only self and mate and two hands left to work ship.

1 August.—Two days of fog and not a sail sighted. Had hoped when in the English Channel to be able to signal for help or get in somewhere. Not having power to work sails, have to run before wind. Dare not lower, as could not raise them again. We seem to be drifting to some terrible doom. Mate now more demoralised than either of men. His stronger nature seems to have worked inwardly against himself. Men are beyond fear, working stolidly and patiently, with minds made up to worst. They are Russian, he Roumanian.

2 August, midnight.—Woke up from few minutes' sleep by hearing a cry, seemingly outside my port. Could see nothing in fog. Rushed on deck, and ran against mate. Tells me heard cry and ran, but no sign of man on watch. One more gone. Lord, help us! Mate says we must be past Straits of Dover, as in a moment of fog lifting he saw North Foreland, just as he heard the man cry out. If so we are now off in the North Sea, and only God can guide us in the fog, which seems to move with us; and God seems to have deserted us.

3 August.—At midnight I went to relieve the man at the wheel, and when I got to it found no one there. The wind was steady, and as we ran before it there was no yawing. I dared not leave it, so shouted for the mate. After a few seconds he rushed up on deck in his flannels. He looked wild-eyed and haggard, and I greatly fear his reason has given way. He came close to me and whispered hoarsely, with his mouth to my ear, as though fearing the very air might hear: *"It* is here; I know it, now. On the watch last night I saw it, like a man, tall and thin, and ghastly pale. It was in the bows, and looking out. I crept behind It, and gave It my knife; but the knife went through It, empty as the air." And as he spoke he took his knife and drove it savagely into space. Then he went on: "But It is here, and I'll find It. It is in the hold, perhaps in one of those boxes. I'll unscrew them one by one and see. You work the helm." And, with a warning look and his finger on his lip, he went below. There was springing up a choppy wind, and I could not leave the helm. I saw him come out on deck again with a tool-chest and a lantern, and go down the forward hatchway. He is mad, stark, raving mad, and it's no use my trying to stop him. He can't hurt those big boxes: they are invoiced as "clay," and to pull them about is as harmless a thing as he can do. So here I stay, and mind the helm, and write these notes. I can only trust in God and wait till the fog clears. Then, if I can't steer to any harbour with the wind that is, I shall cut down sails and lie by, and signal for help.

It is nearly all over now. Just as I was beginning to hope that the mate would come out calmer—for I heard him knocking away at something in the hold, and work is good for him—there came up the hatchway a sudden, startled scream, which made my blood run cold, and up on the deck he came as if shot from a gun—a raging madman, with his eyes rolling and his face convulsed with fear. "Save me! save me!" he cried, and then looked round on the blanket of fog. His horror turned to despair, and in a steady voice he said: "You had better come too, Captain, before it is too late. *He* is there. I know the secret now. The sea will save me from Him, and it is all that is left!" Before I could say a word, or move forward to seize him, he sprang on the bulwark and deliberately threw himself into the sea. I suppose I know the secret too, now. It was this madman who had got rid of the men one by one, and now he has followed them himself. God help me! How am I to account for all these horrors when I get to port? *When* I get to port! Will that ever be?

4 August.—Still fog, which the sunrise cannot pierce. I know there is sunrise because I am a sailor, why else I know not. I dared not go below, I dared not leave the helm; so here all night I stayed, and in the dimness of the night I saw It—Him! God forgive me, but the mate was right to jump overboard. It was better to die like a man; to die like a sailor in blue water no man can object. But I am captain, and I must not leave my ship. But I shall baffle this fiend or monster, for I shall tie my hands to the wheel when my strength begins to fail, and along with them I shall tie that which He—It!—dare not touch; and then, come good wind or foul, I shall save my soul, and my honour as a captain. I am growing weaker, and the night is coming on. If He can look me in the face again, I may not have time to act. . . . If we are wrecked, mayhap this bottle may be found, and those who find it may understand; if not, . . . well, then all men shall know that I have been true to my trust. God and the Blessed Virgin and the saints help a poor ignorant soul trying to do his duty. . . .

Of course the verdict was an open one. There is no evidence to adduce; and whether or not the man himself committed the murders there is now none to say. The folk here hold almost universally that the captain is simply a hero, and he is to be given a public funeral. Already it is arranged that his body is to be taken with a train of boats up the Esk for a piece and then brought back to Tate Hill Pier and up the abbey steps; for he is to be buried in the churchyard on the cliff. The owners of more than a hundred boats have already given in their names as wishing to follow him to the grave.

No trace has ever been found of the great dog; at which there is much mourning, for, with public opinion in its present state, he would, I believe, be adopted by the town. To-morrow will see the funeral; and so will end this one more "mystery of the sea."

MINA MURRAY'S JOURNAL.

8 August.—Lucy was very restless all night, and I, too, could not sleep. The storm was fearful, and as it boomed loudly among the chimney-pots, it made me shudder. When a sharp puff came it seemed to be like a distant gun. Strangely enough, Lucy did not wake; but she got up twice and dressed herself. Fortunately, each time I awoke in time and managed to undress her without waking her, and got her back to bed. It is a very strange thing, this sleep-walking, for as soon as her will is thwarted in any physical way, her intention, if there be any, disappears, and she yields herself almost exactly to the routine of her life.

Early in the morning we both got up and went down to the harbour to see if anything had happened in the night. There were very few people about, and though the sun was bright, and the air clear and fresh, the big, grim-looking waves, that seemed dark themselves because the foam that topped them was like snow, forced themselves in through the narrow mouth of the harbour—like a bullying man going through a crowd. Somehow I felt glad that Jonathan was not on the sea last night, but on land. But, oh, is he on land or sea? Where is he, and how? I am getting fearfully anxious about him. If I only knew what to do, and could do anything!

10 August.—The funeral of the poor sea-captain to-day was most touching. Every boat in the harbour seemed to be there, and the coffin was carried by captains all the way from Tate Hill Pier up to the church-yard. Lucy came with me, and we went early to our old seat, whilst the cortège of boats went up the river to the Viaduct and came down again. We had a lovely view, and saw the procession nearly all the way. The poor fellow was laid to rest quite near our seat so that we stood on it when the time came and saw everything. Poor Lucy seemed much upset. She was restless and uneasy all the time; and I cannot but think that her dreaming at night is telling on her. She is quite odd in one thing: she will not admit to me that there is any cause for restlessness; or if there be, she does not understand it herself. There is an additional cause in that poor old Mr. Swales was found dead this morning on our seat, his neck being broken. He had evidently, as the doctor said, fallen back in the seat in some sort of fright, for there was a look of fear and horror on his face that the men said made them shudder. Poor dear old man! Perhaps he had seen Death with his dying eyes! Lucy is so sweet and sensitive that she feels influences more acutely than other people do. Just now she was quite upset by a little thing which I did not much heed, though I am myself very fond of animals. One of the men who came up here often to look for the boats was followed by his dog. The dog is always with him. They are both quiet persons, and I never saw the man angry, nor heard the dog bark. During the service the dog would not come to its master, who was on the seat with us, but kept a few yards off, barking and howling. Its master spoke to it gently, and then harshly, and then angrily; but it would neither come nor cease to make a noise. It was in a sort of fury, with its eyes savage, and all its hairs bristling out like a cat's tail when puss is on the war-path. Finally the man, too, got angry, and jumped down and kicked the dog, and then took it by the scruff of the neck and half dragged and half threw it on the tombstone on which the seat is fixed. The moment it touched the stone the poor thing became quiet and fell all into a tremble. It did not try to get away, but crouched down, quivering and cowering, and was in such a pitiable state of terror that I tried, though without effect, to comfort it. Lucy was full of pity, too, but she did not attempt to touch the dog, but looked at it in an agonised sort of way. I greatly fear that she is too super-sensitive a nature to go through the world without trouble. She will be dreaming of this tonight, I am sure. The whole agglomeration of things—the ship steered into port by a dead man; his attitude, tied to the wheel with a crucifix and beads; the touching funeral; the dog, now furious and now in terror—will all afford material for her dreams.

I think it will be best for her to go to bed tired out physically, so I shall take her for a long walk by the cliffs to Robin Hood's Bay and back. She ought not to have much inclination for sleep-walking then.

CHAPTER 8.

——◇——

MINA MURRAY'S JOURNAL.

Same day, 11 o'clock p.m.—Oh, but I am tired! If it were not that I had made my diary a duty I should not open it to-night. We had a lovely walk. Lucy, after a while, was in gay spirits, owing, I think, to some dear cows who came nosing towards us in a field close to the lighthouse, and frightened the wits out of us. I believe we forgot everything except, of course, personal fear, and it seemed to wipe the slate clean and give us a fresh start. We had a capital "severe tea" at Robin Hood's Bay in a sweet little old-fashioned inn, with a bow-window right over the seaweed-covered rocks of the strand. I believe we should have shocked the "New Woman" with our appetites. Men are more tolerant, bless them! Then we walked home with some, or rather many, stoppages to rest, and with our hearts full of a constant dread of wild bulls. Lucy was really tired, and we intended to creep off to bed as soon as we could. The young curate came in, however, and Mrs. Westenra asked him to stay for supper. Lucy and I had both a fight for it with the dusty miller; I know it was a hard fight on my part, and I am quite heroic. I think that some day the bishops must get together and see about breeding up a new class of curates, who don't take supper, no matter how they may be pressed to, and who will know when girls are tired. Lucy is asleep and breathing softly. She has more colour in her cheeks than usual, and looks, oh, so sweet. If Mr. Holmwood fell in love with her seeing her only in the drawing-room, I wonder what he would say if he saw her now. Some of the "New Women" writers will some day start an idea that men and women should be allowed to see each other asleep before proposing or accepting. But I suppose the New Woman won't condescend in future to accept; she will do the proposing herself. And a nice job she will make of it, too! There's some consolation in that. I am so happy tonight, because dear Lucy seems better. I really believe she has turned the corner, and that we are over her troubles with dreaming. I should be quite happy if I only knew if Jonathan . . . God bless and keep him.

11 August, 3 a.m.—Diary again. No sleep now, so I may as well write. I am too agitated to sleep. We have had such an adventure, such an agonising experience. I fell asleep as soon as I had closed my diary. . . . Suddenly I became broad awake, and sat up, with a horrible sense of fear upon me, and of some feeling of emptiness around me. The room was dark, so I could not see Lucy's bed; I stole across and felt for her. The bed was empty. I lit a match and found that she was not in the room. The door was shut, but not locked, as I had left it. I feared to wake her mother, who has been more than usually ill lately, so threw on some clothes and got ready to look for her. As I was leaving the room it struck me that the clothes she wore might give me some clue to her dreaming intention. Dressing-gown would mean house; dress, outside. Dressing-gown and dress were both in their places. "Thank God," I said to myself, "she cannot be far, as she is only in her nightdress." I ran downstairs and looked in the sitting-room. Not there! Then I looked in all the other open rooms of the house, with an ever-growing fear chilling my heart. Finally I came to the hall-door and found it open. It was not wide open, but the catch of the lock had not caught. The people of the house are careful to lock the door every night, so I feared that Lucy must have gone out as she was. There was no time to think of what might happen;

a vague, overmastering fear obscured all details. I took a big, heavy shawl and ran out. The clock was striking one as I was in the Crescent, and there was not a soul in sight. I ran along the North Terrace, but could see no sign of the white figure which I expected. At the edge of the West Cliff above the pier I looked across the harbour to the East Cliff, in the hope or fear—I don't know which—of seeing Lucy in our favourite seat. There was a bright full moon, with heavy black, driving clouds, which threw the whole scene into a fleeting diorama of light and shade as they sailed across. For a moment or two I could see nothing, as the shadow of a cloud obscured St. Mary's Church and all around it. Then as the cloud passed I could see the ruins of the abbey coming into view; and as the edge of a narrow band of light as sharp as a sword-cut moved along, the church and the churchyard became gradually visible. Whatever my expectation was, it was not disappointed, for there, on our favourite seat, the silver light of the moon struck a half-reclining figure, snowy white. The coming of the cloud was too quick for me to see much, for shadow shut down on light almost immediately; but it seemed to me as though something dark stood behind the seat where the white figure shone, and bent over it. What it was, whether man or beast, I could not tell; I did not wait to catch another glance, but flew down the steep steps to the pier and along by the fish-market to the bridge, which was the only way to reach the East Cliff. The town seemed as dead, for not a soul did I see; I rejoiced that it was so, for I wanted no witness of poor Lucy's condition. The time and distance seemed endless, and my knees trembled and my breath came laboured as I toiled up the endless steps to the abbey. I must have gone fast, and yet it seemed to me as if my feet were weighted with lead, and as though every joint in my body were rusty. When I got almost to the top I could see the seat and the white figure, for I was now close enough to distinguish it even through the spells of shadow. There was undoubtedly something, long and black, bending over the half-reclining white figure. I called in fright, "Lucy! Lucy!" and something raised a head, and from where I was I could see a white face and red, gleaming eyes. Lucy did not answer, and I ran on to the entrance of the churchyard. As I entered, the church was between me and the seat, and for a minute or so I lost sight of her. When I came in view again the cloud had passed, and the moonlight struck so brilliantly that I could see Lucy half reclining with her head lying over the back of the seat. She was quite alone, and there was not a sign of any living thing about.

When I bent over her I could see that she was still asleep. Her lips were parted, and she was breathing—not softly as usual with her, but in long, heavy gasps, as though striving to get her lungs full at every breath. As I came close, she put up her hand in her sleep and pulled the collar of her nightdress close around her throat. Whilst she did so there came a little shudder through her, as though she felt the cold. I flung the warm shawl over her, and drew the edges tight round her neck, for I dreaded lest she should get some deadly chill from the night air, unclad as she was. I feared to wake her all at once, so, in order to have my hands free that I might help her, I fastened the shawl at her throat with a big safety-pin; but I must have been clumsy in my anxiety and pinched or pricked her with it, for by-and-by, when her breathing became quieter, she put her hand to her throat again and moaned. When I had her carefully wrapped up I put my shoes on her feet, and then began very gently to wake her. At first she did not respond; but gradually she became more and more uneasy in her sleep, moaning and sighing occasionally. At last, as time was passing fast, and, for many other reasons, I wished to get her home at once, I shook her more forcibly, till finally she opened her eyes and awoke. She did not seem surprised to see me, as, of course, she did not realise all at once where she was. Lucy always wakes prettily, and even at such a time, when her body must have been chilled with cold, and her mind somewhat appalled at waking unclad in a churchyard at night, she did not lose her grace. She trembled a little, and clung to me; when I told her to come at once with me home she rose without a word, with the obedience of a child. As we passed along, the gravel hurt my feet, and Lucy noticed me wince. She stopped and wanted to insist upon my taking my shoes; but I would not. However, when we got to the pathway outside the churchyard, where there was a puddle of water, remaining from the storm, I daubed my feet with mud, using each foot in turn on the other, so that as we went home, no one, in case we should meet any one, should notice my bare feet.

Fortune favoured us, and we got home without meeting a soul. Once we saw a man, who seemed not quite sober, passing along a street in front of us; but we hid in a door till he had disappeared up an opening such as there are here, steep little closes, or "wynds," as they call them in Scotland. My heart beat so loud all the time that sometimes I thought I should faint. I was filled with anxiety about Lucy, not only for her health, lest she should suffer from the exposure, but for her reputation in case the story should get wind. When we got in, and had washed our feet, and had said a prayer of thankfulness together, I tucked her into bed. Before falling asleep she asked—even implored—me not to say a word to any one, even her mother, about her sleep-walking adventure. I hesitated at first to promise; but on thinking of the state of her mother's health, and how the knowledge of such a thing would fret her, and thinking, too, of how such a story might become distorted—nay, infallibly would—in case it should leak out, I thought it wiser to do so. I hope I did right. I have locked the door, and the key is tied to my wrist, so perhaps I shall not be again disturbed. Lucy is sleeping soundly; the reflex of the dawn is high and far over the sea. . . .

Same day, noon.—All goes well. Lucy slept till I woke her and seemed not to have even changed her side. The adventure of the night does not seem to have harmed her; on the contrary, it has benefited her, for she looks better this morning than she has done for weeks. I was sorry to notice that my clumsiness with the safety-pin hurt her. Indeed, it might have been serious, for the skin of her throat was pierced. I must have pinched up a piece of loose skin and have transfixed it, for there are two little red points like pin-pricks, and on the band of her nightdress was a drop of blood. When I apologised and was concerned about it, she laughed and petted me, and said she did not even feel it. Fortunately it cannot leave a scar, as it is so tiny.

Same day, night.—We passed a happy day. The air was clear, and the sun bright, and there was a cool breeze. We took our lunch to Mulgrave

Woods, Mrs. Westenra driving by the road and Lucy and I walking by the cliff-path and joining her at the gate. I felt a little sad myself, for I could not but feel how *absolutely* happy it would have been had Jonathan been with me. But there! I must only be patient. In the evening we strolled in the Casino Terrace, and heard some good music by Spohr and Mackenzie, and went to bed early. Lucy seems more restful than she has been for some time, and fell asleep at once. I shall lock the door and secure the key the same as before, though I do not expect any trouble to-night.

12 August.—My expectations were wrong, for twice during the night I was wakened by Lucy trying to get out. She seemed, even in her sleep, to be a little impatient at finding the door shut, and went back to bed under a sort of protest. I woke with the dawn, and heard the birds chirping outside of the window. Lucy woke, too, and, I was glad to see, was even better than on the previous morning. All her old gaiety of manner seemed to have come back, and she came and snuggled in beside me and told me all about Arthur. I told her how anxious I was about Jonathan, and then she tried to comfort me. Well, she succeeded somewhat, for, though sympathy can't alter facts, it can help to make them more bearable.

13 August.—Another quiet day, and to bed with the key on my wrist as before. Again I awoke in the night, and found Lucy sitting up in bed, still asleep, pointing to the window. I got up quietly, and pulling aside the blind, looked out. It was brilliant moonlight, and the soft effect of the light over the sea and sky—merged together in one great, silent mystery—was beautiful beyond words. Between me and the moonlight flitted a great bat, coming and going in great whirling circles. Once or twice it came quite close, but was, I suppose, frightened at seeing me, and flitted away across the harbour towards the abbey. When I came back from the window Lucy had lain down again, and was sleeping peacefully. She did not stir again all night.

14 August.—On the East Cliff, reading and writing all day. Lucy seems to have become as much in love with the spot as I am, and it is hard to get her away from it when it is time to come home for lunch or tea or dinner. This afternoon she made a funny remark. We were coming home for dinner, and had come to the top of the steps up from the West Pier and stopped to look at the view, as we generally do. The setting sun, low down in the sky, was just dropping behind Kettleness; the red light was thrown over on the East Cliff and the old abbey, and seemed to bathe everything in a beautiful rosy glow. We were silent for a while, and suddenly Lucy murmured as if to herself:—

"His red eyes again! They are just the same." It was such an odd expression, coming *apropos* of nothing, that it quite startled me. I slewed round a little, so as to see Lucy well without seeming to stare at her, and saw that she was in a half-dreamy state, with an odd look on her face that I could not quite make out; so I said nothing, but followed her eyes. She appeared to be looking over at our own seat, whereon was a dark figure seated alone. I was a little startled myself, for it seemed for an instant as if the stranger had great eyes like burning flames; but a second look dispelled the illusion. The red sunlight was shining on the windows of St. Mary's Church behind our seat, and as the sun dipped there was just sufficient change in the refraction and reflection to make it appear as if the light moved. I called Lucy's attention to the peculiar effect, and she became herself with a start, but she looked sad all the same; it may have been that she was thinking of that terrible night up there. We never refer to it; so I said nothing, and we went home to dinner. Lucy had a headache and went early to bed. I saw her asleep, and went out for a little stroll myself; I walked along the cliffs to the westward, and was full of sweet sadness, for I was thinking of Jonathan. When coming home—it was then bright moonlight, so bright that, though the front of our part of the Crescent was in shadow, everything could be well seen— I threw a glance up at our window, and saw Lucy's head leaning out. I thought that perhaps she was looking out for me, so I opened my handkerchief and waved it. She did not notice or make any movement whatever. Just then, the moonlight crept round an angle of the building, and the light fell on the window. There distinctly was Lucy with her head lying up against the side of the window-sill and her eyes shut. She was fast asleep, and by her, seated on the window-sill, was something that looked like a good-sized bird. I was afraid she might get a chill, so I ran upstairs, but as I came into the room she was moving back to her bed, fast asleep, and breathing heavily; she was holding her hand to her throat, as though to protect it from cold.

I did not wake her, but tucked her up warmly; I have taken care that the door is locked and the window securely fastened.

She looks so sweet as she sleeps; but she is paler than is her wont, and there is a drawn, haggard look under her eyes which I do not like. I fear she is fretting about something. I wish I could find out what it is.

15 August.—Rose later than usual. Lucy was languid and tired, and slept on after we had been called. We had a happy surprise at breakfast. Arthur's father is better, and wants the marriage to come off soon. Lucy is full of quiet joy, and her mother is glad and sorry at once. Later on in the day she told me the cause. She is grieved to lose Lucy as her very own, but she is rejoiced that she is soon to have some one to protect her. Poor dear, sweet lady! She confided to me that she has got her death-warrant. She has not told Lucy, and made me promise secrecy; her doctor told her that within a few months, at most, she must die, for her heart is weakening. At any time, even now, a sudden shock would be almost sure to kill her. Ah, we were wise to keep from her the affair of the dreadful night of Lucy's sleep-walking.

17 August.—No diary for two whole days. I have not had the heart to write. Some sort of shadowy pall seems to be coming over our happiness. No news from Jonathan, and Lucy seems to be growing weaker, whilst her mother's hours are numbering to a close. I do not understand Lucy's fading away as she is doing. She eats well and sleeps well, and enjoys the fresh air; but all the time the roses in her cheeks are fading, and she gets weaker and more languid day by day; at night I hear her gasping as if for air. I keep the key of our door always fastened to my wrist at night, but she gets up and walks about the room, and sits at the open window. Last night I found her leaning out when I woke up, and when I tried to wake her I could not; she was in a faint. When I managed to restore her she was as weak as water, and cried silently between long, painful struggles for breath. When I asked her how she came to be at the window she shook her head and turned away. I trust her feeling ill may not be from that unlucky prick of the safety-pin. I looked at her throat just now as she lay asleep, and the tiny wounds seem not to have healed. They are still open, and, if anything, larger than before, and the edges of them are faintly white. They are like little white dots with red centres. Unless they heal within a day or two I shall insist on the doctor seeing about them.

LETTER FROM SAMUEL F. BILLINGTON & SON, SOLICITORS, WHITBY, TO MESSRS. CARTER, PATERSON & CO., LONDON.

"*17 August.*

"Dear Sirs,—

"Herewith please receive invoice of goods sent by Great Northern Railway. Same are to be delivered at Carfax, near Purfleet, immediately on receipt at goods station King's Cross. The house is at present empty, but enclosed please find keys, all of which are labelled.

"You will please deposit the boxes, fifty in number, which form the consignment, in the partially ruined building forming part of the house and marked 'A' on rough diagram enclosed. Your agent will easily recognise the locality, as it is the ancient chapel of the mansion. The goods leave by the train at 9:30 to-night, and will be due at King's Cross at 4:30 to-morrow afternoon. As our client wishes the delivery made as soon as possible, we shall be obliged by your having teams ready at King's Cross at the time named and forthwith conveying the goods to destination. In order to obviate any delays possible through any routine requirements as to payment in your departments, we enclose cheque herewith for ten pounds (£10), receipt of which please acknowledge. Should the charge be less than this amount, you can return balance; if greater, we shall at once send cheque for difference on hearing from you. You are to leave the keys on coming away in the main hall of the house, where the proprietor may get them on his entering the house by means of his duplicate key.

"Pray do not take us as exceeding the bounds of business courtesy in pressing you in all ways to use the utmost expedition.

"We are, dear Sirs,

"Faithfully yours,

"SAMUEL F. BILLINGTON & SON."

LETTER FROM MESSRS. CARTER, PATERSON & CO., LONDON, TO MESSRS. SAMUEL F. BILLINGTON & SON, WHITBY.

"*21 August.*

"Dear Sirs,—

"We beg to acknowledge £10 received and to return cheque £1 17s. 9d, amount of overplus, as shown in receipted account herewith. Goods are delivered in exact accordance with instructions, and keys left in parcel in main hall, as directed.

"We are, dear Sirs,

"Yours respectfully,

"*Pro* CARTER, PATERSON & CO."

MINA MURRAY'S JOURNAL.

18 August.—I am happy to-day, and write sitting on the seat in the churchyard. Lucy is ever so much better. Last night she slept well all night, and did not disturb me once. The roses seem coming back already to her cheeks, though she is still sadly pale and wan-looking. If she were in any way anaemic I could understand it, but she is not. She is in gay spirits and full of life and cheerfulness. All the morbid reticence seems to have passed from her, and she has just reminded me, as if I needed any reminding, of *that* night, and that it was here, on this very seat, I found her asleep. As she told me she tapped playfully with the heel of her boot on the stone slab and said:—

"My poor little feet didn't make much noise then! I daresay poor old Mr. Swales would have told me that it was because I didn't want to wake up Geordie." As she was in such a communicative humour, I asked her if she had dreamed at all that night. Before she answered, that sweet, puckered look came into her forehead, which Arthur—I call him Arthur from her habit—says he loves; and, indeed, I don't wonder that he does. Then she went on in a half-dreaming kind of way, as if trying to recall it to herself:—

"I didn't quite dream; but it all seemed to be real. I only wanted to be here in this spot—I don't know why, for I was afraid of something—I don't know what. I remember, though I suppose I was asleep, passing through the streets and over the bridge. A fish leaped as I went by, and I leaned over to look at it, and I heard a lot of dogs howling—the whole town seemed as if it must be full of dogs all howling at once—as I went up the steps. Then I had a vague memory of something long and dark with red eyes, just as we saw in the sunset, and something very sweet and very bitter all around me at once; and then I seemed sinking into deep green water, and there was a singing in my ears, as I have heard there is to drowning men; and then everything seemed passing away from me; my soul seemed to go out from my body and float about the air. I seem to remember that once the West Lighthouse was right under me, and then there was a sort of agonising feeling, as if I were in an earthquake, and I came back and found you shaking my body. I saw you do it before I felt you."

Then she began to laugh. It seemed a little uncanny to me, and I listened to her breathlessly. I did not quite like it, and thought it better not to keep her mind on the subject, so we drifted on to other subjects, and Lucy was like her old self again. When we got home the fresh breeze had braced her up, and her pale cheeks were really more rosy. Her mother rejoiced when she saw her, and we all spent a very happy evening together.

19 August.—Joy, joy, joy! Although not all joy. At last, news of Jonathan. The dear fellow has been ill; that is why he did not write. I am not afraid to think it or say it, now that I know. Mr. Hawkins sent me on the letter, and wrote himself, oh, so kindly. I am to leave in the morning and go over to Jonathan, and to help to nurse him if necessary, and to bring him home. Mr. Hawkins says it would not be a bad thing if we were to be married out there. I have cried over the good Sister's letter till I can feel it wet against my bosom, where it lies. It is of Jonathan, and must be next my heart, for he is *in* my heart. My journey is all mapped out, and my luggage ready. I am only taking one change of dress; Lucy will bring my trunk to London and keep it till I send for it, for it may be that . . . I must write no more; I must keep it to say to Jonathan, my husband. The letter that he has seen and touched must comfort me till we meet.

LETTER FROM SISTER AGATHA, HOSPITAL
OF ST. JOSEPH AND STE. MARY, BUDA-PESTH,
TO MISS WILHELMINA MURRAY.

"*12 August.*

"Dear Madam,—

"I write by desire of Mr. Jonathan Harker, who is himself not strong enough to write, though progressing well, thanks to God and St. Joseph and Ste. Mary. He has been under our care for nearly six weeks, suffering from a violent brain fever. He wishes me to convey his love, and to say that by this post I write for him to Mr. Peter Hawkins, Exeter, to say, with his dutiful respects, that he is sorry for his delay, and that all of his work is completed. He will require some few weeks' rest in our sanatorium in the hills, but will then return. He wishes me to say that he has not sufficient money with him, and that he would like to pay for his staying here, so that others who need shall not be wanting for help.

"Believe me,
    yours, with sympathy and all blessings,
    "SISTER AGATHA.

"P. S.—My patient being asleep, I open this to let you know something more. He has told me all about you, and that you are shortly to be his wife. All blessings to you both! He has had some fearful shock—so says our doctor—and in his delirium his ravings have been dreadful; of wolves and poison and blood; of ghosts and demons; and I fear to say of what. Be careful with him always that there may be nothing to excite him of this kind for a long time to come; the traces of such an illness as his do not lightly die away. We should have written long ago, but we knew nothing of his friends, and there was on him nothing that any one could understand. He came in the train from Klausenburg, and the guard was told by the station-master there that he rushed into the station shouting for a ticket for home. Seeing from his violent demeanour that he was English, they gave him a ticket for the furthest station on the way thither that the train reached.

"Be assured that he is well cared for. He has won all hearts by his sweetness and gentleness. He is truly getting on well, and I have no doubt will in a few weeks be all himself. But be careful of him for safety's sake. There are, I pray God and St. Joseph and Ste. Mary, many, many, happy years for you both."

DR. SEWARD'S DIARY.

19 August.—Strange and sudden change in Renfield last night. About eight o'clock he began to get excited and sniff about as a dog does when setting. The attendant was struck by his manner, and knowing my interest in him, encouraged him to talk. He is usually respectful to the attendant and at times servile; but to-night, the man tells me, he was quite haughty. Would not condescend to talk with him at all. All he would say was:—

"I don't want to talk to you: you don't count now; the Master is at hand."

The attendant thinks it is some sudden form of religious mania which has seized him. If so, we must look out for squalls, for a strong man with homicidal and religious mania at once might be dangerous.

The combination is a dreadful one. At nine o'clock I visited him myself. His attitude to me was the same as that to the attendant; in his sublime self-feeling the difference between myself and the attendant seemed to him as nothing. It looks like religious mania, and he will soon think that he himself is God. These infinitesimal distinctions between man and man are too paltry for an Omnipotent Being. How these madmen give themselves away! The real God taketh heed lest a sparrow fall; but the God created from human vanity sees no difference between an eagle and a sparrow. Oh, if men only knew!

For half an hour or more Renfield kept getting excited in greater and greater degree. I did not pretend to be watching him, but I kept strict observation all the same. All at once that shifty look came into his eyes which we always see when a madman has seized an idea, and with it the shifty movement of the head and back which asylum attendants come to know so well. He became quite quiet; and went and sat on the edge of his bed resignedly, and looked into space with lack-lustre eyes. I thought I would find out if his apathy were real or only assumed, and tried to lead him to talk of his pets, a theme which had never failed to excite his attention. At first he made no reply, but at length said testily:—

"Bother them all! I don't care a pin about them."

"What?" I said. "You don't mean to tell me you don't care about spiders?" (Spiders at present are his hobby and the notebook is filling up with columns of small figures.) To this he answered enigmatically:—

"The bride-maidens rejoice the eyes that wait the coming of the bride; but when the bride draweth nigh, then the maidens shine not to the eyes that are filled."

He would not explain himself, but remained obstinately seated on his bed all the time I remained with him.

I am weary to-night and low in spirits. I cannot but think of Lucy, and how different things might have been. If I don't sleep at once, chloral, the modern Morpheus—C_2HCl_3O. H_2O! I must be careful not to let it grow into a habit. No, I shall take none to-night! I have thought of Lucy, and I shall not dishonour her by mixing the two. If need be, to-night shall be sleepless. . . .

Later.—Glad I made the resolution; gladder that I kept to it. I had lain tossing about, and had heard the clock strike only twice, when the night-watchman came to me, sent up from the ward, to say that Renfield had escaped. I threw on my clothes and ran down at once; my patient is too dangerous a person to be roaming about. Those ideas of his might work out dangerously with strangers. The attendant was waiting for me. He said he had seen him not ten minutes before, seemingly asleep in his bed, when he had looked through the observation-trap in the door. His attention was called by the sound of the window being wrenched out. He ran back and saw his feet disappear through the window, and had at once sent up for me. He was only in his night-gear, and cannot be far off. The attendant thought it would be more useful to watch where he should go than to follow him, as he might lose sight of him whilst getting out of the building by the door. He is a bulky man, and couldn't get through the window. I am thin, so, with his aid, I got out, but feet foremost, and, as we were only a few feet above ground, landed unhurt. The attendant told me the patient had gone to the left, and had taken a straight line, so I ran as quickly as I could. As I got through the belt of trees I saw a white figure scale the high wall which separates our grounds from those of the deserted house.

I ran back at once, told the watchman to get three or four men immediately and follow me into the grounds of Carfax, in case our friend might be dangerous. I got a ladder myself, and crossing the wall, dropped down on the other side. I could see Renfield's figure just disappearing behind the angle of the house, so I ran after him. On the far side of the house I found him pressed close against the old ironbound oak door of the chapel. He was talking, apparently to some one, but I was afraid to go near enough to hear what he was saying, lest I might frighten him, and he should run off. Chasing an errant swarm of bees is nothing to following a naked lunatic, when the fit of escaping is upon him! After a few minutes, however, I could see that he did not take note of anything around him, and so ventured to draw nearer to him— the more so as my men had now crossed the wall and were closing him in. I heard him say:—

"I am here to do Your bidding, Master. I am Your slave, and You will reward me, for I shall be faithful. I have worshipped You long and afar off. Now that You are near, I await Your commands, and You will not pass me by, will You, dear Master, in Your distribution of good things?"

He *is* a selfish old beggar anyhow. He thinks of the loaves and fishes even when he believes he is in a Real Presence. His manias make a startling combination. When we closed in on him he fought like a tiger. He is immensely strong, for he was more like a wild beast than a man. I never saw a lunatic in such a paroxysm of rage before; and I hope I shall not again. It is a mercy that we have found out his strength and his danger in good time. With strength and determination like this, he might have done wild work before he was caged. He is safe now at any rate. Jack Sheppard himself couldn't get free from the strait-waistcoat that keeps him restrained, and he's chained to the wall in the padded room. His cries are at times awful, but the silences that follow are more deadly still, for he means murder in every turn and movement.

Just now he spoke coherent words for the first time:—

"I shall be patient, Master. It is coming—coming—coming!"

So I took the hint and came too. I was too excited to sleep, but this diary has quieted me, and I feel I shall get some sleep to-night.

CHAPTER 9.

LETTER FROM MINA HARKER TO LUCY WESTENRA.

"*Buda-Pesth, 24 August.*

"My dearest Lucy,—

"I know you will be anxious to hear all that has happened since we parted at the railway station at Whitby. Well, my dear, I got to Hull all right, and caught the boat to Hamburg, and then the train on here. I feel that I can hardly recall anything of the journey, except that I knew I was coming to Jonathan, and, that as I should have to do some nursing, I had better get all the sleep I could. . . . I found my dear one, oh, so thin and pale and weak-looking. All the resolution has gone out of his dear eyes, and that quiet dignity which I told you was in his face has vanished. He is only a wreck of himself, and he does not remember anything that has happened to him for a long time past. At least, he wants me to believe so, and I shall never ask. He has had some terrible shock, and I fear it might tax his poor brain if he were to try to recall it. Sister Agatha, who is a good creature and a born nurse, tells me that he raved of dreadful things whilst he was off his head. I wanted her to tell me what they were; but she would only cross herself, and say she would never tell; that the ravings of the sick were the secrets of God, and that if a nurse through her vocation should hear them, she should respect her trust. She is a sweet, good soul, and the next day, when she saw I was troubled, she opened up the subject again, and after saying that she could never mention what my poor dear raved about, added: 'I can tell you this much, my dear: that it was not about anything which he has done wrong himself; and you, as his wife to be, have no cause to be concerned. He has not forgotten you or what he owes to you. His fear was of great and terrible things, which no mortal can treat of.' I do believe the dear soul thought I might be jealous lest my poor dear should have fallen in love with any other girl. The idea of *my* being jealous about Jonathan! And yet, my dear, let me whisper, I felt a thrill of joy through me when I *knew* that no other woman was a cause of trouble. I am now sitting by his bedside, where I can see his face while he sleeps. He is waking! . . .

"When he woke he asked me for his coat, as he wanted to get something from the pocket; I asked Sister Agatha, and she brought all his things. I saw that amongst them was his notebook, and was going to ask him to let me look at it—for I knew then that I might find some clue to his trouble—but I suppose he must have seen my wish in my eyes, for he sent me over to the window, saying he wanted to be quite alone for a moment. Then he called me back, and when I came he had his hand over the notebook, and he said to me very solemnly:—

"'Wilhelmina'—I knew then that he was in deadly earnest, for he has never called me by that name since he asked me to marry him—'you know, dear, my ideas of the trust between husband and wife: there should be no secret, no concealment. I have had a great shock, and when I try to think of what it is I feel my head spin round, and I do not know if it was all real or the dreaming of a madman. You know I have had brain fever, and that is to be mad. The secret is here, and I do not want to know it. I want to take up my life here, with our marriage.' For, my dear, we had decided to be married as soon as the formalities are complete. 'Are you willing, Wilhelmina, to share my ignorance? Here is the book. Take it and keep it, read it if you will, but never let me know;

unless, indeed, some solemn duty should come upon me to go back to the bitter hours, asleep or awake, sane or mad, recorded here.' He fell back exhausted, and I put the book under his pillow, and kissed him. I had asked Sister Agatha to beg the Superior to let our wedding be this afternoon, and am waiting her reply. . . .

"She has come and told me that the chaplain of the English mission church has been sent for. We are to be married in an hour, or as soon after as Jonathan awakes. . . .

"Lucy, the time has come and gone. I feel very solemn, but very, very happy. Jonathan woke a little after the hour, and all was ready, and he sat up in bed, propped up with pillows. He answered his 'I will' firmly and strongly. I could hardly speak; my heart was so full that even those words seemed to choke me. The dear sisters were so kind. Please God, I shall never, never forget them, nor the grave and sweet responsibilities I have taken upon me. I must tell you of my wedding present. When the chaplain and the sisters had left me alone with my husband—oh, Lucy, it is the first time I have written the words 'my husband'—left me alone with my husband, I took the book from under his pillow, and wrapped it up in white paper, and tied it with a little bit of pale blue ribbon which was round my neck, and sealed it over the knot with sealing-wax, and for my seal I used my wedding ring. Then I kissed it and showed it to my husband, and told him that I would keep it so, and then it would be an outward and visible sign for us all our lives that we trusted each other; that I would never open it unless it were for his own dear sake or for the sake of some stern duty. Then he took my hand in his, and oh, Lucy, it was the first time he took *his wife's* hand, and said it was the dearest thing in all the wide world, and that he would go through all the past again to win it, if need be. The poor dear meant to have said a part of the past, but he cannot think of time yet, and I shall not wonder if at first he mixes up not only the month, but the year.

"Well, my dear, what could I say? I could only tell him that I was the happiest woman in all the wide world, and that I had nothing to give him except myself, my life, and my trust, and that with these went my love and duty for all the days of my life. And, my dear, when he kissed me, and drew me to him with his poor weak hands, it was like a very solemn pledge between us. . . .

"Lucy dear, do you know why I tell you all this? It is not only because it is all sweet to me, but because you have been, and are, very dear to me. It was my privilege to be your friend and guide when you came from the schoolroom to prepare for the world of life. I want you to see now, and with the eyes of a very happy wife, whither duty has led me; so that in your own married life you too may be all happy as I am. My dear, please Almighty God, your life may be all it promises: a long day of sunshine, with no harsh wind, no forgetting duty, no distrust. I must not wish you no pain, for that can never be; but I do hope you will be *always* as happy as I am *now*. Good-bye, my dear. I shall post this at once, and, perhaps, write you very soon again. I must stop, for Jonathan is waking—I must attend to my husband!

"Your ever-loving

"MINA HARKER."

LETTER FROM LUCY WESTENRA TO MINA HARKER.

Whitby, 30 August.

"My dearest Mina,—

"Oceans of love and millions of kisses, and may you soon be in your own home with your husband. I wish you could be coming home soon enough to stay with us here. The strong air would soon restore Jonathan; it has quite restored me. I have an appetite like a cormorant, am full of life, and sleep well. You will be glad to know that I have quite given up walking in my sleep. I think I have not stirred out of my bed for a week, that is when I once got into it at night. Arthur says I am getting fat. By the way, I forgot to tell you that Arthur is here. We have such walks and drives, and rides, and rowing, and tennis, and fishing together; and I love him more than ever. He *tells* me that he loves me more, but I doubt that, for at first he told me that he couldn't love me more than he did then. But this is nonsense. There he is, calling to me. So no more just at present from your loving

"LUCY.

"P. S.—Mother sends her love. She seems better, poor dear.

"P. P. S.—We are to be married on 28 September."

DR. SEWARD'S DIARY.

20 August.—The case of Renfield grows even more interesting. He has now so far quieted that there are spells of cessation from his passion. For the first week after his attack he was perpetually violent. Then one night, just as the moon rose, he grew quiet, and kept murmuring to himself: "Now I can wait; now I can wait." The attendant came to tell me, so I ran down at once to have a look at him. He was still in the strait-waistcoat and in the padded room, but the suffused look had gone from his face, and his eyes had something of their old pleading—I might almost say, "cringing"—softness. I was satisfied with his present condition, and directed him to be relieved. The attendants hesitated, but finally carried out my wishes without protest. It was a strange thing that the patient had humour enough to see their distrust, for, coming close to me, he said in a whisper, all the while looking furtively at them:—

"They think I could hurt you! Fancy *me* hurting *you*! The fools!"

It was soothing, somehow, to the feelings to find myself dissociated even in the mind of this poor madman from the others; but all the same I do not follow his thought. Am I to take it that I have anything in common with him, so that we are, as it were, to stand together; or has he to gain from me some good so stupendous that my well-being is needful to him? I must find out later on. To-night he will not speak. Even the offer of a kitten or even a full-grown cat will not tempt him. He will only say: "I don't take any stock in cats. I have more to think of now, and I can wait; I can wait."

After a while I left him. The attendant tells me that he was quiet until just before dawn, and that then he began to get uneasy, and at length violent, until at last he fell into a paroxysm which exhausted him so that he swooned into a sort of coma.

. . . Three nights has the same thing happened—violent all day then quiet from moonrise to sunrise. I wish I could get some clue to the cause. It would almost seem as if there was some influence which came and went. Happy thought! We shall to-night play sane wits against mad ones. He escaped before without our help; to-night he shall escape with it. We shall give him a chance, and have the men ready to follow in case they are required. . . .

23 *August.*—"The unexpected always happens." How well Disraeli knew life. Our bird when he found the cage open would not fly, so all our subtle arrangements were for nought. At any rate, we have proved one thing; that the spells of quietness last a reasonable time. We shall in future be able to ease his bonds for a few hours each day. I have given orders to the night attendant merely to shut him in the padded room, when once he is quiet, until an hour before sunrise. The poor soul's body will enjoy the relief even if his mind cannot appreciate it. Hark! The unexpected again! I am called; the patient has once more escaped.

Later.—Another night adventure. Renfield artfully waited until the attendant was entering the room to inspect. Then he dashed out past him and flew down the passage. I sent word for the attendants to follow. Again he went into the grounds of the deserted house, and we found him in the same place, pressed against the old chapel door. When he saw me he became furious, and had not the attendants seized him in time, he would have tried to kill me. As we were holding him a strange thing happened. He suddenly redoubled his efforts, and then as suddenly grew calm. I looked round instinctively, but could see nothing. Then I caught the patient's eye and followed it, but could trace nothing as it looked into the moonlit sky except a big bat, which was flapping its silent and ghostly way to the west. Bats usually wheel and flit about, but this one seemed to go straight on, as if it knew where it was bound for or had some intention of its own. The patient grew calmer every instant, and presently said:—

"You needn't tie me; I shall go quietly!" Without trouble we came back to the house. I feel there is something ominous in his calm, and shall not forget this night. . . .

LUCY WESTENRA'S DIARY.

Hillingham, 24 August.—I must imitate Mina, and keep writing things down. Then we can have long talks when we do meet. I wonder when it will be. I wish she were with me again, for I feel so unhappy. Last night I seemed to be dreaming again just as I was at Whitby. Perhaps it is the change of air, or getting home again. It is all dark and horrid to me, for I can remember nothing; but I am full of vague fear, and I feel so weak and worn out. When Arthur came to lunch he looked quite grieved when he saw me, and I hadn't the spirit to try to be cheerful. I wonder if I could sleep in mother's room to-night. I shall make an excuse and try.

25 August.—Another bad night. Mother did not seem to take to my proposal. She seems not too well herself, and doubtless she fears to worry me. I tried to keep awake, and succeeded for a while; but when the clock struck twelve it waked me from a doze, so I must have been falling asleep. There was a sort of scratching or flapping at the window, but I did not mind it, and as I remember no more, I suppose I must then have fallen asleep. More bad dreams. I wish I could remember them. This morning I am horribly weak. My face is ghastly pale, and my throat pains me. It must be something wrong with my lungs, for I don't seem ever to get air enough. I shall try to cheer up when Arthur comes, or else I know he will be miserable to see me so.

LETTER FROM ARTHUR HOLMWOOD TO DR. SEWARD.

"Albemarle Hotel, 31 August.

"My dear Jack,—

"I want you to do me a favour. Lucy is ill; that is, she has no special disease, but she looks awful, and is getting worse every day. I have asked her if there is any cause; I do not dare to ask her mother, for to disturb the poor lady's mind about her daughter in her present state of health would be fatal. Mrs. Westenra has confided to me that her doom is spoken—disease of the heart—though poor Lucy does not know it yet. I am sure that there is something preying on my dear girl's mind. I am almost distracted when I think of her; to look at her gives me a pang. I told her I should ask you to see her, and though she demurred at first—I know why, old fellow—she finally consented. It will be a painful task for you, I know, old friend, but it is for *her* sake, and I must not hesitate to ask, or you to act. You are to come to lunch at Hillingham to-morrow, two o'clock, so as not to arouse any suspicion in Mrs. Westenra, and after lunch Lucy will take an opportunity of being alone with you. I shall come in for tea, and we can go away together; I am filled with anxiety, and want to consult with you alone as soon as I can after you have seen her. Do not fail!

"ARTHUR."

TELEGRAM, ARTHUR HOLMWOOD TO DR. SEWARD.

"1 September.—Am summoned to see my father, who is worse. Am writing. Write me fully by to-night's post to Ring. Wire me if necessary."

LETTER FROM DR. SEWARD TO ARTHUR HOLMWOOD.

"2 September.

"My dear old fellow,—

"With regard to Miss Westenra's health I hasten to let you know at once that in my opinion there is not any functional disturbance or any malady that I know of. At the same time, I am not by any means satisfied with her appearance; she is woefully different from what she was when I saw her last. Of course you must bear in mind that I did not have full opportunity of examination such as I should wish; our very friendship makes a little difficulty which not even medical science or custom can bridge over. I had better tell you exactly what happened, leaving you to draw, in a measure, your own conclusions. I shall then say what I have done and propose doing.

"I found Miss Westenra in seemingly gay spirits. Her mother was present, and in a few seconds I made up my mind that she was trying all she knew to mislead her mother and prevent her from being anxious. I have no doubt she guesses, if she does not know, what need of caution there is. We lunched alone, and as we all exerted ourselves to be cheerful, we got, as some kind of reward for our labours, some real cheerfulness amongst us. Then Mrs. Westenra went to lie down, and Lucy was left with me. We went into her boudoir, and till we got there her gaiety remained, for the servants were coming and going. As soon as the door was closed, however, the mask fell from her face, and she sank down into a chair with a great sigh, and hid her eyes with her hand. When I saw that her high spirits had failed, I at once took advantage of her reaction to make a diagnosis. She said to me very sweetly:

"'I cannot tell you how I loathe talking about myself.' I reminded her that a doctor's confidence was sacred, but that you were grievously anxious about her. She caught on to my meaning at once, and settled that matter in a word. 'Tell Arthur everything you choose. I do not care for myself, but all for him!' So I am quite free.

"I could easily see that she is somewhat bloodless, but I could not see the usual anaemic signs, and by a chance I was actually able to test the quality of her blood, for in opening a window which was stiff a cord gave way, and she cut her hand slightly with broken glass. It was a slight matter in itself, but it gave me an evident chance, and I secured a few drops of the blood and have analysed them. The qualitative analysis gives a quite normal condition, and shows, I should infer, in itself a vigorous state of health. In other physical matters I was quite satisfied that there is no need for anxiety; but as there must be a cause somewhere, I have come to the conclusion that it must be something mental. She complains of difficulty in breathing satisfactorily at times, and of heavy, lethargic sleep, with dreams that frighten her, but regarding which she can remember nothing. She says that as a child she used to walk in her sleep, and that when in Whitby the habit came back, and that once she walked out in the night and went to East Cliff, where Miss Murray found her; but she assures me that of late the habit has not returned. I am in doubt, and so have done the best thing I know of; I have written to my old friend and master, Professor Van Helsing, of Amsterdam, who knows as much about obscure diseases as any one in the world. I have asked him to come over, and as you told me that all things were to be at your charge, I have mentioned to him who you are and your relations to Miss Westenra. This, my dear fellow, is in obedience to your wishes, for I am only too proud and happy to do anything I can for her. Van Helsing would, I know, do anything for me for a personal reason, so, no matter on what ground he comes, we must accept his wishes. He is a seemingly arbitrary man, but this because he knows what he is talking about better than any one else. He is a philosopher and a metaphysician, and one of the most advanced scientists of his day; and he has, I believe, an absolutely open mind. This, with an iron nerve, a temper of the icebrook, an indomitable resolution, self-command, and toleration exalted from virtues to blessings, and the kindliest and truest heart that beats—these form his equipment for the noble work that he is doing for mankind—work both in theory and practise, for his views are as wide as his all-embracing sympathy. I tell you these facts that you may know why I have such confidence in him. I have asked him to come at once. I shall see Miss Westenra to-morrow again. She is to meet me at the Stores, so that I may not alarm her mother by too early a repetition of my call.

"Yours always,

"JOHN SEWARD."

LETTER FROM ABRAHAM VAN HELSING, M.D., D.PH., D.LIT., ETC., ETC., TO DR. SEWARD.

"*2 September.*

"My good Friend,—

"When I have received your letter I am already coming to you. By good fortune I can leave just at once, without wrong to any of those who have trusted me. Were fortune other, then it were bad for those who have trusted, for I come to my friend when he call me to aid those he holds dear. Tell your friend that when that time you suck from my wound so swiftly the poison of the gangrene from that knife that our other friend, too nervous, let slip, you did more for him when he wants my aids and you call for them than all his great fortune could do. But it is pleasure added to do for him, your friend; it is to you that I come. Have then rooms for me at the Great Eastern Hotel, so that I may be near to hand, and please it so arrange that we may see the young lady not too late on to-morrow, for it is likely that I may have to return here that night. But if need be I shall come again in three days, and stay longer if it must. Till then good-bye, my friend John.

"VAN HELSING."

LETTER FROM DR. SEWARD TO ARTHUR HOLMWOOD.

"*3 September.*

"My dear Art,—

"Van Helsing has come and gone. He came on with me to Hillingham, and found that, by Lucy's discretion, her mother was lunching out, so that we were alone with her. Van Helsing made a very careful examination of the patient. He is to report to me, and I shall advise you, for of course I was not present all the time. He is, I fear, much concerned, but says he must think. When I told him of our friendship and how you trust to me in the matter, he said: 'You must tell him all you think. Tell him what I think, if you can guess it, if you will. Nay, I am not jesting.

This is no jest, but life and death, perhaps more.' I asked what he meant by that, for he was very serious. This was when we had come back to town, and he was having a cup of tea before starting on his return to Amsterdam. He would not give me any further clue. You must not be angry with me, Art, because his very reticence means that all his brains are working for her good. He will speak plainly enough when the time comes, be sure. So I told him I would simply write an account of our visit, just as if I were doing a descriptive special article for *The Daily Telegraph*. He seemed not to notice, but remarked that the smuts in London were not quite so bad as they used to be when he was a student here. I am to get his report to-morrow if he can possibly make it. In any case I am to have a letter.

"Well, as to the visit. Lucy was more cheerful than on the day I first saw her, and certainly looked better. She had lost something of the ghastly look that so upset you, and her breathing was normal. She was very sweet to the professor (as she always is), and tried to make him feel at ease; though I could see that the poor girl was making a hard struggle for it. I believe Van Helsing saw it, too, for I saw the quick look under his bushy brows that I knew of old. Then he began to chat of all things except ourselves and diseases and with such an infinite geniality that I could see poor Lucy's pretense of animation merge into reality. Then, without any seeming change, he brought the conversation gently round to his visit, and suavely said:—

"'My dear young miss, I have the so great pleasure because you are so much beloved. That is much, my dear, ever were there that which I do not see. They told me you were down in the spirit, and that you were of a ghastly pale. To them I say: "Pouf!"' And he snapped his fingers at me and went on: 'But you and I shall show them how wrong they are. How can he'—and he pointed at me with the same look and gesture as that with which once he pointed me out to his class, on, or rather after, a particular occasion which he never fails to remind me of—'know any-thing of a young ladies? He has his madmen to play with, and to bring them back to happiness, and to those that love them. It is much to do, and, oh, but there are rewards, in that we can bestow such happiness.

But the young ladies! He has no wife nor daughter, and the young do not tell themselves to the young, but to the old, like me, who have known so many sorrows and the causes of them. So, my dear, we will send him away to smoke the cigarette in the garden, whiles you and I have little talk all to ourselves.' I took the hint, and strolled about, and presently the professor came to the window and called me in. He looked grave, but said: 'I have made careful examination, but there is no functional cause. With you I agree that there has been much blood lost; it has been, but is not. But the conditions of her are in no way anaemic. I have asked her to send me her maid, that I may ask just one or two question, that so I may not chance to miss nothing. I know well what she will say. And yet there is cause; there is always cause for everything. I must go back home and think. You must send to me the telegram every day; and if there be cause I shall come again. The disease—for not to be all well is a disease—interest me, and the sweet young dear, she interest me too. She charm me, and for her, if not for you or disease, I come.'

"As I tell you, he would not say a word more, even when we were alone. And so now, Art, you know all I know. I shall keep stern watch. I trust your poor father is rallying. It must be a terrible thing to you, my dear old fellow, to be placed in such a position between two people who are both so dear to you. I know your idea of duty to your father, and you are right to stick to it; but, if need be, I shall send you word to come at once to Lucy; so do not be over-anxious unless you hear from me."

DR. SEWARD'S DIARY.

4 September.—Zoöphagous patient still keeps up our interest in him. He had only one outburst and that was yesterday at an unusual time. Just before the stroke of noon he began to grow restless. The attendant knew the symptoms, and at once summoned aid. Fortunately the men came at a run, and were just in time, for at the stroke of noon he became so violent that it took all their strength to hold him. In about five minutes, however, he began to get more and more quiet, and finally sank into a sort of melancholy, in which state he has remained up to now. The attendant tells me that his screams whilst in the paroxysm were really appalling; I found my hands full when I got in, attending to some of the other patients who were frightened by him. Indeed, I can quite understand the effect, for the sounds disturbed even me, though I was some distance away. It is now after the dinner-hour of the asylum, and as yet my patient sits in a corner brooding, with a dull, sullen, woe-begone look in his face, which seems rather to indicate than to show something directly. I cannot quite understand it.

Later.—Another change in my patient. At five o'clock I looked in on him, and found him seemingly as happy and contented as he used to be. He was catching flies and eating them, and was keeping note of his capture by making nail-marks on the edge of the door between the ridges of padding. When he saw me, he came over and apologised for his bad conduct, and asked me in a very humble, cringing way to be led back to his own room and to have his note-book again. I thought it well to humour him: so he is back in his room with the window open. He has the sugar of his tea spread out on the window-sill, and is reaping quite a harvest of flies. He is not now eating them, but putting them into a box, as of old, and is already examining the corners of his room to find a spider. I tried to get him to talk about the past few days, for any clue to his thoughts would be of immense help to me; but he would not rise. For a moment or two he looked very sad, and said in a sort of far-away voice, as though saying it rather to himself than to me:—

"All over! all over! He has deserted me. No hope for me now unless I do it for myself!" Then suddenly turning to me in a resolute way, he said: "Doctor, won't you be very good to me and let me have a little more sugar? I think it would be good for me."

"And the flies?" I said.

"Yes! The flies like it, too; and I like the flies; therefore I like it." And there are people who know so little as to think that madmen do not argue. I procured him a double supply, and left him as happy a man as, I suppose, any in the world. I wish I could fathom his mind.

Midnight.—Another change in him. I had been to see Miss Westenra, whom I found much better, and had just returned, and was standing at our own gate looking at the sunset, when once more I heard him yelling. As his room is on this side of the house, I could hear it better than in the morning. It was a shock to me to turn from the wonderful smoky beauty of a sunset over London, with its lurid lights and inky shadows and all the marvellous tints that come on foul clouds even as on foul water, and to realise all the grim sternness of my own cold stone building, with its wealth of breathing misery, and my own desolate heart to endure it all. I reached him just as the sun was going down, and from his window saw the red disc sink. As it sank he became less and less frenzied; and just as it dipped he slid from the hands that held him, an inert mass, on the floor. It is wonderful, however, what intellectual recuperative power lunatics have, for within a few minutes he stood up quite calmly and looked around him. I signalled to the attendants not to hold him, for I was anxious to see what he would do. He went straight over to the window and brushed out the crumbs of sugar; then he took his fly-box, and emptied it outside, and threw away the box; then he shut the window, and crossing over, sat down on his bed. All this surprised me, so I asked him: "Are you not going to keep flies any more?"

"No," said he; "I am sick of all that rubbish!" He certainly is a wonderfully interesting study. I wish I could get some glimpse of his mind or of the cause of his sudden passion. Stop; there may be a clue after all, if we can find why to-day his paroxysms came on at high noon and at sunset. Can it be that there is a malign influence of the sun at periods which affects certain natures—as at times the moon does others? We shall see.

TELEGRAM, FROM SEWARD, LONDON, TO
VAN HELSING, AMSTERDAM.

"4 September.—Patient still better to-day."

TELEGRAM, FROM SEWARD, LONDON, TO
VAN HELSING, AMSTERDAM.

"5 September.—Patient greatly improved. Good appetite; sleeps naturally; good spirits; colour coming back."

TELEGRAM, FROM SEWARD, LONDON, TO
VAN HELSING, AMSTERDAM.

"6 September.—Terrible change for the worse. Come at once; do not lose an hour. I hold over telegram to Holmwood till have seen you."

CHAPTER 10.

LETTER FROM DR. SEWARD TO THE
HONOURABLE ARTHUR HOLMWOOD.

"*6 September.*

"My dear Art,—

"My news to-day is not so good. Lucy this morning had gone back a bit. There is, however, one good thing which has arisen from it; Mrs. Westenra was naturally anxious concerning Lucy, and has consulted me professionally about her. I took advantage of the opportunity, and told her that my old master, Van Helsing, the great specialist, was coming to stay with me, and that I would put her in his charge conjointly with myself; so now we can come and go without alarming her unduly, for a shock to her would mean sudden death, and this, in Lucy's weak condition, might be disastrous to her. We are hedged in with difficulties, all of us, my poor old fellow; but, please God, we shall come through them all right. If any need I shall write, so that, if you do not hear from me, take it for granted that I am simply waiting for news. In haste

"Yours ever,

"JOHN SEWARD."

DR. SEWARD'S DIARY.

7 September.—The first thing Van Helsing said to me when we met at Liverpool Street was:—

"Have you said anything to our young friend the lover of her?"

"No," I said. "I waited till I had seen you, as I said in my telegram. I wrote him a letter simply telling him that you were coming, as Miss Westenra was not so well, and that I should let him know if need be."

"Right, my friend," he said, "quite right! Better he not know as yet; perhaps he shall never know. I pray so; but if it be needed, then he shall know all. And, my good friend John, let me caution you. You deal with the madmen. All men are mad in some way or the other; and inasmuch as you deal discreetly with your madmen, so deal with God's madmen, too—the rest of the world. You tell not your madmen what you do nor why you do it; you tell them not what you think. So you shall keep knowledge in its place, where it may rest—where it may gather its kind around it and breed. You and I shall keep as yet what we know here, and here." He touched me on the heart and on the forehead, and then touched himself the same way. "I have for myself thoughts at the present. Later I shall unfold to you."

"Why not now?" I asked. "It may do some good; we may arrive at some decision." He stopped and looked at me, and said:—

"My friend John, when the corn is grown, even before it has ripened—while the milk of its mother-earth is in him, and the sunshine has not yet begun to paint him with his gold, the husbandman he pull the ear and rub him between his rough hands, and blow away the green chaff, and say to you: 'Look! he's good corn; he will make good crop when the time comes!'" I did not see the application, and told him so. For reply he reached over and took my ear in his hand and pulled it playfully, as he used long ago to do at lectures, and said: "The good husbandman tell you so then because he knows, but not till then. But you do not find the good husbandman dig up his planted corn to see if he grow; that is for the children who play at husbandry, and not for those who take it as of the work of their life. See you now, friend John? I have sown my corn, and Nature has her work to do in making it sprout; if he sprout at all, there's some promise; and I wait till the ear begins to swell." He broke off, for he evidently saw that I understood. Then he went on, and very gravely:—

"You were always a careful student, and your case-book was ever more full than the rest. You were only student then; now you are master, and I trust that good habit have not fail. Remember, my friend, that knowledge is stronger than memory, and we should not trust the weaker. Even if you have not kept the good practise, let me tell you that this case of our dear miss is one that may be—mind, I say *may be*—of such interest to us and others that all the rest may not make him kick the beam; as your peoples say. Take then good note of it. Nothing is too small I counsel you, put down in record even your doubts and surmises. Hereafter it may be of interest to you to see how true you guess. We learn from failure, not from success!"

When I described Lucy's symptoms—the same as before, but infinitely more marked—he looked very grave, but said nothing. He took with him a bag in which were many instruments and drugs, "the ghastly paraphernalia of our beneficial trade," as he once called, in one of his lectures, the equipment of a professor of the healing craft. When we were shown in, Mrs. Westenra met us. She was alarmed, but not nearly so much as I expected to find her. Nature in one of her beneficent moods has ordained that even death has some antidote to its own terrors. Here, in a case where any shock may prove fatal, matters are so ordered that, from some cause or other, the things not personal—even the terrible change in her daughter to whom she is so attached—do not seem to reach her. It is something like the way Dame Nature gathers round a foreign body an envelope of some insensitive tissue which can protect from evil that which it would otherwise harm by contact. If this be an ordered selfishness, then we should pause before we condemn any one for the vice of egoism, for there may be deeper root for its cause than we have knowledge of.

I used my knowledge of this phase of spiritual pathology, and laid down a rule that she should not be present with Lucy or think of her illness more than was absolutely required. She assented readily, so readily that I saw again the hand of Nature fighting for life. Van Helsing and I were shown up to Lucy's room. If I was shocked when I saw her yesterday, I was horrified when I saw her to-day. She was ghastly, chalkily pale; the red seemed to have gone even from her lips and gums, and the bones of her face stood out prominently; her breathing was painful to see or hear. Van Helsing's face grew set as marble, and his eyebrows converged till they almost touched over his nose. Lucy lay motionless, and did not seem to have strength to speak, so for a while we were all silent. Then Van Helsing beckoned to me, and we went gently out of the room. The instant we had closed the door he stepped quickly along the passage to the next door, which was open. Then he pulled me quickly in with him and closed the door. "My God!" he said; "this is dreadful. There is no time to be lost. She will die for sheer want of blood to keep the heart's action as it should be. There must be transfusion of blood at once. Is it you or me?"

"I am younger and stronger, Professor. It must be me."

"Then get ready at once. I will bring up my bag. I am prepared."

I went downstairs with him, and as we were going there was a knock at the hall-door. When we reached the hall the maid had just opened the door, and Arthur was stepping quickly in. He rushed up to me, saying in an eager whisper:—

"Jack, I was so anxious. I read between the lines of your letter, and have been in an agony. My dad was better, so I ran down here to see for myself. Is not that gentleman Dr. Van Helsing? I am so thankful to you, sir, for coming." When first the Professor's eye had lit upon him he had been angry at his interruption at such a time; but now, as he took in his stalwart proportions and recognised the strong young manhood which seemed to emanate from him, his eyes gleamed. Without a pause he said to him gravely as he held out his hand:—

"Sir, you have come in time. You are the lover of our dear miss. She is bad, very, very bad. Nay, my child, do not go like that." For he suddenly grew pale and sat down in a chair almost fainting. "You are to help her. You can do more than any that live, and your courage is your best help."

"What can I do?" asked Arthur hoarsely. "Tell me, and I shall do it. My life is hers, and I would give the last drop of blood in my body for her." The Professor has a strongly humorous side, and I could from old knowledge detect a trace of its origin in his answer:—

"My young sir, I do not ask so much as that—not the last!"

"What shall I do?" There was fire in his eyes, and his open nostrils quivered with intent. Van Helsing slapped him on the shoulder. "Come!" he said. "You are a man, and it is a man we want. You are better than me, better than my friend John." Arthur looked bewildered, and the Professor went on by explaining in a kindly way:—

"Young miss is bad, very bad. She wants blood, and blood she must have or die. My friend John and I have consulted; and we are about to perform what we call transfusion of blood to transfer from full veins of one to the empty veins which pine for him. John was to give his blood, as he is the more young and strong than me"—here Arthur took my hand and wrung it hard in silence—"but, now you are here, you are more good than us, old or young, who toil much in the world of thought. Our nerves are not so calm and our blood not so bright than yours!" Arthur turned to him and said:—

"If you only knew how gladly I would die for her you would understand—"

He stopped, with a sort of choke in his voice.

"Good boy!" said Van Helsing. "In the not-so-far-off you will be happy that you have done all for her you love. Come now and be silent. You shall kiss her once before it is done, but then you must go; and you must leave at my sign. Say no word to Madame; you know how it is with her! There must be no shock; any knowledge of this would be one. Come!"

We all went up to Lucy's room. Arthur by direction remained outside. Lucy turned her head and looked at us, but said nothing. She was not asleep, but she was simply too weak to make the effort. Her eyes spoke to us; that was all. Van Helsing took some things from his bag and laid them on a little table out of sight. Then he mixed a narcotic, and coming over to the bed, said cheerily:—

"Now, little miss, here is your medicine. Drink it off, like a good child. See, I lift you so that to swallow is easy. Yes." She had made the effort with success.

It astonished me how long the drug took to act. This, in fact, marked the extent of her weakness. The time seemed endless until sleep began to flicker in her eyelids. At last, however, the narcotic began to manifest its potency; and she fell into a deep sleep. When the Professor was satisfied he called Arthur into the room, and bade him strip off his coat. Then he added: "You may take that one little kiss whiles I bring over the table. Friend John, help to me!" So neither of us looked whilst he bent over her.

Van Helsing turning to me, said:

"He is so young and strong and of blood so pure that we need not defibrinate it."

Then with swiftness, but with absolute method, Van Helsing performed the operation. As the transfusion went on something like life seemed to come back to poor Lucy's cheeks, and through Arthur's growing pallor the joy of his face seemed absolutely to shine. After a bit I began to grow anxious, for the loss of blood was telling on Arthur, strong man as he was. It gave me an idea of what a terrible strain Lucy's system must have undergone that what weakened Arthur only partially restored her. But the Professor's face was set, and he stood watch in hand and with his eyes fixed now on the patient and now on Arthur. I could hear my own heart beat. Presently he said in a soft voice: "Do not stir an instant. It is enough. You attend him; I will look to her." When all was over I could see how much Arthur was weakened. I dressed the wound and took his arm to bring him away, when Van Helsing spoke without turning round—the man seems to have eyes in the back of his head:—

"The brave lover, I think, deserve another kiss, which he shall have presently." And as he had now finished his operation, he adjusted the pillow to the patient's head. As he did so the narrow black velvet band which she seems always to wear round her throat, buckled with an old diamond buckle which her lover had given her, was dragged a little up, and showed a red mark on her throat. Arthur did not notice it, but I could hear the deep hiss of indrawn breath which is one of Van Helsing's ways of betraying emotion. He said nothing at the moment, but turned to me, saying: "Now take down our brave young lover, give him of the port wine, and let him lie down awhile. He must then go home and rest, sleep much and eat much, that he may be recruited of what he has so given to his love. He must not stay here. Hold! a moment. I may take it, sir, that you are anxious of result. Then bring it with you that in all ways the operation is successful. You have saved her life this time, and you can go home and rest easy in mind that all that can be is. I shall tell her all when she is well; she shall love you none the less for what you have done. Good-bye."

When Arthur had gone I went back to the room. Lucy was sleeping gently, but her breathing was stronger; I could see the counterpane move as her breast heaved. By the bedside sat Van Helsing, looking at her intently. The velvet band again covered the red mark. I asked the Professor in a whisper:—

"What do you make of that mark on her throat?"

"What do you make of it?"

"I have not examined it yet," I answered, and then and there proceeded to loose the band. Just over the external jugular vein there were two punctures, not large, but not wholesome-looking. There was no sign of disease, but the edges were white and worn-looking, as if by some trituration. It at once occurred to me that this wound, or whatever it was, might be the means of that manifest loss of blood; but I abandoned the idea as soon as formed, for such a thing could not be. The whole bed would have been drenched to a scarlet with the blood which the girl must have lost to leave such a pallor as she had before the transfusion.

"Well?" said Van Helsing.

"Well," said I, "I can make nothing of it." The Professor stood up. "I must go back to Amsterdam to-night," he said. "There are books and things there which I want. You must remain here all the night, and you must not let your sight pass from her."

"Shall I have a nurse?" I asked.

"We are the best nurses, you and I. You keep watch all night; see that she is well fed, and that nothing disturbs her. You must not sleep all the night. Later on we can sleep, you and I. I shall be back as soon as possible. And then we may begin."

"May begin?" I said. "What on earth do you mean?"

"We shall see!" he answered, as he hurried out. He came back a moment later and put his head inside the door and said with warning finger held up:—

"Remember, she is your charge. If you leave her, and harm befall, you shall not sleep easy hereafter!"

DR. SEWARD'S DIARY—*continued*.

8 September.—I sat up all night with Lucy. The opiate worked itself off towards dusk, and she waked naturally; she looked a different being from what she had been before the operation. Her spirits even were good, and she was full of a happy vivacity, but I could see evidences of the absolute prostration which she had undergone. When I told Mrs. Westenra that Dr. Van Helsing had directed that I should sit up with her she almost pooh-poohed the idea, pointing out her daughter's renewed strength and excellent spirits. I was firm, however, and made preparations for my long vigil. When her maid had prepared her for the night I came in, having in the meantime had supper, and took a seat by the bedside. She did not in any way make objection, but looked at me gratefully whenever I caught her eye. After a long spell she seemed sinking off to sleep, but with an effort seemed to pull herself together and shook it off. This was repeated several times, with greater effort and with shorter pauses as the time moved on. It was apparent that she did not want to sleep, so I tackled the subject at once:—

"You do not want to go to sleep?"

"No; I am afraid."

"Afraid to go to sleep! Why so? It is the boon we all crave for."

"Ah, not if you were like me—if sleep was to you a presage of horror!"

"A presage of horror! What on earth do you mean?"

"I don't know; oh, I don't know. And that is what is so terrible. All this weakness comes to me in sleep; until I dread the very thought."

"But, my dear girl, you may sleep to-night. I am here watching you, and I can promise that nothing will happen."

"Ah, I can trust you!" I seized the opportunity, and said: "I promise you that if I see any evidence of bad dreams I will wake you at once."

"You will? Oh, will you really? How good you are to me. Then I will sleep!" And almost at the word she gave a deep sigh of relief, and sank back, asleep.

All night long I watched by her. She never stirred, but slept on and on in a deep, tranquil, life-giving, health-giving sleep. Her lips were slightly parted, and her breasts rose and fell with the regularity of a pendulum. There was a smile on her face, and it was evident that no bad dreams had come to disturb her peace of mind.

In the early morning her maid came, and I left her in her care and took myself back home, for I was anxious about many things. I sent a short wire to Van Helsing and to Arthur, telling them of the excellent result of the operation. My own work, with its manifold arrears, took me all day to clear off; it was dark when I was able to inquire about my zoöphagous patient. The report was good; he had been quiet for the past day and night. A telegram came from Van Helsing at Amsterdam whilst I was at dinner, suggesting that I should be at Hillingham to-night, as it might be well to be at hand, and stating that he was leaving by the night mail and would join me early in the morning.

9 September.—I was pretty tired and worn out when I got to Hillingham. For two nights I had hardly had a wink of sleep, and my brain was beginning to feel that numbness which marks cerebral exhaustion. Lucy was up and in cheerful spirits. When she shook hands with me she looked sharply in my face and said:—

"No sitting up to-night for you. You are worn out. I am quite well again; indeed, I am; and if there is to be any sitting up, it is I who will sit up with you." I would not argue the point, but went and had my supper.

Lucy came with me, and, enlivened by her charming presence, I made an excellent meal, and had a couple of glasses of the more than excellent port. Then Lucy took me upstairs, and showed me a room next to her own, where a cozy fire was burning. "Now," she said, "you must stay here. I shall leave this door open and my door too. You can lie on the sofa for I know that nothing would induce any of you doctors to go to bed whilst there is a patient above the horizon. If I want anything I shall call out, and you can come to me at once." I could not but acquiesce, for I was "dog-tired," and could not have sat up had I tried. So, on her renewing her promise to call me if she should want anything, I lay on the sofa, and forgot all about everything.

LUCY WESTENRA'S DIARY.

9 September.—I feel so happy to-night. I have been so miserably weak, that to be able to think and move about is like feeling sunshine after a long spell of east wind out of a steel sky. Somehow Arthur feels very, very close to me. I seem to feel his presence warm about me. I suppose it is that sickness and weakness are selfish things and turn our inner eyes and sympathy on ourselves, whilst health and strength give Love rein, and in thought and feeling he can wander where he wills. I know where my thoughts are. If Arthur only knew! My dear, my dear, your ears must tingle as you sleep, as mine do waking. Oh, the blissful rest of last night! How I slept, with that dear, good Dr. Seward watching me. And to-night I shall not fear to sleep, since he is close at hand and within call. Thank everybody for being so good to me! Thank God! Good-night, Arthur.

DR. SEWARD'S DIARY.

10 September.—I was conscious of the Professor's hand on my head, and started awake all in a second. That is one of the things that we learn in an asylum, at any rate.

"And how is our patient?"

"Well, when I left her, or rather when she left me," I answered.

"Come, let us see," he said. And together we went into the room.

The blind was down, and I went over to raise it gently, whilst Van Helsing stepped, with his soft, cat-like tread, over to the bed.

As I raised the blind, and the morning sunlight flooded the room, I heard the Professor's low hiss of inspiration, and knowing its rarity, a deadly fear shot through my heart. As I passed over he moved back, and his exclamation of horror, "Gott in Himmel!" needed no enforcement from his agonised face. He raised his hand and pointed to the bed, and his iron face was drawn and ashen white. I felt my knees begin to tremble.

There on the bed, seemingly in a swoon, lay poor Lucy, more horribly white and wan-looking than ever. Even the lips were white, and the gums seemed to have shrunken back from the teeth, as we sometimes see in a corpse after a prolonged illness. Van Helsing raised his foot to stamp in anger, but the instinct of his life and all the long years of habit stood to him, and he put it down again softly. "Quick!" he said. "Bring the brandy." I flew to the dining-room, and returned with the decanter. He wetted the poor white lips with it, and together we rubbed palm and wrist and heart. He felt her heart, and after a few moments of agonising suspense said:—

"It is not too late. It beats, though but feebly. All our work is undone; we must begin anew. There is no young Arthur here now; I have to call on you yourself this time, friend John." As he spoke, he was dipping into his bag and producing the instruments for transfusion; I had taken off my coat and rolled up my shirtsleeve. There was no possibility of an opiate just at present, and no need of one; and so, without a moment's delay, we began the operation. After a time—it did not seem a short time either, for the draining away of one's blood, no matter how willingly it be given, is a terrible feeling—Van Helsing held up a warning finger. "Do not stir," he said, "but I fear that with growing strength she may wake; and that would make danger, oh, so much danger. But I shall precaution take. I shall give hypodermic injection of morphia." He proceeded then, swiftly and deftly, to carry out his intent. The effect on

Lucy was not bad, for the faint seemed to merge subtly into the narcotic sleep. It was with a feeling of personal pride that I could see a faint tinge of colour steal back into the pallid cheeks and lips. No man knows, till he experiences it, what it is to feel his own life-blood drawn away into the veins of the woman he loves.

The Professor watched me critically. "That will do," he said. "Already?" I remonstrated. "You took a great deal more from Art." To which he smiled a sad sort of smile as he replied:—

"He is her lover, her *fiancé*. You have work, much work, to do for her and for others; and the present will suffice."

When we stopped the operation, he attended to Lucy, whilst I applied digital pressure to my own incision. I laid down, whilst I waited his leisure to attend to me, for I felt faint and a little sick. By-and-by he bound up my wound, and sent me down-stairs to get a glass of wine for myself. As I was leaving the room, he came after me, and half whispered:—

"Mind, nothing must be said of this. If our young lover should turn up unexpected, as before, no word to him. It would at once frighten him and enjealous him, too. There must be none. So!"

When I came back he looked at me carefully, and then said:—

"You are not much the worse. Go into the room, and lie on your sofa, and rest awhile; then have much breakfast, and come here to me."

I followed out his orders, for I knew how right and wise they were. I had done my part, and now my next duty was to keep up my strength. I felt very weak, and in the weakness lost something of the amazement at what had occurred. I fell asleep on the sofa, however, wondering over and over again how Lucy had made such a retrograde movement, and how she could have been drained of so much blood with no sign anywhere to show for it. I think I must have continued my wonder in my dreams, for, sleeping and waking, my thoughts always came back to the little punctures in her throat and the ragged, exhausted appearance of their edges—tiny though they were.

Lucy slept well into the day, and when she woke she was fairly well and strong, though not nearly so much so as the day before. When Van

Helsing had seen her, he went out for a walk, leaving me in charge, with strict injunctions that I was not to leave her for a moment. I could hear his voice in the hall, asking the way to the nearest telegraph office.

Lucy chatted with me freely, and seemed quite unconscious that anything had happened. I tried to keep her amused and interested. When her mother came up to see her, she did not seem to notice any change whatever, but said to me gratefully:—

"We owe you so much, Dr. Seward, for all you have done, but you really must now take care not to overwork yourself. You are looking pale yourself. You want a wife to nurse and look after you a bit; that you do!" As she spoke, Lucy turned crimson, though it was only momentarily, for her poor wasted veins could not stand for long such an unwonted drain to the head. The reaction came in excessive pallor as she turned imploring eyes on me. I smiled and nodded, and laid my finger on my lips; with a sigh, she sank back amid her pillows.

Van Helsing returned in a couple of hours, and presently said to me: "Now you go home, and eat much and drink enough. Make yourself strong. I stay here to-night, and I shall sit up with little miss myself. You and I must watch the case, and we must have none other to know. I have grave reasons. No, do not ask them; think what you will. Do not fear to think even the most not-probable. Good-night."

In the hall two of the maids came to me, and asked if they or either of them might not sit up with Miss Lucy. They implored me to let them; and when I said it was Dr. Van Helsing's wish that either he or I should sit up, they asked me quite piteously to intercede with the "foreign gentleman." I was much touched by their kindness. Perhaps it is because I am weak at present, and perhaps because it was on Lucy's account, that their devotion was manifested; for over and over again have I seen similar instances of woman's kindness. I got back here in time for a late dinner; went my rounds—all well; and set this down whilst waiting for sleep. It is coming.

11 September.—This afternoon I went over to Hillingham. Found Van Helsing in excellent spirits, and Lucy much better. Shortly after I had arrived, a big parcel from abroad came for the Professor. He opened it with much impressment—assumed, of course—and showed a great bundle of white flowers.

"These are for you, Miss Lucy," he said.

"For me? Oh, Dr. Van Helsing!"

"Yes, my dear, but not for you to play with. These are medicines." Here Lucy made a wry face. "Nay, but they are not to take in a decoction or in nauseous form, so you need not snub that so charming nose, or I shall point out to my friend Arthur what woes he may have to endure in seeing so much beauty that he so loves so much distort. Aha, my pretty miss, that bring the so nice nose all straight again. This is medicinal, but you do not know how. I put him in your window, I make pretty wreath, and hang him round your neck, so that you sleep well. Oh yes! they, like the lotus flower, make your trouble forgotten. It smell so like the waters of Lethe, and of that fountain of youth that the Conquistadores sought for in the Floridas, and find him all too late."

Whilst he was speaking, Lucy had been examining the flowers and smelling them. Now she threw them down, saying, with half-laughter, and half-disgust:—

"Oh, Professor, I believe you are only putting up a joke on me. Why, these flowers are only common garlic."

To my surprise, Van Helsing rose up and said with all his sternness, his iron jaw set and his bushy eyebrows meeting:—

"No trifling with me! I never jest! There is grim purpose in all I do; and I warn you that you do not thwart me. Take care, for the sake of others if not for your own." Then seeing poor Lucy scared, as she might well be, he went on more gently: "Oh, little miss, my dear, do not fear me. I only do for your good; but there is much virtue to you in those so common flowers. See, I place them myself in your room. I make myself the wreath that you are to wear. But hush! no telling to others that make so inquisitive questions. We must obey, and silence is a part of obedience; and obedience is to bring you strong and well into loving arms that wait for you. Now sit still awhile. Come with me, friend John, and you shall help me deck the room with my garlic, which is all the way from Haarlem, where my friend Vanderpool raise herb in his glass-houses all the year. I had to telegraph yesterday, or they would not have been here."

We went into the room, taking the flowers with us. The Professor's actions were certainly odd and not to be found in any pharmacopoeia that I ever heard of. First he fastened up the windows and latched them securely; next, taking a handful of the flowers, he rubbed them all over the sashes, as though to ensure that every whiff of air that might get in would be laden with the garlic smell. Then with the wisp he rubbed all over the jamb of the door, above, below, and at each side, and round the fireplace in the same way. It all seemed grotesque to me, and presently I said:—

"Well, Professor, I know you always have a reason for what you do, but this certainly puzzles me. It is well we have no sceptic here, or he would say that you were working some spell to keep out an evil spirit."

"Perhaps I am!" he answered quietly as he began to make the wreath which Lucy was to wear round her neck.

We then waited whilst Lucy made her toilet for the night, and when she was in bed he came and himself fixed the wreath of garlic round her neck. The last words he said to her were:—

"Take care you do not disturb it; and even if the room feel close, do not to-night open the window or the door."

"I promise," said Lucy, "and thank you both a thousand times for all your kindness to me! Oh, what have I done to be blessed with such friends?"

As we left the house in my fly, which was waiting, Van Helsing said:—

"To-night I can sleep in peace, and sleep I want—two nights of travel, much reading in the day between, and much anxiety on the day to follow, and a night to sit up, without to wink. To-morrow in the morning early you call for me, and we come together to see our pretty miss, so much more strong for my 'spell' which I have work. Ho! ho!"

He seemed so confident that I, remembering my own confidence two nights before and with the baneful result, felt awe and vague terror. It must have been my weakness that made me hesitate to tell it to my friend, but I felt it all the more, like unshed tears.

CHAPTER 11.

———◇———

LUCY WESTENRA'S DIARY.

12 September.—How good they all are to me. I quite love that dear Dr. Van Helsing. I wonder why he was so anxious about these flowers. He positively frightened me, he was so fierce. And yet he must have been right, for I feel comfort from them already. Somehow, I do not dread being alone to-night, and I can go to sleep without fear. I shall not mind any flapping outside the window. Oh, the terrible struggle that I have had against sleep so often of late; the pain of the sleeplessness, or the pain of the fear of sleep, with such unknown horror as it has for me! How blessed are some people, whose lives have no fears, no dreads; to whom sleep is a blessing that comes nightly, and brings nothing but sweet dreams. Well, here I am to-night, hoping for sleep, and lying like Ophelia in the play, with "virgin crants and maiden strewments." I never liked garlic before, but to-night it is delightful! There is peace in its smell; I feel sleep coming already. Good-night, everybody.

DR. SEWARD'S DIARY.

13 September.—Called at the Berkeley and found Van Helsing, as usual, up to time. The carriage ordered from the hotel was waiting. The Professor took his bag, which he always brings with him now.

Let all be put down exactly. Van Helsing and I arrived at Hillingham at eight o'clock. It was a lovely morning; the bright sunshine and all the fresh feeling of early autumn seemed like the completion of nature's annual work. The leaves were turning to all kind of beautiful colours, but had not yet begun to drop from the trees. When we entered we met Mrs. Westenra coming out of the morning room. She is always an early riser. She greeted us warmly and said:—

"You will be glad to know that Lucy is better. The dear child is still asleep. I looked into her room and saw her, but did not go in, lest I should disturb her." The Professor smiled, and looked quite jubilant. He rubbed his hands together and said:—

"Aha! I thought I had diagnosed the case. My treatment is working," to which she answered:—

"You must not take all the credit to yourself, Doctor. Lucy's state this morning is due in part to me."

"How you do mean, ma'am?" asked the Professor.

"Well, I was anxious about the dear child in the night, and went into her room. She was sleeping soundly—so soundly that even my coming did not wake her. But the room was awfully stuffy. There were a lot of those horrible, strong-smelling flowers about everywhere, and she had actually a bunch of them round her neck. I feared that the heavy odour would be too much for the dear child in her weak state, so I took them all away and opened a bit of the window to let in a little fresh air. You will be pleased with her, I am sure."

She moved off into her boudoir, where she usually breakfasted early. As she had spoken, I watched the Professor's face, and saw it turn ashen grey. He had been able to retain his self-command whilst the poor lady was present, for he knew her state and how mischievous a shock would be; he actually smiled on her as he held open the door for her to pass into her room. But the instant she had disappeared he pulled me, suddenly and forcibly, into the dining-room and closed the door.

Then for the first time in my life, I saw Van Helsing break down. He raised his hands over his head in a sort of mute despair, and then beat his palms together in a helpless way; finally he sat down on a chair, and putting his hands before his face, began to sob, with loud, dry sobs that seemed to come from the very racking of his heart. Then he raised his arms again, as though appealing to the whole universe. "God! God! God!" he said. "What have we done, what has this poor thing done, that we are so sore beset? Is there fate amongst us still, sent down from the pagan world of old, that such things must be, and in such way? This poor mother, all unknowing, and all for the best as she think, does such thing as lose her daughter body and soul; and we must not tell her, we must not even warn her, or she die, and then both die. Oh, how we are beset! How are all the powers of the devils against us!" Suddenly he jumped to his feet. "Come," he said, "come, we must see and act. Devils or no devils, or all the devils at once, it matters not; we fight him all the same." He went to the hall-door for his bag; and together we went up to Lucy's room.

Once again I drew up the blind, whilst Van Helsing went towards the bed. This time he did not start as he looked on the poor face with the same awful, waxen pallor as before. He wore a look of stern sadness and infinite pity.

"As I expected," he murmured, with that hissing inspiration of his which meant so much. Without a word he went and locked the door, and then began to set out on the little table the instruments for yet another operation of transfusion of blood. I had long ago recognised the necessity, and begun to take off my coat, but he stopped me with a warning hand. "No!" he said. "To-day you must operate. I shall provide. You are weakened already." As he spoke he took off his coat and rolled up his shirtsleeve.

Again the operation; again the narcotic; again some return of colour to the ashy cheeks, and the regular breathing of healthy sleep. This time I watched whilst Van Helsing recruited himself and rested.

Presently he took an opportunity of telling Mrs. Westenra that she must not remove anything from Lucy's room without consulting him; that the flowers were of medicinal value, and that the breathing of their odour was a part of the system of cure. Then he took over the care of the case himself, saying that he would watch this night and the next and would send me word when to come.

After another hour Lucy waked from her sleep, fresh and bright and seemingly not much the worse for her terrible ordeal.

What does it all mean? I am beginning to wonder if my long habit of life amongst the insane is beginning to tell upon my own brain.

LUCY WESTENRA'S DIARY.

17 September.—Four days and nights of peace. I am getting so strong again that I hardly know myself. It is as if I had passed through some long nightmare, and had just awakened to see the beautiful sunshine and feel the fresh air of the morning around me. I have a dim half-remembrance of long, anxious times of waiting and fearing; darkness in which there was not even the pain of hope to make present distress more poignant: and then long spells of oblivion, and the rising back to life as a diver coming up through a great press of water. Since, however, Dr. Van Helsing has been with me, all this bad dreaming seems to have passed away; the noises that used to frighten me out of my wits—the flapping against the windows, the distant voices which seemed so close to me, the harsh sounds that came from I know not where and commanded me to do I know not what—have all ceased. I go to bed now without any fear of sleep. I do not even try to keep awake. I have grown quite fond of the garlic, and a boxful arrives for me every day from Haarlem. To-night Dr. Van Helsing is going away, as he has to be for a day in Amsterdam. But I need not be watched; I am well enough to be left alone. Thank God for mother's sake, and dear Arthur's, and for all our friends who have been so kind! I shall not even feel the change, for last night Dr. Van Helsing slept in his chair a lot of the time. I found him asleep twice when I awoke; but I did not fear to go to sleep again; although the boughs or bats or something flapped almost angrily against the window-panes.

"The Pall Mall Gazette," 18 September.

THE ESCAPED WOLF.
PERILOUS ADVENTURE OF OUR INTERVIEWER

Interview with the Keeper in the Zooaulogical Gardens.

After many inquiries and almost as many refusals, and perpetually using the words, "Pall Mall Gazette" as a sort of talisman, I managed to find the keeper of the section of the Zooaulogical Gardens in which the wolf department is included. Thomas Bilder lives in one of the cottages in the enclosure behind the elephant house, and was just sitting down to his tea when I found him. Thomas and his wife are hospitable folk, elderly, and without children, and if the specimen I enjoyed of their hospitality be of the average kind, their lives must be pretty comfortable. The keeper would not enter on what he called "business" until the supper was over, and we were all satisfied. Then when the table was cleared, and he had lit his pipe, he said:—

"Now, sir, you can go on and arsk me what you want. You'll excoose me refoosin' to talk of perfeshunal subjects afore meals. I gives the wolves and the jackals and the hyenas in all our section their tea afore I begins to arsk them questions."

"How do you mean, ask them questions?" I queried, wishful to get him into a talkative humour.

" 'Ittin' of them over the 'ead with a pole is one way; scratchin' of their hears is another, when gents as is flush wants a bit of a show-orf to their gals. I don't so much mind the fust—the 'ittin' with a pole afore I chucks in their dinner; but I waits till they've 'ad their sherry and kawffee, so to speak, afore I tries on with the ear-scratchin'. Mind you," he added philosophically, "there's a deal of the same nature in us as in them theer animiles. Here's you a-comin' and arskin' of me questions about my business, and I that grumpy-like that only for your bloomin' 'arf-quid I'd 'a' seen you blowed fust 'fore I'd answer. Not even when you arsked me sarcastic-like if I'd like you to arsk the Superintendent if you might arsk me questions. Without offence did I tell yer to go to 'ell?"

"You did."

"An' when you said you'd report me for usin' of obscene language that was 'ittin' me over the 'ead; but the 'arf-quid made that all right. I weren't a-goin' to fight, so I waited for the food, and did with my 'owl as the wolves, and lions, and tigers does. But, Lor' love yer 'art, now that the old 'ooman has stuck a chunk of her tea-cake in me, an' rinsed me out with her bloomin' old teapot, and I've lit hup, you may scratch my ears for all you're worth, and won't git even a growl out of me. Drive along with your questions. I know what yer a-comin' at, that 'ere escaped wolf."

"Exactly. I want you to give me your view of it. Just tell me how it happened; and when I know the facts I'll get you to say what you consider was the cause of it, and how you think the whole affair will end."

"All right, guv'nor. This 'ere is about the 'ole story. That 'ere wolf what we called Bersicker was one of three grey ones that came from Norway to Jamrach's, which we bought off him four years ago. He was a nice well-behaved wolf, that never gave no trouble to talk of. I'm more surprised at 'im for wantin' to get out nor any other animile in the place. But, there, you can't trust wolves no more nor women."

"Don't you mind him, sir!" broke in Mrs. Tom, with a cheery laugh. "'E's got mindin' the animiles so long that blest if he ain't like an old wolf 'isself! But there ain't no 'arm in 'im."

"Well, sir, it was about two hours after feedin' yesterday when I first hear my disturbance. I was makin' up a litter in the monkey-house for a young puma which is ill; but when I heard the yelpin' and 'owlin' I kem away straight. There was Bersicker a-tearin' like a mad thing at the bars as if he wanted to get out. There wasn't much people about that day, and close at hand was only one man, a tall, thin chap, with a 'ook nose and a pointed beard, with a few white hairs runnin' through it. He had a 'ard, cold look and red eyes, and I took a sort of mislike to him, for it seemed as if it was 'im as they was hirritated at. He 'ad white kid gloves on 'is 'ands, and he pointed out the animiles to me and says: 'Keeper, these wolves seem upset at something.'

"'Maybe it's you,' says I, for I did not like the airs as he give 'isself. He didn't git angry, as I 'oped he would, but he smiled a kind of insolent smile, with a mouth full of white, sharp teeth. 'Oh no, they wouldn't like me,' 'e says.

"'Ow yes, they would,' says I, a-imitatin' of him. 'They always like a bone or two to clean their teeth on about tea-time, which you 'as a bag-ful.'

"Well, it was a odd thing, but when the animiles see us a-talkin' they lay down, and when I went over to Bersicker he let me stroke his ears same as ever. That there man kem over, and blessed but if he didn't put in his hand and stroke the old wolf's ears too!

"'Tyke care,' says I. 'Bersicker is quick.'

"'Never mind,' he says. 'I'm used to 'em!'

"'Are you in the business yourself?' I says, tyking off my 'at, for a man what trades in wolves, anceterer, is a good friend to keepers.

"'No,' says he, 'not exactly in the business, but I 'ave made pets of several.' And with that he lifts his 'at as perlite as a lord, and walks away. Old Bersicker kep' a-lookin' arter 'im till 'e was out of sight, and then went and lay down in a corner and wouldn't come hout the 'ole hevening. Well, larst night, so soon as the moon was hup, the wolves here all began a-'owling. There warn't nothing for them to 'owl at. There warn't no one near, except some one that was evidently a-callin' a dog some-wheres out back of the gardings in the Park road. Once or twice I went out to see that all was right, and it was, and then the 'owling stopped. Just before twelve o'clock I just took a look round afore turnin' in, an', bust me, but when I kem opposite to old Bersicker's cage I see the rails broken and twisted about and the cage empty. And that's all I know for certing."

"Did any one else see anything?"

"One of our gard'ners was a-comin' 'ome about that time from a 'armony, when he sees a big grey dog comin' out through the garding 'edges. At least, so he says, but I don't give much for it myself, for if he did 'e never said a word about it to his missis when 'e got 'ome, and it was only after the escape of the wolf was made known, and we had been up all night-a-huntin' of the Park for Bersicker, that he remembered seein' anything. My own belief was that the 'armony 'ad got into his 'ead."

"Now, Mr. Bilder, can you account in any way for the escape of the wolf?"

"Well, sir," he said, with a suspicious sort of modesty, "I think I can; but I don't know as 'ow you'd be satisfied with the theory."

"Certainly I shall. If a man like you, who knows the animals from experience, can't hazard a good guess at any rate, who is even to try?"

"Well then, sir, I accounts for it this way; it seems to me that 'ere wolf escaped—simply because he wanted to get out."

From the hearty way that both Thomas and his wife laughed at the joke I could see that it had done service before, and that the whole explanation was simply an elaborate sell. I couldn't cope in badinage with the worthy Thomas, but I thought I knew a surer way to his heart, so I said:—

"Now, Mr. Bilder, we'll consider that first half-sovereign worked off, and this brother of his is waiting to be claimed when you've told me what you think will happen."

"Right y'are, sir," he said briskly. "Ye'll excoose me, I know, for a-chaffin' of ye, but the old woman here winked at me, which was as much as telling me to go on."

"Well, I never!" said the old lady.

"My opinion is this: that 'ere wolf is a-'idin' of, somewheres. The gard'ner wot didn't remember said he was a-gallopin' northward faster than a horse could go; but I don't believe him, for, yer see, sir, wolves don't gallop no more nor dogs does, they not bein' built that way. Wolves is fine things in a story-book, and I dessay when they gets in packs and does be chivyin' somethin' that's more afeared than they is they can make a devil of a noise and chop it up, whatever it is. But, Lor' bless you, in real life a wolf is only a low creature, not half so clever or bold as a good dog; and not half a quarter so much fight in 'im. This one ain't been used to fightin' or even to providin' for hisself, and more like he's somewhere round the Park a-'idin' an' a-shiverin' of, and, if he thinks at all, wonderin' where he is to get his breakfast from; or maybe he's got down some area and is in a coal-cellar. My eye, won't some cook get a rum start when she sees his green eyes a-shining at her out of the dark! If he can't get food he's bound to look for it, and mayhap he may chance to light on a butcher's shop in time. If he doesn't, and some nursemaid goes a-walkin' orf with a soldier, leavin' of the hinfant in the perambulator—well, then I shouldn't be surprised if the census is one baby the less. That's all."

I was handing him the half-sovereign, when something came bobbing up against the window, and Mr. Bilder's face doubled its natural length with surprise.

"God bless me!" he said. "If there ain't old Bersicker come back by 'isself!"

He went to the door and opened it; a most unnecessary proceeding it seemed to me. I have always thought that a wild animal never looks so well as when some obstacle of pronounced durability is between us; a personal experience has intensified rather than diminished that idea.

After all, however, there is nothing like custom, for neither Bilder nor his wife thought any more of the wolf than I should of a dog. The animal itself was as peaceful and well-behaved as that father of all picture-wolves—Red Riding Hood's quondam friend, whilst moving her confidence in masquerade.

The whole scene was an unutterable mixture of comedy and pathos. The wicked wolf that for half a day had paralysed London and set all the children in the town shivering in their shoes, was there in a sort of penitent mood, and was received and petted like a sort of vulpine prodigal son. Old Bilder examined him all over with most tender solicitude, and when he had finished with his penitent said:—

"There, I knew the poor old chap would get into some kind of trouble; didn't I say it all along? Here's his head all cut and full of broken glass. 'E's been a-gettin' over some bloomin' wall or other. It's a shyme that people are allowed to top their walls with broken bottles. This 'ere's what comes of it. Come along, Bersicker."

He took the wolf and locked him up in a cage, with a piece of meat that satisfied, in quantity at any rate, the elementary conditions of the fatted calf, and went off to report.

I came off, too, to report the only exclusive information that is given to-day regarding the strange escapade at the Zoo.

DR. SEWARD'S DIARY.

17 September.—I was engaged after dinner in my study posting up my books, which, through press of other work and the many visits to Lucy, had fallen sadly into arrear. Suddenly the door was burst open, and in rushed my patient, with his face distorted with passion. I was thunderstruck, for such a thing as a patient getting of his own accord into the Superintendent's study is almost unknown. Without an instant's pause he made straight at me. He had a dinner-knife in his hand, and, as I saw he was dangerous, I tried to keep the table between us. He was too quick and too strong for me, however; for before I could get my balance he had struck at me and cut my left wrist rather severely. Before he could strike again, however, I got in my right and he was sprawling on his back on the floor. My wrist bled freely, and quite a little pool trickled on to the carpet. I saw that my friend was not intent on further effort, and occupied myself binding up my wrist, keeping a wary eye on the prostrate figure all the time. When the attendants rushed in, and we turned our attention to him, his employment positively sickened me. He was lying on his belly on the floor licking up, like a dog, the blood which had fallen from my wounded wrist. He was easily secured, and, to my surprise, went with the attendants quite placidly, simply repeating over and over again: "The blood is the life! The blood is the life!"

I cannot afford to lose blood just at present; I have lost too much of late for my physical good, and then the prolonged strain of Lucy's illness and its horrible phases is telling on me. I am over-excited and weary, and I need rest, rest, rest. Happily Van Helsing has not summoned me, so I need not forego my sleep; to-night I could not well do without it.

TELEGRAM, VAN HELSING, ANTWERP,
TO SEWARD, CARFAX.
(Sent to Carfax, Sussex, as no county given; delivered late by twenty-two hours.)

"*17 September.*—Do not fail to be at Hillingham to-night. If not watching all the time frequently, visit and see that flowers are as placed; very important; do not fail. Shall be with you as soon as possible after arrival."

DR. SEWARD'S DIARY.

18 September.—Just off for train to London. The arrival of Van Helsing's telegram filled me with dismay. A whole night lost, and I know by bitter experience what may happen in a night. Of course it is possible that all may be well, but what *may* have happened? Surely there is some horrible doom hanging over us that every possible accident should thwart us in all we try to do. I shall take this cylinder with me, and then I can complete my entry on Lucy's phonograph.

MEMORANDUM LEFT BY LUCY WESTENRA.

17 September, night.—I write this and leave it to be seen, so that no one may by any chance get into trouble through me. This is an exact record of what took place to-night. I feel I am dying of weakness, and have barely strength to write, but it must be done if I die in the doing.

I went to bed as usual, taking care that the flowers were placed as Dr. Van Helsing directed, and soon fell asleep.

I was waked by the flapping at the window, which had begun after that sleep-walking on the cliff at Whitby when Mina saved me, and which now I know so well. I was not afraid, but I did wish that Dr. Seward was in the next room—as Dr. Van Helsing said he would be—so that I might have called him. I tried to go to sleep, but could not. Then there came to me the old fear of sleep, and I determined to keep awake. Perversely sleep would try to come then when I did not want it; so, as I feared to be alone, I opened my door and called out: "Is there anybody there?" There was no answer. I was afraid to wake mother, and so closed my door again. Then outside in the shrubbery I heard a sort of howl like a dog's, but more fierce and deeper. I went to the window and looked out, but could see nothing, except a big bat, which had evidently been buffeting its wings against the window. So I went back to bed again, but determined not to go to sleep. Presently the door opened, and mother looked in; seeing by my moving that I was not asleep, came in, and sat by me. She said to me even more sweetly and softly than her wont:—

"I was uneasy about you, darling, and came in to see that you were all right."

I feared she might catch cold sitting there, and asked her to come in and sleep with me, so she came into bed, and lay down beside me; she did not take off her dressing-gown, for she said she would only stay awhile and then go back to her own bed. As she lay there in my arms, and I in hers, the flapping and buffeting came to the window again. She was startled and a little frightened, and cried out: "What is that?" I tried to pacify her, and at last succeeded, and she lay quiet; but I could hear her poor dear heart still beating terribly. After a while there was the low howl again out in the shrubbery, and shortly after there was a crash at the window, and a lot of broken glass was hurled on the floor. The window blind blew back with the wind that rushed in, and in the aperture of the broken panes there was the head of a great, gaunt grey wolf. Mother cried out in a fright, and struggled up into a sitting posture, and clutched wildly at anything that would help her. Amongst other things, she clutched the wreath of flowers that Dr. Van Helsing insisted on my wearing round my neck, and tore it away from me. For a second or two she sat up, pointing at the wolf, and there was a strange and horrible gurgling in her throat; then she fell over—as if struck with lightning, and her head hit my forehead and made me dizzy for a moment or two. The room and all round seemed to spin round. I kept my eyes fixed on the window, but the wolf drew his head back, and a whole myriad of little specks seemed to come blowing in through the broken window, and wheeling and circling round like the pillar of dust that travellers describe when there is a simoon in the desert. I tried to stir, but there was some spell upon me, and dear mother's poor body, which seemed to grow cold already—for her dear heart had ceased to beat—weighed me down; and I remembered no more for a while.

The time did not seem long, but very, very awful, till I recovered consciousness again. Somewhere near, a passing bell was tolling; the dogs all round the neighbourhood were howling; and in our shrubbery, seemingly just outside, a nightingale was singing. I was dazed and stupid with pain and terror and weakness, but the sound of the nightingale seemed like the voice of my dead mother come back to comfort me. The sounds seemed to have awakened the maids, too, for I could hear their bare feet pattering outside my door. I called to them, and they came in, and when they saw what had happened, and what it was that lay over me on the bed, they screamed out. The wind rushed in through the broken window, and the door slammed to. They lifted off the body of my dear mother, and laid her, covered up with a sheet, on the bed after I had got up. They were all so frightened and nervous that I directed them to go to the dining-room and have each a glass of wine. The door flew open for an instant and closed again. The maids shrieked, and then went in a body to the dining-room; and I laid what flowers I had on my dear mother's breast. When they were there I remembered what Dr. Van Helsing had told me, but I didn't like to remove them, and, besides, I would have some of the servants to sit up with me now. I was surprised that the maids did not come back. I called them, but got no answer, so I went to the dining-room to look for them.

My heart sank when I saw what had happened. They all four lay helpless on the floor, breathing heavily. The decanter of sherry was on the table half full, but there was a queer, acrid smell about. I was suspicious, and examined the decanter. It smelt of laudanum, and looking on the sideboard, I found that the bottle which mother's doctor uses for her—oh! did use—was empty. What am I to do? what am I to do? I am back in the room with mother. I cannot leave her, and I am alone, save for the sleeping servants, whom some one has drugged. Alone with the dead! I dare not go out, for I can hear the low howl of the wolf through the broken window.

The air seems full of specks, floating and circling in the draught from the window, and the lights burn blue and dim. What am I to do? God shield me from harm this night! I shall hide this paper in my breast, where they shall find it when they come to lay me out. My dear mother gone! It is time that I go too. Good-bye, dear Arthur, if I should not survive this night. God keep you, dear, and God help me!

CHAPTER 12.

———◇———

DR. SEWARD'S DIARY.

18 September.—I drove at once to Hillingham and arrived early. Keeping my cab at the gate, I went up the avenue alone. I knocked gently and rang as quietly as possible, for I feared to disturb Lucy or her mother, and hoped to only bring a servant to the door. After a while, finding no response, I knocked and rang again; still no answer. I cursed the laziness of the servants that they should lie abed at such an hour— for it was now ten o'clock—and so rang and knocked again, but more impatiently, but still without response. Hitherto I had blamed only the servants, but now a terrible fear began to assail me. Was this desolation but another link in the chain of doom which seemed drawing tight around us? Was it indeed a house of death to which I had come, too late? I knew that minutes, even seconds of delay, might mean hours of danger to Lucy, if she had had again one of those frightful relapses; and I went round the house to try if I could find by chance an entry anywhere.

I could find no means of ingress. Every window and door was fastened and locked, and I returned baffled to the porch. As I did so, I heard the rapid pit-pat of a swiftly driven horse's feet. They stopped at the gate, and a few seconds later I met Van Helsing running up the avenue. When he saw me, he gasped out:—

"Then it was you, and just arrived. How is she? Are we too late? Did you not get my telegram?"

I answered as quickly and coherently as I could that I had only got his telegram early in the morning, and had not lost a minute in coming here, and that I could not make any one in the house hear me. He paused and raised his hat as he said solemnly:—

"Then I fear we are too late. God's will be done!" With his usual recuperative energy, he went on: "Come. If there be no way open to get in, we must make one. Time is all in all to us now."

We went round to the back of the house, where there was a kitchen window. The Professor took a small surgical saw from his case, and handing it to me, pointed to the iron bars which guarded the window. I attacked them at once and had very soon cut through three of them. Then with a long, thin knife we pushed back the fastening of the sashes and opened the window. I helped the Professor in, and followed him. There was no one in the kitchen or in the servants' rooms, which were close at hand. We tried all the rooms as we went along, and in the dining-room, dimly lit by rays of light through the shutters, found four servant-women lying on the floor. There was no need to think them dead, for their stertorous breathing and the acrid smell of laudanum in the room left no doubt as to their condition. Van Helsing and I looked at each other, and as we moved away he said: "We can attend to them later." Then we ascended to Lucy's room. For an instant or two we paused at the door to listen, but there was no sound that we could hear. With white faces and trembling hands, we opened the door gently, and entered the room.

How shall I describe what we saw? On the bed lay two women, Lucy and her mother. The latter lay farthest in, and she was covered with a white sheet, the edge of which had been blown back by the draught through the broken window, showing the drawn, white face, with a look of terror fixed upon it. By her side lay Lucy, with face white and still more drawn. The flowers which had been round her neck we found upon her mother's bosom, and her throat was bare, showing the two little wounds which we had noticed before, but looking horribly white and mangled. Without a word the Professor bent over the bed, his head almost touching poor Lucy's breast; then he gave a quick turn of his head, as of one who listens, and leaping to his feet, he cried out to me:—

"It is not yet too late! Quick! quick! Bring the brandy!"

I flew downstairs and returned with it, taking care to smell and taste it, lest it, too, were drugged like the decanter of sherry which I found on the table. The maids were still breathing, but more restlessly, and I fancied that the narcotic was wearing off. I did not stay to make sure, but returned to Van Helsing. He rubbed the brandy, as on another occasion, on her lips and gums and on her wrists and the palms of her hands. He said to me:—

"I can do this, all that can be at the present. You go wake those maids. Flick them in the face with a wet towel, and flick them hard. Make them get heat and fire and a warm bath. This poor soul is nearly as cold as that beside her. She will need be heated before we can do anything more."

I went at once, and found little difficulty in waking three of the women. The fourth was only a young girl, and the drug had evidently affected her more strongly, so I lifted her on the sofa and let her sleep. The others were dazed at first, but as remembrance came back to them they cried and sobbed in a hysterical manner. I was stern with them, however, and would not let them talk. I told them that one life was bad enough to lose, and that if they delayed they would sacrifice Miss Lucy. So, sobbing and crying, they went about their way, half clad as they were, and prepared fire and water. Fortunately, the kitchen and boiler fires were still alive, and there was no lack of hot water. We got a bath and carried Lucy out as she was and placed her in it. Whilst we were busy chafing her limbs there was a knock at the hall-door. One of the maids ran off, hurried on some more clothes, and opened it. Then she returned and whispered to us that there was a gentleman who had come with a message from Mr. Holmwood. I bade her simply tell him that he must wait, for we could see no one now. She went away with the message, and, engrossed with our work, I clean forgot all about him.

I never saw in all my experience the Professor work in such deadly earnest. I knew—as he knew—that it was a stand-up fight with death, and in a pause told him so. He answered me in a way that I did not understand, but with the sternest look that his face could wear:—

"If that were all, I would stop here where we are now, and let her fade away into peace, for I see no light in life over her horizon." He went on with his work with, if possible, renewed and more frenzied vigour.

Presently we both began to be conscious that the heat was beginning to be of some effect. Lucy's heart beat a trifle more audibly to the stethoscope, and her lungs had a perceptible movement. Van Helsing's face almost beamed, and as we lifted her from the bath and rolled her in a hot sheet to dry her he said to me:—

"The first gain is ours! Check to the King!"

We took Lucy into another room, which had by now been prepared, and laid her in bed and forced a few drops of brandy down her throat. I noticed that Van Helsing tied a soft silk handkerchief round her throat. She was still unconscious, and was quite as bad, if not worse than, we had ever seen her.

Van Helsing called in one of the women, and told her to stay with her and not to take her eyes off her till we returned, and then beckoned me out of the room.

"We must consult as to what is to be done," he said as we descended the stairs. In the hall he opened the dining-room door, and we passed in, he closing the door carefully behind him. The shutters had been opened, but the blinds were already down, with that obedience to the etiquette of death which the British women of the lower classes always rigidly observe. The room was, therefore, dimly dark. It was, however, light enough for our purposes. Van Helsing's sternness was somewhat relieved by a look of perplexity. He was evidently torturing his mind about something, so I waited for an instant, and he spoke:—

"What are we to do now? Where are we to turn for help? We must have another transfusion of blood, and that soon, or that poor girl's life won't be worth an hour's purchase. You are exhausted already; I am exhausted too. I fear to trust those women, even if they would have courage to submit. What are we to do for some one who will open his veins for her?"

"What's the matter with me, anyhow?"

The voice came from the sofa across the room, and its tones brought relief and joy to my heart, for they were those of Quincey Morris. Van Helsing started angrily at the first sound, but his face softened and a glad look came into his eyes as I cried out: "Quincey Morris!" and rushed towards him with outstretched hands.

"What brought you here?" I cried as our hands met.

"I guess Art is the cause."

He handed me a telegram:—

"Have not heard from Seward for three days, and am terribly anxious. Cannot leave. Father still in same condition. Send me word how Lucy is. Do not delay.—HOLMWOOD."

"I think I came just in the nick of time. You know you have only to tell me what to do."

Van Helsing strode forward, and took his hand, looking him straight in the eyes as he said:—

"A brave man's blood is the best thing on this earth when a woman is in trouble. You're a man and no mistake. Well, the devil may work against us for all he's worth, but God sends us men when we want them."

Once again we went through that ghastly operation. I have not the heart to go through with the details. Lucy had got a terrible shock and it told on her more than before, for though plenty of blood went into her veins, her body did not respond to the treatment as well as on the other occasions. Her struggle back into life was something frightful to see and hear. However, the action of both heart and lungs improved, and Van Helsing made a subcutaneous injection of morphia, as before, and with good effect. Her faint became a profound slumber. The Professor watched whilst I went downstairs with Quincey Morris, and sent one of the maids to pay off one of the cabmen who were waiting. I left Quincey lying down after having a glass of wine, and told the cook to get ready a good breakfast. Then a thought struck me, and I went back to the room where Lucy now was. When I came softly in, I found Van Helsing with a sheet or two of note-paper in his hand. He had evidently read it, and was thinking it over as he sat with his hand to his brow. There was a look of grim satisfaction in his face, as of one who has had a doubt solved. He handed me the paper saying only: "It dropped from Lucy's breast when we carried her to the bath."

When I had read it, I stood looking at the Professor, and after a pause asked him: "In God's name, what does it all mean? Was she, or is she, mad; or what sort of horrible danger is it?" I was so bewildered that I did not know what to say more. Van Helsing put out his hand and took the paper, saying:—

"Do not trouble about it now. Forget it for the present. You shall know and understand it all in good time; but it will be later. And now what is it that you came to me to say?" This brought me back to fact, and I was all myself again.

"I came to speak about the certificate of death. If we do not act properly and wisely, there may be an inquest, and that paper would have to be produced. I am in hopes that we need have no inquest, for if we had it would surely kill poor Lucy, if nothing else did. I know, and you know, and the other doctor who attended her knows, that Mrs. Westenra had disease of the heart, and we can certify that she died of it. Let us fill up the certificate at once, and I shall take it myself to the registrar and go on to the undertaker."

"Good, oh my friend John! Well thought of! Truly Miss Lucy, if she be sad in the foes that beset her, is at least happy in the friends that love her. One, two, three, all open their veins for her, besides one old man. Ah, yes, I know, friend John; I am not blind! I love you all the more for it! Now go."

In the hall I met Quincey Morris, with a telegram for Arthur telling him that Mrs. Westenra was dead; that Lucy also had been ill, but was now going on better, and that Van Helsing and I were with her. I told him where I was going, and he hurried me out, but as I was going said:—

"When you come back, Jack, may I have two words with you all to ourselves?" I nodded in reply and went out. I found no difficulty about the registration, and arranged with the local undertaker to come up in the evening to measure for the coffin and to make arrangements.

When I got back Quincey was waiting for me. I told him I would see him as soon as I knew about Lucy, and went up to her room. She was still sleeping, and the Professor seemingly had not moved from his seat at her side. From his putting his finger to his lips, I gathered that he expected her to wake before long and was afraid of forestalling nature. So I went down to Quincey and took him into the breakfast-room, where the blinds were not drawn down, and which was a little more cheerful, or rather less cheerless, than the other rooms. When we were alone, he said to me:—

"Jack Seward, I don't want to shove myself in anywhere where I've no right to be; but this is no ordinary case. You know I loved that girl and wanted to marry her; but although that's all past and gone, I can't help feeling anxious about her all the same. What is it that's wrong with her? The Dutchman—and a fine old fellow he is; I can see that—said, that time you two came into the room, that you must have *another* transfusion of blood, and that both you and he were exhausted. Now I know well that you medical men speak *in camera*, and that a man must not expect to know what they consult about in private. But this is no common matter, and, whatever it is, I have done my part. Is not that so?"

"That's so," I said, and he went on:—

"I take it that both you and Van Helsing had done already what I did to-day. Is not that so?"

"That's so."

"And I guess Art was in it too. When I saw him four days ago down at his own place he looked queer. I have not seen anything pulled down so quick since I was on the Pampas and had a mare that I was fond of go to grass all in a night. One of those big bats that they call vampires had got at her in the night, and what with his gorge and the vein left open, there wasn't enough blood in her to let her stand up, and I had to put a bullet through her as she lay. Jack, if you may tell me without betraying confidence, Arthur was the first, is not that so?" As he spoke the poor fellow looked terribly anxious. He was in a torture of suspense regarding the woman he loved, and his utter ignorance of the terrible mystery which seemed to surround her intensified his pain. His very heart was bleeding, and it took all the manhood of him—and there was a royal lot of it, too—to keep him from breaking down. I paused before answering, for I felt that I must not betray anything which the Professor wished kept secret; but already he knew so much, and guessed so much, that there could be no reason for not answering, so I answered in the same phrase: "That's so."

"And how long has this been going on?"

"About ten days."

"Ten days! Then I guess, Jack Seward, that that poor pretty creature that we all love has had put into her veins within that time the blood of four strong men. Man alive, her whole body wouldn't hold it." Then, coming close to me, he spoke in a fierce half-whisper; "What took it out?"

I shook my head. "That," I said, "is the crux. Van Helsing is simply frantic about it, and I am at my wits' end. I can't even hazard a guess. There has been a series of little circumstances which have thrown out all our calculations as to Lucy being properly watched. But these shall not occur again. Here we stay until all be well,—or ill." Quincey held out his hand. "Count me in," he said. "You and the Dutchman will tell me what to do, and I'll do it."

When she woke late in the afternoon, Lucy's first movement was to feel in her breast, and, to my surprise, produce the paper which Van Helsing had given me to read. The careful Professor had replaced it where it had come from, lest on waking she should be alarmed. Her eye then lit on Van Helsing and on me too, and gladdened. Then she looked around the room, and seeing where she was, shuddered; she gave a loud cry, and put her poor thin hands before her pale face. We both under-stood what that meant—that she had realised to the full her mother's death; so we tried what we could to comfort her. Doubtless sympathy eased her somewhat, but she was very low in thought and spirit, and wept silently and weakly for a long time. We told her that either or both of us would now remain with her all the time, and that seemed to comfort her. Towards dusk she fell into a doze. Here a very odd thing occurred. Whilst still asleep she took the paper from her breast and tore it in two. Van Helsing stepped over and took the pieces from her. All the same, however, she went on with the action of tearing, as though the material were still in her hands; finally she lifted her hands and opened them as though scattering the fragments. Van Helsing seemed surprised, and his brows gathered as if in thought, but he said nothing.

19 September.—All last night she slept fitfully, being always afraid to sleep, and something weaker when she woke from it. The Professor and I took it in turns to watch, and we never left her for a moment unattended. Quincey Morris said nothing about his intention, but I knew that all night long he patrolled round and round the house.

When the day came, its searching light showed the ravages in poor Lucy's strength. She was hardly able to turn her head, and the little nourishment which she could take seemed to do her no good. At times she slept, and both Van Helsing and I noticed the difference in her, between sleeping and waking. Whilst asleep she looked stronger, although more haggard, and her breathing was softer; her open mouth showed the pale gums drawn back from the teeth, which thus looked positively longer and sharper than usual; when she woke the softness of her eyes evidently changed the expression, for she looked her own self, although a dying one. In the afternoon she asked for Arthur, and we telegraphed for him. Quincey went off to meet him at the station.

When he arrived it was nearly six o'clock, and the sun was setting full and warm, and the red light streamed in through the window and gave more colour to the pale cheeks. When he saw her, Arthur was simply choking with emotion, and none of us could speak. In the hours that had passed, the fits of sleep, or the comatose condition that passed for it, had grown more frequent, so that the pauses when conversation was possible were shortened. Arthur's presence, however, seemed to act as a stimulant; she rallied a little, and spoke to him more brightly than she had done since we arrived. He too pulled himself together, and spoke as cheerily as he could, so that the best was made of everything.

It was now nearly one o'clock, and he and Van Helsing are sitting with her. I am to relieve them in a quarter of an hour, and I am entering this on Lucy's phonograph. Until six o'clock they are to try to rest. I fear that to-morrow will end our watching for the shock has been too great; the poor child cannot rally. God help us all.

LETTER FROM MINA HARKER TO LUCY WESTENRA.
(*Unopened by her.*)

"*17 September.*

"My dearest Lucy,—

"It seems *an age* since I heard from you, or indeed since I wrote. You will pardon me, I know, for all my faults when you have read all my budget of news. Well, I got my husband back all right; when we arrived at Exeter there was a carriage waiting for us, and in it, though he had an attack of gout, Mr. Hawkins. He took us to his house, where there were rooms for us all nice and comfortable, and we dined together. After dinner Mr. Hawkins said:—

"'My dears, I want to drink your health and prosperity; and may every blessing attend you both. I know you both from children, and have, with love and pride, seen you grow up. Now I want you to make your home here with me. I have left to me neither chick nor child; all are gone, and in my will I have left you everything.' I cried, Lucy dear, as Jonathan and the old man clasped hands. Our evening was a very, very happy one.

"So here we are, installed in this beautiful old house, and from both my bedroom and the drawing-room I can see the great elms of the cathedral close, with their great black stems standing out against the old yellow stone of the cathedral and I can hear the rooks overhead cawing and cawing and chattering and gossiping all day, after the manner of rooks—and humans. I am busy, I need not tell you, arranging things and housekeeping. Jonathan and Mr. Hawkins are busy all day; for, now that Jonathan is a partner, Mr. Hawkins wants to tell him all about the clients.

"How is your dear mother getting on? I wish I could run up to town for a day or two to see you, dear, but I dare not go yet, with so much on my shoulders; and Jonathan wants looking after still. He is beginning to put some flesh on his bones again, but he was terribly weakened by the long illness; even now he sometimes starts out of his sleep in a sudden way and awakes all trembling until I can coax him back to his usual placidity. However, thank God, these occasions grow less frequent as the days go on, and they will in time pass away altogether, I trust. And now I have told you my news, let me ask yours. When are you to be married, and where, and who is to perform the ceremony, and what are you to wear, and is it to be a public or a private wedding? Tell me all about it, dear; tell me all about everything, for there is nothing which interests you which will not be dear to me. Jonathan asks me to send his 'respectful duty,' but I do not think that is good enough from the junior partner of the important firm Hawkins & Harker; and so, as you love me, and he loves me, and I love you with all the moods and tenses of the verb, I send you simply his 'love' instead. Good-bye, my dearest Lucy, and all blessings on you.

"Yours,

"MINA HARKER."

REPORT FROM PATRICK HENNESSEY, M.D., M.R.C.S.L.K., Q.C.P.I., ETC., ETC., TO JOHN SEWARD, M.D.

"20 September.

"My dear Sir,—

"In accordance with your wishes, I enclose report of the conditions of everything left in my charge. . . . With regard to patient, Renfield, there is more to say. He has had another outbreak, which might have had a dreadful ending, but which, as it fortunately happened, was unattended with any unhappy results. This afternoon a carrier's cart with two men made a call at the empty house whose grounds abut on ours—the house to which, you will remember, the patient twice ran away. The men stopped at our gate to ask the porter their way, as they were strangers. I was myself looking out of the study window, having a smoke after dinner, and saw one of them come up to the house. As he passed the window of Renfield's room, the patient began to rate him from within, and called him all the foul names he could lay his tongue to. The man, who seemed a decent fellow enough, contented himself by telling him to 'shut up for a foul-mouthed beggar,' whereon our man accused him of robbing him and wanting to murder him and said that he would hinder him if he were to swing for it. I opened the window and signed to the man not to notice, so he contented himself after looking the place over and making up his mind as to what kind of a place he had got to by saying: 'Lor' bless yer, sir, I wouldn't mind what was said to me in a bloomin' madhouse. I pity ye and the guv'nor for havin' to live in the house with a wild beast like that.' Then he asked his way civilly enough, and I told him where the gate of the empty house was; he went away, followed by threats and curses and revilings from our man. I went down to see if I could make out any cause of his anger, since he is usually such a well-behaved man, and except his violent fits nothing of the kind had ever occurred. I found him, to my astonishment, quite composed and most genial in his manner. I tried to get him to talk of the incident, but he blandly asked me questions as to what I meant, and led me to believe that he was completely oblivious of the affair. It was, I am sorry to say, however, only another instance of his cunning, for within half an hour I heard of him again. This time he had broken out through the window of his room, and was running down the avenue. I called to the attendants to follow me, and ran after him, for I feared he was intent on some mischief. My fear was justified when I saw the same cart which had passed before coming down the road, having on it some great wooden boxes. The men were wiping their foreheads, and were flushed in the face, as if with violent exercise. Before I could get up to him the patient rushed at them, and pulling one of them off the cart, began to knock his head against the ground. If I had not seized him just at the moment I believe he would have killed the man there and then. The other fellow jumped down and struck him over the head with the butt-end of his heavy whip. It was a terrible blow; but he did not seem to mind it, but seized him also, and struggled with the three of us, pulling us to and fro as if we were kittens. You know I am no light weight, and the others were both burly men. At first he was silent in his fighting; but as we began to master him, and the attendants were putting a strait-waistcoat on him, he began to shout: 'I'll frustrate them! They shan't rob me! they shan't murder me by inches! I'll fight for my Lord and Master!' and all sorts of similar incoherent ravings. It was with very considerable difficulty that they got him back to the house and put him in the padded room. One of the attendants, Hardy, had a finger broken. However, I set it all right; and he is going on well.

"The two carriers were at first loud in their threats of actions for damages, and promised to rain all the penalties of the law on us. Their threats were, however, mingled with some sort of indirect apology for the defeat of the two of them by a feeble madman. They said that if it had not been for the way their strength had been spent in carrying and raising the heavy boxes to the cart they would have made short work of him. They gave as another reason for their defeat the extraordinary state of drouth to which they had been reduced by the dusty nature of their occupation and the reprehensible distance from the scene of their labours of any place of public entertainment. I quite understood their drift, and after a stiff glass of grog, or rather more of the same, and with each a sovereign in hand, they made light of the attack, and swore that they would encounter a worse madman any day for the pleasure of meeting so 'bloomin' good a bloke' as your correspondent. I took their names and addresses, in case they might be needed. They are as follows: —Jack Smollet, of Dudding's Rents, King George's Road, Great Walworth, and Thomas Snelling, Peter Farley's Row, Guide Court, Bethnal Green. They are both in the employment of Harris & Sons, Moving and Shipment Company, Orange Master's Yard, Soho.

"I shall report to you any matter of interest occurring here, and shall wire you at once if there is anything of importance.

"Believe me, dear Sir,

"Yours faithfully,

"PATRICK HENNESSEY."

LETTER FROM MINA HARKER TO LUCY WESTENRA.
(*Unopened by her.*)

"*18 September.*

"My dearest Lucy,—

"Such a sad blow has befallen us. Mr. Hawkins has died very suddenly. Some may not think it so sad for us, but we had both come to so love him that it really seems as though we had lost a father. I never knew either father or mother, so that the dear old man's death is a real blow to me. Jonathan is greatly distressed. It is not only that he feels sorrow, deep sorrow, for the dear, good man who has befriended him all his life, and now at the end has treated him like his own son and left him a fortune which to people of our modest bringing up is wealth beyond the dream of avarice, but Jonathan feels it on another account. He says the amount of responsibility which it puts upon him makes him nervous. He begins to doubt himself. I try to cheer him up, and *my* belief in *him* helps him to have a belief in himself. But it is here that the grave shock that he experienced tells upon him the most. Oh, it is too hard that a sweet, simple, noble, strong nature such as his—a nature which enabled him by our dear, good friend's aid to rise from clerk to master in a few years—should be so injured that the very essence of its strength is gone. Forgive me, dear, if I worry you with my troubles in the midst of your own happiness; but, Lucy dear, I must tell some one, for the strain of keeping up a brave and cheerful appearance to Jonathan tries me, and I have no one here that I can confide in. I dread coming up to London, as we must do the day after to-morrow; for poor Mr. Hawkins left in his will that he was to be buried in the grave with his father. As there are no relations at all, Jonathan will have to be chief mourner. I shall try to run over to see you, dearest, if only for a few minutes. Forgive me for troubling you. With all blessings,

"Your loving
"MINA HARKER."

DR. SEWARD'S DIARY.

20 September.—Only resolution and habit can let me make an entry to-night. I am too miserable, too low-spirited, too sick of the world and all in it, including life itself, that I would not care if I heard this moment the flapping of the wings of the angel of death. And he has been flapping those grim wings to some purpose of late—Lucy's mother and Arthur's father, and now. . . . Let me get on with my work.

I duly relieved Van Helsing in his watch over Lucy. We wanted Arthur to go to rest also, but he refused at first. It was only when I told him that we should want him to help us during the day, and that we must not all break down for want of rest, lest Lucy should suffer, that he agreed to go. Van Helsing was very kind to him. "Come, my child," he said; "come with me. You are sick and weak, and have had much sorrow and much mental pain, as well as that tax on your strength that we know of. You must not be alone; for to be alone is to be full of fears and alarms. Come to the drawing-room, where there is a big fire, and there are two sofas. You shall lie on one, and I on the other, and our sympathy will be comfort to each other, even though we do not speak, and even if we sleep." Arthur went off with him, casting back a longing look on Lucy's face, which lay in her pillow, almost whiter than the lawn. She lay quite still, and I looked round the room to see that all was as it should be. I could see that the Professor had carried out in this room, as in the other, his purpose of using the garlic; the whole of the window-sashes reeked with it, and round Lucy's neck, over the silk handkerchief which Van Helsing made her keep on, was a rough chaplet of the same odorous flowers. Lucy was breathing somewhat stertorously, and her face was at its worst, for the open mouth showed the pale gums. Her teeth, in the dim, uncertain light, seemed longer and sharper than they had been in the morning. In particular, by some trick of the light, the canine teeth looked longer and sharper than the rest. I sat down by her, and presently she moved uneasily. At the same moment there came a sort of dull flapping or buffeting at the window. I went over to it softly, and peeped out by the corner of the blind. There was a full moonlight, and I could see that the noise was made by a great bat, which wheeled round—doubtless attracted by the light, although so dim—and every now and again struck the window with its wings. When I came back to my seat, I found that Lucy had moved slightly and had torn away the garlic flowers from her throat. I replaced them as well as I could, and sat watching her.

Presently she woke, and I gave her food, as Van Helsing had prescribed. She took but a little, and that languidly. There did not seem to be with her now the unconscious struggle for life and strength that had hitherto so marked her illness. It struck me as curious that the moment she became conscious she pressed the garlic flowers close to her. It was certainly odd that whenever she got into that lethargic state, with the stertorous breathing, she put the flowers from her; but that when she waked she clutched them close. There was no possibility of making any mistake about this, for in the long hours that followed, she had many spells of sleeping and waking and repeated both actions many times.

At six o'clock Van Helsing came to relieve me. Arthur had then fallen into a doze, and he mercifully let him sleep on. When he saw Lucy's face I could hear the hissing indraw of his breath, and he said to me in a sharp whisper: "Draw up the blind; I want light!" Then he bent down, and, with his face almost touching Lucy's, examined her carefully. He removed the flowers and lifted the silk handkerchief from her throat. As he did so he started back, and I could hear his ejaculation, "Mein Gott!" as it was smothered in his throat. I bent over and looked, too, and as I noticed some queer chill came over me.

The wounds on the throat had absolutely disappeared.

For fully five minutes Van Helsing stood looking at her, with his face at its sternest. Then he turned to me and said calmly:—

"She is dying. It will not be long now. It will be much difference, mark me, whether she dies conscious or in her sleep. Wake that poor boy, and let him come and see the last; he trusts us, and we have promised him."

I went to the dining-room and waked him. He was dazed for a moment, but when he saw the sunlight streaming in through the edges of the shutters he thought he was late, and expressed his fear. I assured him that Lucy was still asleep, but told him as gently as I could that both Van Helsing and I feared that the end was near. He covered his face with his hands, and slid down on his knees by the sofa, where he remained, perhaps a minute, with his head buried, praying, whilst his shoulders shook with grief. I took him by the hand and raised him up. "Come," I said, "my dear old fellow, summon all your fortitude: it will be best and easiest for her."

When we came into Lucy's room I could see that Van Helsing had, with his usual forethought, been putting matters straight and making everything look as pleasing as possible. He had even brushed Lucy's hair, so that it lay on the pillow in its usual sunny ripples. When we came into the room she opened her eyes, and seeing him, whispered softly:—

"Arthur! Oh, my love, I am so glad you have come!" He was stooping to kiss her, when Van Helsing motioned him back. "No," he whispered, "not yet! Hold her hand; it will comfort her more."

So Arthur took her hand and knelt beside her, and she looked her best, with all the soft lines matching the angelic beauty of her eyes. Then gradually her eyes closed, and she sank to sleep. For a little bit her breasts heaved softly, and her breath came and went like a tired child's.

And then insensibly there came the strange change which I had noticed in the night. Her breathing grew stertorous, the mouth opened, and the pale gums, drawn back, made the teeth look longer and sharper than ever. In a sort of sleep-waking, vague, unconscious way she opened her eyes, which were now dull and hard at once, and said in a soft, voluptuous voice, such as I had never heard from her lips:—

"Arthur! Oh, my love, I am so glad you have come! Kiss me!" Arthur bent eagerly over to kiss her; but at that instant Van Helsing, who, like me, had been startled by her voice, swooped upon him, and catching him by the neck with a fury of strength which I never thought he could have possessed, and actually hurled him almost across the room.

"Not for your life!" he said; "not for your living soul and hers!" And he stood between them like a lion at bay.

Arthur was so taken aback that he did not for a moment know what to do or say; and before any impulse of violence could seize him he realised the place and the occasion, and stood silent, waiting.

I kept my eyes fixed on Lucy, as did Van Helsing, and we saw a spasm as of rage flit like a shadow over her face; the sharp teeth champed together. Then her eyes closed, and she breathed heavily.

Very shortly after she opened her eyes in all their softness, and putting out her poor, pale, thin hand, took Van Helsing's great brown one; drawing it to her, she kissed it. "My true friend," she said, in a faint voice, but with untellable pathos. "My true friend, and his! Oh, guard him, and give me peace!"

"I swear it!" he said solemnly, kneeling beside her and holding up his hand, as one who registers an oath. Then he turned to Arthur, and said to him: "Come, my child, take her hand in yours, and kiss her on the forehead, and only once."

Their eyes met instead of their lips; and so they parted.

Lucy's eyes closed; and Van Helsing, who had been watching closely, took Arthur's arm, and drew him away.

And then Lucy's breathing became stertorous again, and all at once it ceased.

"It is all over," said Van Helsing. "She is dead!"

I took Arthur by the arm, and led him away to the drawing-room, where he sat down, and covered his face with his hands, sobbing in a way that nearly broke me down to see.

I went back to the room, and found Van Helsing looking at poor Lucy, and his face was sterner than ever. Some change had come over her body. Death had given back part of her beauty, for her brow and cheeks had recovered some of their flowing lines; even the lips had lost their deadly pallor. It was as if the blood, no longer needed for the working of the heart, had gone to make the harshness of death as little rude as might be.

"We thought her dying whilst she slept,

And sleeping when she died."

I stood beside Van Helsing, and said:—

"Ah, well, poor girl, there is peace for her at last. It is the end!"

He turned to me, and said with grave solemnity:—

"Not so; alas! not so. It is only the beginning!"

When I asked him what he meant, he only shook his head and answered:—

"We can do nothing as yet. Wait and see."

CHAPTER 13.

———◇———

DR. SEWARD'S DIARY—*continued.*

The funeral was arranged for the next succeeding day, so that Lucy and her mother might be buried together. I attended to all the ghastly formalities, and the urbane undertaker proved that his staff were afflicted—or blessed—with something of his own obsequious suavity. Even the woman who performed the last offices for the dead remarked to me, in a confidential, brother-professional way, when she had come out from the death-chamber:—

"She makes a very beautiful corpse, sir. It's quite a privilege to attend on her. It's not too much to say that she will do credit to our establishment!"

I noticed that Van Helsing never kept far away. This was possible from the disordered state of things in the household. There were no relatives at hand; and as Arthur had to be back the next day to attend at his father's funeral, we were unable to notify any one who should have been bidden. Under the circumstances, Van Helsing and I took it upon ourselves to examine papers, etc. He insisted upon looking over Lucy's papers himself. I asked him why, for I feared that he, being a foreigner, might not be quite aware of English legal requirements, and so might in ignorance make some unnecessary trouble. He answered me:—

"I know; I know. You forget that I am a lawyer as well as a doctor. But this is not altogether for the law. You knew that, when you avoided the coroner. I have more than him to avoid. There may be papers more— such as this."

As he spoke he took from his pocket-book the memorandum which had been in Lucy's breast, and which she had torn in her sleep.

"When you find anything of the solicitor who is for the late Mrs. Westenra, seal all her papers, and write him to-night. For me, I watch here in the room and in Miss Lucy's old room all night, and I myself search for what may be. It is not well that her very thoughts go into the hands of strangers."

I went on with my part of the work, and in another half hour had found the name and address of Mrs. Westenra's solicitor and had written to him. All the poor lady's papers were in order; explicit directions regarding the place of burial were given. I had hardly sealed the letter, when, to my surprise, Van Helsing walked into the room, saying:—

"Can I help you, friend John? I am free, and if I may, my service is to you."

"Have you got what you looked for?" I asked, to which he replied:—

"I did not look for any specific thing. I only hoped to find, and find I have, all that there was—only some letters and a few memoranda, and a diary new begun. But I have them here, and we shall for the present say nothing of them. I shall see that poor lad to-morrow evening, and, with his sanction, I shall use some."

When we had finished the work in hand, he said to me:—

"And now, friend John, I think we may to bed. We want sleep, both you and I, and rest to recuperate. To-morrow we shall have much to do, but for the to-night there is no need of us. Alas!"

Before turning in we went to look at poor Lucy. The undertaker had certainly done his work well, for the room was turned into a small *chapelle ardente.* There was a wilderness of beautiful white flowers, and death was made as little repulsive as might be. The end of the winding-sheet was laid over the face; when the Professor bent over and turned it gently back, we both started at the beauty before us, the tall wax candles showing a sufficient light to note it well. All Lucy's loveliness had come back to her in death, and the hours that had passed, instead of leaving traces of "decay's effacing fingers," had but restored the beauty of life, till positively I could not believe my eyes that I was looking at a corpse.

The Professor looked sternly grave. He had not loved her as I had, and there was no need for tears in his eyes. He said to me: "Remain till I return," and left the room. He came back with a handful of wild garlic from the box waiting in the hall, but which had not been opened, and placed the flowers amongst the others on and around the bed. Then he took from his neck, inside his collar, a little gold crucifix, and placed it over the mouth. He restored the sheet to its place and we came away.

I was undressing in my own room, when, with a premonitory tap at the door, he entered, and at once began to speak:—

"To-morrow I want you to bring me, before night, a set of post-mortem knives."

"Must we make an autopsy?" I asked.

"Yes and no. I want to operate, but not as you think. Let me tell you, now, but not a word to another. I want to cut off her head and take out her heart. Ah! you a surgeon, and so shocked! You, whom I have seen with no tremble of hand or heart, do operations of life and death that make the rest shudder. Oh, but I must not forget, my dear friend John, that you loved her; and I have not forgotten it, for it is I that shall operate, and you must only help. I would like to do it to-night, but for Arthur I must not; he will be free after his father's funeral to-morrow, and he will want to see her—to see *it*. Then, when she is coffined ready for the next day, you and I shall come when all sleep. We shall unscrew the coffin-lid, and shall do our operation; and then replace all, so that none know, save we alone."

"But why do it at all? The girl is dead. Why mutilate her poor body without need? And if there is no necessity for a post-mortem and nothing to gain by it—no good to her, to us, to science, to human knowledge—why do it? Without such it is monstrous."

For answer he put his hand on my shoulder, and said, with infinite tenderness:—

"Friend John. I pity your poor bleeding heart; and I love you the more because it does so bleed. If I could, I would take on myself the burden that you do bear. But there are things that you know not, but that you shall know, and bless me for knowing, though they are not pleasant things. John, my child, you have been my friend now many years, and yet did you ever know me to do any without good cause? I may err—I am but man; but I believe in all I do. Was it not for these causes that you send for me when the great trouble came? Yes! Were you not amazed, nay horrified, when I would not let Arthur kiss his love—though she was dying—and snatched him away by all my strength? Yes! And yet you saw how she thanked me, with her so beautiful dying eyes, her voice, too, so weak, and she kiss my rough old hand and bless me? Yes! And did you not hear me swear promise to her, that so she closed her eyes grateful? Yes!

"Well, I have good reason now for all I want to do. You have for many years trust me; you have believe me weeks past, when there be things so strange that you might have well doubt. Believe me yet a little, friend John. If you trust me not, then I must tell what I think; and that is not perhaps well. And if I work—as work I shall, no matter trust or not trust—without my friend trust in me, I work with heavy heart and feel, oh! so lonely when I want all help and courage that may be!" He paused a moment and went on solemnly: "Friend John, there are strange and terrible days before us. Let us not be two, but one, that so we work to a good end. Will you not have faith in me?"

I took his hand, and promised him. I held my door open as he went away, and watched him go into his room and close the door. As I stood without moving, I saw one of the maids pass silently along the passage—she had her back towards me, so did not see me—and go into the room where Lucy lay. The sight touched me. Devotion is so rare, and we are so grateful to those who show it unasked to those we love. Here was a poor girl putting aside the terrors which she naturally had of death to go watch alone by the bier of the mistress whom she loved, so that the poor clay might not be lonely till laid to eternal rest. . . .

I must have slept long and soundly, for it was broad daylight when Van Helsing waked me by coming into my room. He came over to my bedside and said:—

"You need not trouble about the knives; we shall not do it."

"Why not?" I asked. For his solemnity of the night before had greatly impressed me.

"Because," he said sternly, "it is too late—or too early. See!" Here he held up the little golden crucifix. "This was stolen in the night."

"How, stolen," I asked in wonder, "since you have it now?"

"Because I get it back from the worthless wretch who stole it, from the woman who robbed the dead and the living. Her punishment will surely come, but not through me; she knew not altogether what she did, and thus unknowing, she only stole. Now we must wait."

He went away on the word, leaving me with a new mystery to think of, a new puzzle to grapple with.

The forenoon was a dreary time, but at noon the solicitor came: Mr. Marquand, of Wholeman, Sons, Marquand Lidderdale. He was very genial and very appreciative of what we had done, and took off our hands all cares as to details. During lunch he told us that Mrs. Westenra had for some time expected sudden death from her heart, and had put her affairs in absolute order; he informed us that, with the exception of a certain entailed property of Lucy's father's which now, in default of direct issue, went back to a distant branch of the family, the whole estate, real and personal, was left absolutely to Arthur Holmwood. When he had told us so much he went on:—

"Frankly we did our best to prevent such a testamentary disposition, and pointed out certain contingencies that might leave her daughter either penniless or not so free as she should be to act regarding a matrimonial alliance. Indeed, we pressed the matter so far that we almost came into collision, for she asked us if we were or were not prepared to carry out her wishes. Of course, we had then no alternative but to accept.

We were right in principle, and ninety-nine times out of a hundred we should have proved, by the logic of events, the accuracy of our judgment. Frankly, however, I must admit that in this case any other form of disposition would have rendered impossible the carrying out of her wishes. For by her predeceasing her daughter the latter would have come into possession of the property, and, even had she only survived her mother by five minutes, her property would, in case there were no will—and a will was a practical impossibility in such a case—have been treated at her decease as under intestacy. In which case Lord Godalming, though so dear a friend, would have had no claim in the world; and the inheritors, being remote, would not be likely to abandon their just right, for sentimental reasons regarding an entire stranger. I assure you, my dear sirs, I am rejoiced at the result, perfectly rejoiced."

He was a good fellow, but his rejoicing at the one little part—in which he was officially interested—of so great a tragedy, was an object-lesson in the limitations of sympathetic understanding.

He did not remain long, but said he would look in later in the day and see Lord Godalming. His coming, however, had been a certain comfort to us, since it assured us that we should not have to dread hostile criticism as to any of our acts. Arthur was expected at five o'clock, so a little before that time we visited the death-chamber. It was so in very truth, for now both mother and daughter lay in it. The undertaker, true to his craft, had made the best display he could of his goods, and there was a mortuary air about the place that lowered our spirits at once. Van Helsing ordered the former arrangement to be adhered to, explaining that, as Lord Godalming was coming very soon, it would be less harrowing to his feelings to see all that was left of his *fiancée* quite alone. The undertaker seemed shocked at his own stupidity and exerted himself to restore things to the condition in which we left them the night before, so that when Arthur came such shocks to his feelings as we could avoid were saved.

Poor fellow! He looked desperately sad and broken; even his stalwart manhood seemed to have shrunk somewhat under the strain of his much-tried emotions. He had, I knew, been very genuinely and devotedly attached to his father; and to lose him, and at such a time, was a bitter blow to him. With me he was warm as ever, and to Van Helsing he was sweetly courteous; but I could not help seeing that there was some constraint with him. The Professor noticed it, too, and motioned me to bring him upstairs. I did so, and left him at the door of the room, as I felt he would like to be quite alone with her, but he took my arm and led me in, saying huskily:—

"You loved her too, old fellow; she told me all about it, and there was no friend had a closer place in her heart than you. I don't know how to thank you for all you have done for her. I can't think yet. . . ."

Here he suddenly broke down, and threw his arms round my shoulders and laid his head on my breast, crying:—

"Oh, Jack! Jack! What shall I do! The whole of life seems gone from me at once, and there is nothing in the wide world for me to live for."

I comforted him as well as I could. In such cases men do not need much expression. A grip of the hand, the tightening of an arm over the shoulder, a sob in unison, are expressions of sympathy dear to a man's heart. I stood still and silent till his sobs died away, and then I said softly to him:—

"Come and look at her."

Together we moved over to the bed, and I lifted the lawn from her face. God! how beautiful she was. Every hour seemed to be enhancing her loveliness. It frightened and amazed me somewhat; and as for Arthur, he fell a-trembling, and finally was shaken with doubt as with an ague. At last, after a long pause, he said to me in a faint whisper:—

"Jack, is she really dead?"

I assured him sadly that it was so, and went on to suggest—for I felt that such a horrible doubt should not have life for a moment longer than I could help—that it often happened that after death faces became softened and even resolved into their youthful beauty; that this was especially so when death had been preceded by any acute or prolonged suffering. It seemed to quite do away with any doubt, and, after kneeling beside the couch for a while and looking at her lovingly and long, he turned aside. I told him that that must be good-bye, as the coffin had to be prepared; so he went back and took her dead hand in his and kissed it, and bent over and kissed her forehead. He came away, fondly looking back over his shoulder at her as he came.

I left him in the drawing-room, and told Van Helsing that he had said good-bye; so the latter went to the kitchen to tell the undertaker's men to proceed with the preparations and to screw up the coffin. When he came out of the room again I told him of Arthur's question, and he replied:—

"I am not surprised. Just now I doubted for a moment myself!"

We all dined together, and I could see that poor Art was trying to make the best of things. Van Helsing had been silent all dinner-time; but when we had lit our cigars he said:—

"Lord ——"; but Arthur interrupted him:—

"No, no, not that, for God's sake! not yet at any rate. Forgive me, sir: I did not mean to speak offensively; it is only because my loss is so recent."

The Professor answered very sweetly:—

"I only used that name because I was in doubt. I must not call you 'Mr.' and I have grown to love you—yes, my dear boy, to love you—as Arthur."

Arthur held out his hand, and took the old man's warmly.

"Call me what you will," he said. "I hope I may always have the title of a friend. And let me say that I am at a loss for words to thank you for your goodness to my poor dear." He paused a moment, and went on: "I know that she understood your goodness even better than I do; and if I was rude or in any way wanting at that time you acted so—you remember"—the Professor nodded—"you must forgive me."

He answered with a grave kindness:—

"I know it was hard for you to quite trust me then, for to trust such violence needs to understand; and I take it that you do not—that you cannot—trust me now, for you do not yet understand. And there may be more times when I shall want you to trust when you cannot—and may not—and must not yet understand. But the time will come when your trust shall be whole and complete in me, and when you shall understand as though the sunlight himself shone through. Then you shall bless me from first to last for your own sake, and for the sake of others, and for her dear sake to whom I swore to protect."

"And, indeed, indeed, sir," said Arthur warmly, "I shall in all ways trust you. I know and believe you have a very noble heart, and you are Jack's friend, and you were hers. You shall do what you like."

The Professor cleared his throat a couple of times, as though about to speak, and finally said:—

"May I ask you something now?"

"Certainly."

"You know that Mrs. Westenra left you all her property?"

"No, poor dear; I never thought of it."

"And as it is all yours, you have a right to deal with it as you will. I want you to give me permission to read all Miss Lucy's papers and letters. Believe me, it is no idle curiosity. I have a motive of which, be sure, she would have approved. I have them all here. I took them before we knew that all was yours, so that no strange hand might touch them—no strange eye look through words into her soul. I shall keep them, if I may; even you may not see them yet, but I shall keep them safe. No word shall be lost; and in the good time I shall give them back to you. It's a hard thing I ask, but you will do it, will you not, for Lucy's sake?"

Arthur spoke out heartily, like his old self:—

"Dr. Van Helsing, you may do what you will. I feel that in saying this I am doing what my dear one would have approved. I shall not trouble you with questions till the time comes."

The old Professor stood up as he said solemnly:—

"And you are right. There will be pain for us all; but it will not be all pain, nor will this pain be the last. We and you too—you most of all, my dear boy—will have to pass through the bitter water before we reach the sweet. But we must be brave of heart and unselfish, and do our duty, and all will be well!"

I slept on a sofa in Arthur's room that night. Van Helsing did not go to bed at all. He went to and fro, as if patrolling the house, and was never out of sight of the room where Lacy lay in her coffin, strewn with the wild garlic flowers, which sent, through the odour of lily and rose, a heavy, overpowering smell into the night.

MINA HARKER'S JOURNAL.

22 September.—In the train to Exeter. Jonathan sleeping.

It seems only yesterday that the last entry was made, and yet how much between then, in Whitby and all the world before me, Jonathan away and no news of him; and now, married to Jonathan, Jonathan a solicitor, a partner, rich, master of his business, Mr. Hawkins dead and buried, and Jonathan with another attack that may harm him. Some day he may ask me about it. Down it all goes. I am rusty in my shorthand— see what unexpected prosperity does for us—so it may be as well to freshen it up again with an exercise anyhow. . . .

The service was very simple and very solemn. There were only our- selves and the servants there, one or two old friends of his from Exeter, his London agent, and a gentleman representing Sir John Paxton, the President of the Incorporated Law Society. Jonathan and I stood hand in hand, and we felt that our best and dearest friend was gone from us. . . .

We came back to town quietly, taking a 'bus to Hyde Park Corner. Jonathan thought it would interest me to go into the Row for a while, so we sat down; but there were very few people there, and it was sad-looking and desolate to see so many empty chairs. It made us think of the empty chair at home; so we got up and walked down Piccadilly. Jonathan was holding me by the arm, the way he used to in the old days before I went to school. I felt it very improper, for you can't go on for some years teaching etiquette and decorum to other girls without the pedantry of it biting into yourself a bit; but it was Jonathan, and he was my husband, and we didn't know anybody who saw us—and we didn't care if they did—so on we walked. I was looking at a very beautiful girl, in a big cart-wheel hat, sitting in a victoria outside Guiliano's, when I felt Jona- than clutch my arm so tight that he hurt me, and he said under his breath: "My God!" I am always anxious about Jonathan, for I fear that some nervous fit may upset him again; so I turned to him quickly, and asked him what it was that disturbed him.

He was very pale, and his eyes seemed bulging out as, half in terror and half in amazement, he gazed at a tall, thin man, with a beaky nose and black moustache and pointed beard, who was also observing the pretty girl. He was looking at her so hard that he did not see either of us, and so I had a good view of him. His face was not a good face; it was hard, and cruel, and sensual, and his big white teeth, that looked all the whiter because his lips were so red, were pointed like an animal's. Jonathan kept staring at him, till I was afraid he would notice. I feared he might take it ill, he looked so fierce and nasty. I asked Jonathan why he was disturbed, and he answered, evidently thinking that I knew as much about it as he did: "Do you see who it is?"

"No, dear," I said; "I don't know him; who is it?" His answer seemed to shock and thrill me, for it was said as if he did not know that it was to me, Mina, to whom he was speaking:—

"It is the man himself!"

The poor dear was evidently terrified at something—very greatly terrified; I do believe that if he had not had me to lean on and to support him he would have sunk down. He kept staring; a man came out of the shop with a small parcel, and gave it to the lady, who then drove off. The dark man kept his eyes fixed on her, and when the carriage moved up Piccadilly he followed in the same direction, and hailed a hansom. Jonathan kept looking after him, and said, as if to himself:—

"I believe it is the Count, but he has grown young. My God, if this be so! Oh, my God! my God! If I only knew! if I only knew!" He was distressing himself so much that I feared to keep his mind on the subject by asking him any questions, so I remained silent. I drew him away quietly, and he, holding my arm, came easily. We walked a little further, and then went in and sat for a while in the Green Park. It was a hot day for autumn, and there was a comfortable seat in a shady place. After a few minutes' staring at nothing, Jonathan's eyes closed, and he went quietly into a sleep, with his head on my shoulder. I thought it was the best thing for him, so did not disturb him. In about twenty minutes he woke up, and said to me quite cheerfully:—

"Why, Mina, have I been asleep! Oh, do forgive me for being so rude. Come, and we'll have a cup of tea somewhere." He had evidently forgotten all about the dark stranger, as in his illness he had forgotten all that this episode had reminded him of. I don't like this lapsing into forgetfulness; it may make or continue some injury to the brain. I must not ask him, for fear I shall do more harm than good; but I must somehow learn the facts of his journey abroad. The time is come, I fear, when I must open that parcel, and know what is written. Oh, Jonathan, you will, I know, forgive me if I do wrong, but it is for your own dear sake.

Later.—A sad home-coming in every way—the house empty of the dear soul who was so good to us; Jonathan still pale and dizzy under a slight relapse of his malady; and now a telegram from Van Helsing, whoever he may be:—

"You will be grieved to hear that Mrs. Westenra died five days ago, and that Lucy died the day before yesterday. They were both buried to-day."

Oh, what a wealth of sorrow in a few words! Poor Mrs. Westenra! poor Lucy! Gone, gone, never to return to us! And poor, poor Arthur, to have lost such sweetness out of his life! God help us all to bear our troubles.

DR. SEWARD'S DIARY.

22 September.—It is all over. Arthur has gone back to Ring, and has taken Quincey Morris with him. What a fine fellow is Quincey! I believe in my heart of hearts that he suffered as much about Lucy's death as any of us; but he bore himself through it like a moral Viking. If America can go on breeding men like that, she will be a power in the world indeed. Van Helsing is lying down, having a rest preparatory to his journey. He goes over to Amsterdam to-night, but says he returns to-morrow night;

that he only wants to make some arrangements which can only be made personally. He is to stop with me then, if he can; he says he has work to do in London which may take him some time. Poor old fellow! I fear that the strain of the past week has broken down even his iron strength. All the time of the burial he was, I could see, putting some terrible restraint on himself. When it was all over, we were standing beside Arthur, who, poor fellow, was speaking of his part in the operation where his blood had been transfused to his Lucy's veins; I could see Van Helsing's face grow white and purple by turns. Arthur was saying that he felt since then as if they two had been really married and that she was his wife in the sight of God. None of us said a word of the other operations, and none of us ever shall. Arthur and Quincey went away together to the station, and Van Helsing and I came on here. The moment we were alone in the carriage he gave way to a regular fit of hysterics. He has denied to me since that it was hysterics, and insisted that it was only his sense of humour asserting itself under very terrible conditions. He laughed till he cried, and I had to draw down the blinds lest any one should see us and misjudge; and then he cried, till he laughed again; and laughed and cried together, just as a woman does. I tried to be stern with him, as one is to a woman under the circumstances; but it had no effect. Men and women are so different in manifestations of nervous strength or weakness! Then when his face grew grave and stern again I asked him why his mirth, and why, at such a time. His reply was in a way characteristic of him, for it was logical and forceful and mysterious. He said:—

"Ah, you don't comprehend, friend John. Do not think that I am not sad, though I laugh. See, I have cried even when the laugh did choke me. But no more think that I am all sorry when I cry, for the laugh he comes just the same. Keep it always with you that laughter who knock at your door and say, 'May I come in?' is not the true laughter. No! he is a king, and he come when and how he like. He ask no person; he choose no time of suitability. He say, 'I am here.' Behold, in example I grieve my heart out for that so sweet young girl; I give my blood for her, though I am old and worn; I give my time, my skill, my sleep; I let my other sufferers want that so she may have all. And yet I can laugh at her very grave—laugh when the clay from the spade of the sexton drop upon her coffin and say 'Thud! thud!' to my heart, till it send back the blood from my cheek. My heart bleed for that poor boy—that dear boy, so of the age of mine own boy had I been so blessed that he live, and with his hair and eyes the same. There, you know now why I love him so. And yet when he say things that touch my husband-heart to the quick, and make my father-heart yearn to him as to no other man—not even to you, friend John, for we are more level in experiences than father and son—yet even at such moment King Laugh he come to me and shout and bellow in my ear, 'Here I am! here I am!' till the blood come dance back and bring some of the sunshine that he carry with him to my cheek. Oh, friend John, it is a strange world, a sad world, a world full of miseries, and woes, and troubles; and yet when King Laugh come he make them all dance to the tune he play. Bleeding hearts, and dry bones of the church-yard, and tears that burn as they fall—all dance together to the music that he make with that smileless mouth of him. And believe me, friend John, that he is good to come, and kind. Ah, we men and women are like ropes drawn tight with strain that pull us different ways. Then tears come; and, like the rain on the ropes, they brace us up, until perhaps the strain become too great, and we break. But King Laugh he come like the sunshine, and he ease off the strain again; and we bear to go on with our labour, what it may be."

I did not like to wound him by pretending not to see his idea; but, as I did not yet understand the cause of his laughter, I asked him. As he answered me his face grew stern, and he said in quite a different tone:—

"Oh, it was the grim irony of it all—this so lovely lady garlanded with flowers, that looked so fair as life, till one by one we wondered if she were truly dead; she laid in that so fine marble house in that lonely churchyard, where rest so many of her kin, laid there with the mother who loved her, and whom she loved; and that sacred bell going 'Toll! toll! toll!' so sad and slow; and those holy men, with the white garments of the angel, pretending to read books, and yet all the time their eyes never on the page; and all of us with the bowed head. And all for what? She is dead; so! Is it not?"

"Well, for the life of me, Professor," I said, "I can't see anything to laugh at in all that. Why, your explanation makes it a harder puzzle than before. But even if the burial service was comic, what about poor Art and his trouble? Why, his heart was simply breaking."

"Just so. Said he not that the transfusion of his blood to her veins had made her truly his bride?"

"Yes, and it was a sweet and comforting idea for him."

"Quite so. But there was a difficulty, friend John. If so that, then what about the others? Ho, ho! Then this so sweet maid is a polyandrist, and me, with my poor wife dead to me, but alive by Church's law, though no wits, all gone—even I, who am faithful husband to this now-no-wife, am bigamist."

"I don't see where the joke comes in there either!" I said; and I did not feel particularly pleased with him for saying such things. He laid his hand on my arm, and said:—

"Friend John, forgive me if I pain. I showed not my feeling to others when it would wound, but only to you, my old friend, whom I can trust. If you could have looked into my very heart then when I want to laugh; if you could have done so when the laugh arrived; if you could do so now; when King Laugh have pack up his crown, and all that is to him—for he go far, far away from me, and for a long, long time—maybe you would perhaps pity me the most of all."

I was touched by the tenderness of his tone, and asked why.

"Because I know!"

And now we are all scattered; and for many a long day loneliness will sit over our roofs with brooding wings. Lucy lies in the tomb of her kin, a lordly deathhouse in a lonely churchyard, away from teeming London; where the air is fresh, and the sun rises over Hampstead Hill and where wild flowers grow of their own accord.

So I can finish this diary; and God only knows if I shall ever begin another. If I do, or if I even open this again, it will be to deal with different people and different themes; for here at the end, where the romance of my life is told, ere I go back to take up the thread of my lifework, I say sadly and without hope "finis."

"THE WESTMINSTER GAZETTE,"
25 SEPTEMBER.

A HAMPSTEAD MYSTERY.

The neighbourhood of Hampstead is just at present exercised with a series of events which seem to run on lines parallel to those of what was known to the writers of headlines as "The Kensington Horror," or "The Stabbing Woman," or "The Woman in Black." During the past two or three days several cases have occurred of young children straying from home or neglecting to return from their playing on the Heath. In all these cases the children were too young to give any properly intelligible account of themselves, but the consensus of their excuses is that they had been with a "bloofer lady." It has always been late in the evening when they have been missed, and on two occasions the children have not been found until early in the following morning. It is generally supposed in the neighbourhood that, as the first child missed gave as his reason for being away that a "bloofer lady" had asked him to come for a walk, the others had picked up the phrase and used it as occasion served. This is the more natural as the favourite game of the little ones at present is luring each other away by wiles. A correspondent writes us that to see some of the tiny tots pretending to be the "bloofer lady" is supremely funny. Some of our caricaturists might, he says, take a lesson in the irony of grotesque by comparing the reality and the picture. It is only in accordance with general principles of human nature that the "bloofer lady" should be the popular rôle at these *al fresco* performances. Our correspondent naïvely says that even Ellen Terry could not be so winningly attractive as some of these grubby-faced little children pretend—and even imagine themselves—to be.

There is, however, possibly a serious side to the question, for some of the children, indeed all who have been missed at night, have been slightly torn or wounded in the throat. The wounds seem such as might be made by a rat or a small dog, and although of not much importance individually, would tend to show that whatever animal inflicts them has a system or method of its own. The police of the division have been instructed to keep a sharp look-out for straying children, especially when very young, in and around Hampstead Heath, and for any stray dog which may be about.

"THE WESTMINSTER GAZETTE," 25 SEPTEMBER.
EXTRA SPECIAL.

THE HAMPSTEAD HORROR.
ANOTHER CHILD INJURED.
THE "BLOOFER LADY."

We have just received intelligence that another child, missed last night, was only discovered late in the morning under a furze bush at the Shooter's Hill side of Hampstead Heath, which is, perhaps, less frequented than the other parts. It has the same tiny wound in the throat as has been noticed in other cases. It was terribly weak, and looked quite emaciated. It too, when partially restored, had the common story to tell of being lured away by the "bloofer lady."

CHAPTER 14.

‡———◇———‡

MINA HARKER'S JOURNAL.

23 September.—Jonathan is better after a bad night. I am so glad that he has plenty of work to do, for that keeps his mind off the terrible things; and oh, I am rejoiced that he is not now weighed down with the responsibility of his new position. I knew he would be true to himself, and now how proud I am to see my Jonathan rising to the height of his advancement and keeping pace in all ways with the duties that come upon him. He will be away all day till late, for he said he could not lunch at home. My household work is done, so I shall take his foreign journal, and lock myself up in my room and read it. . . .

24 September.—I hadn't the heart to write last night; that terrible record of Jonathan's upset me so. Poor dear! How he must have suffered, whether it be true or only imagination. I wonder if there is any truth in it at all. Did he get his brain fever, and then write all those terrible things, or had he some cause for it all? I suppose I shall never know, for I dare not open the subject to him. . . . And yet that man we saw yesterday! He seemed quite certain of him. . . . Poor fellow! I suppose it was the funeral upset him and sent his mind back on some train of thought. . . . He believes it all himself. I remember how on our wedding-day he said: "Unless some solemn duty come upon me to go back to the bitter hours, asleep or awake, mad or sane." There seems to be through it all some thread of continuity. . . . That fearful Count was coming to London. . . . If it should be, and he came to London, with his teeming millions. . . . There may be solemn duty; and if it come we must not shrink from it. . . . I shall be prepared. I shall get my typewriter this very hour and begin transcribing. Then we shall be ready for other eyes if required. And if it be wanted; then, perhaps, if I am ready, poor Jonathan may not be upset, for I can speak for him and never let him be troubled or worried with it at all. If ever Jonathan quite gets over the nervousness he may want to tell me of it all, and I can ask him questions and find out things, and see how I may comfort him.

LETTER, VAN HELSING TO MRS. HARKER.

"*24 September.*
(*Confidence*)
"Dear Madam,—

"I pray you to pardon my writing, in that I am so far friend as that I sent you sad news of Miss Lucy Westenra's death. By the kindness of Lord Godalming, I am empowered to read her letters and papers, for I am deeply concerned about certain matters vitally important. In them I find some letters from you, which show how great friends you were and how you love her. Oh, Madam Mina, by that love, I implore you, help me. It is for others' good that I ask—to redress great wrong, and to lift much and terrible troubles—that may be more great than you can know. May it be that I see you? You can trust me. I am friend of Dr. John Seward and of Lord Godalming (that was Arthur of Miss Lucy). I must keep it private for the present from all. I should come to Exeter to see you at once if you tell me I am privilege to come, and where and when. I implore your pardon, madam. I have read your letters to poor Lucy, and know how good you are and how your husband suffer; so I pray you, if it may be, enlighten him not, lest it may harm. Again your pardon, and forgive me.

"VAN HELSING."

TELEGRAM FROM MRS. HARKER TO VAN HELSING.

"*25 September.*—Come to-day by quarter-past ten train if you can catch it. Can see you any time you call. Wilhelmina Harker."

MINA HARKER'S JOURNAL.

25 September.—I cannot help feeling terribly excited as the time draws near for the visit of Dr. Van Helsing, for somehow I expect that it will throw some light upon Jonathan's sad experience; and as he attended poor dear Lucy in her last illness, he can tell me all about her. That is the reason of his coming; it is concerning Lucy and her sleep-walking, and not about Jonathan. Then I shall never know the real truth now! How silly I am. That awful journal gets hold of my imagination and tinges everything with something of its own colour. Of course it is about Lucy. That habit came back to the poor dear, and that awful night on the cliff must have made her ill. I had almost forgotten in my own affairs how ill she was afterwards. She must have told him of her sleep-walking adventure on the cliff, and that I knew all about it; and now he wants me to tell him what she knows, so that he may understand. I hope I did right in not saying anything of it to Mrs. Westenra; I should never forgive myself if any act of mine, were it even a negative one, brought harm on poor dear Lucy. I hope, too, Dr. Van Helsing will not blame me; I have had so much trouble and anxiety of late that I feel I cannot bear more just at present.

I suppose a cry does us all good at times—clears the air as other rain does. Perhaps it was reading the journal yesterday that upset me, and then Jonathan went away this morning to stay away from me a whole day and night, the first time we have been parted since our marriage. I do hope the dear fellow will take care of himself, and that nothing will occur to upset him. It is two o'clock, and the doctor will be here soon now. I shall say nothing of Jonathan's journal unless he asks me. I am so glad I have typewritten out my own journal, so that, in case he asks about Lucy, I can hand it to him; it will save much questioning.

Later.—He has come and gone. Oh, what a strange meeting, and how it all makes my head whirl round! I feel like one in a dream. Can it be all possible, or even a part of it? If I had not read Jonathan's journal first, I should never have accepted even a possibility. Poor, poor, dear Jonathan! How he must have suffered. Please the good God, all this may not upset him again. I shall try to save him from it; but it may be even a consolation and a help to him—terrible though it be and awful in its consequences—to know for certain that his eyes and ears and brain did not deceive him, and that it is all true. It may be that it is the doubt which haunts him; that when the doubt is removed, no matter which— waking or dreaming—may prove the truth, he will be more satisfied and better able to bear the shock. Dr. Van Helsing must be a good man as well as a clever one if he is Arthur's friend and Dr. Seward's, and if they brought him all the way from Holland to look after Lucy. I feel from having seen him that he *is* good and kind and of a noble nature. When he comes to-morrow I shall ask him about Jonathan; and then, please God, all this sorrow and anxiety may lead to a good end. I used to think I would like to practice interviewing; Jonathan's friend on "The Exeter News" told him that memory was everything in such work—that you must be able to put down exactly almost every word spoken, even if you had to refine some of it afterwards. Here was a rare interview; I shall try to record it *verbatim*.

It was half-past two o'clock when the knock came. I took my courage *à deux mains* and waited. In a few minutes Mary opened the door, and announced "Dr. Van Helsing."

I rose and bowed, and he came towards me; a man of medium weight, strongly built, with his shoulders set back over a broad, deep chest and a neck well balanced on the trunk as the head is on the neck. The poise of the head strikes one at once as indicative of thought and power; the head is noble, well-sized, broad, and large behind the ears. The face, clean-shaven, shows a hard, square chin, a large, resolute, mobile mouth, a good-sized nose, rather straight, but with quick, sensitive nostrils, that seem to broaden as the big, bushy brows come down and the mouth tightens. The forehead is broad and fine, rising at first almost straight and then sloping back above two bumps on ridges wide apart; such a forehead that the reddish hair cannot possibly tumble over it, but falls naturally back and to the sides. Big, dark blue eyes are set widely apart, and are quick and tender or stern with the man's moods. He said to me:—

"Mrs. Harker, is it not?" I bowed assent.

"That was Miss Mina Murray?" Again I assented.

"It is Mina Murray that I came to see that was friend of that poor dear child Lucy Westenra. Madam Mina, it is on account of the dead I come."

"Sir," I said, "you could have no better claim on me than that you were a friend and helper of Lucy Westenra." And I held out my hand. He took it and said tenderly:—

"Oh, Madam Mina, I knew that the friend of that poor lily girl must be good, but I had yet to learn——" He finished his speech with a courtly bow. I asked him what it was that he wanted to see me about, so he at once began:—

"I have read your letters to Miss Lucy. Forgive me, but I had to begin to inquire somewhere, and there was none to ask. I know that you were with her at Whitby. She sometimes kept a diary—you need not look surprised, Madam Mina; it was begun after you had left, and was in imitation of you—and in that diary she traces by inference certain things to a sleep-walking in which she puts down that you saved her. In great perplexity then I come to you, and ask you out of your so much kindness to tell me all of it that you can remember."

"I can tell you, I think, Dr. Van Helsing, all about it."

"Oh, then you have good memory for facts, for details? It is not always so with young ladies."

"No, Doctor, but I wrote it all down at the time. I can show it to you if you like."

"Oh, Madam Mina, I will be grateful; you will do me much favour." I could not resist the temptation of mystifying him a bit—I suppose it is some of the taste of the original apple that remains still in our mouths—so I handed him the shorthand diary. He took it with a grateful bow, and said:—

"May I read it?"

"If you wish," I answered as demurely as I could. He opened it, and for an instant his face fell. Then he stood up and bowed.

"Oh, you so clever woman!" he said. "I knew long that Mr. Jonathan was a man of much thankfulness; but see, his wife have all the good things. And will you not so much honour me and so help me as to read it for me? Alas! I know not the shorthand." By this time my little joke was over, and I was almost ashamed; so I took the typewritten copy from my workbasket and handed it to him.

"Forgive me," I said: "I could not help it; but I had been thinking that it was of dear Lucy that you wished to ask, and so that you might not have time to wait—not on my account, but because I know your time must be precious—I have written it out on the typewriter for you."

He took it and his eyes glistened. "You are so good," he said. "And may I read it now? I may want to ask you some things when I have read."

"By all means," I said, "read it over whilst I order lunch; and then you can ask me questions whilst we eat." He bowed and settled himself in a chair with his back to the light, and became absorbed in the papers, whilst I went to see after lunch chiefly in order that he might not be disturbed. When I came back, I found him walking hurriedly up and down the room, his face all ablaze with excitement. He rushed up to me and took me by both hands.

"Oh, Madam Mina," he said, "how can I say what I owe to you? This paper is as sunshine. It opens the gate to me. I am daze, I am dazzle, with so much light, and yet clouds roll in behind the light every time. But that you do not, cannot, comprehend. Oh, but I am grateful to you, you so clever woman. Madam"—he said this very solemnly—"if ever

Abraham Van Helsing can do anything for you or yours, I trust you will let me know. It will be pleasure and delight if I may serve you as a friend; as a friend, but all I have ever learned, all I can ever do, shall be for you and those you love. There are darknesses in life, and there are lights; you are one of the lights. You will have happy life and good life, and your husband will be blessed in you."

"But, doctor, you praise me too much, and—and you do not know me."

"Not know you—I, who am old, and who have studied all my life men and women; I, who have made my specialty the brain and all that belongs to him and all that follow from him! And I have read your diary that you have so goodly written for me, and which breathes out truth in every line. I, who have read your so sweet letter to poor Lucy of your marriage and your trust, not know you! Oh, Madam Mina, good women tell all their lives, and by day and by hour and by minute, such things that angels can read; and we men who wish to know have in us something of angels' eyes. Your husband is noble nature, and you are noble too, for you trust, and trust cannot be where there is mean nature. And your husband—tell me of him. Is he quite well? Is all that fever gone, and is he strong and hearty?" I saw here an opening to ask him about Jonathan, so I said:—

"He was almost recovered, but he has been greatly upset by Mr. Hawkins's death." He interrupted:—

"Oh, yes, I know, I know. I have read your last two letters." I went on:—

"I suppose this upset him, for when we were in town on Thursday last he had a sort of shock."

"A shock, and after brain fever so soon! That was not good. What kind of a shock was it?"

"He thought he saw some one who recalled something terrible, something which led to his brain fever." And here the whole thing seemed to overwhelm me in a rush. The pity for Jonathan, the horror which he experienced, the whole fearful mystery of his diary, and the fear that has been brooding over me ever since, all came in a tumult. I suppose I was hysterical, for I threw myself on my knees and held up my hands to him, and implored him to make my husband well again. He took my hands and raised me up, and made me sit on the sofa, and sat by me; he held my hand in his, and said to me with, oh, such infinite sweetness:—

"My life is a barren and lonely one, and so full of work that I have not had much time for friendships; but since I have been summoned to here by my friend John Seward I have known so many good people and seen such nobility that I feel more than ever—and it has grown with my advancing years—the loneliness of my life. Believe me, then, that I come here full of respect for you, and you have given me hope—hope, not in what I am seeking of, but that there are good women still left to make life happy—good women, whose lives and whose truths may make good lesson for the children that are to be. I am glad, glad, that I may here be of some use to you; for if your husband suffer, he suffer within the range of my study and experience, I promise you that I will gladly do *all* for him that I can—all to make his life strong and manly, and your life a happy one. Now you must eat. You are overwrought and perhaps over-anxious. Husband Jonathan would not like to see you so pale; and what he like not where he love, is not to his good. Therefore for his sake you must eat and smile. You have told me all about Lucy, and so now we shall not speak of it, lest it distress. I shall stay in Exeter to-night, for I want to think much over what you have told me, and when I have thought I will ask you questions, if I may. And then, too, you will tell me of husband Jonathan's trouble so far as you can, but not yet. You must eat now; afterwards you shall tell me all."

After lunch, when we went back to the drawing-room, he said to me:—

"And now tell me all about him." When it came to speaking to this great learned man, I began to fear that he would think me a weak fool, and Jonathan a madman—that journal is all so strange—and I hesitated to go on. But he was so sweet and kind, and he had promised to help, and I trusted him, so I said:—

"Dr. Van Helsing, what I have to tell you is so queer that you must not laugh at me or at my husband. I have been since yesterday in a sort of fever of doubt; you must be kind to me, and not think me foolish that

I have even half believed some very strange things." He reassured me by his manner as well as his words when he said:—

"Oh, my dear, if you only know how strange is the matter regarding which I am here, it is you who would laugh. I have learned not to think little of any one's belief, no matter how strange it be. I have tried to keep an open mind; and it is not the ordinary things of life that could close it, but the strange things, the extraordinary things, the things that make one doubt if they be mad or sane."

"Thank you, thank you, a thousand times! You have taken a weight off my mind. If you will let me, I shall give you a paper to read. It is long, but I have typewritten it out. It will tell you my trouble and Jonathan's. It is the copy of his journal when abroad, and all that happened. I dare not say anything of it; you will read for yourself and judge. And then when I see you, perhaps, you will be very kind and tell me what you think."

"I promise," he said as I gave him the papers; "I shall in the morning, so soon as I can, come to see you and your husband, if I may."

"Jonathan will be here at half-past eleven, and you must come to lunch with us and see him then; you could catch the quick 3:34 train, which will leave you at Paddington before eight." He was surprised at my knowledge of the trains offhand, but he does not know that I have made up all the trains to and from Exeter, so that I may help Jonathan in case he is in a hurry.

So he took the papers with him and went away, and I sit here thinking—thinking I don't know what.

LETTER (BY HAND) FROM VAN HELSING TO MRS. HARKER.

"*25 September, 6 o'clock.*

"Dear Madam Mina,—

"I have read your husband's so wonderful diary. You may sleep without doubt. Strange and terrible as it is, it is *true*! I will pledge my life on it. It may be worse for others; but for him and you there is no dread. He is a noble fellow; and let me tell you from experience of men, that one who would do as he did in going down that wall and to that room—ay, and going a second time—is not one to be injured in permanence by a shock. His brain and his heart are all right; this I swear, before I have even seen him; so be at rest. I shall have much to ask him of other things. I am blessed that to-day I come to see you, for I have learn all at once so much that again I am dazzle—dazzle more than ever, and I must think.

"Yours the most faithful,

"ABRAHAM VAN HELSING."

LETTER FROM MRS. HARKER TO VAN HELSING.

"*25 September, 6:30 p.m.*

"My dear Dr. Van Helsing,—

"A thousand thanks for your kind letter, which has taken a great weight off my mind. And yet, if it be true, what terrible things there are in the world, and what an awful thing if that man, that monster, be really in London! I fear to think. I have this moment, whilst writing, had a wire from Jonathan, saying that he leaves by the 6:25 to-night from Launceston and will be here at 10:18, so that I shall have no fear to-night. Will you, therefore, instead of lunching with us, please come to breakfast at eight o'clock, if this be not too early for you? You can get away, if you are in a hurry, by the 10:30 train, which will bring you to Paddington by 2:35. Do not answer this, as I shall take it that, if I do not hear, you will come to breakfast.

"Believe me,

"Your faithful and grateful friend,

"MINA HARKER."

JONATHAN HARKER'S JOURNAL.

26 September.—I thought never to write in this diary again, but the time has come. When I got home last night Mina had supper ready, and when we had supped she told me of Van Helsing's visit, and of her having given him the two diaries copied out, and of how anxious she has been about me. She showed me in the doctor's letter that all I wrote down was true. It seems to have made a new man of me. It was the doubt as to the reality of the whole thing that knocked me over. I felt impotent, and in the dark, and distrustful. But, now that I *know*, I am not afraid, even of the Count. He has succeeded after all, then, in his design in getting to London, and it was he I saw. He has got younger, and how? Van Helsing is the man to unmask him and hunt him out, if he is anything like what Mina says. We sat late, and talked it all over. Mina is dressing, and I shall call at the hotel in a few minutes and bring him over. . . .

He was, I think, surprised to see me. When I came into the room where he was, and introduced myself, he took me by the shoulder, and turned my face round to the light, and said, after a sharp scrutiny:—

"But Madam Mina told me you were ill, that you had had a shock." It was so funny to hear my wife called "Madam Mina" by this kindly, strong-faced old man. I smiled, and said:—

"I *was* ill, I *have* had a shock; but you have cured me already."

"And how?"

"By your letter to Mina last night. I was in doubt, and then everything took a hue of unreality, and I did not know what to trust, even the evidence of my own senses. Not knowing what to trust, I did not know what to do; and so had only to keep on working in what had hitherto been the groove of my life. The groove ceased to avail me, and I mistrusted myself. Doctor, you don't know what it is to doubt everything, even yourself. No, you don't; you couldn't with eyebrows like yours." He seemed pleased, and laughed as he said:—

"So! You are physiognomist. I learn more here with each hour. I am with so much pleasure coming to you to breakfast: and, oh, sir, you will pardon praise from an old man, but you are blessed in your wife." I would listen to him go on praising Mina for a day; so I simply nodded and stood silent.

"She is one of God's women, fashioned by His own hand to show us men and other women that there is a heaven where we can enter, and that its lights can be here on earth. So true, so sweet, so noble, so little an egoist—and that, let me tell you, is much in this age, so sceptical and selfish. And you, sir—I have read all the letters to poor Miss Lucy, and some of them speak of you, so I know you since some days from the knowing of others; but I have seen your true self since last night. You will give me your hand, will you not? And let us be friends for all our lives."

We shook hands, and he was so earnest and so kind that it made me quite choky.

"And now," he said, "may I ask you for some more help? I have a great task to do, and at the beginning it is to know. You can help me here. Can you tell me what went before your going to Transylvania? Later on I may ask more help, and of a different kind; but at first this will do."

"Look here, sir," I said, "does what you have to do concern the Count?"

"It does," he said solemnly.

"Then I am with you heart and soul. As you go by the 10:30 train, you will not have time to read them; but I shall get the bundle of papers. You can take them with you and read them in the train."

After breakfast I saw him to the station. When we were parting he said:—

"Perhaps you will come to town if I send to you, and take Madam Mina too."

"We shall both come when you will," I said.

I had got him the morning papers and the London papers of the previous night, and while we were talking at the carriage window, waiting for the train to start, he was turning them over. His eyes suddenly seemed to catch something in one of them, "The Westminster Gazette"—I knew it by the colour—and he grew quite white. He read something intently, groaning to himself: "Mein Gott! Mein Gott! So soon! so soon!" I do not think he remembered me at the moment. Just then the whistle blew, and the train moved off. This recalled him to himself, and he leaned out of the window and waved his hand, calling out: "Love to Madam Mina; I shall write so soon as ever I can."

DR. SEWARD'S DIARY.

26 September.—Truly there is no such thing as finality. Not a week since I said "Finis," and yet here I am starting fresh again, or rather going on with the same record. Until this afternoon I had no cause to think of what is done. Renfield had become, to all intents, as sane as he ever was. He was already well ahead with his fly business; and he had just started in the spider line also; so he had not been of any trouble to me. I had a letter from Arthur, written on Sunday, and from it I gather that he is bearing up wonderfully well. Quincey Morris is with him, and that is much of a help, for he himself is a bubbling well of good spirits. Quincey wrote me a line too, and from him I hear that Arthur is beginning to recover something of his old buoyancy; so as to them all my mind is at rest. As for myself, I was settling down to my work with the enthusiasm which I used to have for it, so that I might fairly have said that the wound which poor Lucy left on me was becoming cicatrised. Everything is, however, now reopened; and what is to be the end God only knows. I have an idea that Van Helsing thinks he knows, too, but he will only let out enough at a time to whet curiosity. He went to Exeter yesterday, and stayed there all night. To-day he came back, and almost bounded into the room at about half-past five o'clock, and thrust last night's "Westminster Gazette" into my hand.

"What do you think of that?" he asked as he stood back and folded his arms.

I looked over the paper, for I really did not know what he meant; but he took it from me and pointed out a paragraph about children being decoyed away at Hampstead. It did not convey much to me, until I reached a passage where it described small puncture wounds on their throats. An idea struck me, and I looked up. "Well?" he said.

"It is like poor Lucy's."

"And what do you make of it?"

"Simply that there is some cause in common. Whatever it was that injured her has injured them." I did not quite understand his answer:—

"That is true indirectly, but not directly."

"How do you mean, Professor?" I asked. I was a little inclined to take his seriousness lightly—for, after all, four days of rest and freedom from burning, harrowing anxiety does help to restore one's spirits—but when I saw his face, it sobered me. Never, even in the midst of our despair about poor Lucy, had he looked more stern.

"Tell me!" I said. "I can hazard no opinion. I do not know what to think, and I have no data on which to found a conjecture."

"Do you mean to tell me, friend John, that you have no suspicion as to what poor Lucy died of; not after all the hints given, not only by events, but by me?"

"Of nervous prostration following on great loss or waste of blood."

"And how the blood lost or waste?" I shook my head. He stepped over and sat down beside me, and went on:—

"You are a clever man, friend John; you reason well, and your wit is bold; but you are too prejudiced. You do not let your eyes see nor your ears hear, and that which is outside your daily life is not of account to you. Do you not think that there are things which you cannot understand, and yet which are; that some people see things that others cannot? But there are things old and new which must not be contemplate by men's eyes, because they know—or think they know—some things which other men have told them. Ah, it is the fault of our science that it wants to explain all; and if it explain not, then it says there is nothing to explain. But yet we see around us every day the growth of new beliefs, which think themselves new; and which are yet but the old, which pretend to be young—like the fine ladies at the opera. I suppose now you do not believe in corporeal transference. No? Nor in materialisation. No? Nor in astral bodies. No? Nor in the reading of thought. No? Nor in hypnotism——"

"Yes," I said. "Charcot has proved that pretty well." He smiled as he went on: "Then you are satisfied as to it. Yes? And of course then you understand how it act, and can follow the mind of the great Charcot—alas that he is no more!—into the very soul of the patient that he influence. No? Then, friend John, am I to take it that you simply accept fact, and are satisfied to let from premise to conclusion be a blank? No? Then tell me—for I am student of the brain—how you accept the hypnotism and reject the thought reading. Let me tell you, my friend, that there are things done to-day in electrical science which would have been deemed unholy by the very men who discovered electricity—who would themselves not so long before have been burned as wizards. Where are always mysteries in life. Why was it that Methuselah lived nine hundred years, and 'Old Parr' one hundred and sixty-nine, and yet that poor Lucy, with four men's blood in her poor veins, could not live even one day? For, had she live one more day, we could have save her. Do you know all the mystery of life and death? Do you know the altogether of comparative anatomy and can say wherefore the qualities of brutes are in some men, and not in others? Can you tell me why, when other spiders die small and soon, that one great spider lived for centuries in the tower of the old Spanish church and grew and grew, till, on descending, he could drink the oil of all the church lamps? Can you tell me why in the Pampas, ay and elsewhere, there are bats that come at night and open the veins of cattle and horses and suck dry their veins; how in some islands of the Western seas there are bats which hang on the trees all day, and those who have seen describe as like giant nuts or pods, and that when the sailors sleep on the deck, because that it is hot, flit down on them, and then—and then in the morning are found dead men, white as even Miss Lucy was?"

"Good God, Professor!" I said, starting up. "Do you mean to tell me that Lucy was bitten by such a bat; and that such a thing is here in London in the nineteenth century?" He waved his hand for silence, and went on:—

"Can you tell me why the tortoise lives more long than generations of men; why the elephant goes on and on till he have seen dynasties; and why the parrot never die only of bite of cat or dog or other complaint? Can you tell me why men believe in all ages and places that there are some few who live on always if they be permit; that there are men and women who cannot die? We all know—because science has vouched for the fact—that there have been toads shut up in rocks for thousands of years, shut in one so small hole that only hold him since the youth of the world. Can you tell me how the Indian fakir can make himself to die and have been buried,

CHAPTER 15.

———◇———

DR. SEWARD'S DIARY—*continued.*

For a while sheer anger mastered me; it was as if he had during her life struck Lucy on the face. I smote the table hard and rose up as I said to him:—

"Dr. Van Helsing, are you mad?" He raised his head and looked at me, and somehow the tenderness of his face calmed me at once. "Would I were!" he said. "Madness were easy to bear compared with truth like this. Oh, my friend, why, think you, did I go so far round, why take so long to tell you so simple a thing? Was it because I hate you and have hated you all my life? Was it because I wished to give you pain? Was it that I wanted, now so late, revenge for that time when you saved my life, and from a fearful death? Ah no!"

"Forgive me," said I. He went on:—

"My friend, it was because I wished to be gentle in the breaking to you, for I know you have loved that so sweet lady. But even yet I do not expect you to believe. It is so hard to accept at once any abstract truth, that we may doubt such to be possible when we have always believed the 'no' of it; it is more hard still to accept so sad a concrete truth, and of such a one as Miss Lucy. To-night I go to prove it. Dare you come with me?"

This staggered me. A man does not like to prove such a truth. Byron excepted from the category, jealousy.

"And prove the very truth he most abhorred."

He saw my hesitation and spoke:—

"The logic is simple, no madman's logic this time, jumping from tussock to tussock in a misty bog. If it be not true, then proof will be relief; at worst it will not harm. If it be true! Ah, there is the dread; yet very dread should help my cause, for in it is some need of belief. Come, I tell you what I propose: first, that we go off now and see that child in the hospital. Dr. Vincent, of the North Hospital, where the papers say the child is, is friend of mine, and I think of yours since you were in class at Amsterdam. He will let two scientists see his case, if he will not let two friends. We shall tell him nothing, but only that we wish to learn. And then—"

"And then?" He took a key from his pocket and held it up. "And then we spend the night, you and I, in the churchyard where Lucy lies. This is the key that lock the tomb. I had it from the coffin-man to give to Arthur." My heart sank within me, for I felt that there was some fearful ordeal before us. I could do nothing, however, so I plucked up what heart I could and said that we had better hasten, as the afternoon was passing. . . .

We found the child awake. It had had a sleep and taken some food, and altogether was going on well. Dr. Vincent took the bandage from its throat, and showed us the punctures. There was no mistaking the similarity to those which had been on Lucy's throat. They were smaller, and the edges looked fresher; that was all. We asked Vincent to what he attributed them, and he replied that it must have been a bite of some animal, perhaps a rat; but, for his own part, he was inclined to think that it was one of the bats which are so numerous on the northern heights of London. "Out of so many harmless ones," he said, "there may be some wild specimen from the South of a more malignant species. Some sailor may have brought one home, and it managed to escape; or even from the Zoölogical Gardens a young one may have got loose, or one be bred there from a vampire. These things do occur, you know. Only ten days ago a wolf got out, and was, I believe, traced up in this direction. For a week after, the children were playing nothing but Red Riding Hood on the Heath and in every alley in the place until this 'bloofer lady' scare came along, since when it has been quite a gala-time with them. Even this poor little mite, when he woke up to-day, asked the nurse if he might go away. When she asked him why he wanted to go, he said he wanted to play with the 'bloofer lady.'"

"I hope," said Van Helsing, "that when you are sending the child home you will caution its parents to keep strict watch over it. These fancies to stray are most dangerous; and if the child were to remain out another night, it would probably be fatal. But in any case I suppose you will not let it away for some days?"

"Certainly not, not for a week at least: longer if the wound is not healed."

Our visit to the hospital took more time than we had reckoned on, and the sun had dipped before we came out. When Van Helsing saw how dark it was, he said:—

"There is no hurry. It is more late than I thought. Come, let us seek somewhere that we may eat, and then we shall go on our way."

We dined at "Jack Straw's Castle" along with a little crowd of bicyclists and others who were genially noisy. About ten o'clock we started from the inn. It was then very dark, and the scattered lamps made the darkness greater when we were once outside their individual radius. The Professor had evidently noted the road we were to go, for he went on unhesitatingly; but, as for me, I was in quite a mixup as to locality. As we went further, we met fewer and fewer people, till at last we were somewhat surprised when we met even the patrol of horse police going their usual suburban round. At last we reached the wall of the church-yard, which we climbed over. With some little difficulty—for it was very dark, and the whole place seemed so strange to us—we found the

Westenra tomb. The Professor took the key, opened the creaky door, and standing back, politely, but quite unconsciously, motioned me to precede him. There was a delicious irony in the offer, in the courtliness of giving preference on such a ghastly occasion. My companion followed me quickly, and cautiously drew the door to, after carefully ascertaining that the lock was a falling, and not a spring, one. In the latter case we should have been in a bad plight. Then he fumbled in his bag, and taking out a matchbox and a piece of candle, proceeded to make a light. The tomb in the day-time, and when wreathed with fresh flowers, had looked grim and gruesome enough; but now, some days afterwards, when the flowers hung lank and dead, their whites turning to rust and their greens to browns; when the spider and the beetle had resumed their accustomed dominance; when time-discoloured stone, and dust-encrusted mortar, and rusty, dank iron and tarnished brass, and clouded silver-plating gave back the feeble glimmer of a candle, the effect was more miserable and sordid than could have been imagined. It conveyed irresistibly the idea that life—animal life—was not the only thing which could pass away.

Van Helsing went about his work systematically. Holding his candle so that he could read the coffin plates, and so holding it that the sperm dropped in white patches which congealed as they touched the metal, he made assurance of Lucy's coffin. Another search in his bag and he took out a turnscrew.

"What are you going to do?" I asked.

"To open the coffin. You shall yet be convinced." Straightway he began taking out the screws, and finally lifted off the lid, showing the casing of lead beneath. The sight was almost too much for me. It seemed to be as much an affront to the dead as it would have been to have stripped off her clothing in her sleep whilst living; I actually took hold of his hand to stop him. He only said: "You shall see," and again fumbling in his bag, took out a tiny fret-saw. Striking the turnscrew through the lead with a swift downward stab, which made me wince, he made a small hole, which was, however, big enough to admit the point of the saw. I had expected a rush of gas from the week-old corpse. We doctors, who have had to study our dangers, have to become accustomed to such things, and I drew back towards the door. But the Professor never stopped for a moment; he sawed down a couple of feet along one side of the lead coffin, and then across, and down the other side. Taking the edge of the loose flange, he bent it back toward the foot of the coffin, and holding up the candle into the aperture, motioned to me to look.

I drew near and looked. The coffin was empty.

It was certainly a surprise to me, and gave me a considerable shock, but Van Helsing was unmoved. He was now more sure than ever of his ground, and so emboldened to proceed in his task. "Are you satisfied now, friend John?" he asked.

I felt all the dogged argumentativeness of my nature awake within me as I answered him:—

"I am satisfied that Lucy's body is not in that coffin; but that only proves one thing."

"And what is that, friend John?"

"That it is not there."

"That is good logic," he said, "so far as it goes. But how do you—how can you—account for it not being there?"

"Perhaps a body-snatcher," I suggested. "Some of the undertaker's people may have stolen it." I felt that I was speaking folly, and yet it was the only real cause which I could suggest. The Professor sighed. "Ah well!" he said, "we must have more proof. Come with me."

He put on the coffin-lid again, gathered up all his things and placed them in the bag, blew out the light, and placed the candle also in the bag. We opened the door, and went out. Behind us he closed the door and locked it. He handed me the key, saying: "Will you keep it? You had better be assured." I laughed—it was not a very cheerful laugh, I am bound to say—as I motioned him to keep it. "A key is nothing," I said; "there may be duplicates; and anyhow it is not difficult to pick a lock of that kind." He said nothing, but put the key in his pocket. Then he told me to watch at one side of the churchyard whilst he would watch at the other. I took up my place behind a yew-tree, and I saw his dark figure move until the intervening headstones and trees hid it from my sight.

It was a lonely vigil. Just after I had taken my place I heard a distant clock strike twelve, and in time came one and two. I was chilled and unnerved, and angry with the Professor for taking me on such an errand and with myself for coming. I was too cold and too sleepy to be keenly observant, and not sleepy enough to betray my trust; so altogether I had a dreary, miserable time.

Suddenly, as I turned round, I thought I saw something like a white streak, moving between two dark yew-trees at the side of the church-yard farthest from the tomb; at the same time a dark mass moved from the Professor's side of the ground, and hurriedly went towards it. Then I too moved; but I had to go round headstones and railed-off tombs, and I stumbled over graves. The sky was overcast, and somewhere far off an early cock crew. A little way off, beyond a line of scattered juniper-trees, which marked the pathway to the church, a white, dim figure flitted in the direction of the tomb. The tomb itself was hidden by trees, and I could not see where the figure disappeared. I heard the rustle of actual movement where I had first seen the white figure, and coming over, found the Professor holding in his arms a tiny child. When he saw me he held it out to me, and said—

"Are you satisfied now?"

"No," I said, in a way that I felt was aggressive.

"Do you not see the child?"

"Yes, it is a child, but who brought it here? And is it wounded?" I asked.

"We shall see," said the Professor, and with one impulse we took our way out of the churchyard, he carrying the sleeping child.

When we had got some little distance away, we went into a clump of trees, and struck a match, and looked at the child's throat. It was without a scratch or scar of any kind.

"Was I right?" I asked triumphantly.

"We were just in time," said the Professor thankfully.

We had now to decide what we were to do with the child, and so consulted about it. If we were to take it to a police-station we should have to give some account of our movements during the night; at least, we should have had to make some statement as to how we had come to find the child. So finally we decided that we would take it to the Heath, and when we heard a policeman coming, would leave it where he could not fail to find it; we would then seek our way home as quickly as we could. All fell out well. At the edge of Hampstead Heath we heard a policeman's heavy tramp, and laying the child on the pathway, we waited and watched until he saw it as he flashed his lantern to and fro. We heard his exclamation of astonishment, and then we went away silently. By good chance we got a cab near the "Spaniards," and drove to town.

I cannot sleep, so I make this entry. But I must try to get a few hours' sleep, as Van Helsing is to call for me at noon. He insists that I shall go with him on another expedition.

27 September.—It was two o'clock before we found a suitable opportunity for our attempt. The funeral held at noon was all completed, and the last stragglers of the mourners had taken themselves lazily away, when, looking carefully from behind a clump of alder-trees, we saw the sexton lock the gate after him. We knew then that we were safe till morning did we desire it; but the Professor told me that we should not want more than an hour at most. Again I felt that horrid sense of the reality of things, in which any effort of imagination seemed out of place; and I realised distinctly the perils of the law which we were incurring in our unhallowed work. Besides, I felt it was all so useless. Outrageous as it was to open a leaden coffin, to see if a woman dead nearly a week were really dead, it now seemed the height of folly to open the tomb again, when we knew, from the evidence of our own eyesight, that the coffin was empty. I shrugged my shoulders, however, and rested silent, for Van Helsing had a way of going on his own road, no matter who remonstrated. He took the key, opened the vault, and again courteously motioned me to precede. The place was not so gruesome as last night, but oh, how unutterably mean-looking when the sunshine streamed in. Van Helsing walked over to Lucy's coffin, and I followed. He bent over and again forced back the leaden flange; and then a shock of surprise and dismay shot through me.

There lay Lucy, seemingly just as we had seen her the night before her funeral. She was, if possible, more radiantly beautiful than ever; and I could not believe that she was dead. The lips were red, nay redder than before; and on the cheeks was a delicate bloom.

"Is this a juggle?" I said to him.

"Are you convinced now?" said the Professor in response, and as he spoke he put over his hand, and in a way that made me shudder, pulled back the dead lips and showed the white teeth.

"See," he went on, "see, they are even sharper than before. With this and this"—and he touched one of the canine teeth and that below it—"the little children can be bitten. Are you of belief now, friend John?" Once more, argumentative hostility woke within me. I could not accept such an overwhelming idea as he suggested; so, with an attempt to argue of which I was even at the moment ashamed, I said:—

"She may have been placed here since last night."

"Indeed? That is so, and by whom?"

"I do not know. Some one has done it."

"And yet she has been dead one week. Most peoples in that time would not look so." I had no answer for this, so was silent. Van Helsing did not seem to notice my silence; at any rate, he showed neither chagrin nor triumph. He was looking intently at the face of the dead woman, raising the eyelids and looking at the eyes, and once more opening the lips and examining the teeth. Then he turned to me and said:—

"Here, there is one thing which is different from all recorded; here is some dual life that is not as the common. She was bitten by the vampire when she was in a trance, sleep-walking—oh, you start; you do not know that, friend John, but you shall know it all later—and in trance could he best come to take more blood. In trance she died, and in trance she is Un-Dead, too. So it is that she differ from all other. Usually when the Un-Dead sleep at home"—as he spoke he made a comprehensive sweep of his arm to designate what to a vampire was "home"—"their face show what they are, but this so sweet that was when she not Un-Dead she go back to the nothings of the common dead. There is no malign there, see, and so it make hard that I must kill her in her sleep."

This turned my blood cold, and it began to dawn upon me that I was accepting Van Helsing's theories; but if she were really dead, what was there of terror in the idea of killing her? He looked up at me, and evidently saw the change in my face, for he said almost joyously:—

"Ah, you believe now?"

I answered: "Do not press me too hard all at once. I am willing to accept. How will you do this bloody work?"

"I shall cut off her head and fill her mouth with garlic, and I shall drive a stake through her body." It made me shudder to think of so mutilating the body of the woman whom I had loved. And yet the feeling was not so strong as I had expected. I was, in fact, beginning to shudder at the presence of this being, this Un-Dead, as Van Helsing called it, and to loathe it. Is it possible that love is all subjective, or all objective?

I waited a considerable time for Van Helsing to begin, but he stood as if wrapped in thought. Presently he closed the catch of his bag with a snap, and said:—

"I have been thinking, and have made up my mind as to what is best. If I did simply follow my inclining I would do now, at this moment, what is to be done; but there are other things to follow, and things that are thousand times more difficult in that them we do not know. This is simple. She have yet no life taken, though that is of time; and to act now would be to take danger from her for ever. But then we may have to want Arthur, and how shall we tell him of this? If you, who saw the wounds on Lucy's throat, and saw the wounds so similar on the child's at the hospital; if you, who saw the coffin empty last night and full to-day with a woman who have not change only to be more rose and more beautiful in a whole week, after she die—if you know of this and know of the white figure last night that brought the child to the churchyard, and yet of your own senses you did not believe, how, then, can I expect Arthur, who know none of those things, to believe? He doubted me when I took him from her kiss when she was dying. I know he has forgiven me because in some mistaken idea I have done things that prevent him say good-bye as he ought; and he may think that in some more mistaken idea this woman was buried alive; and that in most mistake of all we have killed her. He will then argue back that it is we, mistaken ones, that have killed her by our ideas; and so he will be much unhappy always. Yet he never can be sure; and that is the worst of all. And he will sometimes think that she he loved was buried alive, and that will paint his dreams with horrors of what she must have suffered; and again, he will think that we may be right, and that his so beloved was, after all, an Un-Dead. No! I told him once, and since then I learn much. Now, since I know it is all true, a hundred thousand times more do I know that he must pass through the bitter waters to reach the sweet. He, poor fellow, must have one hour that will make the very face of heaven grow black to him; then we can act for good all round and send him peace. My mind is made up. Let us go. You return home for to-night to your asylum, and see that all be well. As for me, I shall spend the night here in this churchyard in my own way. To-morrow night you will come to me to the Berkeley Hotel at ten of the clock. I shall send for Arthur to come too, and also that so fine young man of America that gave his blood. Later we shall have work to do. I come with you so far as Piccadilly and there dine, for I must be back here before the sun set."

So we locked the tomb and came away, and got over the wall of the churchyard, which was not much of a task, and drove back to Piccadilly.

NOTE LEFT BY VAN HELSING IN HIS PORTMANTEAU, BERKELEY HOTEL, DIRECTED TO JOHN SEWARD, M.D.
(Not delivered.)

"*27 September.*
"Friend John,—
"I write this in case anything should happen. I go alone to watch in that churchyard. It pleases me that the Un-Dead, Miss Lucy, shall not leave to-night, that so on the morrow night she may be more eager. Therefore I shall fix some things she like not—garlic and a crucifix—

and so seal up the door of the tomb. She is young as Un-Dead, and will heed. Moreover, these are only to prevent her coming out; they may not prevail on her wanting to get in; for then the Un-Dead is desperate, and must find the line of least resistance, whatsoever it may be. I shall be at hand all the night from sunset till after the sunrise, and if there be aught that may be learned I shall learn it. For Miss Lucy or from her, I have no fear; but that other to whom is there that she is Un-Dead, he have now the power to seek her tomb and find shelter. He is cunning, as I know from Mr. Jonathan and from the way that all along he have fooled us when he played with us for Miss Lucy's life and we lost; and in many ways the Un-Dead are strong. He have always the strength in his hand of twenty men; even we four who gave our strength to Miss Lucy it also is all to him. Besides, he can summon his wolf and I know not what. So if it be that he come thither on this night he shall find me; but none other shall—until it be too late. But it may be that he will not attempt the place. There is no reason why he should; his hunting ground is more full of game than the churchyard where the Un-Dead woman sleep and the one old man watch.

"Therefore I write this in case. . . . Take the papers that are with this, the diaries of Harker and the rest, and read them, and then find this great Un-Dead, and cut off his head and burn his heart or drive a stake through it, so that the world may rest from him.

"If it be so, farewell.

"VAN HELSING."

DR. SEWARD'S DIARY.

28 September.—It is wonderful what a good night's sleep will do for one. Yesterday I was almost willing to accept Van Helsing's monstrous ideas; but now they seem to start out lurid before me as outrages on common sense. I have no doubt that he believes it all. I wonder if his mind can have become in any way unhinged. Surely there must be *some* rational explanation of all these mysterious things. Is it possible that the Professor can have done it himself? He is so abnormally clever that if he went off his head he would carry out his intent with regard to some fixed idea in a wonderful way. I am loath to think it, and indeed it would be almost as great a marvel as the other to find that Van Helsing was mad; but anyhow I shall watch him carefully. I may get some light on the mystery.

29 September, morning. . . . Last night, at a little before ten o'clock, Arthur and Quincey came into Van Helsing's room; he told us all that he wanted us to do, but especially addressing himself to Arthur, as if all our wills were centred in his. He began by saying that he hoped we would all come with him too, "for," he said, "there is a grave duty to be done there. You were doubtless surprised at my letter?" This query was directly addressed to Lord Godalming.

"I was. It rather upset me for a bit. There has been so much trouble around my house of late that I could do without any more. I have been curious, too, as to what you mean. Quincey and I talked it over; but the more we talked, the more puzzled we got, till now I can say for myself that I'm about up a tree as to any meaning about anything."

"Me too," said Quincey Morris laconically.

"Oh," said the Professor, "then you are nearer the beginning, both of you, than friend John here, who has to go a long way back before he can even get so far as to begin."

It was evident that he recognised my return to my old doubting frame of mind without saying a word. Then, turning to the other two, he said with intense gravity:—

"I want your permission to do what I think good this night. It is, I know, much to ask; and when you know what it is I propose to do you will know, and only then, how much. Therefore may I ask that you promise me in the dark, so that afterwards, though you may be angry with me for a time—I must not disguise from myself the possibility that such may be—you shall not blame yourselves for anything."

"That's frank anyhow," broke in Quincey. "I'll answer for the Professor. I don't quite see his drift, but I swear he's honest; and that's good enough for me."

"I thank you, sir," said Van Helsing proudly. "I have done myself the honour of counting you one trusting friend, and such endorsement is dear to me." He held out a hand, which Quincey took.

Then Arthur spoke out:—

"Dr. Van Helsing, I don't quite like to 'buy a pig in a poke,' as they say in Scotland, and if it be anything in which my honour as a gentleman or my faith as a Christian is concerned, I cannot make such a promise. If you can assure me that what you intend does not violate either of these two, then I give my consent at once; though for the life of me, I cannot understand what you are driving at."

"I accept your limitation," said Van Helsing, "and all I ask of you is that if you feel it necessary to condemn any act of mine, you will first consider it well and be satisfied that it does not violate your reservations."

"Agreed!" said Arthur; "that is only fair. And now that the *pourparlers* are over, may I ask what it is we are to do?"

"I want you to come with me, and to come in secret, to the churchyard at Kingstead."

Arthur's face fell as he said in an amazed sort of way:—

"Where poor Lucy is buried?" The Professor bowed. Arthur went on: "And when there?"

"To enter the tomb!" Arthur stood up.

"Professor, are you in earnest; or is it some monstrous joke? Pardon me, I see that you are in earnest." He sat down again, but I could see that he sat firmly and proudly, as one who is on his dignity. There was silence until he asked again:—

"And when in the tomb?"

"To open the coffin."

"This is too much!" he said, angrily rising again. "I am willing to be patient in all things that are reasonable; but in this—this desecration of the grave—of one who—" He fairly choked with indignation. The Professor looked pityingly at him.

"If I could spare you one pang, my poor friend," he said, "God knows I would. But this night our feet must tread in thorny paths; or later, and for ever, the feet you love must walk in paths of flame!"

Arthur looked up with set white face and said:—

"Take care, sir, take care!"

"Would it not be well to hear what I have to say?" said Van Helsing. "And then you will at least know the limit of my purpose. Shall I go on?"

"That's fair enough," broke in Morris.

After a pause Van Helsing went on, evidently with an effort:—

"Miss Lucy is dead; is it not so? Yes! Then there can be no wrong to her. But if she is not dead—"

Arthur jumped to his feet.

"Good God!" he cried. "What do you mean? Has there been any mistake; has she been buried alive?" He groaned in anguish that not even hope could soften.

"I did not say she was alive, my child; I did not think it. I go no further than to say that she might be Un-Dead."

"Un-Dead! Not alive! What do you mean? Is this all a nightmare, or what is it?"

"There are mysteries which men can only guess at, which age by age they may solve only in part. Believe me, we are now on the verge of one. But I have not done. May I cut off the head of dead Miss Lucy?"

"Heavens and earth, no!" cried Arthur in a storm of passion. "Not for the wide world will I consent to any mutilation of her dead body. Dr. Van Helsing, you try me too far. What have I done to you that you should torture me so? What did that poor, sweet girl do that you should want to cast such dishonour on her grave? Are you mad that speak such things, or am I mad to listen to them? Don't dare to think more of such a desecration; I shall not give my consent to anything you do. I have a duty to do in protecting her grave from outrage; and, by God, I shall do it!"

Van Helsing rose up from where he had all the time been seated, and said, gravely and sternly:—

"My Lord Godalming, I, too, have a duty to do, a duty to others, a duty to you, a duty to the dead; and, by God, I shall do it! All I ask you now is that you come with me, that you look and listen; and if when later I make the same request you do not be more eager for its fulfilment even

than I am, then—then I shall do my duty, whatever it may seem to me. And then, to follow your Lordship's wishes I shall hold myself at your disposal to render an account to you, when and where you will." His voice broke a little, and he went on with a voice full of pity:—

"But, I beseech you, do not go forth in anger with me. In a long life of acts which were often not pleasant to do, and which sometimes did wring my heart, I have never had so heavy a task as now. Believe me that if the time comes for you to change your mind towards me, one look from you will wipe away all this so sad hour, for I would do what a man can to save you from sorrow. Just think. For why should I give myself so much of labour and so much of sorrow? I have come here from my own land to do what I can of good; at the first to please my friend John, and then to help a sweet young lady, whom, too, I came to love. For her—I am ashamed to say so much, but I say it in kindness—I gave what you gave; the blood of my veins; I gave it, I, who was not, like you, her lover, but only her physician and her friend. I gave to her my nights and days—before death, after death; and if my death can do her good even now, when she is the dead Un-Dead, she shall have it freely." He said this with a very grave, sweet pride, and Arthur was much affected by it. He took the old man's hand and said in a broken voice:—

"Oh, it is hard to think of it, and I cannot understand; but at least I shall go with you and wait."

CHAPTER 16.

—◆—

DR. SEWARD'S DIARY—*continued.*

It was just a quarter before twelve o'clock when we got into the churchyard over the low wall. The night was dark with occasional gleams of moonlight between the rents of the heavy clouds that scudded across the sky. We all kept somehow close together, with Van Helsing slightly in front as he led the way. When we had come close to the tomb I looked well at Arthur, for I feared that the proximity to a place laden with so sorrowful a memory would upset him; but he bore himself well. I took it that the very mystery of the proceeding was in some way a counteractant to his grief. The Professor unlocked the door, and seeing a natural hesitation amongst us for various reasons, solved the difficulty by entering first himself. The rest of us followed, and he closed the door. He then lit a dark lantern and pointed to the coffin. Arthur stepped forward hesitatingly; Van Helsing said to me:—

"You were with me yesterday. Was the body of Miss Lucy in that coffin?"

"It was." The Professor turned to the rest saying:—

"You hear; and yet there is no one who does not believe with me." He took his screwdriver and again took off the lid of the coffin. Arthur looked on, very pale but silent; when the lid was removed he stepped forward. He evidently did not know that there was a leaden coffin, or, at any rate, had not thought of it. When he saw the rent in the lead, the blood rushed to his face for an instant, but as quickly fell away again, so that he remained of a ghastly whiteness; he was still silent. Van Helsing forced back the leaden flange, and we all looked in and recoiled.

The coffin was empty!

For several minutes no one spoke a word. The silence was broken by Quincey Morris:—

"Professor, I answered for you. Your word is all I want. I wouldn't ask such a thing ordinarily—I wouldn't so dishonour you as to imply a doubt; but this is a mystery that goes beyond any honour or dishonour. Is this your doing?"

"I swear to you by all that I hold sacred that I have not removed nor touched her. What happened was this: Two nights ago my friend Seward and I came here—with good purpose, believe me. I opened that coffin, which was then sealed up, and we found it, as now, empty. We then waited, and saw something white come through the trees. The next day we came here in daytime, and she lay there. Did she not, friend John?"

"Yes."

"That night we were just in time. One more so small child was missing, and we find it, thank God, unharmed amongst the graves. Yesterday I came here before sundown, for at sundown the Un-Dead can move. I waited here all the night till the sun rose, but I saw nothing. It was most probable that it was because I had laid over the clamps of those doors garlic, which the Un-Dead cannot bear, and other things which they shun. Last night there was no exodus, so to-night before the sundown I took away my garlic and other things. And so it is we find this coffin empty. But bear with me. So far there is much that is strange. Wait you with me outside, unseen and unheard, and things much stranger are yet to be. So"—here he shut the dark slide of his lantern—"now to the outside." He opened the door, and we filed out, he coming last and locking the door behind him.

Oh! but it seemed fresh and pure in the night air after the terror of that vault. How sweet it was to see the clouds race by, and the passing gleams of the moonlight between the scudding clouds crossing and passing—like the gladness and sorrow of a man's life; how sweet it was to breathe the fresh air, that had no taint of death and decay; how humanising to see the red lighting of the sky beyond the hill, and to hear far away the muffled roar that marks the life of a great city. Each in his own way was solemn and overcome. Arthur was silent, and was, I could see, striving to grasp the purpose and the inner meaning of the mystery. I was myself tolerably patient, and half inclined again to throw aside doubt and to accept Van Helsing's conclusions. Quincey Morris was phlegmatic in the way of a man who accepts all things, and accepts them in the spirit of cool bravery, with hazard of all he has to stake. Not being able to smoke, he cut himself a good-sized plug of tobacco and began to chew. As to Van Helsing, he was employed in a definite way. First he took from his bag a mass of what looked like thin, wafer-like biscuit, which was carefully rolled up in a white napkin; next he took out a double-handful of some whitish stuff, like dough or putty. He crumbled the wafer up fine and worked it into the mass between his hands. This he then took, and rolling it into thin strips, began to lay them into the crevices between the door and its setting in the tomb. I was somewhat puzzled at this, and being close, asked him what it was that he was doing. Arthur and Quincey drew near also, as they too were curious. He answered:—

"I am closing the tomb, so that the Un-Dead may not enter."

"And is that stuff you have put there going to do it?" asked Quincey. "Great Scott! Is this a game?"

"It is."

"What is that which you are using?" This time the question was by Arthur. Van Helsing reverently lifted his hat as he answered:—

"The Host. I brought it from Amsterdam. I have an Indulgence." It was an answer that appalled the most sceptical of us, and we felt individually that in the presence of such earnest purpose as the Professor's, a purpose which could thus use the to him most sacred of things, it was impossible to distrust. In respectful silence we took the places assigned to us close round the tomb, but hidden from the sight of any one approaching. I pitied the others, especially Arthur. I had myself been apprenticed by my former visits to this watching horror, and yet I, who had up to an hour ago repudiated the proofs, felt my heart sink within me. Never did tombs look so ghastly white; never did cypress, or yew, or juniper so seem the embodiment of funereal gloom; never did tree or grass wave or rustle so ominously; never did bough creak so mysteriously; and never did the far-away howling of dogs send such a woeful presage through the night.

There was a long spell of silence, a big, aching void, and then from the Professor a keen "S-s-s-s!" He pointed; and far down the avenue of yews we saw a white figure advance—a dim white figure, which held something dark at its breast. The figure stopped, and at the moment a ray of moonlight fell upon the masses of driving clouds and showed in startling prominence a dark-haired woman, dressed in the cerements of the grave. We could not see the face, for it was bent down over what we saw to be a fair-haired child. There was a pause and a sharp little cry, such as a child gives in sleep, or a dog as it lies before the fire and dreams. We were starting forward, but the Professor's warning hand, seen by us as he stood behind a yew-tree, kept us back; and then as we looked the white figure moved forwards again. It was now near enough for us to see clearly, and the moonlight still held. My own heart grew cold as ice, and I could hear the gasp of Arthur, as we recognised the features of Lucy Westenra. Lucy Westenra, but yet how changed. The sweetness was turned to adamantine, heartless cruelty, and the purity to voluptuous wantonness. Van Helsing stepped out, and, obedient to his gesture, we all advanced too; the four of us ranged in a line before the door of the tomb. Van Helsing raised his lantern and drew the slide; by the concentrated light that fell on Lucy's face we could see that the lips were crimson with fresh blood, and that the stream had trickled over her chin and stained the purity of her lawn death-robe.

We shuddered with horror. I could see by the tremulous light that even Van Helsing's iron nerve had failed. Arthur was next to me, and if I had not seized his arm and held him up, he would have fallen.

When Lucy—I call the thing that was before us Lucy because it bore her shape—saw us she drew back with an angry snarl, such as a cat gives when taken unawares; then her eyes ranged over us. Lucy's eyes in form and colour; but Lucy's eyes unclean and full of hell-fire, instead of the pure, gentle orbs we knew. At that moment the remnant of my love passed into hate and loathing; had she then to be killed, I could have done it with savage delight. As she looked, her eyes blazed with unholy light, and the face became wreathed with a voluptuous smile. Oh, God, how it made me shudder to see it! With a careless motion, she flung to the ground, callous as a devil, the child that up to now she had clutched strenuously to her breast, growling over it as a dog growls over a bone. The child gave a sharp cry, and lay there moaning. There was a cold-bloodedness in the act which wrung a groan from Arthur; when she advanced to him with outstretched arms and a wanton smile he fell back and hid his face in his hands.

She still advanced, however, and with a languorous, voluptuous grace, said:—

"Come to me, Arthur. Leave these others and come to me. My arms are hungry for you. Come, and we can rest together. Come, my husband, come!"

There was something diabolically sweet in her tones—something of the tingling of glass when struck—which rang through the brains even of us who heard the words addressed to another. As for Arthur, he seemed under a spell; moving his hands from his face, he opened wide his arms. She was leaping for them, when Van Helsing sprang forward and held between them his little golden crucifix. She recoiled from it, and, with a suddenly distorted face, full of rage, dashed past him as if to enter the tomb.

When within a foot or two of the door, however, she stopped, as if arrested by some irresistible force. Then she turned, and her face was shown in the clear burst of moonlight and by the lamp, which had now no quiver from Van Helsing's iron nerves. Never did I see such baffled malice on a face; and never, I trust, shall such ever be seen again by mortal eyes. The beautiful colour became livid, the eyes seemed to throw out sparks of hell-fire, the brows were wrinkled as though the folds of the flesh were the coils of Medusa's snakes, and the lovely, bloodstained mouth grew to an open square, as in the passion masks of the Greeks and Japanese. If ever a face meant death—if looks could kill—we saw it at that moment.

And so for full half a minute, which seemed an eternity, she remained between the lifted crucifix and the sacred closing of her means of entry. Van Helsing broke the silence by asking Arthur:—

"Answer me, oh my friend! Am I to proceed in my work?"

Arthur threw himself on his knees, and hid his face in his hands, as he answered:—

"Do as you will, friend; do as you will. There can be no horror like this ever any more"; and he groaned in spirit. Quincey and I simultaneously moved towards him, and took his arms. We could hear the click of the closing lantern as Van Helsing held it down; coming close to the tomb, he began to remove from the chinks some of the sacred emblem which he had placed there. We all looked on in horrified amazement as we saw, when he stood back, the woman, with a corporeal body as real at that moment as our own, pass in through the interstice where scarce a knife-blade could have gone. We all felt a glad sense of relief when we saw the Professor calmly restoring the strings of putty to the edges of the door.

When this was done, he lifted the child and said:

"Come now, my friends; we can do no more till to-morrow. There is a funeral at noon, so here we shall all come before long after that. The friends of the dead will all be gone by two, and when the sexton lock the gate we shall remain. Then there is more to do; but not like this of to-night. As for this little one, he is not much harm, and by to-morrow night he shall be well. We shall leave him where the police will find him, as on the other night; and then to home." Coming close to Arthur, he said:—

"My friend Arthur, you have had a sore trial; but after, when you look back, you will see how it was necessary. You are now in the bitter waters, my child. By this time to-morrow you will, please God, have passed them, and have drunk of the sweet waters; so do not mourn over-much. Till then I shall not ask you to forgive me."

Arthur and Quincey came home with me, and we tried to cheer each other on the way. We had left the child in safety, and were tired; so we all slept with more or less reality of sleep.

29 September, night.—A little before twelve o'clock we three—Arthur, Quincey Morris, and myself—called for the Professor. It was odd to notice that by common consent we had all put on black clothes. Of course, Arthur wore black, for he was in deep mourning, but the rest of us wore it by instinct. We got to the churchyard by half-past one, and strolled about, keeping out of official observation, so that when the gravediggers had completed their task and the sexton, under the belief that every one had gone, had locked the gate, we had the place all to ourselves. Van Helsing, instead of his little black bag, had with him a long leather one, something like a cricketing bag; it was manifestly of fair weight.

When we were alone and had heard the last of the footsteps die out up the road, we silently, and as if by ordered intention, followed the Professor to the tomb. He unlocked the door, and we entered, closing it behind us. Then he took from his bag the lantern, which he lit, and also two wax candles, which, when lighted, he stuck, by melting their own ends, on other coffins so that they might give light sufficient to work by. When he again lifted the lid off Lucy's coffin we all looked—Arthur trembling like an aspen—and saw that the body lay there in all its death-beauty. But there was no love in my own heart, nothing but loathing for the foul Thing which had taken Lucy's shape without her soul. I could see even Arthur's face grow hard as he looked. Presently he said to Van Helsing:—

"Is this really Lucy's body, or only a demon in her shape?"

"It is her body, and yet not it. But wait a while, and you shall see her as she was, and is."

She seemed like a nightmare of Lucy as she lay there; the pointed teeth, the bloodstained, voluptuous mouth—which it made one shudder to see—the whole carnal and unspiritual appearance, seeming like a devilish mockery of Lucy's sweet purity. Van Helsing, with his usual methodicalness, began taking the various contents from his bag and placing them ready for use. First he took out a soldering iron and some plumbing solder, and then a small oil-lamp, which gave out, when lit in a corner of the tomb, gas which burned at fierce heat with a blue flame; then his operating knives, which he placed to hand; and last a round wooden stake, some two and a half or three inches thick and about three feet long. One end of it was hardened by charring in the fire, and was sharpened to a fine point. With this stake came a heavy hammer, such as in households is used in the coal-cellar for breaking the lumps. To me, a doctor's preparations for work of any kind are stimulating and bracing, but the effect of these things on both Arthur and Quincey was to cause them a sort of consternation. They both, however, kept their courage, and remained silent and quiet.

When all was ready, Van Helsing said:—

"Before we do anything, let me tell you this: it is out of the lore and experience of the ancients and of all those who have studied the powers of the Un-Dead. When they become such, there comes with the change the curse of immortality; they cannot die, but must go on age after age adding new victims and multiplying the evils of the world, for all that die from the preying of the Un-Dead becomes themselves Un-Dead, and prey on their kind. And so the circle goes on ever widening, like as the ripples from a stone thrown in the water. Friend Arthur, if you had met that kiss which you know of before poor Lucy die; or again, last night when you open your arms to her, you would in time, when you had died, have become *nosferatu*, as they call it in Eastern Europe, and would all time make more of those Un-Deads that so have fill us with horror. The career of this so unhappy dear lady is but just begun. Those children whose blood she suck are not as yet so much the worse; but if she live on, Un-Dead, more and more they lose their blood and by her power over them they come to her; and so she draw their blood with that so wicked mouth. But if she die in truth, then all cease; the tiny wounds of the throats disappear, and they go back to their plays unknowing ever of what has been. But of the most blessed of all, when this now Un-Dead be made to rest as true dead, then the soul of the poor lady whom we love shall again be free. Instead of working wickedness by night and growing more debased in the assimilating of it by day, she shall take her place with the other Angels. So that, my friend, it will be a blessed hand for her that shall strike the blow that sets her free. To this I am willing; but is there none amongst us who has a better right? Will it be no joy to think of hereafter in the silence of the night when sleep is not: 'It was my hand that sent her to the stars; it was the hand of him that loved her best; the hand that of all she would herself have chosen, had it been to her to choose?' Tell me if there be such a one amongst us?"

We all looked at Arthur. He saw, too, what we all did, the infinite kindness which suggested that his should be the hand which would restore Lucy to us as a holy, and not an unholy, memory; he stepped forward and said bravely, though his hand trembled, and his face was as pale as snow:—

"My true friend, from the bottom of my broken heart I thank you. Tell me what I am to do, and I shall not falter!" Van Helsing laid a hand on his shoulder, and said:—

"Brave lad! A moment's courage, and it is done. This stake must be driven through her. It will be a fearful ordeal—be not deceived in that—but it will be only a short time, and you will then rejoice more than your pain was great; from this grim tomb you will emerge as though you tread on air. But you must not falter when once you have begun. Only think that we, your true friends, are round you, and that we pray for you all the time."

"Go on," said Arthur hoarsely. "Tell me what I am to do."

"Take this stake in your left hand, ready to place the point over the heart, and the hammer in your right. Then when we begin our prayer for the dead—I shall read him, I have here the book, and the others shall follow—strike in God's name, that so all may be well with the dead that we love and that the Un-Dead pass away."

Arthur took the stake and the hammer, and when once his mind was set on action his hands never trembled nor even quivered. Van Helsing opened his missal and began to read, and Quincey and I followed as well as we could. Arthur placed the point over the heart, and as I looked I could see its dint in the white flesh. Then he struck with all his might.

The Thing in the coffin writhed; and a hideous, blood-curdling screech came from the opened red lips. The body shook and quivered and twisted in wild contortions; the sharp white teeth champed together till the lips were cut, and the mouth was smeared with a crimson foam. But Arthur never faltered. He looked like a figure of Thor as his untrembling arm rose and fell, driving deeper and deeper the mercy-bearing stake, whilst the blood from the pierced heart welled and spurted up around it. His face was set, and high duty seemed to shine through it; the sight of it gave us courage so that our voices seemed to ring through the little vault.

And then the writhing and quivering of the body became less, and the teeth seemed to champ, and the face to quiver. Finally it lay still. The terrible task was over.

The hammer fell from Arthur's hand. He reeled and would have fallen had we not caught him. The great drops of sweat sprang from his forehead, and his breath came in broken gasps. It had indeed been an awful strain on him; and had he not been forced to his task by more than human considerations he could never have gone through with it. For a few minutes we were so taken up with him that we did not look towards the coffin. When we did, however, a murmur of startled surprise ran from one to the other of us. We gazed so eagerly that Arthur rose, for he had been seated on the ground, and came and looked too; and then a glad, strange light broke over his face and dispelled altogether the gloom of horror that lay upon it.

There, in the coffin lay no longer the foul Thing that we had so dreaded and grown to hate that the work of her destruction was yielded as a privilege to the one best entitled to it, but Lucy as we had seen her in her life, with her face of unequalled sweetness and purity. True that there were there, as we had seen them in life, the traces of care and pain and waste; but these were all dear to us, for they marked her truth to what we knew. One and all we felt that the holy calm that lay like sun-shine over the wasted face and form was only an earthly token and sym-bol of the calm that was to reign for ever.

Van Helsing came and laid his hand on Arthur's shoulder, and said to him:—

"And now, Arthur my friend, dear lad, am I not forgiven?"

The reaction of the terrible strain came as he took the old man's hand in his, and raising it to his lips, pressed it, and said:—

"Forgiven! God bless you that you have given my dear one her soul again, and me peace." He put his hands on the Professor's shoulder, and laying his head on his breast, cried for a while silently, whilst we stood unmoving. When he raised his head Van Helsing said to him:—

"And now, my child, you may kiss her. Kiss her dead lips if you will, as she would have you to, if for her to choose. For she is not a grinning devil now—not any more a foul Thing for all eternity. No longer she is the devil's Un-Dead. She is God's true dead, whose soul is with Him!"

Arthur bent and kissed her, and then we sent him and Quincey out of the tomb; the Professor and I sawed the top off the stake, leaving the point of it in the body. Then we cut off the head and filled the mouth with garlic. We soldered up the leaden coffin, screwed on the coffin-lid, and gathering up our belongings, came away. When the Professor locked the door he gave the key to Arthur.

Outside the air was sweet, the sun shone, and the birds sang, and it seemed as if all nature were tuned to a different pitch. There was glad-ness and mirth and peace everywhere, for we were at rest ourselves on one account, and we were glad, though it was with a tempered joy.

Before we moved away Van Helsing said:—

"Now, my friends, one step of our work is done, one the most har-rowing to ourselves. But there remains a greater task: to find out the author of all this our sorrow and to stamp him out. I have clues which we can follow; but it is a long task, and a difficult, and there is danger in it, and pain. Shall you not all help me? We have learned to believe, all of us—is it not so? And since so, do we not see our duty? Yes! And do we not promise to go on to the bitter end?"

Each in turn, we took his hand, and the promise was made. Then said the Professor as we moved off:—

"Two nights hence you shall meet with me and dine together at seven of the clock with friend John. I shall entreat two others, two that you know not as yet; and I shall be ready to all our work show and our plans unfold. Friend John, you come with me home, for I have much to consult about, and you can help me. To-night I leave for Amsterdam, but shall return to-morrow night. And then begins our great quest. But first I shall have much to say, so that you may know what is to do and to dread. Then our promise shall be made to each other anew; for there is a terrible task before us, and once our feet are on the ploughshare we must not draw back."

CHAPTER 17.

DR. SEWARD'S DIARY—*continued.*

When we arrived at the Berkeley Hotel, Van Helsing found a telegram waiting for him:—

> "Am coming up by train. Jonathan at Whitby.
> Important news.—MINA HARKER."

The Professor was delighted. "Ah, that wonderful Madam Mina," he said, "pearl among women! She arrive, but I cannot stay. She must go to your house, friend John. You must meet her at the station. Telegraph her *en route*, so that she may be prepared."

When the wire was despatched he had a cup of tea; over it he told me of a diary kept by Jonathan Harker when abroad, and gave me a typewritten copy of it, as also of Mrs. Harker's diary at Whitby. "Take these," he said, "and study them well. When I have returned you will be master of all the facts, and we can then better enter on our inquisition. Keep them safe, for there is in them much of treasure. You will need all your faith, even you who have had such an experience as that of to-day. What is here told," he laid his hand heavily and gravely on the packet of papers as he spoke, "may be the beginning of the end to you and me and many another; or it may sound the knell of the Un-Dead who walk the earth. Read all, I pray you, with the open mind; and if you can add in any way to the story here told do so, for it is all-important. You have kept diary of all these so strange things; is it not so? Yes! Then we shall go through all these together when we meet." He then made ready for his departure, and shortly after drove off to Liverpool Street. I took my way to Paddington, where I arrived about fifteen minutes before the train came in.

The crowd melted away, after the bustling fashion common to arrival platforms; and I was beginning to feel uneasy, lest I might miss my guest, when a sweet-faced, dainty-looking girl stepped up to me, and, after a quick glance, said: "Dr. Seward, is it not?"

"And you are Mrs. Harker!" I answered at once; whereupon she held out her hand.

"I knew you from the description of poor dear Lucy; but——" She stopped suddenly, and a quick blush overspread her face.

The blush that rose to my own cheeks somehow set us both at ease, for it was a tacit answer to her own. I got her luggage, which included a typewriter, and we took the Underground to Fenchurch Street, after I had sent a wire to my housekeeper to have a sitting-room and bedroom prepared at once for Mrs. Harker.

In due time we arrived. She knew, of course, that the place was a lunatic asylum, but I could see that she was unable to repress a shudder when we entered.

She told me that, if she might, she would come presently to my study, as she had much to say. So here I am finishing my entry in my phonograph diary whilst I await her. As yet I have not had the chance of looking at the papers which Van Helsing left with me, though they lie open before me. I must get her interested in something, so that I may have an opportunity of reading them. She does not know how precious time is, or what a task we have in hand. I must be careful not to frighten her. Here she is!

MINA HARKER'S JOURNAL.

29 September.—After I had tidied myself, I went down to Dr. Seward's study. At the door I paused a moment, for I thought I heard him talking with some one. As, however, he had pressed me to be quick, I knocked at the door, and on his calling out, "Come in," I entered.

To my intense surprise, there was no one with him. He was quite alone, and on the table opposite him was what I knew at once from the description to be a phonograph. I had never seen one, and was much interested.

"I hope I did not keep you waiting," I said; "but I stayed at the door as I heard you talking, and thought there was some one with you."

"Oh," he replied with a smile, "I was only entering my diary—"

"Your diary?" I asked him in surprise.

"Yes," he answered. "I keep it in this." As he spoke he laid his hand on the phonograph. I felt quite excited over it, and blurted out:—

"Why, this beats even shorthand! May I hear it say something?"

"Certainly," he replied with alacrity, and stood up to put it in train for speaking. Then he paused, and a troubled look overspread his face.

"The fact is," he began awkwardly, "I only keep my diary in it; and as it is entirely—almost entirely—about my cases, it may be awkward— that is, I mean——" He stopped, and I tried to help him out of his embarrassment:—

"You helped to attend dear Lucy at the end. Let me hear how she died; for all that I know of her, I shall be very grateful. She was very, very dear to me."

To my surprise, he answered, with a horrorstruck look in his face:—

"Tell you of her death? Not for the wide world!"

"Why not?" I asked, for some grave, terrible feeling was coming over me. Again he paused, and I could see that he was trying to invent an excuse. At length he stammered out:—

"You see, I do not know how to pick out any particular part of the diary." Even while he was speaking an idea dawned upon him, and he said with unconscious simplicity, in a different voice, and with the naïveté of a child: "That's quite true, upon my honour. Honest Indian!" I could not but smile, at which he grimaced. "I gave myself away that time!" he said. "But do you know that, although I have kept the diary for months past, it never once struck me how I was going to find any particular part of it in case I wanted to look it up?" By this time my mind was made up that the diary of a doctor who attended Lucy might have something to add to the sum of our knowledge of that terrible Being, and I said boldly:—

"Then, Dr. Seward, you had better let me copy it out for you on my typewriter." He grew to a positively deathly pallor as he said:—

"No! no! no! For all the world, I wouldn't let you know that terrible story!"

Then it was terrible; my intuition was right! For a moment I thought, and as my eyes ranged the room, unconsciously looking for something or some opportunity to aid me, they lit on a great batch of typewriting on the table. His eyes caught the look in mine, and, without his thinking, followed their direction. As they saw the parcel he realised my meaning.

"You do not know me," I said. "When you have read those papers— my own diary and my husband's also, which I have typed—you will know me better. I have not faltered in giving every thought of my own heart in this cause; but, of course, you do not know me—yet; and I must not expect you to trust me so far."

He is certainly a man of noble nature: poor dear Lucy was right about him. He stood up and opened a large drawer, in which were arranged in order a number of hollow cylinders of metal covered with dark wax, and said:—

"You are quite right. I did not trust you because I did not know you. But I know you now; and let me say that I should have known you long ago. I know that Lucy told you of me; she told me of you too. May I make the only atonement in my power? Take the cylinders and hear them—the first half-dozen of them are personal to me, and they will not horrify you; then you will know me better. Dinner will by then be ready. In the meantime I shall read over some of these documents, and shall be better able to understand certain things." He carried the phonograph himself up to my sitting-room and adjusted it for me. Now I shall learn something pleasant, I am sure; for it will tell me the other side of a true love episode of which I know one side already. . . .

DR. SEWARD'S DIARY.

29 September.—I was so absorbed in that wonderful diary of Jonathan Harker and that other of his wife that I let time run on without thinking. Mrs. Harker was not down when the maid came running to announce dinner, so I said: "She is possibly tired; let dinner wait an hour," and I went on with my work. I had just finished Mrs. Harker's diary, when she came in. She looked sweetly pretty, but very sad, and her eyes were flushed with crying. This somehow moved me much. Of late I have had cause for tears, God knows! but the relief of them was denied me; and now the sight of those sweet eyes, brightened with recent tears, went straight to my heart. So I said as gently as I could:—

"I greatly fear I have distressed you."

"Oh, no, not distressed me," she replied, "but I have been more touched than I can say by your grief. That is a wonderful machine, but it is cruelly true. It told me, in its very tones, the anguish of your heart. It was like a soul crying out to Almighty God. No one must hear them spoken ever again! See, I have tried to be useful. I have copied out the words on my typewriter, and none other need now hear your heart beat, as I did."

"No one need ever know, shall ever know," I said in a low voice. She laid her hand on mine and said very gravely:—

"Ah, but they must!"

"Must! But why?" I asked.

"Because it is a part of the terrible story, a part of poor dear Lucy's death and all that led to it; because in the struggle which we have before us to rid the earth of this terrible monster we must have all the knowledge and all the help which we can get. I think that the cylinders which you gave me contained more than you intended me to know; but I can see that there are in your record many lights to this dark mystery. You will let me help, will you not? I know all up to a certain point; and I see already, though your diary only took me to 7 September, how poor Lucy was beset, and how her terrible doom was being wrought out. Jonathan and I have been working day and night since Professor Van Helsing saw us. He is gone to Whitby to get more information, and he will be here to-morrow to help us. We need have no secrets amongst us; working together and with absolute trust, we can surely be stronger than if some of us were in the dark." She looked at me so appealingly, and at the same time manifested such courage and resolution in her bearing, that I gave in at once to her wishes. "You shall," I said, "do as you like in the matter. God forgive me if I do wrong! There are terrible things yet to learn of; but if you have so far travelled on the road to poor Lucy's death, you will not be content, I know, to remain in the dark. Nay, the end—the very end—may give you a gleam of peace. Come, there is dinner. We must keep one another strong for what is before us; we have a cruel and dreadful task. When you have eaten you shall learn the rest, and I shall answer any questions you ask—if there be anything which you do not understand, though it was apparent to us who were present."

MINA HARKER'S JOURNAL.

29 September.—After dinner I came with Dr. Seward to his study. He brought back the phonograph from my room, and I took my typewriter. He placed me in a comfortable chair, and arranged the phonograph so that I could touch it without getting up, and showed me how to stop it in case I should want to pause. Then he very thoughtfully took a chair, with his back to me, so that I might be as free as possible, and began to read. I put the forked metal to my ears and listened.

When the terrible story of Lucy's death, and—and all that followed, was done, I lay back in my chair powerless. Fortunately I am not of a fainting disposition. When Dr. Seward saw me he jumped up with a horrified exclamation, and hurriedly taking a case-bottle from a cupboard, gave me some brandy, which in a few minutes somewhat restored me. My brain was all in a whirl, and only that there came through all the multitude of horrors, the holy ray of light that my dear, dear Lucy was at last at peace, I do not think I could have borne it without making a scene. It is all so wild, and mysterious, and strange that if I had not known Jonathan's experience in Transylvania I could not have believed. As it was, I didn't know what to believe, and so got out of my difficulty by attending to something else. I took the cover off my typewriter, and said to Dr. Seward:—

"Let me write this all out now. We must be ready for Dr. Van Helsing when he comes. I have sent a telegram to Jonathan to come on here when he arrives in London from Whitby. In this matter dates are everything, and I think that if we get all our material ready, and have every item put in chronological order, we shall have done much. You tell me that Lord Godalming and Mr. Morris are coming too. Let us be able to tell them when they come." He accordingly set the phonograph at a slow pace, and I began to typewrite from the beginning of the seventh cylinder. I used manifold, and so took three copies of the diary, just as I had done with all the rest. It was late when I got through, but Dr. Seward went about his work of going his round of the patients; when he had finished he came back and sat near me, reading, so that I did not feel too lonely whilst I worked. How good and thoughtful he is; the world seems full of good men—even if there *are* monsters in it. Before I left him I remembered what Jonathan put in his diary of the Professor's perturbation at reading something in an evening paper at the station at Exeter; so, seeing that Dr. Seward keeps his newspapers, I borrowed the files of "The Westminster Gazette" and "The Pall Mall Gazette," and took them to my room. I remember how much "The Dailygraph" and "The Whitby Gazette," of which I had made cuttings, helped us to understand the terrible events at Whitby when Count Dracula landed, so I shall look through the evening papers since then, and perhaps I shall get some new light. I am not sleepy, and the work will help to keep me quiet.

DR. SEWARD'S DIARY.

30 September.—Mr. Harker arrived at nine o'clock. He had got his wife's wire just before starting. He is uncommonly clever, if one can judge from his face, and full of energy. If this journal be true—and judging by one's own wonderful experiences, it must be—he is also a man of great nerve. That going down to the vault a second time was a remarkable piece of daring. After reading his account of it I was prepared to meet a good specimen of manhood, but hardly the quiet, business-like gentleman who came here to-day.

Later.—After lunch Harker and his wife went back to their own room, and as I passed a while ago I heard the click of the typewriter. They are hard at it. Mrs. Harker says that they are knitting together in chronological order every scrap of evidence they have. Harker has got the letters between the consignee of the boxes at Whitby and the carriers in London who took charge of them. He is now reading his wife's typescript of my diary. I wonder what they make out of it. Here it is. . . .

Strange that it never struck me that the very next house might be the Count's hiding-place! Goodness knows that we had enough clues from the conduct of the patient Renfield! The bundle of letters relating to the purchase of the house were with the typescript. Oh, if we had only had them earlier we might have saved poor Lucy! Stop; that way madness lies! Harker has gone back, and is again collating his material. He says that by dinner-time they will be able to show a whole connected narrative. He thinks that in the meantime I should see Renfield, as hitherto he has been a sort of index to the coming and going of the Count. I hardly see this yet, but when I get at the dates I suppose I shall. What a good thing that Mrs. Harker put my cylinders into type! We never could have found the dates otherwise. . . .

I found Renfield sitting placidly in his room with his hands folded, smiling benignly. At the moment he seemed as sane as any one I ever saw. I sat down and talked with him on a lot of subjects, all of which he treated naturally. He then, of his own accord, spoke of going home, a subject he has never mentioned to my knowledge during his sojourn here. In fact, he spoke quite confidently of getting his discharge at once. I believe that, had I not had the chat with Harker and read the letters and the dates of his outbursts, I should have been prepared to sign for him after a brief time of observation. As it is, I am darkly suspicious. All those outbreaks were in some way linked with the proximity of the Count. What then does this absolute content mean? Can it be that his instinct is satisfied as to the vampire's ultimate triumph? Stay; he is himself zoöphagous, and in his wild ravings spoke of "master." This all seems confirmation of our idea. However, after a while I came away; my friend is just a little too sane at present to make it safe to probe him too deep with questions. He might begin to think, and then—! So I came away. I mistrust these quiet moods of his; so I have given the attendant a hint to look closely after him, and to have a strait-waistcoat ready in case of need.

JONATHAN HARKER'S JOURNAL.

29 September, in train to London.—When I received Mr. Billington's courteous message that he would give me any information in his power I thought it best to go down to Whitby and make, on the spot, such inquiries as I wanted. It was now my object to trace that horrid cargo of the Count's to its place in London. Later, we may be able to deal with it. Billington Junior, a nice lad, met me at the station, and brought me to his father's house, where they had decided that I must stay the night. They are hospitable, with true Yorkshire hospitality: give a guest everything, and leave him free to do as he likes. They all knew that I was busy, and that my stay was short, and Mr. Billington had ready in his office all the papers concerning the consignment of boxes. It gave me almost a turn to see again one of the letters which I had seen on the Count's table before I knew of his diabolical plans. Everything had been carefully thought out, and done systematically and with precision. He seemed to have been prepared for every obstacle which might be placed by accident in the way of his intentions being carried out. To use an Americanism, he had "taken no chances," and the absolute accuracy with which his instructions were fulfilled, was simply the logical result of his care. I saw the invoice, and took note of it: "Fifty cases of common earth, to be used for experimental purposes." Also the copy of the letter to Carter, Paterson, and their reply; of both of these I got copies. This was all the information Mr. Billington could give me, so I went down to the port and saw the coastguards, the Customs officers and the harbour-master. They had all something to say of the strange entry of the ship, which is already taking its place in local tradition; but no one could add to the simple description "Fifty cases of common earth." I then saw the station-master, who kindly put me in communication with the men who had actually received the boxes. Their tally was exact with the list, and they had nothing to add except that the boxes were "main and mortal heavy," and that shifting them was dry work. One of them added that it was hard lines that there wasn't any gentleman "such-like as yourself, squire," to show some sort of appreciation of their efforts in a liquid form; another put in a rider that the thirst then generated was such that even the time which had elapsed had not completely allayed it. Needless to add, I took care before leaving to lift, for ever and adequately, this source of reproach.

30 September.—The station-master was good enough to give me a line to his old companion the station-master at King's Cross, so that when I arrived there in the morning I was able to ask him about the arrival of the boxes. He, too, put me at once in communication with the proper officials, and I saw that their tally was correct with the original invoice. The opportunities of acquiring an abnormal thirst had been here limited; a noble use of them had, however, been made, and again I was compelled to deal with the result in an *ex post facto* manner.

From thence I went on to Carter, Paterson's central office, where I met with the utmost courtesy. They looked up the transaction in their day-book and letter-book, and at once telephoned to their King's Cross office for more details. By good fortune, the men who did the teaming were waiting for work, and the official at once sent them over, sending also by one of them the way-bill and all the papers connected with the delivery of the boxes at Carfax. Here again I found the tally agreeing exactly; the carriers' men were able to supplement the paucity of the written words with a few details. These were, I shortly found, connected almost solely with the dusty nature of the job, and of the consequent thirst engendered in the operators. On my affording an opportunity, through the medium of the currency of the realm, of the allaying, at a later period, this beneficial evil, one of the men remarked:—

"That 'ere 'ouse, guv'nor, is the rummiest I ever was in. Blyme! but it ain't been touched sence a hundred years. There was dust that thick in the place that you might have slep' on it without 'urtin' of yer bones; an' the place was that neglected that yer might 'ave smelled old Jerusalem in it. But the ole chapel—that took the cike, that did! Me and my mate, we thort we wouldn't never git out quick enough. Lor', I wouldn't take less nor a quid a moment to stay there arter dark."

Having been in the house, I could well believe him; but if he knew what I know, he would, I think, have raised his terms.

Of one thing I am now satisfied: that *all* the boxes which arrived at Whitby from Varna in the *Demeter* were safely deposited in the old chapel at Carfax. There should be fifty of them there, unless any have since been removed—as from Dr. Seward's diary I fear.

I shall try to see the carter who took away the boxes from Carfax when Renfield attacked them. By following up this clue we may learn a good deal.

Later.—Mina and I have worked all day, and we have put all the papers into order.

MINA HARKER'S JOURNAL.

30 September.—I am so glad that I hardly know how to contain myself. It is, I suppose, the reaction from the haunting fear which I have had: that this terrible affair and the reopening of his old wound might act detrimentally on Jonathan. I saw him leave for Whitby with as brave a face as I could, but I was sick with apprehension. The effort has, however, done him good. He was never so resolute, never so strong, never so full of volcanic energy, as at present. It is just as that dear, good Professor Van Helsing said: he is true grit, and he improves under strain that would kill a weaker nature. He came back full of life and hope and determination; we have got everything in order for to-night. I feel myself quite wild with excitement. I suppose one ought to pity any thing so hunted as is the Count. That is just it: this Thing is not human—not even beast. To read Dr. Seward's account of poor Lucy's death, and what followed, is enough to dry up the springs of pity in one's heart.

Later.—Lord Godalming and Mr. Morris arrived earlier than we expected. Dr. Seward was out on business, and had taken Jonathan with him, so I had to see them. It was to me a painful meeting, for it brought back all poor dear Lucy's hopes of only a few months ago. Of course they had heard Lucy speak of me, and it seemed that Dr. Van Helsing, too, has been quite "blowing my trumpet," as Mr. Morris expressed it. Poor fellows, neither of them is aware that I know all about the proposals they made to Lucy. They did not quite know what to say or do, as they were ignorant of the amount of my knowledge; so they had to keep on neutral subjects. However, I thought the matter over, and came to the conclusion that the best thing I could do would be to post them in affairs right up to date. I knew from Dr. Seward's diary that they had been at Lucy's death—her real death—and that I need not fear to betray any secret before the time. So I told them, as well as I could, that I had read all the papers and diaries, and that my husband and I, having typewritten them, had just finished putting them in order. I gave them each a copy to read in the library. When Lord Godalming got his and turned it over—it does make a pretty good pile—he said:—

"Did you write all this, Mrs. Harker?"

I nodded, and he went on:—

"I don't quite see the drift of it; but you people are all so good and kind, and have been working so earnestly and so energetically, that all I can do is to accept your ideas blindfold and try to help you. I have had one lesson already in accepting facts that should make a man humble to the last hour of his life. Besides, I know you loved my poor Lucy—" Here he turned away and covered his face with his hands. I could hear the tears in his voice. Mr. Morris, with instinctive delicacy, just laid a hand for a moment on his shoulder, and then walked quietly out of the room. I suppose there is something in woman's nature that makes a man free to break down before her and express his feelings on the tender or emotional side without feeling it derogatory to his manhood; for when Lord Godalming found himself alone with me he sat down on the sofa and gave way utterly and openly. I sat down beside him and took his hand. I hope he didn't think it forward of me, and that if he ever thinks of it afterwards he never will have such a thought. There I wrong him; I *know* he never will—he is too true a gentleman. I said to him, for I could see that his heart was breaking:—

"I loved dear Lucy, and I know what she was to you, and what you were to her. She and I were like sisters; and now she is gone, will you not let me be like a sister to you in your trouble? I know what sorrows you have had, though I cannot measure the depth of them. If sympathy and pity can help in your affliction, won't you let me be of some little service— for Lucy's sake?"

In an instant the poor dear fellow was overwhelmed with grief. It seemed to me that all he had of late been suffering in silence found a vent at once. He grew quite hysterical, and raising his open hands, beat his palms together in a perfect agony of grief. He stood up and then sat down again, and the tears rained down his cheeks. I felt an infinite pity for him, and opened my arms unthinkingly. With a sob he laid his head on my shoulder and cried like a wearied child, whilst he shook with emotion.

We women have something of the mother in us that makes us rise above smaller matters when the mother-spirit is invoked; I felt this big sorrowing man's head resting on me, as though it were that of the baby that some day may lie on my bosom, and I stroked his hair as though he were my own child. I never thought at the time how strange it all was.

After a little bit his sobs ceased, and he raised himself with an apology, though he made no disguise of his emotion. He told me that for days and nights past—weary days and sleepless nights—he had been unable to speak with any one, as a man must speak in his time of sorrow. There was no woman whose sympathy could be given to him, or with whom, owing to the terrible circumstances with which his sorrow was surrounded, he could speak freely. "I know now how I suffered," he said, as he dried his eyes, "but I do not know even yet—and none other can ever know—how much your sweet sympathy has been to me to-day. I shall know better in time; and believe me that, though I am not ungrateful now, my gratitude will grow with my understanding. You will let me be like a brother, will you not, for all our lives—for dear Lucy's sake?"

"For dear Lucy's sake," I said as we clasped hands. "Ay, and for your own sake," he added, "for if a man's esteem and gratitude are ever worth the winning, you have won mine to-day. If ever the future should bring to you a time when you need a man's help, believe me, you will not call in vain. God grant that no such time may ever come to you to break the sunshine of your life; but if it should ever come, promise me that you will let me know." He was so earnest, and his sorrow was so fresh, that I felt it would comfort him, so I said:—

"I promise."

As I came along the corridor I saw Mr. Morris looking out of a window. He turned as he heard my footsteps. "How is Art?" he said. Then noticing my red eyes, he went on: "Ah, I see you have been comforting him. Poor old fellow! he needs it. No one but a woman can help a man when he is in trouble of the heart; and he had no one to comfort him."

He bore his own trouble so bravely that my heart bled for him. I saw the manuscript in his hand, and I knew that when he read it he would realise how much I knew; so I said to him:—

"I wish I could comfort all who suffer from the heart. Will you let me be your friend, and will you come to me for comfort if you need it? You will know, later on, why I speak." He saw that I was in earnest, and stooping, took my hand, and raising it to his lips, kissed it. It seemed but poor comfort to so brave and unselfish a soul, and impulsively I bent over and kissed him. The tears rose in his eyes, and there was a momentary choking in his throat; he said quite calmly:—

"Little girl, you will never regret that true-hearted kindness, so long as ever you live!" Then he went into the study to his friend.

"Little girl!"—the very words he had used to Lucy, and oh, but he proved himself a friend!

CHAPTER 18.

—◦—

DR. SEWARD'S DIARY.

30 September.—I got home at five o'clock, and found that Godalming and Morris had not only arrived, but had already studied the transcript of the various diaries and letters which Harker and his wonderful wife had made and arranged. Harker had not yet returned from his visit to the carriers' men, of whom Dr. Hennessey had written to me. Mrs. Harker gave us a cup of tea, and I can honestly say that, for the first time since I have lived in it, this old house seemed like *home*. When we had finished, Mrs. Harker said:—

"Dr. Seward, may I ask a favour? I want to see your patient, Mr. Renfield. Do let me see him. What you have said of him in your diary interests me so much!" She looked so appealing and so pretty that I could not refuse her, and there was no possible reason why I should; so I took her with me. When I went into the room, I told the man that a lady would like to see him; to which he simply answered: "Why?"

"She is going through the house, and wants to see every one in it," I answered. "Oh, very well," he said; "let her come in, by all means; but just wait a minute till I tidy up the place." His method of tidying was peculiar: he simply swallowed all the flies and spiders in the boxes before I could stop him. It was quite evident that he feared, or was jealous of, some interference. When he had got through his disgusting task, he said cheerfully: "Let the lady come in," and sat down on the edge of his bed with his head down, but with his eyelids raised so that he could see her as she entered. For a moment I thought that he might have some homicidal intent; I remembered how quiet he had been just before he attacked me in my own study, and I took care to stand where I could seize him at once if he attempted to make a spring at her. She came into the room with an easy gracefulness which would at once command the respect of any lunatic—for easiness is one of the qualities mad people most respect. She walked over to him, smiling pleasantly, and held out her hand.

"Good-evening, Mr. Renfield," said she. "You see, I know you, for Dr. Seward has told me of you." He made no immediate reply, but eyed her all over intently with a set frown on his face. This look gave way to one of wonder, which merged in doubt; then, to my intense astonishment, he said:—

"You're not the girl the doctor wanted to marry, are you? You can't be, you know, for she's dead." Mrs. Harker smiled sweetly as she replied:—

"Oh no! I have a husband of my own, to whom I was married before I ever saw Dr. Seward, or he me. I am Mrs. Harker."

"Then what are you doing here?"

"My husband and I are staying on a visit with Dr. Seward."

"Then don't stay."

"But why not?" I thought that this style of conversation might not be pleasant to Mrs. Harker, any more than it was to me, so I joined in:—

"How did you know I wanted to marry any one?" His reply was simply contemptuous, given in a pause in which he turned his eyes from Mrs. Harker to me, instantly turning them back again:—

"What an asinine question!"

"I don't see that at all, Mr. Renfield," said Mrs. Harker, at once championing me. He replied to her with as much courtesy and respect as he had shown contempt to me:—

"You will, of course, understand, Mrs. Harker, that when a man is so loved and honoured as our host is, everything regarding him is of interest in our little community. Dr. Seward is loved not only by his household and his friends, but even by his patients, who, being some of them hardly in mental equilibrium, are apt to distort causes and effects. Since I myself have been an inmate of a lunatic asylum, I cannot but notice that the sophistic tendencies of some of its inmates lean towards the errors of *non causa* and *ignoratio elenchi.*" I positively opened my eyes at this new development. Here was my own pet lunatic—the most pronounced of his type that I had ever met with—talking elemental philosophy, and with the manner of a polished gentleman. I wonder if it was Mrs. Harker's presence which had touched some chord in his memory. If this new phase was spontaneous, or in any way due to her unconscious influence, she must have some rare gift or power.

We continued to talk for some time; and, seeing that he was seemingly quite reasonable, she ventured, looking at me questioningly as she began, to lead him to his favourite topic. I was again astonished, for he addressed himself to the question with the impartiality of the completest sanity; he even took himself as an example when he mentioned certain things.

"Why, I myself am an instance of a man who had a strange belief. Indeed, it was no wonder that my friends were alarmed, and insisted on my being put under control. I used to fancy that life was a positive and perpetual entity, and that by consuming a multitude of live things, no matter how low in the scale of creation, one might indefinitely prolong life. At times I held the belief so strongly that I actually tried to take human life. The doctor here will bear me out that on one occasion I tried to kill him for the purpose of strengthening my vital powers by the assimilation with my own body of life through the medium of his blood—relying, of course, upon the Scriptural phrase, 'For the blood is the life.' Though, indeed, the vendor of a certain nostrum has vulgarised the truism to the very point of contempt. Isn't that true, Doctor?" I nodded assent, for I was so amazed that I hardly knew what to either think or say; it was hard to imagine that I had seen him eat up his spiders and flies not five minutes before. Looking at my watch, I saw that I should go to the station to meet Van Helsing, so I told Mrs. Harker that it was time to leave. She came at once, after saying pleasantly to Mr. Renfield: "Good-bye, and I hope I may see you often, under auspices pleasanter to yourself," to which, to my astonishment, he replied:—

"Good-bye, my dear. I pray God I may never see your sweet face again. May He bless and keep you!"

When I went to the station to meet Van Helsing I left the boys behind me. Poor Art seemed more cheerful than he has been since Lucy first took ill, and Quincey is more like his own bright self than he has been for many a long day.

Van Helsing stepped from the carriage with the eager nimbleness of a boy. He saw me at once, and rushed up to me, saying:—

"Ah, friend John, how goes all? Well? So! I have been busy, for I come here to stay if need be. All affairs are settled with me, and I have much to tell. Madam Mina is with you? Yes. And her so fine husband? And Arthur and my friend Quincey, they are with you, too? Good!"

As I drove to the house I told him of what had passed, and of how my own diary had come to be of some use through Mrs. Harker's suggestion; at which the Professor interrupted me:—

"Ah, that wonderful Madam Mina! She has man's brain—a brain that a man should have were he much gifted—and a woman's heart. The good God fashioned her for a purpose, believe me, when He made that so good combination. Friend John, up to now fortune has made that woman of help to us; after to-night she must not have to do with this so terrible affair. It is not good that she run a risk so great. We men are determined—nay, are we not pledged?—to destroy this monster; but it is no part for a woman. Even if she be not harmed, her heart may fail her in so much and so many horrors; and hereafter she may suffer—both in waking, from her nerves, and in sleep, from her dreams. And, besides, she is young woman and not so long married; there may be other things to think of some time, if not now. You tell me she has wrote all, then she must consult with us; but to-morrow she say good-bye to this work, and we go alone." I agreed heartily with him, and then I told him what we had found in his absence: that the house which Dracula had bought was the very next one to my own. He was amazed, and a great concern seemed to come on him. "Oh that we had known it before!" he said, "for then we might have reached him in time to save poor Lucy. However, 'the milk that is spilt cries not out afterwards,' as you say. We shall not think of that, but go on our way to the end." Then he fell into a silence that lasted till we entered my own gateway. Before we went to prepare for dinner he said to Mrs. Harker:—

"I am told, Madam Mina, by my friend John that you and your husband have put up in exact order all things that have been, up to this moment."

"Not up to this moment, Professor," she said impulsively, "but up to this morning."

"But why not up to now? We have seen hitherto how good light all the little things have made. We have told our secrets, and yet no one who has told is the worse for it."

Mrs. Harker began to blush, and taking a paper from her pockets, she said:—

"Dr. Van Helsing, will you read this, and tell me if it must go in. It is my record of to-day. I too have seen the need of putting down at present everything, however trivial; but there is little in this except what is personal. Must it go in?" The Professor read it over gravely, and handed it back, saying:—

"It need not go in if you do not wish it; but I pray that it may. It can but make your husband love you the more, and all us, your friends, more honour you—as well as more esteem and love." She took it back with another blush and a bright smile.

And so now, up to this very hour, all the records we have are complete and in order. The Professor took away one copy to study after dinner, and before our meeting, which is fixed for nine o'clock. The rest of us have already read everything; so when we meet in the study we shall all be informed as to facts, and can arrange our plan of battle with this terrible and mysterious enemy.

MINA HARKER'S JOURNAL.

30 September.—When we met in Dr. Seward's study two hours after dinner, which had been at six o'clock, we unconsciously formed a sort of board or committee. Professor Van Helsing took the head of the table, to which Dr. Seward motioned him as he came into the room. He made me sit next to him on his right, and asked me to act as secretary; Jonathan sat next to me. Opposite us were Lord Godalming, Dr. Seward, and Mr. Morris—Lord Godalming being next the Professor, and Dr. Seward in the centre. The Professor said:—

"I may, I suppose, take it that we are all acquainted with the facts that are in these papers." We all expressed assent, and he went on:—

"Then it were, I think, good that I tell you something of the kind of enemy with which we have to deal. I shall then make known to you something of the history of this man, which has been ascertained for me. So we then can discuss how we shall act, and can take our measure according.

"There are such beings as vampires; some of us have evidence that they exist. Even had we not the proof of our own unhappy experience, the teachings and the records of the past give proof enough for sane peoples. I admit that at the first I was sceptic. Were it not that through long years I have train myself to keep an open mind, I could not have believe until such time as that fact thunder on my ear. 'See! see! I prove; I prove.' Alas! Had I known at the first what now I know—nay, had I ever guess at him—one so precious life had been spared to many of us who did love her. But that is gone; and we must so work, that other poor souls perish not, whilst we can save. The *nosferatu* do not die like the bee when he sting once. He is only stronger; and being stronger, have yet more power to work evil. This vampire which is amongst us is of himself so strong in person as twenty men; he is of cunning more than mortal, for his cunning be the growth of ages; he have still the aids of necromancy, which is, as his etymology imply, the divination by the dead, and all the dead that he can come nigh to are for him at command; he is brute, and more than brute; he is devil in callous, and the heart of him is not; he can, within limitations, appear at will when, and where, and in any of the forms that are to him; he can, within his range, direct the elements; the storm, the fog, the thunder; he can command all the meaner things: the rat, and the owl, and the bat—the moth, and the fox, and the wolf; he can grow and become small; and he can at times vanish and come unknown. How then are we to begin our strike to destroy him? How shall we find his where; and having found it, how can we destroy? My friends, this is much; it is a terrible task that we undertake, and there may be consequence to make the brave shudder. For if we fail in this our fight he must surely win; and then where end we? Life is nothings; I heed him not. But to fail here, is not mere life or death. It is that we become as him; that we henceforward become foul things of the night like him—without heart or conscience, preying on the bodies and the souls of those we love best. To us for ever are the gates of heaven shut; for who shall open them to us again? We go on for all time abhorred by all; a blot on the face of God's sunshine; an arrow in the side of Him who died for man. But we are face to face with duty; and in such case must we shrink? For me, I say, no; but then I am old, and life, with his sunshine, his fair places, his song of birds, his music and his love, lie far behind. You others are young. Some have seen sorrow; but there are fair days yet in store. What say you?"

Whilst he was speaking, Jonathan had taken my hand. I feared, oh so much, that the appalling nature of our danger was overcoming him when I saw his hand stretch out; but it was life to me to feel its touch—so strong, so self-reliant, so resolute. A brave man's hand can speak for itself; it does not even need a woman's love to hear its music.

When the Professor had done speaking my husband looked in my eyes, and I in his; there was no need for speaking between us.

"I answer for Mina and myself," he said.

"Count me in, Professor," said Mr. Quincey Morris, laconically as usual.

"I am with you," said Lord Godalming, "for Lucy's sake, if for no other reason."

Dr. Seward simply nodded. The Professor stood up and, after laying his golden crucifix on the table, held out his hand on either side. I took his right hand, and Lord Godalming his left; Jonathan held my right with his left and stretched across to Mr. Morris. So as we all took hands our solemn compact was made. I felt my heart icy cold, but it did not even occur to me to draw back. We resumed our places, and Dr. Van Helsing went on with a sort of cheerfulness which showed that the serious work had begun. It was to be taken as gravely, and in as business-like a way, as any other transaction of life:—

"Well, you know what we have to contend against; but we, too, are not without strength. We have on our side power of combination—a power denied to the vampire kind; we have sources of science; we are free to act and think; and the hours of the day and the night are ours equally. In fact, so far as our powers extend, they are unfettered, and we are free to use them. We have self-devotion in a cause, and an end to achieve which is not a selfish one. These things are much.

"Now let us see how far the general powers arrayed against us are restrict, and how the individual cannot. In fine, let us consider the limitations of the vampire in general, and of this one in particular.

"All we have to go upon are traditions and superstitions. These do not at the first appear much, when the matter is one of life and death—nay of more than either life or death. Yet must we be satisfied; in the first place because we have to be—no other means is at our control—and secondly, because, after all, these things—tradition and superstition— are everything. Does not the belief in vampires rest for others—though not, alas! for us—on them? A year ago which of us would have received such a possibility, in the midst of our scientific, sceptical, matter-of-fact nineteenth century? We even scouted a belief that we saw justified under our very eyes. Take it, then, that the vampire, and the belief in his limitations and his cure, rest for the moment on the same base. For, let me tell you, he is known everywhere that men have been. In old Greece, in old Rome; he flourish in Germany all over, in France, in India; even in the Chernosese; and in China, so far from us in all ways, there even he is, and the peoples fear him at this day. He have follow the wake of the berserker Icelander, the devil-begotten Hun, the Slav, the Saxon, the

Magyar. So far, then, we have all we may act upon; and let me tell you that very much of the beliefs are justified by what we have seen in our own so unhappy experience. The vampire live on, and cannot die by mere passing of the time; he can flourish when that he can fatten on the blood of the living. Even more, we have seen amongst us that he can even grow younger; that his vital faculties grow strenuous, and seem as though they refresh themselves when his special pabulum is plenty. But he cannot flourish without this diet; he eat not as others. Even friend Jonathan, who lived with him for weeks, did never see him to eat, never! He throws no shadow; he make in the mirror no reflect, as again Jonathan observe. He has the strength of many of his hand—witness again Jonathan when he shut the door against the wolves, and when he help him from the diligence too. He can transform himself to wolf, as we gather from the ship arrival in Whitby, when he tear open the dog; he can be as bat, as Madam Mina saw him on the window at Whitby, and as friend John saw him fly from this so near house, and as my friend Quincey saw him at the window of Miss Lucy. He can come in mist which he create—that noble ship's captain proved him of this; but, from what we know, the distance he can make this mist is limited, and it can only be round himself. He come on moonlight rays as elemental dust—as again Jonathan saw those sisters in the castle of Dracula. He become so small—we ourselves saw Miss Lucy, ere she was at peace, slip through a hairbreadth space at the tomb door. He can, when once he find his way, come out from anything or into anything, no matter how close it be bound or even fused up with fire— solder you call it. He can see in the dark—no small power this, in a world which is one half shut from the light. Ah, but hear me through. He can do all these things, yet he is not free. Nay; he is even more prisoner than the slave of the galley, than the madman in his cell. He cannot go where he lists; he who is not of nature has yet to obey some of nature's laws— why we know not. He may not enter anywhere at the first, unless there be some one of the household who bid him to come; though afterwards he can come as he please. His power ceases, as does that of all evil things, at the coming of the day. Only at certain times can he have limited freedom. If he be not at the place whither he is bound, he can only change himself at noon or at exact sunrise or sunset. These things are we told, and in this record of ours we have proof by inference. Thus, whereas he can do as he will within his limit, when he have his earth-home, his coffin-home, his hell-home, the place unhallowed, as we saw when he went to the grave of the suicide at Whitby; still at other time he can only change when the time come. It is said, too, that he can only pass running water at the slack or the flood of the tide. Then there are things which so afflict him that he has no power, as the garlic that we know of; and as for things sacred, as this symbol, my crucifix, that was amongst us even now when we resolve, to them he is nothing, but in their presence he take his place far off and silent with respect. There are others, too, which I shall tell you of, lest in our seeking we may need them. The branch of wild rose on his coffin keep him that he move not from it; a sacred bullet fired into the coffin kill him so that he be true dead; and as for the stake through him, we know already of its peace; or the cut-off head that giv-eth rest. We have seen it with our eyes.

"Thus when we find the habitation of this man-that-was, we can con-fine him to his coffin and destroy him, if we obey what we know. But he is clever. I have asked my friend Arminius, of Buda-Pesth University, to make his record; and, from all the means that are, he tell me of what he has been. He must, indeed, have been that Voivode Dracula who won his name against the Turk, over the great river on the very frontier of Turkey-land. If it be so, then was he no common man; for in that time, and for centuries after, he was spoken of as the cleverest and the most cunning, as well as the bravest of the sons of the 'land beyond the forest.' That mighty brain and that iron resolution went with him to his grave, and are even now arrayed against us. The Draculas were, says Arminius, a great and noble race, though now and again were scions who were held by their coevals to have had dealings with the Evil One. They learned his secrets in the Scholo-mance, amongst the mountains over Lake Hermanstadt, where the devil claims the tenth scholar as his due. In the records are such words as 'stre-goica'—witch, 'ordog,' and 'pokol'—Satan and hell; and in one manuscript this very Dracula is spoken of as 'wampyr,' which we all understand too well. There have been from the loins of this very one great men and good women, and their graves make sacred the earth where alone this foulness can dwell. For it is not the least of its terrors that this evil thing is rooted deep in all good; in soil barren of holy memories it cannot rest."

Whilst they were talking Mr. Morris was looking steadily at the window, and he now got up quietly, and went out of the room. There was a little pause, and then the Professor went on:—

"And now we must settle what we do. We have here much data, and we must proceed to lay out our campaign. We know from the inquiry of Jonathan that from the castle to Whitby came fifty boxes of earth, all of which were delivered at Carfax; we also know that at least some of these boxes have been removed. It seems to me, that our first step should be to ascertain whether all the rest remain in the house beyond that wall where we look to-day; or whether any more have been removed. If the latter, we must trace—"

Here we were interrupted in a very startling way. Outside the house came the sound of a pistol-shot; the glass of the window was shattered with a bullet, which, ricocheting from the top of the embrasure, struck the far wall of the room. I am afraid I am at heart a coward, for I shrieked out. The men all jumped to their feet; Lord Godalming flew over to the window and threw up the sash. As he did so we heard Mr. Morris's voice without:—

"Sorry! I fear I have alarmed you. I shall come in and tell you about it." A minute later he came in and said:—

"It was an idiotic thing of me to do, and I ask your pardon, Mrs. Harker, most sincerely; I fear I must have frightened you terribly. But the fact is that whilst the Professor was talking there came a big bat and sat on the windowsill. I have got such a horror of the damned brutes from recent events that I cannot stand them, and I went out to have a shot, as I have been doing of late of evenings, whenever I have seen one. You used to laugh at me for it then, Art."

"Did you hit it?" asked Dr. Van Helsing.

"I don't know; I fancy not, for it flew away into the wood." Without saying any more he took his seat, and the Professor began to resume his statement:—

"We must trace each of these boxes; and when we are ready, we must either capture or kill this monster in his lair; or we must, so to speak, sterilise the earth, so that no more he can seek safety in it. Thus in the end we may find him in his form of man between the hours of noon and sunset, and so engage with him when he is at his most weak.

"And now for you, Madam Mina, this night is the end until all be well. You are too precious to us to have such risk. When we part to-night, you no more must question. We shall tell you all in good time. We are men and are able to bear; but you must be our star and our hope, and we shall act all the more free that you are not in the danger, such as we are."

All the men, even Jonathan, seemed relieved; but it did not seem to me good that they should brave danger and, perhaps, lessen their safety—strength being the best safety—through care of me; but their minds were made up, and, though it was a bitter pill for me to swallow, I could say nothing, save to accept their chivalrous care of me.

Mr. Morris resumed the discussion:—

"As there is no time to lose, I vote we have a look at his house right now. Time is everything with him; and swift action on our part may save another victim."

I own that my heart began to fail me when the time for action came so close, but I did not say anything, for I had a greater fear that if I appeared as a drag or a hindrance to their work, they might even leave me out of their counsels altogether. They have now gone off to Carfax, with means to get into the house.

Man-like, they had told me to go to bed and sleep; as if a woman can sleep when those she loves are in danger! I shall lie down and pretend to sleep, lest Jonathan have added anxiety about me when he returns.

DR. SEWARD'S DIARY.

1 October, 4 a.m.—Just as we were about to leave the house, an urgent message was brought to me from Renfield to know if I would see him at once, as he had something of the utmost importance to say to me. I told the messenger to say that I would attend to his wishes in the morning; I was busy just at the moment. The attendant added:—

"He seems very importunate, sir. I have never seen him so eager. I don't know but what, if you don't see him soon, he will have one of his violent fits." I knew the man would not have said this without some cause, so I said: "All right; I'll go now"; and I asked the others to wait a few minutes for me, as I had to go and see my "patient."

"Take me with you, friend John," said the Professor. "His case in your diary interest me much, and it had bearing, too, now and again on *our* case. I should much like to see him, and especial when his mind is disturbed."

"May I come also?" asked Lord Goldalming.

"Me too?" said Quincey Morris. "May I come?" said Harker. I nodded, and we all went down the passage together.

We found him in a state of considerable excitement, but far more rational in his speech and manner than I had ever seen him. There was an unusual understanding of himself, which was unlike anything I had ever met with in a lunatic; and he took it for granted that his reasons would prevail with others entirely sane. We all four went into the room, but none of the others at first said anything. His request was that I would at once release him from the asylum and send him home. This he backed up with arguments regarding his complete recovery, and adduced his own existing sanity. "I appeal to your friends," he said, "they will, perhaps, not mind sitting in judgment on my case. By the way, you have not introduced me." I was so much astonished, that the oddness of introducing a madman in an asylum did not strike me at the moment; and, besides, there was a certain dignity in the man's manner, so much of the habit of equality, that I at once made the introduction: "Lord Godalming; Professor Van Helsing; Mr. Quincey Morris, of Texas; Mr. Renfield." He shook hands with each of them, saying in turn:—

"Lord Godalming, I had the honour of seconding your father at the Windham; I grieve to know, by your holding the title, that he is no more. He was a man loved and honoured by all who knew him; and in his youth was, I have heard, the inventor of a burnt rum punch, much patronised on Derby night. Mr. Morris, you should be proud of your great state. Its reception into the Union was a precedent which may have far-reaching effects hereafter, when the Pole and the Tropics may hold alliance to the Stars and Stripes. The power of Treaty may yet prove a vast engine of enlargement, when the Monroe doctrine takes its true place as a political fable. What shall any man say of his pleasure at meeting Van Helsing? Sir, I make no apology for dropping all forms of conventional prefix. When an individual has revolutionised therapeutics by his discovery of the continuous evolution of brain-matter, conventional forms are unfitting, since they would seem to limit him to one of a class. You, gentlemen, who by nationality, by heredity, or by the possession of natural gifts, are fitted to hold your respective places in the moving world, I take to witness that I am as sane as at least the majority of men who are in full possession of their liberties. And I am sure that you, Dr. Seward, humanitarian and medico-jurist as well as scientist, will deem it a moral duty to deal with me as one to be considered as under exceptional circumstances." He made this last appeal with a courtly air of conviction which was not without its own charm.

I think we were all staggered. For my own part, I was under the conviction, despite my knowledge of the man's character and history, that his reason had been restored; and I felt under a strong impulse to tell him that I was satisfied as to his sanity, and would see about the necessary formalities for his release in the morning. I thought it better to wait, however, before making so grave a statement, for of old I knew the sudden changes to which this particular patient was liable. So I contented myself with making a general statement that he appeared to be improving very rapidly; that I would have a longer chat with him in the morning, and would then see what I could do in the direction of meeting his wishes. This did not at all satisfy him, for he said quickly:—

"But I fear, Dr. Seward, that you hardly apprehend my wish. I desire to go at once—here—now—this very hour—this very moment, if I may. Time presses, and in our implied agreement with the old scytheman it is of the essence of the contract. I am sure it is only necessary to put before so admirable a practitioner as Dr. Seward so simple, yet so momentous a wish, to ensure its fulfilment." He looked at me keenly, and seeing the negative in my face, turned to the others, and scrutinised them closely. Not meeting any sufficient response, he went on:—

"Is it possible that I have erred in my supposition?"

"You have," I said frankly, but at the same time, as I felt, brutally. There was a considerable pause, and then he said slowly:—

"Then I suppose I must only shift my ground of request. Let me ask for this concession—boon, privilege, what you will. I am content to implore in such a case, not on personal grounds, but for the sake of others. I am not at liberty to give you the whole of my reasons; but you may, I assure you, take it from me that they are good ones, sound and unselfish, and spring from the highest sense of duty. Could you look, sir, into my heart, you would approve to the full the sentiments which animate me. Nay, more, you would count me amongst the best and truest of your friends." Again he looked at us all keenly. I had a growing conviction that this sudden change of his entire intellectual method was but yet another form or phase of his madness, and so determined to let him go on a little longer, knowing from experience that he would, like all lunatics, give himself away in the end. Van Helsing was gazing at him with a look of utmost intensity, his bushy eyebrows almost meeting with the fixed concentration of his look. He said to Renfield in a tone which did not surprise me at the time, but only when I thought of it afterwards— for it was as of one addressing an equal:—

"Can you not tell frankly your real reason for wishing to be free to-night? I will undertake that if you will satisfy even me—a stranger, without prejudice, and with the habit of keeping an open mind—Dr. Seward will give you, at his own risk and on his own responsibility, the privilege you seek." He shook his head sadly, and with a look of poignant regret on his face. The Professor went on:—

"Come, sir, bethink yourself. You claim the privilege of reason in the highest degree, since you seek to impress us with your complete reasonableness. You do this, whose sanity we have reason to doubt, since you are not yet released from medical treatment for this very defect. If you will not help us in our effort to choose the wisest course, how can we perform the duty which you yourself put upon us? Be wise, and help us; and if we can we shall aid you to achieve your wish." He still shook his head as he said:—

"Dr. Van Helsing, I have nothing to say. Your argument is complete, and if I were free to speak I should not hesitate a moment; but I am not my own master in the matter. I can only ask you to trust me. If I am refused, the responsibility does not rest with me." I thought it was now time to end the scene, which was becoming too comically grave, so I went towards the door, simply saying:—

"Come, my friends, we have work to do. Good-night."

As, however, I got near the door, a new change came over the patient. He moved towards me so quickly that for the moment I feared that he was about to make another homicidal attack. My fears, however, were groundless, for he held up his two hands imploringly, and made his petition in a moving manner. As he saw that the very excess of his emotion was militating against him, by restoring us more to our old relations, he became still more demonstrative. I glanced at Van Helsing, and saw my conviction reflecting in his eyes; so I became a little more fixed in my manner, if not more stern, and motioned to him that his efforts were unavailing. I had previously seen something of the same constantly growing excitement in him when he had to make some request of which at the time he had thought much, such, for instance, as when he wanted a cat; and I was prepared to see the collapse into the same sullen acquiescence on this occasion. My expectation was not realised, for, when he found that his appeal would not be successful, he got into quite a frantic condition. He threw himself on his knees, and held up his hands, wringing them in plaintive supplication, and poured forth a torrent of entreaty, with the tears rolling down his cheeks, and his whole face and form expressive of the deepest emotion:—

"Let me entreat you, Dr. Seward, oh, let me implore you, to let me out of this house at once. Send me away how you will and where you will; send keepers with me with whips and chains; let them take me in a strait-waistcoat, manacled and leg-ironed, even to a gaol; but let me go out of this. You don't know what you do by keeping me here. I am speaking from the depths of my heart—of my very soul. You don't know whom you wrong, or how; and I may not tell. Woe is me! I may not tell. By all you hold sacred—by all you hold dear—by your love that is lost— by your hope that lives—for the sake of the Almighty, take me out of this and save my soul from guilt! Can't you hear me, man? Can't you understand? Will you never learn? Don't you know that I am sane and earnest now; that I am no lunatic in a mad fit, but a sane man fighting for his soul? Oh, hear me! hear me! Let me go! let me go! let me go!"

I thought that the longer this went on the wilder he would get, and so would bring on a fit; so I took him by the hand and raised him up.

"Come," I said sternly, "no more of this; we have had quite enough already. Get to your bed and try to behave more discreetly."

He suddenly stopped and looked at me intently for several moments. Then, without a word, he rose and moving over, sat down on the side of the bed. The collapse had come, as on the former occasion, just as I had expected.

When I was leaving the room, last of our party, he said to me in a quiet, well-bred voice:—

"You will, I trust, Dr. Seward, do me the justice to bear in mind, later on, that I did what I could to convince you to-night."

CHAPTER 19.

——◇——

JONATHAN HARKER'S JOURNAL.

1 October, 5 a.m.—I went with the party to the search with an easy mind, for I think I never saw Mina so absolutely strong and well. I am so glad that she consented to hold back and let us men do the work. Somehow, it was a dread to me that she was in this fearful business at all; but now that her work is done, and that it is due to her energy and brains and foresight that the whole story is put together in such a way that every point tells, she may well feel that her part is finished, and that she can henceforth leave the rest to us. We were, I think, all a little upset by the scene with Mr. Renfield. When we came away from his room we were silent till we got back to the study. Then Mr. Morris said to Dr. Seward:—

"Say, Jack, if that man wasn't attempting a bluff, he is about the sanest lunatic I ever saw. I'm not sure, but I believe that he had some serious purpose, and if he had, it was pretty rough on him not to get a chance." Lord Godalming and I were silent, but Dr. Van Helsing added:—

"Friend John, you know more of lunatics than I do, and I'm glad of it, for I fear that if it had been to me to decide I would before that last hysterical outburst have given him free. But we live and learn, and in our present task we must take no chance, as my friend Quincey would say. All is best as they are." Dr. Seward seemed to answer them both in a dreamy kind of way:—

"I don't know but that I agree with you. If that man had been an ordinary lunatic I would have taken my chance of trusting him; but he seems so mixed up with the Count in an indexy kind of way that I am afraid of doing anything wrong by helping his fads. I can't forget how he prayed with almost equal fervour for a cat, and then tried to tear my throat out with his teeth. Besides, he called the Count 'lord and master,' and he may want to get out to help him in some diabolical way. That horrid thing has the wolves and the rats and his own kind to help him, so I suppose he isn't above trying to use a respectable lunatic. He certainly did seem earnest, though. I only hope we have done what is best. These things, in conjunction with the wild work we have in hand, help to unnerve a man." The Professor stepped over, and laying his hand on his shoulder, said in his grave, kindly way:—

"Friend John, have no fear. We are trying to do our duty in a very sad and terrible case; we can only do as we deem best. What else have we to hope for, except the pity of the good God?" Lord Godalming had slipped away for a few minutes, but now he returned. He held up a little silver whistle, as he remarked:—

"That old place may be full of rats, and if so, I've got an antidote on call." Having passed the wall, we took our way to the house, taking care to keep in the shadows of the trees on the lawn when the moonlight shone out. When we got to the porch the Professor opened his bag and took out a lot of things, which he laid on the step, sorting them into four little groups, evidently one for each. Then he spoke:—

"My friends, we are going into a terrible danger, and we need arms of many kinds. Our enemy is not merely spiritual. Remember that he has the strength of twenty men, and that, though our necks or our windpipes are of the common kind—and therefore breakable or crushable—his are not amenable to mere strength. A stronger man, or a body of men more strong in all than him, can at certain times hold him; but they cannot hurt him as we can be hurt by him. We must, therefore, guard ourselves from his touch. Keep this near your heart"—as he spoke he lifted a little silver crucifix and held it out to me, I being nearest to him—"put these flowers round your neck"—here he handed to me a wreath of withered garlic blossoms—"for other enemies more mundane, this revolver and this knife; and for aid in all, these so small electric lamps, which you can fasten to your breast; and for all, and above all at the last, this, which we must not desecrate needless." This was a portion of Sacred Wafer, which he put in an envelope and handed to me. Each of the others was similarly equipped. "Now," he said, "friend John, where are the skeleton keys? If so that we can open the door, we need not break house by the window, as before at Miss Lucy's."

Dr. Seward tried one or two skeleton keys, his mechanical dexterity as a surgeon standing him in good stead. Presently he got one to suit; after a little play back and forward the bolt yielded, and, with a rusty clang, shot back. We pressed on the door, the rusty hinges creaked, and it slowly opened. It was startlingly like the image conveyed to me in Dr. Seward's diary of the opening of Miss Westenra's tomb; I fancy that the same idea seemed to strike the others, for with one accord they shrank back. The Professor was the first to move forward, and stepped into the open door.

"In manus tuas, Domine!" he said, crossing himself as he passed over the threshold. We closed the door behind us, lest when we should have lit our lamps we should possibly attract attention from the road. The Professor carefully tried the lock, lest we might not be able to open it from within should we be in a hurry making our exit. Then we all lit our lamps and proceeded on our search.

The light from the tiny lamps fell in all sorts of odd forms, as the rays crossed each other, or the opacity of our bodies threw great shadows. I could not for my life get away from the feeling that there was some one else amongst us. I suppose it was the recollection, so powerfully brought home to me by the grim surroundings, of that terrible experience in Transylvania. I think the feeling was common to us all, for I noticed that the others kept looking over their shoulders at every sound and every new shadow, just as I felt myself doing.

The whole place was thick with dust. The floor was seemingly inches deep, except where there were recent footsteps, in which on holding down my lamp I could see marks of hobnails where the dust was cracked. The walls were fluffy and heavy with dust, and in the corners were masses of spiders' webs, whereon the dust had gathered till they looked like old tattered rags as the weight had torn them partly down. On a table in the hall was a great bunch of keys, with a time-yellowed label on each. They had been used several times, for on the table were several similar rents in the blanket of dust, similar to that exposed when the Professor lifted them. He turned to me and said:—

"You know this place, Jonathan. You have copied maps of it, and you know it at least more than we do. Which is the way to the chapel?" I had an idea of its direction, though on my former visit I had not been able to get admission to it; so I led the way, and after a few wrong turnings found myself opposite a low, arched oaken door, ribbed with iron bands. "This is the spot," said the Professor as he turned his lamp on a small map of the house, copied from the file of my original correspondence regarding the purchase. With a little trouble we found the key on the bunch and opened the door. We were prepared for some unpleasantness, for as we were opening the door a faint, malodorous air seemed to exhale through the gaps, but none of us ever expected such an odour as we encountered. None of the others had met the Count at all at close quarters, and when I had seen him he was either in the fasting stage of his existence in his rooms or, when he was bloated with fresh blood, in a ruined building open to the air; but here the place was small and close, and the long disuse had made the air stagnant and foul. There was an earthy smell, as of some dry miasma, which came through the fouler air. But as to the odour itself, how shall I describe it? It was not alone that it was composed of all the ills of mortality and with the pungent, acrid smell of blood, but it seemed as though corruption had become itself corrupt. Faugh! it sickens me to think of it. Every breath exhaled by that monster seemed to have clung to the place and intensified its loathsomeness.

Under ordinary circumstances such a stench would have brought our enterprise to an end; but this was no ordinary case, and the high and terrible purpose in which we were involved gave us a strength which rose above merely physical considerations. After the involuntary shrinking consequent on the first nauseous whiff, we one and all went about our work as though that loathsome place were a garden of roses.

We made an accurate examination of the place, the Professor saying as we began:—

"The first thing is to see how many of the boxes are left; we must then examine every hole and corner and cranny and see if we cannot get some clue as to what has become of the rest." A glance was sufficient to show how many remained, for the great earth chests were bulky, and there was no mistaking them.

There were only twenty-nine left out of the fifty! Once I got a fright, for, seeing Lord Godalming suddenly turn and look out of the vaulted door into the dark passage beyond, I looked too, and for an instant my heart stood still. Somewhere, looking out from the shadow, I seemed to see the high lights of the Count's evil face, the ridge of the nose, the red eyes, the red lips, the awful pallor. It was only for a moment, for, as Lord Godalming said, "I thought I saw a face, but it was only the shadows," and resumed his inquiry, I turned my lamp in the direction, and stepped into the passage. There was no sign of any one; and as there were no corners, no doors, no aperture of any kind, but only the solid walls of the passage, there could be no hiding-place even for *him*. I took it that fear had helped imagination and said nothing.

A few minutes later I saw Morris step suddenly back from a corner, which he was examining. We all followed his movements with our eyes, for undoubtedly some nervousness was growing on us, and we saw a whole mass of phosphorescence, which twinkled like stars. We all instinctively drew back. The whole place was becoming alive with rats.

For a moment or two we stood appalled, all save Lord Godalming, who was seemingly prepared for such an emergency. Rushing over to the great iron-bound oaken door, which Dr. Seward had described from the outside, and which I had seen myself, he turned the key in the lock, drew the huge bolts, and swung the door open. Then, taking his little silver whistle from his pocket, he blew a low, shrill call. It was answered from behind Dr. Seward's house by the yelping of dogs, and after about a minute three terriers came dashing round the corner of the house. Unconsciously we had all moved towards the door, and as we moved I noticed that the dust had been much disturbed: the boxes which had been taken out had been brought this way. But even in the minute that had elapsed the number of the rats had vastly increased. They seemed to swarm over the place all at once, till the lamplight, shining on their moving dark bodies and glittering, baleful eyes, made the place look like a bank of earth set with fireflies. The dogs dashed on, but at the threshold suddenly stopped and snarled, and then, simultaneously lifting their noses, began to howl in most lugubrious fashion. The rats were multiplying in thousands, and we moved out.

Lord Godalming lifted one of the dogs, and carrying him in, placed him on the floor. The instant his feet touched the ground he seemed to recover his courage, and rushed at his natural enemies. They fled before him so fast that before he had shaken the life out of a score, the other dogs, who had by now been lifted in the same manner, had but small prey ere the whole mass had vanished.

With their going it seemed as if some evil presence had departed, for the dogs frisked about and barked merrily as they made sudden darts at their prostrate foes, and turned them over and over and tossed them in the air with vicious shakes. We all seemed to find our spirits rise. Whether it was the purifying of the deadly atmosphere by the opening of the chapel door, or the relief which we experienced by finding ourselves in the open I know not; but most certainly the shadow of dread seemed to slip from us like a robe, and the occasion of our coming lost something of its grim significance, though we did not slacken a whit in our resolution. We closed the outer door and barred and locked it, and bringing the dogs with us, began our search of the house. We found nothing throughout except dust in extraordinary proportions, and all untouched save for my own footsteps when I had made my first visit. Never once did the dogs exhibit any symptom of uneasiness, and even when we returned to the chapel they frisked about as though they had been rabbit hunting in a summer wood.

The morning was quickening in the east when we emerged from the front. Dr. Van Helsing had taken the key of the hall-door from the bunch, and locked the door in orthodox fashion, putting the key into his pocket when he had done.

"So far," he said, "our night has been eminently successful. No harm has come to us such as I feared might be and yet we have ascertained how many boxes are missing. More than all do I rejoice that this, our first—and perhaps our most difficult and dangerous—step has been accomplished without the bringing thereinto our most sweet Madam Mina or troubling her waking or sleeping thoughts with sights and sounds and smells of horror which she might never forget. One lesson, too, we have learned, if it be allowable to argue *a particulari*: that the brute beasts which are to the Count's command are yet themselves not amenable to his spiritual power; for look, these rats that would come to his call, just as from his castle top he summon the wolves to your going and to that poor mother's cry, though they come to him, they run pell-mell from the so little dogs of my friend Arthur. We have other matters before us, other dangers, other fears; and that monster—he has not used his power over the brute world for the only or the last time to-night. So be it that he has gone elsewhere. Good! It has given us opportunity to cry 'check' in some ways in this chess game, which we play for the stake of human souls. And now let us go home. The dawn is close at hand, and we have reason to be content with our first night's work. It may be ordained that we have many nights and days to follow, if full of peril; but we must go on, and from no danger shall we shrink."

The house was silent when we got back, save for some poor creature who was screaming away in one of the distant wards, and a low, moaning sound from Renfield's room. The poor wretch was doubtless torturing himself, after the manner of the insane, with needless thoughts of pain.

I came tiptoe into our own room, and found Mina asleep, breathing so softly that I had to put my ear down to hear it. She looks paler than usual. I hope the meeting to-night has not upset her. I am truly thankful that she is to be left out of our future work, and even of our deliberations. It is too great a strain for a woman to bear. I did not think so at first, but I know better now. Therefore I am glad that it is settled. There may be things which would frighten her to hear; and yet to conceal them from her might be worse than to tell her if once she suspected that there was any concealment. Henceforth our work is to be a sealed book to her, till at least such time as we can tell her that all is finished, and the earth free from a monster of the nether world. I daresay it will be difficult to begin to keep silence after such confidence as ours; but I must be resolute, and to-morrow I shall keep dark over to-night's doings, and shall refuse to speak of anything that has happened. I rest on the sofa, so as not to disturb her.

1 October, later.—I suppose it was natural that we should have all overslept ourselves, for the day was a busy one, and the night had no rest at all. Even Mina must have felt its exhaustion, for though I slept till the sun was high, I was awake before her, and had to call two or three times before she awoke. Indeed, she was so sound asleep that for a few seconds she did not recognise me, but looked at me with a sort of blank terror, as one looks who has been waked out of a bad dream. She complained a little of being tired, and I let her rest till later in the day. We now know of twenty-one boxes having been removed, and if it be that several were taken in any of these removals we may be able to trace them all. Such will, of course, immensely simplify our labour, and the sooner the matter is attended to the better. I shall look up Thomas Snelling to-day.

DR. SEWARD'S DIARY.

1 October.—It was towards noon when I was awakened by the Professor walking into my room. He was more jolly and cheerful than usual, and it is quite evident that last night's work has helped to take some of the brooding weight off his mind. After going over the adventure of the night he suddenly said:—

"Your patient interests me much. May it be that with you I visit him this morning? Or if that you are too occupy, I can go alone if it may be. It is a new experience to me to find a lunatic who talk philosophy, and reason so sound." I had some work to do which pressed, so I told him that if he would go alone I would be glad, as then I should not have to keep him waiting; so I called an attendant and gave him the necessary instructions. Before the Professor left the room I cautioned him against getting any false impression from my patient. "But," he answered, "I want him to talk of himself and of his delusion as to consuming live things. He said to Madam Mina, as I see in your diary of yesterday, that he had once had such a belief. Why do you smile, friend John?"

"Excuse me," I said, "but the answer is here." I laid my hand on the typewritten matter. "When our sane and learned lunatic made that very statement of how he *used* to consume life, his mouth was actually nauseous with the flies and spiders which he had eaten just before Mrs. Harker entered the room." Van Helsing smiled in turn. "Good!" he said. "Your memory is true, friend John. I should have remembered. And yet it is this very obliquity of thought and memory which makes mental disease such a fascinating study. Perhaps I may gain more knowledge out of the folly of this madman than I shall from the teaching of the most wise. Who knows?" I went on with my work, and before long was through that in hand. It seemed that the time had been very short indeed, but there was Van Helsing back in the study. "Do I interrupt?" he asked politely as he stood at the door.

"Not at all," I answered. "Come in. My work is finished, and I am free. I can go with you now, if you like."

"It is needless; I have seen him!"

"Well?"

"I fear that he does not appraise me at much. Our interview was short. When I entered his room he was sitting on a stool in the centre, with his elbows on his knees, and his face was the picture of sullen discontent. I spoke to him as cheerfully as I could, and with such a measure of respect as I could assume. He made no reply whatever. 'Don't you know me?' I asked. His answer was not reassuring: 'I know you well enough; you are the old fool Van Helsing. I wish you would take your-self and your idiotic brain theories somewhere else. Damn all thick-headed Dutchmen!' Not a word more would he say, but sat in his implacable sullenness as indifferent to me as though I had not been in the room at all. Thus departed for this time my chance of much learning from this so clever lunatic; so I shall go, if I may, and cheer myself with a few happy words with that sweet soul Madam Mina. Friend John, it does rejoice me unspeakable that she is no more to be pained, no more to be worried with our terrible things. Though we shall much miss her help, it is better so."

"I agree with you with all my heart," I answered earnestly, for I did not want him to weaken in this matter. "Mrs. Harker is better out of it. Things are quite bad enough for us, all men of the world, and who have been in many tight places in our time; but it is no place for a woman, and if she had remained in touch with the affair, it would in time infallibly have wrecked her."

So Van Helsing has gone to confer with Mrs. Harker and Harker; Quincey and Art are all out following up the clues as to the earth-boxes. I shall finish my round of work and we shall meet to-night.

MINA HARKER'S JOURNAL.

1 October.—It is strange to me to be kept in the dark as I am to-day; after Jonathan's full confidence for so many years, to see him manifestly avoid certain matters, and those the most vital of all. This morning I slept late after the fatigue of yesterday, and though Jonathan was late too, he was the earlier. He spoke to me before he went out, never more sweetly or tenderly, but he never mentioned a word of what had hap-pened in the visit to the Count's house. And yet he must have known how terribly anxious I was. Poor dear fellow! I suppose it must have distressed him even more than it did me. They all agreed that it was best that I should not be drawn further into this awful work, and I acqui-esced. But to think that he keeps anything from me! And now I am crying like a silly fool, when I *know* it comes from my husband's great love and from the good, good wishes of those other strong men.

That has done me good. Well, some day Jonathan will tell me all; and lest it should ever be that he should think for a moment that I kept anything from him, I still keep my journal as usual. Then if he has feared of my trust I shall show it to him, with every thought of my heart put down for his dear eyes to read. I feel strangely sad and low-spirited to-day. I suppose it is the reaction from the terrible excitement.

Last night I went to bed when the men had gone, simply because they told me to. I didn't feel sleepy, and I did feel full of devouring anxiety. I kept thinking over everything that has been ever since Jonathan came to see me in London, and it all seems like a horrible tragedy, with fate pressing on relentlessly to some destined end. Everything that one does seems, no matter how right it may be, to bring on the very thing which is most to be deplored. If I hadn't gone to Whitby, perhaps poor dear Lucy would be with us now. She hadn't taken to visiting the churchyard till I came, and if she hadn't come there in the day-time with me she wouldn't have walked there in her sleep; and if she hadn't gone there at night and asleep, that monster couldn't have destroyed her as he did. Oh, why did I ever go to Whitby? There now, crying again! I wonder what has come over me to-day. I must hide it from Jonathan, for if he knew that I had been crying twice in one morning—I, who never cried on my own account, and whom he has never caused to shed a tear—the dear fellow would fret his heart out. I shall put a bold face on, and if I do feel weepy, he shall never see it. I suppose it is one of the lessons that we poor women have to learn. . . .

I can't quite remember how I fell asleep last night. I remember hearing the sudden barking of the dogs and a lot of queer sounds, like praying on a very tumultuous scale, from Mr. Renfield's room, which is somewhere under this. And then there was silence over everything, silence so profound that it startled me, and I got up and looked out of the window. All was dark and silent, the black shadows thrown by the moonlight seeming full of a silent mystery of their own. Not a thing seemed to be stirring, but all to be grim and fixed as death or fate; so that a thin streak of white mist, that crept with almost imperceptible slowness across the grass towards the house, seemed to have a sentience and a vitality of its own. I think that the digression of my thoughts must have done me good, for when I got back to bed I found a lethargy creeping over me. I lay awhile, but could not quite sleep, so I got out and looked out of the window again. The mist was spreading, and was now close up to the house, so that I could see it lying thick against the wall, as though it were stealing up to the windows. The poor man was more loud than ever, and though I could not distinguish a word he said, I could in some way recognise in his tones some passionate entreaty on his part. Then there was the sound of a struggle, and I knew that the attendants were dealing with him. I was so frightened that I crept into bed, and pulled the clothes over my head, putting my fingers in my ears. I was not then a bit sleepy, at least so I thought; but I must have fallen asleep, for, except dreams, I do not remember anything until the morning, when Jonathan woke me. I think that it took me an effort and a little time to realise where I was, and that it was Jonathan who was bending over me. My dream was very peculiar, and was almost typical of the way that waking thoughts become merged in, or continued in, dreams.

I thought that I was asleep, and waiting for Jonathan to come back. I was very anxious about him, and I was powerless to act; my feet and my mind and my brain were weighted, so that nothing could proceed at the usual pace. And so I slept uneasily and thought. Then it began to dawn upon me that the air was heavy, and dank, and cold. I put back the clothes from my face, and found, to my surprise, that all was dim around. The gaslight which I had left lit for Jonathan, but turned down, came only like a tiny red spark through the fog, which had evidently grown thicker and poured into the room. Then it occurred to me that I had shut the window before I had come to bed. I would have got out to make certain on the point, but some leaden lethargy seemed to chain my limbs and even my will. I lay still and endured; that was all. I closed my eyes, but could still see through my eyelids. (It is wonderful what tricks our dreams play us, and how conveniently we can imagine.) The mist grew thicker and I could see now how it came in, for I could see it like smoke—or with the white energy of boiling water—pouring in, not through the window, but through the joinings of the door. It got thicker and thicker, till it seemed as if it became concentrated into a sort of pillar of cloud in the room, through the top of which I could see the light of the gas shining like a red eye. Things began to whirl through my brain just as the cloudy column was now whirling in the room, and through it all came the scriptural words "a pillar of cloud by day and of fire by night." Was it indeed some such spiritual guidance that was coming to me in my sleep? But the pillar was composed of both the day- and the night-guiding, for the fire was in the red eye, which at the thought got a new fascination for me; till, as I looked, the fire divided, and seemed to shine on me through the fog like two red eyes, such as Lucy told me of in her momentary mental wandering when, on the cliff, the dying sunlight struck the windows of St. Mary's Church. Suddenly the horror burst upon me that it was thus that Jonathan had seen those awful women growing into reality through the whirling mist in the moonlight, and in my dream I must have fainted, for all became black darkness. The last conscious effort which imagination made was to show me a livid white face bending over me out of the mist. I must be careful of such dreams, for they would unseat one's reason if there were too much of them. I would get Dr. Van Helsing or Dr. Seward to prescribe something for me which would make me sleep, only that I fear to alarm them. Such a dream at the present time would become woven into their fears for me. To-night I shall strive hard to sleep naturally. If I do not, I shall to-morrow night get them to give me a dose of chloral; that cannot hurt me for once, and it will give me a good night's sleep. Last night tired me more than if I had not slept at all.

2 October, 10 p.m.—Last night I slept, but did not dream. I must have slept soundly, for I was not waked by Jonathan coming to bed; but the sleep has not refreshed me, for to-day I feel terribly weak and spiritless. I spent all yesterday trying to read, or lying down dozing. In the afternoon Mr. Renfield asked if he might see me. Poor man, he was very gentle, and when I came away he kissed my hand and bade God bless me. Some way it affected me much; I am crying when I think of him. This is a new weakness, of which I must be careful. Jonathan would be miserable if he knew I had been crying. He and the others were out till dinner-time, and they all came in tired. I did what I could to brighten them up, and I suppose that the effort did me good, for I forgot how tired I was. After dinner they sent me to bed, and all went off to smoke together, as they said, but I knew that they wanted to tell each other of what had occurred to each during the day; I could see from Jonathan's manner that he had something important to communicate. I was not so sleepy as I should have been; so before they went I asked Dr. Seward to give me a little opiate of some kind, as I had not slept well the night before. He very kindly made me up a sleeping draught, which he gave to me, telling me that it would do me no harm, as it was very mild. . . . I have taken it, and am waiting for sleep, which still keeps aloof. I hope I have not done wrong, for as sleep begins to flirt with me, a new fear comes: that I may have been foolish in thus depriving myself of the power of waking. I might want it. Here comes sleep. Good-night.

CHAPTER 20.

———◇———

JONATHAN HARKER'S JOURNAL.

1 October, evening.—I found Thomas Snelling in his house at Bethnal Green, but unhappily he was not in a condition to remember anything. The very prospect of beer which my expected coming had opened to him had proved too much, and he had begun too early on his expected debauch. I learned, however, from his wife, who seemed a decent, poor soul, that he was only the assistant to Smollet, who of the two mates was the responsible person. So off I drove to Walworth, and found Mr. Jack Smollet at home and in his shirtsleeves, taking a late tea out of a saucer. He is a decent, intelligent fellow, distinctly a good, reliable type of workman, and with a headpiece of his own. He remembered all about the incident of the boxes, and from a wonderful dog's-eared notebook, which he produced from some mysterious receptacle about the seat of his trousers, and which had hieroglyphical entries in thick, half-obliterated pencil, he gave me the destinations of the boxes. There were, he said, six in the cartload which he took from Carfax and left at 197, Chicksand Street, Mile End, New Town, and another six which he deposited at Jamaica Lane, Bermondsey. If then the Count meant to scatter these ghastly refuges of his over London, these places were chosen as the first of delivery, so that later he might distribute more fully. The systematic manner in which this was done made me think that he could not mean to confine himself to two sides of London. He was now fixed on the far east of the northern shore, on the east of the southern shore, and on the south. The north and west were surely never meant to be left out of his diabolical scheme—let alone the City itself and the very heart of fashionable London in the south-west and west. I went back to Smollet, and asked him if he could tell us if any other boxes had been taken from Carfax.

He replied:—

"Well, guv'nor, you've treated me very 'an'some"—I had given him half a sovereign—"an' I'll tell yer all I know. I heard a man by the name of Bloxam say four nights ago in the 'Are an' 'Ounds, in Pincher's Alley, as 'ow he an' his mate 'ad 'ad a rare dusty job in a old 'ouse at Purfleet. There ain't a-many such jobs as this 'ere, an' I'm thinkin' that maybe Sam Bloxam could tell ye summut." I asked if he could tell me where to find him. I told him that if he could get me the address it would be worth another half-sovereign to him. So he gulped down the rest of his tea and stood up, saying that he was going to begin the search then and there. At the door he stopped, and said:—

"Look 'ere, guv'nor, there ain't no sense in me a keepin' you 'ere. I may find Sam soon, or I mayn't; but anyhow he ain't like to be in a way to tell ye much to-night. Sam is a rare one when he starts on the booze. If you can give me a envelope with a stamp on it, and put yer address on it, I'll find out where Sam is to be found and post it ye to-night. But ye'd better be up arter 'im soon in the mornin', or maybe ye won't ketch 'im; for Sam gets off main early, never mind the booze the night afore."

This was all practical, so one of the children went off with a penny to buy an envelope and a sheet of paper, and to keep the change. When she came back, I addressed the envelope and stamped it, and when Smollet had again faithfully promised to post the address when found, I took my way to home. We're on the track anyhow. I am tired to-night, and want sleep. Mina is fast asleep, and looks a little too pale; her eyes look as though she had been crying. Poor dear, I've no doubt it frets her to be kept in the dark, and it may make her doubly anxious about me and the others. But it is best as it is. It is better to be disappointed and worried in such a way now than to have her nerve broken. The doctors were quite right to insist on her being kept out of this dreadful business. I must be firm, for on me this particular burden of silence must rest. I shall not ever enter on the subject with her under any circumstances. Indeed, it may not be a hard task, after all, for she herself has become reticent on the subject, and has not spoken of the Count or his doings ever since we told her of our decision.

2 October, evening.—A long and trying and exciting day. By the first post I got my directed envelope with a dirty scrap of paper enclosed, on which was written with a carpenter's pencil in a sprawling hand:—

"Sam Bloxam, Korkrans, 4, Poters Cort, Bartel Street, Walworth. Arsk for the depite."

I got the letter in bed, and rose without waking Mina. She looked heavy and sleepy and pale, and far from well. I determined not to wake her, but that, when I should return from this new search, I would arrange for her going back to Exeter. I think she would be happier in our own home, with her daily tasks to interest her, than in being here amongst us and in ignorance. I only saw Dr. Seward for a moment, and told him where I was off to, promising to come back and tell the rest so soon as I should have found out anything. I drove to Walworth and found, with some difficulty, Potter's Court. Mr. Smollet's spelling misled me, as I asked for Poter's Court instead of Potter's Court. However, when I had found the court, I had no difficulty in discovering Corcoran's lodging-house. When I asked the man who came to the door for the "depite," he shook his head, and said: "I dunno 'im. There ain't no such a person 'ere; I never 'eard of 'im in all my bloomin' days. Don't believe there ain't nobody of that kind livin' 'ere or anywheres." I took out Smollet's letter, and as I read it it seemed to me that the lesson of the spelling of the name of the court might guide me. "What are you?" I asked.

"I'm the depity," he answered. I saw at once that I was on the right

dust, and the shutters were up. All the framework was black with time, and from the iron the paint had mostly scaled away. It was evident that up to lately there had been a large notice-board in front of the balcony; it had, however, been roughly torn away, the uprights which had supported it still remaining. Behind the rails of the balcony I saw there were some loose boards, whose raw edges looked white. I would have given a good deal to have been able to see the notice-board intact, as it would, perhaps, have given some clue to the ownership of the house. I remembered my experience of the investigation and purchase of Carfax, and I could not but feel that if I could find the former owner there might be some means discovered of gaining access to the house.

There was at present nothing to be learned from the Piccadilly side, and nothing could be done; so I went round to the back to see if anything could be gathered from this quarter. The mews were active, the Piccadilly houses being mostly in occupation. I asked one or two of the grooms and helpers whom I saw around if they could tell me anything about the empty house. One of them said that he heard it had lately been taken, but he couldn't say from whom. He told me however, that up to very lately there had been a notice-board of "For Sale" up, and that perhaps Mitchell, Sons & Candy, the house agents, could tell me something, as he thought he remembered seeing the name of that firm on the board. I did not wish to seem too eager, or to let my informant know or guess too much, so, thanking him in the usual manner, I strolled away. It was now growing dusk, and the autumn night was closing in, so I did not lose any time. Having learned the address of Mitchell, Sons & Candy from a directory at the Berkeley, I was soon at their office in Sackville Street.

The gentleman who saw me was particularly suave in manner, but uncommunicative in equal proportion. Having once told me that the Piccadilly house—which throughout our interview he called a "mansion"—was sold, he considered my business as concluded. When I asked who had purchased it, he opened his eyes a thought wider, and paused a few seconds before replying:—

"It is sold, sir."

"Pardon me," I said, with equal politeness, "but I have a special reason for wishing to know who purchased it."

Again he paused longer, and raised his eyebrows still more. "It is sold, sir," was again his laconic reply.

"Surely," I said, "you do not mind letting me know so much."

"But I do mind," he answered. "The affairs of their clients are absolutely safe in the hands of Mitchell, Sons & Candy." This was manifestly a prig of the first water, and there was no use arguing with him. I thought I had best meet him on his own ground, so I said:—

"Your clients, sir, are happy in having so resolute a guardian of their confidence. I am myself a professional man." Here I handed him my card. "In this instance I am not prompted by curiosity; I act on the part of Lord Godalming, who wishes to know something of the property which was, he understood, lately for sale." These words put a different complexion on affairs. He said:—

"I would like to oblige you if I could, Mr. Harker, and especially would I like to oblige his lordship. We once carried out a small matter of renting some chambers for him when he was the Honourable Arthur Holmwood. If you will let me have his lordship's address I will consult the House on the subject, and will, in any case, communicate with his lordship by to-night's post. It will be a pleasure if we can so far deviate from our rules as to give the required information to his lordship."

I wanted to secure a friend, and not to make an enemy, so I thanked him, gave the address at Dr. Seward's and came away. It was now dark, and I was tired and hungry. I got a cup of tea at the Aërated Bread Company and came down to Purfleet by the next train.

I found all the others at home. Mina was looking tired and pale, but she made a gallant effort to be bright and cheerful. It wrung my heart to think that I had had to keep anything from her and so caused her inquietude. Thank God, this will be the last night of her looking on at our conferences, and feeling the sting of our not showing our confidence. It took all my courage to hold to the wise resolution of keeping her out of our grim task. She seemed somehow more reconciled; or else the very subject seems to have become repugnant to her, for when any accidental allusion is made she actually shudders. I am glad we made our resolution in time, as with such a feeling as this, our growing knowledge would be torture to her.

I could not tell the others of the day's discovery till we were alone; so after dinner—followed by a little music to save appearances even amongst ourselves—I took Mina to her room and left her to go to bed. The dear girl was more affectionate with me than ever, and clung to me as though she would detain me; but there was much to be talked of and I came away. Thank God, the ceasing of telling things has made no difference between us.

When I came down again I found the others all gathered round the fire in the study. In the train I had written my diary so far, and simply read it off to them as the best means of letting them get abreast of my own information; when I had finished Van Helsing said:—

"This has been a great day's work, friend Jonathan. Doubtless we are on the track of the missing boxes. If we find them all in that house, then our work is near the end. But if there be some missing, we must search until we find them. Then shall we make our final *coup*, and hunt the wretch to his real death." We all sat silent awhile and all at once Mr. Morris spoke:—

"Say! how are we going to get into that house?"

"We got into the other," answered Lord Godalming quickly.

"But, Art, this is different. We broke house at Carfax, but we had night and a walled park to protect us. It will be a mighty different thing to commit burglary in Piccadilly, either by day or night. I confess I don't see how we are going to get in unless that agency duck can find us a key of some sort; perhaps we shall know when you get his letter in the morning." Lord Godalming's brows contracted, and he stood up and walked about the room. By-and-by he stopped and said, turning from one to another of us:—

"Quincey's head is level. This burglary business is getting serious; we got off once all right; but we have now a rare job on hand—unless we can find the Count's key basket."

As nothing could well be done before morning, and as it would be at least advisable to wait till Lord Godalming should hear from Mitchell's, we decided not to take any active step before breakfast time. For a good while we sat and smoked, discussing the matter in its various lights and bearings; I took the opportunity of bringing this diary right up to the moment. I am very sleepy and shall go to bed. . . .

Just a line. Mina sleeps soundly and her breathing is regular. Her forehead is puckered up into little wrinkles, as though she thinks even in her sleep. She is still too pale, but does not look so haggard as she did this morning. To-morrow will, I hope, mend all this; she will be herself at home in Exeter. Oh, but I am sleepy!

DR. SEWARD'S DIARY.

1 October.—I am puzzled afresh about Renfield. His moods change so rapidly that I find it difficult to keep touch of them, and as they always mean something more than his own well-being, they form a more than interesting study. This morning, when I went to see him after his repulse of Van Helsing, his manner was that of a man commanding destiny. He was, in fact, commanding destiny—subjectively. He did not really care for any of the things of mere earth; he was in the clouds and looked down on all the weaknesses and wants of us poor mortals. I thought I would improve the occasion and learn something, so I asked him:—

"What about the flies these times?" He smiled on me in quite a superior sort of way—such a smile as would have become the face of Malvolio—as he answered me:—

"The fly, my dear sir, has one striking feature; its wings are typical of the aërial powers of the psychic faculties. The ancients did well when they typified the soul as a butterfly!"

I thought I would push his analogy to its utmost logically, so I said quickly:—

"Oh, it is a soul you are after now, is it?" His madness foiled his reason, and a puzzled look spread over his face as, shaking his head with a decision which I had but seldom seen in him, he said:—

"Oh, no, oh no! I want no souls. Life is all I want." Here he brightened up; "I am pretty indifferent about it at present. Life is all right; I have all I want. You must get a new patient, Doctor, if you wish to study zoöphagy!"

This puzzled me a little, so I drew him on:—

"Then you command life; you are a god, I suppose?" He smiled with an ineffably benign superiority.

"Oh no! Far be it from me to arrogate to myself the attributes of the Deity. I am not even concerned in His especially spiritual doings. If I may state my intellectual position I am, so far as concerns things purely terrestrial, somewhat in the position which Enoch occupied spiritually!" This was a poser to me. I could not at the moment recall Enoch's appositeness; so I had to ask a simple question, though I felt that by so doing I was lowering myself in the eyes of the lunatic:—

"And why with Enoch?"

"Because he walked with God." I could not see the analogy, but did not like to admit it; so I harked back to what he had denied:—

"So you don't care about life and you don't want souls. Why not?" I put my question quickly and somewhat sternly, on purpose to disconcert him. The effort succeeded; for an instant he unconsciously relapsed into his old servile manner, bent low before me, and actually fawned upon me as he replied:—

"I don't want any souls, indeed, indeed! I don't. I couldn't use them if I had them; they would be no manner of use to me. I couldn't eat them or——" He suddenly stopped and the old cunning look spread over his face, like a wind-sweep on the surface of the water. "And Doctor, as to life, what is it after all? When you've got all you require, and you know that you will never want, that is all. I have friends—good friends—like you, Dr. Seward"; this was said with a leer of inexpressible cunning. "I know that I shall never lack the means of life!"

I think that through the cloudiness of his insanity he saw some antagonism in me, for he at once fell back on the last refuge of such as he—a dogged silence. After a short time I saw that for the present it was useless to speak to him. He was sulky, and so I came away.

Later in the day he sent for me. Ordinarily I would not have come without special reason, but just at present I am so interested in him that I would gladly make an effort. Besides, I am glad to have anything to help to pass the time. Harker is out, following up clues; and so are Lord Godalming and Quincey. Van Helsing sits in my study poring over the record prepared by the Harkers; he seems to think that by accurate knowledge of all details he will light upon some clue. He does not wish to be disturbed in the work, without cause. I would have taken him with me to see the patient, only I thought that after his last repulse he might not care to go again. There was also another reason: Renfield might not speak so freely before a third person as when he and I were alone.

I found him sitting out in the middle of the floor on his stool, a pose which is generally indicative of some mental energy on his part. When I came in, he said at once, as though the question had been waiting on his lips:—

"What about souls?" It was evident then that my surmise had been correct. Unconscious cerebration was doing its work, even with the lunatic. I determined to have the matter out. "What about them yourself?" I asked. He did not reply for a moment but looked all round him, and up and down, as though he expected to find some inspiration for an answer.

"I don't want any souls!" he said in a feeble, apologetic way. The matter seemed preying on his mind, and so I determined to use it—to "be cruel only to be kind." So I said:—

"You like life, and you want life?"

"Oh yes! but that is all right; you needn't worry about that!"

"But," I asked, "how are we to get the life without getting the soul also?" This seemed to puzzle him, so I followed it up:—

"A nice time you'll have some time when you're flying out there, with the souls of thousands of flies and spiders and birds and cats buzzing and twittering and miauing all round you. You've got their lives, you know, and you must put up with their souls!" Something seemed to affect his imagination, for he put his fingers to his ears and shut his eyes, screwing them up tightly just as a small boy does when his face is being soaped. There was something pathetic in it that touched me; it also gave me a lesson, for it seemed that before me was a child—only a child, though the features were worn, and the stubble on the jaws was white. It was evident that he was undergoing some process of mental disturbance, and, knowing how his past moods had interpreted things seemingly foreign to himself, I thought I would enter into his mind as well as I could and go with him. The first step was to restore confidence, so I asked him, speaking pretty loud so that he would hear me through his closed ears:—

"Would you like some sugar to get your flies round again?" He seemed to wake up all at once, and shook his head. With a laugh he replied:—

"Not much! flies are poor things, after all!" After a pause he added, "But I don't want their souls buzzing round me, all the same."

"Or spiders?" I went on.

"Blow spiders! What's the use of spiders? There isn't anything in them to eat or—" He stopped suddenly, as though reminded of a forbidden topic.

"So, so!" I thought to myself, "this is the second time he has suddenly stopped at the word 'drink'; what does it mean?" Renfield seemed himself aware of having made a lapse, for he hurried on, as though to distract my attention from it:—

"I don't take any stock at all in such matters. 'Rats and mice and such small deer,' as Shakespeare has it, 'chicken-feed of the larder' they might be called. I'm past all that sort of nonsense. You might as well ask a man to eat molecules with a pair of chopsticks, as to try to interest me about the lesser carnivora, when I know of what is before me."

"I see," I said. "You want big things that you can make your teeth meet in? How would you like to breakfast on elephant?"

"What ridiculous nonsense you are talking!" He was getting too wide awake, so I thought I would press him hard. "I wonder," I said reflectively, "what an elephant's soul is like!"

The effect I desired was obtained, for he at once fell from his high-horse and became a child again.

"I don't want an elephant's soul, or any soul at all!" he said. For a few moments he sat despondently. Suddenly he jumped to his feet, with his eyes blazing and all the signs of intense cerebral excitement. "To hell with you and your souls!" he shouted. "Why do you plague me about souls! Haven't I got enough to worry, and pain, and distract me already, without thinking of souls!" He looked so hostile that I thought he was in for another homicidal fit, so I blew my whistle. The instant, however, that I did so he became calm, and said apologetically:—

"Forgive me, Doctor; I forgot myself. You do not need any help. I am so worried in my mind that I am apt to be irritable. If you only knew the problem I have to face, and that I am working out, you would pity, and tolerate, and pardon me. Pray do not put me in a strait-waistcoat. I want to think and I cannot think freely when my body is confined. I am sure you will understand!" He had evidently self-control; so when the attendants came I told them not to mind, and they withdrew. Renfield watched them go; when the door was closed he said, with considerable dignity and sweetness:—

"Dr. Seward, you have been very considerate towards me. Believe me that I am very, very grateful to you!" I thought it well to leave him in this mood, and so I came away. There is certainly something to ponder over in this man's state. Several points seem to make what the American interviewer calls "a story," if one could only get them in proper order. Here they are:—

Will not mention "drinking."

Fears the thought of being burdened with the "soul" of anything.

Has no dread of wanting "life" in the future.

Despises the meaner forms of life altogether, though he dreads being haunted by their souls.

Logically all these things point one way! he has assurance of some kind that he will acquire some higher life. He dreads the consequence— the burden of a soul. Then it is a human life he looks to!

And the assurance—?

Merciful God! the Count has been to him, and there is some new scheme of terror afoot!

Later.—I went after my round to Van Helsing and told him my suspicion. He grew very grave; and, after thinking the matter over for a while asked me to take him to Renfield. I did so. As we came to the door we heard the lunatic within singing gaily, as he used to do in the time which now seems so long ago. When we entered we saw with amazement that he had spread out his sugar as of old; the flies, lethargic with the autumn, were beginning to buzz into the room. We tried to make him talk of the subject of our previous conversation, but he would not attend. He went on with his singing, just as though we had not been present. He had got a scrap of paper and was folding it into a notebook. We had to come away as ignorant as we went in.

His is a curious case indeed; we must watch him tonight.

LETTER FROM MITCHELL, SONS & CANDY TO LORD GODALMING.

"*1 October.*

"My Lord,

"We are at all times only too happy to meet your wishes. We beg, with regard to the desire of your Lordship, expressed by Mr. Harker on your behalf, to supply the following information concerning the sale and purchase of No. 347, Piccadilly. The original vendors are the executors of the late Mr. Archibald Winter-Suffield. The purchaser is a foreign nobleman, Count de Ville, who effected the purchase himself paying the purchase money in notes 'over the counter,' if your Lordship will pardon us using so vulgar an expression. Beyond this we know nothing whatever of him.

"We are, my Lord,

"Your Lordship's humble servants,

"MITCHELL, SONS & CANDY."

DR. SEWARD'S DIARY.

2 October.—I placed a man in the corridor last night, and told him to make an accurate note of any sound he might hear from Renfield's room, and gave him instructions that if there should be anything strange he was to call me. After dinner, when we had all gathered round the fire in the study—Mrs. Harker having gone to bed—we discussed the attempts and discoveries of the day. Harker was the only one who had any result, and we are in great hopes that his clue may be an important one.

Before going to bed I went round to the patient's room and looked in through the observation trap. He was sleeping soundly, and his heart rose and fell with regular respiration.

This morning the man on duty reported to me that a little after midnight he was restless and kept saying his prayers somewhat loudly. I asked him if that was all; he replied that it was all he heard. There was something about his manner so suspicious that I asked him point-blank if he had been asleep. He denied sleep, but admitted to having "dozed" for a while. It is too bad that men cannot be trusted unless they are watched.

To-day Harker is out following up his clue, and Art and Quincey are looking after horses. Godalming thinks that it will be well to have horses always in readiness, for when we get the information which we seek there will be no time to lose. We must sterilise all the imported earth between sunrise and sunset; we shall thus catch the Count at his weakest, and without a refuge to fly to. Van Helsing is off to the British Museum looking up some authorities on ancient medicine. The old physicians took account of things which their followers do not accept, and the Professor is searching for witch and demon cures which may be useful to us later.

I sometimes think we must be all mad and that we shall wake to sanity in strait-waistcoats.

Later.—We have met again. We seem at last to be on the track, and our work of to-morrow may be the beginning of the end. I wonder if Renfield's quiet has anything to do with this. His moods have so followed the doings of the Count, that the coming destruction of the monster may be carried to him in some subtle way. If we could only get some hint as to what passed in his mind, between the time of my argument with him to-day and his resumption of fly-catching, it might afford us a valuable clue. He is now seeming quiet for a spell. . . . Is he?—— That wild yell seemed to come from his room. . . .

The attendant came bursting into my room and told me that Renfield had somehow met with some accident. He had heard him yell; and when he went to him found him lying on his face on the floor, all covered with blood. I must go at once. . . .

CHAPTER 21.

DR. SEWARD'S DIARY.

3 October.—Let me put down with exactness all that happened, as well as I can remember it, since last I made an entry. Not a detail that I can recall must be forgotten; in all calmness I must proceed.

When I came to Renfield's room I found him lying on the floor on his left side in a glittering pool of blood. When I went to move him, it became at once apparent that he had received some terrible injuries; there seemed none of that unity of purpose between the parts of the body which marks even lethargic sanity. As the face was exposed I could see that it was horribly bruised, as though it had been beaten against the floor—indeed it was from the face wounds that the pool of blood originated. The attendant who was kneeling beside the body said to me as we turned him over:—

"I think, sir, his back is broken. See, both his right arm and leg and the whole side of his face are paralysed." How such a thing could have happened puzzled the attendant beyond measure. He seemed quite bewildered, and his brows were gathered in as he said:—

"I can't understand the two things. He could mark his face like that by beating his own head on the floor. I saw a young woman do it once at the Eversfield Asylum before anyone could lay hands on her. And I suppose he might have broke his neck by falling out of bed, if he got in an awkward kink. But for the life of me I can't imagine how the two things occurred. If his back was broke, he couldn't beat his head; and if his face was like that before the fall out of bed, there would be marks of it." I said to him:—

"Go to Dr. Van Helsing, and ask him to kindly come here at once. I want him without an instant's delay." The man ran off, and within a few minutes the Professor, in his dressing-gown and slippers, appeared. When he saw Renfield on the ground, he looked keenly at him a moment, and then turned to me. I think he recognised my thought in my eyes, for he said very quietly, manifestly for the ears of the attendant:—

"Ah, a sad accident! He will need very careful watching, and much attention. I shall stay with you myself; but I shall first dress myself. If you will remain I shall in a few minutes join you."

The patient was now breathing stertorously and it was easy to see that he had suffered some terrible injury. Van Helsing returned with extraordinary celerity, bearing with him a surgical case. He had evidently been thinking and had his mind made up; for, almost before he looked at the patient, he whispered to me:—

"Send the attendant away. We must be alone with him when he becomes conscious, after the operation." So I said:—

"I think that will do now, Simmons. We have done all that we can at present. You had better go your round, and Dr. Van Helsing will operate. Let me know instantly if there be anything unusual anywhere."

The man withdrew, and we went into a strict examination of the patient. The wounds of the face were superficial; the real injury was a depressed fracture of the skull, extending right up through the motor area. The Professor thought a moment and said:—

"We must reduce the pressure and get back to normal conditions, as far as can be; the rapidity of the suffusion shows the terrible nature of his injury. The whole motor area seems affected. The suffusion of the brain will increase quickly, so we must trephine at once or it may be too late." As he was speaking there was a soft tapping at the door. I went over and opened it and found in the corridor without, Arthur and Quincey in pajamas and slippers: the former spoke:—

"I heard your man call up Dr. Van Helsing and tell him of an accident. So I woke Quincey or rather called for him as he was not asleep. Things are moving too quickly and too strangely for sound sleep for any of us these times. I've been thinking that to-morrow night will not see things as they have been. We'll have to look back—and forward a little more than we have done. May we come in?" I nodded, and held the door open till they had entered; then I closed it again. When Quincey saw the attitude and state of the patient, and noted the horrible pool on the floor, he said softly:—

"My God! what has happened to him? Poor, poor devil!" I told him briefly, and added that we expected he would recover consciousness after the operation—for a short time, at all events. He went at once and sat down on the edge of the bed, with Godalming beside him; we all watched in patience.

"We shall wait," said Van Helsing, "just long enough to fix the best spot for trephining, so that we may most quickly and perfectly remove the blood clot; for it is evident that the haemorrhage is increasing."

The minutes during which we waited passed with fearful slowness. I had a horrible sinking in my heart, and from Van Helsing's face I gathered that he felt some fear or apprehension as to what was to come. I dreaded the words that Renfield might speak. I was positively afraid to think; but the conviction of what was coming was on me, as I have read of men who have heard the deathwatch. The poor man's breathing came in uncertain gasps. Each instant he seemed as though he would open his eyes and speak; but then would follow a prolonged stertorous breath, and he would relapse into a more fixed insensibility. Inured as I was to sick beds and death, this suspense grew, and grew upon me. I could almost hear the beating of my own heart; and the blood surging through my temples sounded like blows from a hammer. The silence finally became agonising. I looked at my companions, one after another, and saw from

their flushed faces and damp brows that they were enduring equal torture. There was a nervous suspense over us all, as though overhead some
dread bell would peal out powerfully when we should least expect it.

At last there came a time when it was evident that the patient was
sinking fast; he might die at any moment. I looked up at the Professor
and caught his eyes fixed on mine. His face was sternly set as he
spoke:—

"There is no time to lose. His words may be worth many lives; I have
been thinking so, as I stood here. It may be there is a soul at stake! We
shall operate just above the ear."

Without another word he made the operation. For a few moments
the breathing continued to be stertorous. Then there came a breath so
prolonged that it seemed as though it would tear open his chest. Suddenly his eyes opened, and became fixed in a wild, helpless stare. This
was continued for a few moments; then it softened into a glad surprise,
and from the lips came a sigh of relief. He moved convulsively, and as he
did so, said:—

"I'll be quiet, Doctor. Tell them to take off the strait-waistcoat. I have
had a terrible dream, and it has left me so weak that I cannot move.
What's wrong with my face? it feels all swollen, and it smarts dreadfully." He tried to turn his head; but even with the effort his eyes seemed
to grow glassy again so I gently put it back. Then Van Helsing said in a
quiet grave tone:—

"Tell us your dream, Mr. Renfield." As he heard the voice his face
brightened, through its mutilation, and he said:—

"That is Dr. Van Helsing. How good it is of you to be here. Give me
some water, my lips are dry; and I shall try to tell you. I dreamed"—he
stopped and seemed fainting. I called quietly to Quincey—"The
brandy—it is in my study—quick!" He flew and returned with a glass,
the decanter of brandy and a carafe of water. We moistened the parched
lips, and the patient quickly revived. It seemed, however, that his poor
injured brain had been working in the interval, for, when he was quite
conscious, he looked at me piercingly with an agonised confusion which
I shall never forget, and said:—

"I must not deceive myself; it was no dream, but all a grim reality." Then his eyes roved round the room: as they caught sight of the two figures sitting patiently on the edge of the bed he went on:—

"If I were not sure already, I would know from them." For an instant his eyes closed—not with pain or sleep but voluntarily, as though he were bringing all his faculties to bear; when he opened them he said, hurriedly, and with more energy than he had yet displayed:—

"Quick, Doctor, quick. I am dying! I feel that I have but a few minutes; and then I must go back to death—or worse! Wet my lips with brandy again. I have something that I must say before I die; or before my poor crushed brain dies anyhow. Thank you! It was that night after you left me, when I implored you to let me go away. I couldn't speak then, for I felt my tongue was tied; but I was as sane then, except in that way, as I am now. I was in an agony of despair for a long time after you left me; it seemed hours. Then there came a sudden peace to me. My brain seemed to become cool again, and I realised where I was. I heard the dogs bark behind our house, but not where he was!" As he spoke, Van Helsing's eyes never blinked, but his hand came out and met mine and gripped it hard. He did not, however, betray himself; he nodded slightly and said: "Go on," in a low voice. Renfield proceeded:—

"He came up to the window in the mist, as I had seen him often before; but he was solid then—not a ghost, and his eyes were fierce like a man's when angry. He was laughing with his red mouth; the sharp white teeth glinted in the moonlight when he turned to look back over the belt of trees, to where the dogs were barking. I wouldn't ask him to come in at first, though I knew he wanted to—just as he had wanted all along. Then he began promising me things—not in words but by doing them." He was interrupted by a word from the Professor:—

"How?"

"By making them happen; just as he used to send in the flies when the sun was shining. Great big fat ones with steel and sapphire on their wings; and big moths, in the night, with skull and cross-bones on their backs." Van Helsing nodded to him as he whispered to me unconsciously:—

"The *Acherontia Aitetropos of the Sphinges*—what you call the 'Death's-head Moth'?" The patient went on without stopping.

"Then he began to whisper: 'Rats, rats, rats! Hundreds, thousands, millions of them, and every one a life; and dogs to eat them, and cats too. All lives! all red blood, with years of life in it; and not merely buzzing flies!' I laughed at him, for I wanted to see what he could do. Then the dogs howled, away beyond the dark trees in his house. He beckoned me to the window. I got up and looked out, and he raised his hands, and seemed to call out without using any words. A dark mass spread over the grass, coming on like the shape of a flame of fire; and then he moved the mist to the right and left, and I could see that there were thousands of rats with their eyes blazing red—like his, only smaller. He held up his hand, and they all stopped; and I thought he seemed to be saying: 'All these lives will I give you, ay, and many more and greater, through countless ages, if you will fall down and worship me!' And then a red cloud, like the colour of blood, seemed to close over my eyes; and before I knew what I was doing, I found myself opening the sash and saying to him: 'Come in, Lord and Master!' The rats were all gone, but he slid into the room through the sash, though it was only open an inch wide— just as the Moon herself has often come in through the tiniest crack and has stood before me in all her size and splendour."

His voice was weaker, so I moistened his lips with the brandy again, and he continued; but it seemed as though his memory had gone on working in the interval for his story was further advanced. I was about to call him back to the point, but Van Helsing whispered to me: "Let him go on. Do not interrupt him; he cannot go back, and maybe could not proceed at all if once he lost the thread of his thought." He proceeded:—

"All day I waited to hear from him, but he did not send me anything, not even a blow-fly, and when the moon got up I was pretty angry with him. When he slid in through the window, though it was shut, and did not even knock, I got mad with him. He sneered at me, and his white face looked out of the mist with his red eyes gleaming, and he went on as though he owned the whole place, and I was no one. He didn't even smell the same as he went by me. I couldn't hold him. I thought that, somehow, Mrs. Harker had come into the room."

The two men sitting on the bed stood up and came over, standing behind him so that he could not see them, but where they could hear better. They were both silent, but the Professor started and quivered; his face, however, grew grimmer and sterner still. Renfield went on without noticing:—

"When Mrs. Harker came in to see me this afternoon she wasn't the same: It was like tea after the teapot had been watered." Here we all moved, but no one said a word; he went on:—

"I didn't know that she was here till she spoke; and she didn't look the same. I don't care for the pale people; I like them with lots of blood in them, and hers had all seemed to have run out. I didn't think of it at the time; but when she went away I began to think, and it made me mad to know that he had been taking the life out of her." I could feel that the rest quivered, as I did, but we remained otherwise still. "So when he came to-night I was ready for him. I saw the mist stealing in, and I grabbed it tight. I had heard that madmen have unnatural strength; and as I knew I was a madman—at times anyhow—I resolved to use my power. Ay, and he felt it too, for he had come out of the mist to struggle with me. I held tight; and I thought I was going to win, for I didn't mean him to take any more of her life, till I saw his eyes. They burned into me, and my strength became like water. He slipped through it, and when I tried to cling to him, he raised me up and flung me down. There was a red cloud before me, and a noise like thunder, and the mist seemed to steal away under the door." His voice was becoming fainter and his breath more stertorous. Van Helsing stood up instinctively.

"We know the worst now," he said. "He is here, and we know his purpose. It may not be too late. Let us be armed—the same as we were the other night, but lose no time; there is not an instant to spare." There was no need to put our fear, nay our conviction, into words—we shared them in common. We all hurried and took from our rooms the same things that we had when we entered the Count's house. The Professor had his ready, and as we met in the corridor he pointed to them significantly as he said:—

"They never leave me; and they shall not till this unhappy business is over. Be wise also, my friends. It is no common enemy that we deal with. Alas! alas; that that dear Madam Mina should suffer!" He stopped; his voice was breaking, and I do not know if rage or terror predominated in my own heart.

Outside the Harkers' door we paused. Art and Quincey held back, and the latter said:—

"Should we disturb her?"

"We must," said Van Helsing grimly. "If the door be locked, I shall break it in."

"May it not frighten her terribly? It is unusual to break into a lady's room!"

Van Helsing said solemnly, "You are always right; but this is life and death. All chambers are alike to the doctor; and even were they not they are all as one to me to-night. Friend John, when I turn the handle, if the door does not open, do you put your shoulder down and shove; and you too, my friends. Now!"

He turned the handle as he spoke, but the door did not yield. We threw ourselves against it; with a crash it burst open, and we almost fell headlong into the room. The Professor did actually fall, and I saw across him as he gathered himself up from hands and knees. What I saw appalled me. I felt my hair rise like bristles on the back of my neck, and my heart seemed to stand still.

The moonlight was so bright that through the thick yellow blind the room was light enough to see. On the bed beside the window lay Jonathan Harker, his face flushed and breathing heavily as though in a stupor. Kneeling on the near edge of the bed facing outwards was the white-clad figure of his wife. By her side stood a tall, thin man, clad in black. His face was turned from us, but the instant we saw we all recognised the Count—in every way, even to the scar on his forehead. With his left hand he held both Mrs. Harker's hands, keeping them away with her arms at full tension; his right hand gripped her by the back of the neck, forcing her face down on his bosom. Her white night-dress was smeared with blood, and a thin stream trickled down the man's bare breast which was shown by his torn-open dress. The attitude of the two had a terrible resemblance to a child forcing a kitten's nose into a saucer of milk to compel it to drink. As we burst into the room, the Count turned his face, and the hellish look that I had heard described seemed to leap into it. His eyes flamed red with devilish passion; the great nostrils of the white aquiline nose opened wide and quivered at the edge; and the white sharp teeth, behind the full lips of the blood-dripping mouth, clamped together like those of a wild beast. With a wrench, which threw his victim back upon the bed as though hurled from a height, he turned and sprang at us. But by this time the Professor had gained his feet, and was holding towards him the envelope which contained the Sacred Wafer. The Count suddenly stopped, just as poor Lucy had done outside the tomb, and cowered back. Further and further back he cowered, as we, lifting our crucifixes, advanced. The moonlight suddenly failed, as a great black cloud sailed across the sky; and when the gaslight sprang up under Quincey's match, we saw nothing but a faint vapour. This, as we looked, trailed under the door, which with the recoil from its bursting open, had swung back to its old position. Van Helsing, Art, and I moved forward to Mrs. Harker, who by this time had drawn her breath and with it had given a scream so wild, so ear-piercing, so despairing that it seems to me now that it will ring in my ears till my dying day. For a few seconds she lay in her helpless attitude and disarray. Her face was ghastly, with a pallor which was accentuated by the blood which smeared her lips and cheeks and chin; from her throat trickled a thin stream of blood; her eyes were mad with terror. Then she put before her face her poor crushed hands, which bore on their whiteness the red mark of the Count's terrible grip, and from behind them came a low desolate wail which made the terrible scream seem only the quick expression of an endless grief. Van Helsing stepped forward and drew the coverlet gently over her body, whilst Art, after looking at her face for an instant despairingly, ran out of the room. Van Helsing whispered to me:—

"Jonathan is in a stupor such as we know the Vampire can produce. We can do nothing with poor Madam Mina for a few moments till she recovers herself; I must wake him!" He dipped the end of a towel in cold water and with it began to flick him on the face, his wife all the while holding her face between her hands and sobbing in a way that was heartbreaking to hear. I raised the blind, and looked out of the window. There was much moonshine; and as I looked I could see Quincey Morris run across the lawn and hide himself in the shadow of a great yew-tree. It puzzled me to think why he was doing this; but at the instant I heard Harker's quick exclamation as he woke to partial consciousness, and turned to the bed. On his face, as there might well be, was a look of wild amazement. He seemed dazed for a few seconds, and then full consciousness seemed to burst upon him all at once, and he started up. His wife was aroused by the quick movement, and turned to him with her arms stretched out, as though to embrace him; instantly, however, she drew them in again, and putting her elbows together, held her hands before her face, and shuddered till the bed beneath her shook.

"In God's name what does this mean?" Harker cried out. "Dr. Seward, Dr. Van Helsing, what is it? What has happened? What is wrong? Mina, dear, what is it? What does that blood mean? My God, my God! has it come to this!" and, raising himself to his knees, he beat his hands wildly together. "Good God help us! help her! oh, help her!" With a quick movement he jumped from bed, and began to pull on his clothes,—all the man in him awake at the need for instant exertion. "What has happened? Tell me all about it!" he cried without pausing. "Dr. Van Helsing, you love Mina, I know. Oh, do something to save her. It cannot have gone too far yet. Guard her while I look for *him*!" His wife, through her terror and horror and distress, saw some sure danger to him: instantly forgetting her own grief, she seized hold of him and cried out:—

"No! no! Jonathan, you must not leave me. I have suffered enough to-night, God knows, without the dread of his harming you. You must stay with me. Stay with these friends who will watch over you!" Her expression became frantic as she spoke; and, he yielding to her, she pulled him down sitting on the bed side, and clung to him fiercely.

Van Helsing and I tried to calm them both. The Professor held up his little golden crucifix, and said with wonderful calmness:—

"Do not fear, my dear. We are here; and whilst this is close to you no foul thing can approach. You are safe for to-night; and we must be calm and take counsel together." She shuddered and was silent, holding down her head on her husband's breast. When she raised it, his white night-robe was stained with blood where her lips had touched, and where the thin open wound in her neck had sent forth drops. The instant she saw it she drew back, with a low wail, and whispered, amidst choking sobs:—

"Unclean, unclean! I must touch him or kiss him no more. Oh, that it should be that it is I who am now his worst enemy, and whom he may have most cause to fear." To this he spoke out resolutely:—

"Nonsense, Mina. It is a shame to me to hear such a word. I would not hear it of you; and I shall not hear it from you. May God judge me by my deserts, and punish me with more bitter suffering than even this hour, if by any act or will of mine anything ever come between us!" He put out his arms and folded her to his breast; and for a while she lay there sobbing. He looked at us over her bowed head, with eyes that blinked damply above his quivering nostrils; his mouth was set as steel. After a while her sobs became less frequent and more faint, and then he said to me, speaking with a studied calmness which I felt tried his nervous power to the utmost:—

"And now, Dr. Seward, tell me all about it. Too well I know the broad fact; tell me all that has been." I told him exactly what had happened, and he listened with seeming impassiveness; but his nostrils twitched and his eyes blazed as I told how the ruthless hands of the Count had held his wife in that terrible and horrid position, with her mouth to the open wound in his breast. It interested me, even at that moment, to see, that, whilst the face of white set passion worked convulsively over the bowed head, the hands tenderly and lovingly stroked the ruffled hair. Just as I had finished, Quincey and Godalming knocked at the door. They entered in obedience to our summons. Van Helsing looked at me questioningly. I understood him to mean if we were to take advantage of their coming to divert if possible the thoughts of the unhappy husband and wife from each other and from themselves; so on nodding acquiescence to him he asked them what they had seen or done. To which Lord Godalming answered:—

"I could not see him anywhere in the passage, or in any of our rooms. I looked in the study but, though he had been there, he had gone. He had, however—" He stopped suddenly, looking at the poor drooping figure on the bed. Van Helsing said gravely:—

"Go on, friend Arthur. We want here no more concealments. Our hope now is in knowing all. Tell freely!" So Art went on:—

"He had been there, and though it could only have been for a few seconds, he made rare hay of the place. All the manuscripts had been burned, and the blue flames were flickering amongst the white ashes; the cylinders of your phonograph too were thrown on the fire, and the wax had helped the flames." Here I interrupted. "Thank God there is the other copy in the safe!" His face lit for a moment, but fell again as he went on: "I ran downstairs then, but could see no sign of him. I looked into Renfield's room; but there was no trace there except——!" Again he paused. "Go on," said Harker hoarsely; so he bowed his head and moistening his lips with his tongue, added: "except that the poor fellow is dead." Mrs. Harker raised her head, looking from one to the other of us as she said solemnly:—

"God's will be done!" I could not but feel that Art was keeping back something; but, as I took it that it was with a purpose, I said nothing. Van Helsing turned to Morris and asked:—

"And you, friend Quincey, have you any to tell?"

"A little," he answered. "It may be much eventually, but at present I can't say. I thought it well to know if possible where the Count would go when he left the house. I did not see him; but I saw a bat rise from Renfield's window, and flap westward. I expected to see him in some shape go back to Carfax; but he evidently sought some other lair. He will not be back to-night; for the sky is reddening in the east, and the dawn is close. We must work to-morrow!"

He said the latter words through his shut teeth. For a space of perhaps a couple of minutes there was silence, and I could fancy that I could hear the sound of our hearts beating; then Van Helsing said, placing his hand very tenderly on Mrs. Harker's head:—

"And now, Madam Mina—poor, dear, dear Madam Mina—tell us exactly what happened. God knows that I do not want that you be pained; but it is need that we know all. For now more than ever has all work to be done quick and sharp, and in deadly earnest. The day is close to us that must end all, if it may be so; and now is the chance that we may live and learn."

The poor, dear lady shivered, and I could see the tension of her nerves as she clasped her husband closer to her and bent her head lower and lower still on his breast. Then she raised her head proudly, and held out one hand to Van Helsing who took it in his, and, after stooping and kissing it reverently, held it fast. The other hand was locked in that of her husband, who held his other arm thrown round her protectingly. After a pause in which she was evidently ordering her thoughts, she began:—

"I took the sleeping draught which you had so kindly given me, but for a long time it did not act. I seemed to become more wakeful, and myriads of horrible fancies began to crowd in upon my mind—all of them connected with death, and vampires; with blood, and pain, and trouble." Her husband involuntarily groaned as she turned to him and said lovingly: "Do not fret, dear. You must be brave and strong, and help me through the horrible task. If you only knew what an effort it is to me to tell of this fearful thing at all, you would understand how much I need your help. Well, I saw I must try to help the medicine to its work with my will, if it was to do me any good, so I resolutely set myself to sleep. Sure enough sleep must soon have come to me, for I remember no more. Jonathan coming in had not waked me, for he lay by my side when next I remember. There was in the room the same thin white mist that I had before noticed. But I forget now if you know of this; you will find it in my diary which I shall show you later. I felt the same vague terror which had come to me before and the same sense of some presence. I turned to wake Jonathan, but found that he slept so soundly that it seemed as if it was he who had taken the sleeping draught, and not I. I tried, but I could not wake him. This caused me a great fear, and I looked around terrified. Then indeed, my heart sank within me: beside the bed, as if he had stepped out of the mist—or rather as if the mist had turned into his figure, for it had entirely disappeared—stood a tall, thin man, all in black. I knew him at once from the description of the others. The waxen face; the high aquiline nose, on which the light fell in a thin white line; the parted red lips, with the sharp white teeth showing between; and the red eyes that I had seemed to see in the sunset on the windows of St. Mary's Church at Whitby. I knew, too, the red scar on his forehead where Jonathan had struck him. For an instant my heart stood still, and I would have screamed out, only that I was paralysed. In the pause he spoke in a sort of keen, cutting whisper, pointing as he spoke to Jonathan:—

"'Silence! If you make a sound I shall take him and dash his brains out before your very eyes.' I was appalled and was too bewildered to do or say anything. With a mocking smile, he placed one hand upon my shoulder and, holding me tight, bared my throat with the other, saying as he did so, 'First, a little refreshment to reward my exertions. You may as well be quiet; it is not the first time, or the second, that your veins have appeased my thirst!' I was bewildered, and, strangely enough, I did not want to hinder him. I suppose it is a part of the horrible curse that such is, when his touch is on his victim. And oh, my God, my God, pity me! He placed his reeking lips upon my throat!" Her husband groaned again. She clasped his hand harder, and looked at him pityingly, as if he were the injured one, and went on:—

"I felt my strength fading away, and I was in a half swoon. How long this horrible thing lasted I know not; but it seemed that a long time must have passed before he took his foul, awful, sneering mouth away. I saw it drip with the fresh blood!" The remembrance seemed for a while to overpower her, and she drooped and would have sunk down but for her husband's sustaining arm. With a great effort she recovered herself and went on:—

"Then he spoke to me mockingly, 'And so you, like the others, would play your brains against mine. You would help these men to hunt me and frustrate me in my designs! You know now, and they know in part already, and will know in full before long what it is to cross my path. They should have kept their energies for use closer to home. Whilst they played wits against me—against me who commanded nations, and intrigued for them, and fought for them, hundreds of years before they were born—I was countermining them. And you, their best beloved one, are now to me, flesh of my flesh; blood of my blood; kin of my kin; my bountiful wine-press for a while; and shall be later on my companion and my helper. You shall be avenged in turn; for not one of them but shall minister to your needs. But as yet you are to be punished for what you have done. You have aided in thwarting me; now you shall come to my call. When my brain says "Come!" to you, you shall cross land or sea to do my bidding; and to that end this!' With that he pulled open his shirt, and with his long sharp nails opened a vein in his breast. When the blood began to spurt out, he took my hands in one of his, holding them tight, and with the other seized my neck and pressed my mouth to the wound, so that I must either suffocate or swallow some of the— Oh my God! my God! what have I done? What have I done to deserve such a fate, I who have tried to walk in meekness and righteousness all my days. God pity me! Look down on a poor soul in worse than mortal peril; and in mercy pity those to whom she is dear!" Then she began to rub her lips as though to cleanse them from pollution.

As she was telling her terrible story, the eastern sky began to quicken, and everything became more and more clear. Harker was still and quiet; but over his face, as the awful narrative went on, came a grey look which deepened and deepened in the morning light, till when the first red streak of the coming dawn shot up, the flesh stood darkly out against the whitening hair.

We have arranged that one of us is to stay within call of the unhappy pair till we can meet together and arrange about taking action.

Of this I am sure: the sun rises to-day on no more miserable house in all the great round of its daily course.

CHAPTER 22.

JONATHAN HARKER'S JOURNAL.

3 October.—As I must do something or go mad, I write this diary. It is now six o'clock, and we are to meet in the study in half an hour and take something to eat; for Dr. Van Helsing and Dr. Seward are agreed that if we do not eat we cannot work our best. Our best will be, God knows, required to-day. I must keep writing at every chance, for I dare not stop to think. All, big and little, must go down; perhaps at the end the little things may teach us most. The teaching, big or little, could not have landed Mina or me anywhere worse than we are to-day. However, we must trust and hope. Poor Mina told me just now, with the tears running down her dear cheeks, that it is in trouble and trial that our faith is tested—that we must keep on trusting; and that God will aid us up to the end. The end! oh my God! what end? . . . To work! To work!

When Dr. Van Helsing and Dr. Seward had come back from seeing poor Renfield, we went gravely into what was to be done. First, Dr. Seward told us that when he and Dr. Van Helsing had gone down to the room below they had found Renfield lying on the floor, all in a heap. His face was all bruised and crushed in, and the bones of the neck were broken.

Dr. Seward asked the attendant who was on duty in the passage if he had heard anything. He said that he had been sitting down—he confessed to half dozing—when he heard loud voices in the room, and then Renfield had called out loudly several times, "God! God! God!" after that there was a sound of falling, and when he entered the room he found him lying on the floor, face down, just as the doctors had seen him. Van Helsing asked if he had heard "voices" or "a voice," and he said he could not say; that at first it had seemed to him as if there were two, but as there was no one in the room it could have been only one. He could swear to it, if required, that the word "God" was spoken by the patient. Dr. Seward said to us, when we were alone, that he did not wish to go into the matter; the question of an inquest had to be considered, and it would never do to put forward the truth, as no one would believe it. As it was, he thought that on the attendant's evidence he could give a certificate of death by misadventure in falling from bed. In case the coroner should demand it, there would be a formal inquest, necessarily to the same result.

When the question began to be discussed as to what should be our next step, the very first thing we decided was that Mina should be in full confidence; that nothing of any sort—no matter how painful—should be kept from her. She herself agreed as to its wisdom, and it was pitiful to see her so brave and yet so sorrowful, and in such a depth of despair. "There must be no concealment," she said. "Alas! we have had too much already. And besides there is nothing in all the world that can give me more pain than I have already endured—than I suffer now! Whatever may happen, it must be of new hope or of new courage to me!" Van Helsing was looking at her fixedly as she spoke, and said, suddenly but quietly:—

"But dear Madam Mina, are you not afraid; not for yourself, but for others from yourself, after what has happened?" Her face grew set in its lines, but her eyes shone with the devotion of a martyr as she answered:—

"Ah no! for my mind is made up!"

"To what?" he asked gently, whilst we were all very still; for each in

our own way we had a sort of vague idea of what she meant. Her answer
came with direct simplicity, as though she were simply stating a fact:—

"Because if I find in myself—and I shall watch keenly for it—a sign
of harm to any that I love, I shall die!"

"You would not kill yourself?" he asked, hoarsely.

"I would; if there were no friend who loved me, who would save me
such a pain, and so desperate an effort!" She looked at him meaningly as
she spoke. He was sitting down; but now he rose and came close to her
and put his hand on her head as he said solemnly:—

"My child, there is such an one if it were for your good. For myself I
could hold it in my account with God to find such an euthanasia for you,
even at this moment if it were best. Nay, were it safe! But my child—"
for a moment he seemed choked, and a great sob rose in his throat; he
gulped it down and went on:—

"There are here some who would stand between you and death. You
must not die. You must not die by any hand; but least of all by your own.
Until the other, who has fouled your sweet life, is true dead you must
not die; for if he is still with the quick Un-Dead, your death would make
you even as he is. No, you must live! You must struggle and strive to live,
though death would seem a boon unspeakable. You must fight Death
himself, though he come to you in pain or in joy; by the day, or the
night; in safety or in peril! On your living soul I charge you that you do
not die—nay, nor think of death—till this great evil be past." The poor
dear grew white as death, and shook and shivered, as I have seen a
quicksand shake and shiver at the incoming of the tide. We were all
silent; we could do nothing. At length she grew more calm and turning
to him said, sweetly, but oh! so sorrowfully, as she held out her
hand:—

"I promise you, my dear friend, that if God will let me live, I shall
strive to do so; till, if it may be in His good time, this horror may have
passed away from me." She was so good and brave that we all felt that
our hearts were strengthened to work and endure for her, and we began
to discuss what we were to do. I told her that she was to have all the
papers in the safe, and all the papers or diaries and phonographs we

might hereafter use; and was to keep the record as she had done before. She was pleased with the prospect of anything to do—if "pleased" could be used in connection with so grim an interest.

As usual Van Helsing had thought ahead of everyone else, and was prepared with an exact ordering of our work.

"It is perhaps well," he said, "that at our meeting after our visit to Carfax we decided not to do anything with the earth-boxes that lay there. Had we done so, the Count must have guessed our purpose, and would doubtless have taken measures in advance to frustrate such an effort with regard to the others; but now he does not know our intentions. Nay, more, in all probability, he does not know that such a power exists to us as can sterilise his lairs, so that he cannot use them as of old. We are now so much further advanced in our knowledge as to their disposition that, when we have examined the house in Piccadilly, we may track the very last of them. To-day, then, is ours; and in it rests our hope. The sun that rose on our sorrow this morning guards us in its course. Until it sets to-night, that monster must retain whatever form he now has. He is confined within the limitations of his earthly envelope. He cannot melt into thin air nor disappear through cracks or chinks or crannies. If he go through a doorway, he must open the door like a mortal. And so we have this day to hunt out all his lairs and sterilise them. So we shall, if we have not yet catch him and destroy him, drive him to bay in some place where the catching and the destroying shall be, in time, sure." Here I started up for I could not contain myself at the thought that the minutes and seconds so preciously laden with Mina's life and happiness were flying from us, since whilst we talked action was impossible. But Van Helsing held up his hand warningly. "Nay, friend Jonathan," he said, "in this, the quickest way home is the longest way, so your proverb say. We shall all act and act with desperate quick, when the time has come. But think, in all probable the key of the situation is in that house in Piccadilly. The Count may have many houses which he has bought. Of them he will have deeds of purchase, keys and other things. He will have paper that he write on; he will have his book of cheques. There are many belongings that he must have somewhere; why not in this place so central, so quiet, where he come and go by the front or the back at all hour, when in the very vast of the traffic there is none to notice. We shall go there and search that house; and when we learn what it holds, then we do what our friend Arthur call, in his phrases of hunt, 'stop the earths' and so we run down our old fox—so? is it not?"

"Then let us come at once," I cried, "we are wasting the precious, precious time!" The Professor did not move, but simply said:—

"And how are we to get into that house in Piccadilly?"

"Any way!" I cried. "We shall break in if need be."

"And your police; where will they be, and what will they say?"

I was staggered; but I knew that if he wished to delay he had a good reason for it. So I said, as quietly as I could:—

"Don't wait more than need be; you know, I am sure, what torture I am in."

"Ah, my child, that I do; and indeed there is no wish of me to add to your anguish. But just think, what can we do, until all the world be at movement. Then will come our time. I have thought and thought, and it seems to me that the simplest way is the best of all. Now we wish to get into the house, but we have no key; is it not so?" I nodded.

"Now suppose that you were, in truth, the owner of that house, and could not still get it; and think there was to you no conscience of the housebreaker, what would you do?"

"I should get a respectable locksmith, and set him to work to pick the lock for me."

"And your police, they would interfere, would they not?"

"Oh, no! not if they knew the man was properly employed."

"Then," he looked at me keenly as he spoke, "all that is in doubt is the conscience of the employer, and the belief of your policemen as to whether or no that employer has a good conscience or a bad one. Your police must indeed be zealous men and clever—oh, so clever!—in reading the heart, that they trouble themselves in such matter. No, no, my friend Jonathan, you go take the lock off a hundred empty house in this your London, or of any city in the world; and if you do it as such things are rightly done, and at the time such things are rightly done, no one will interfere. I have read of a gentleman who owned a so fine house in London, and when he went for months of summer to Switzerland and lock up his house, some burglar came and broke window at back and got in. Then he went and made open the shutters in front and walk out and in through the door, before the very eyes of the police. Then he have an auction in that house, and advertised it, and put up big notice; and when the day come he sell off by a great auctioneer all the goods of that other man who own them. Then he go to a builder, and he sell him that house, making an agreement that he pull it down and take all away within a certain time. And your police and other authority help him all they can. And when that owner come back from his holiday in Switzerland he find only an empty hole where his house had been. This was all done *en règle*; and in our work we shall be *en règle* too. We shall not go so early that the policemen, who have then little to think of, shall deem it strange; but we shall go after ten o'clock, when there are many about, and such things would be done were we indeed owners of the house."

I could not but see how right he was and the terrible despair of Mina's face became relaxed in thought; there was hope in such good counsel. Van Helsing went on:—

"When once within that house we may find more clues; at any rate some of us can remain there whilst the rest find the other places where there be more earth-boxes—at Bermondsey and Mile End."

Lord Godalming stood up. "I can be of some use here," he said. "I shall wire to my people to have horses and carriages where they will be most convenient."

"Look here, old fellow," said Morris, "it is a capital idea to have all ready in case we want to go horsebacking; but don't you think that one of your snappy carriages with its heraldic adornments in a byway of Walworth or Mile End would attract too much attention for our purposes? It seems to me that we ought to take cabs when we go south or east; and even leave them somewhere near the neighbourhood we are going to."

"Friend Quincey is right!" said the Professor. "His head is what you call in plane with the horizon. It is a difficult thing that we go to do, and we do not want no peoples to watch us if so it may."

Mina took a growing interest in everything and I was rejoiced to see that the exigency of affairs was helping her to forget for a time the terrible experience of the night. She was very, very pale—almost ghastly, and so thin that her lips were drawn away, showing her teeth in somewhat of prominence. I did not mention this last, lest it should give her needless pain; but it made my blood run cold in my veins to think of what had occurred with poor Lucy when the Count had sucked her blood. As yet there was no sign of the teeth growing sharper; but the time as yet was short, and there was time for fear.

When we came to the discussion of the sequence of our efforts and of the disposition of our forces, there were new sources of doubt. It was finally agreed that before starting for Piccadilly we should destroy the Count's lair close at hand. In case he should find it out too soon, we should thus be still ahead of him in our work of destruction; and his presence in his purely material shape, and at his weakest, might give us some new clue.

As to the disposal of forces, it was suggested by the Professor that, after our visit to Carfax, we should all enter the house in Piccadilly; that the two doctors and I should remain there, whilst Lord Godalming and Quincey found the lairs at Walworth and Mile End and destroyed them. It was possible, if not likely, the Professor urged, that the Count might appear in Piccadilly during the day, and that if so we might be able to cope with him then and there. At any rate, we might be able to follow him in force. To this plan I strenuously objected, in so far as my going was concerned, for I said that I intended to stay and protect Mina. I thought that my mind was made up on the subject; but Mina would not listen to my objection. She said that there might be some law matter in which I could be useful; that amongst the Count's papers might be some clue which I could understand out of my experience in Transylvania; and that, as it was, all the strength we could muster was required to cope with the Count's extraordinary power. I had to give in, for Mina's resolution was fixed; she said that it was the last hope for *her* that we should all work together. "As for me," she said, "I have no fear. Things have been as bad as they can be; and whatever may happen must have in it some element of hope or comfort. Go, my husband! God can, if He wishes it, guard me as well alone as with any one present." So I started up crying out: "Then in God's name let us come at once, for we are losing time. The Count may come to Piccadilly earlier than we think."

"Not so!" said Van Helsing, holding up his hand.

"But why?" I asked.

"Do you forget," he said, with actually a smile, "that last night he banqueted heavily, and will sleep late?"

Did I forget! shall I ever—can I ever! Can any of us ever forget that terrible scene! Mina struggled hard to keep her brave countenance; but the pain overmastered her and she put her hands before her face, and shuddered whilst she moaned. Van Helsing had not intended to recall her frightful experience. He had simply lost sight of her and her part in the affair in his intellectual effort. When it struck him what he said, he was horrified at his thoughtlessness and tried to comfort her. "Oh, Madam Mina," he said, "dear, dear Madam Mina, alas! that I of all who so reverence you should have said anything so forgetful. These stupid old lips of mine and this stupid old head do not deserve so; but you will forget it, will you not?" He bent low beside her as he spoke; she took his hand, and looking at him through her tears, said hoarsely:—

"No, I shall not forget, for it is well that I remember; and with it I have so much in memory of you that is sweet, that I take it all together. Now, you must all be going soon. Breakfast is ready, and we must all eat that we may be strong."

Breakfast was a strange meal to us all. We tried to be cheerful and encourage each other, and Mina was the brightest and most cheerful of us. When it was over, Van Helsing stood up and said:—

"Now, my dear friends, we go forth to our terrible enterprise. Are we all armed, as we were on that night when first we visited our enemy's lair; armed against ghostly as well as carnal attack?" We all assured him. "Then it is well. Now, Madam Mina, you are in any case *quite* safe here until the sunset; and before then we shall return—if—— We shall return! But before we go let me see you armed against personal attack. I have myself, since you came down, prepared your chamber by the placing of things of which we know, so that He may not enter. Now let me guard yourself. On your forehead I touch this piece of Sacred Wafer in the name of the Father, the Son, and——"

There was a fearful scream which almost froze our hearts to hear. As he had placed the Wafer on Mina's forehead, it had seared it—had burned into the flesh as though it had been a piece of white-hot metal. My poor darling's brain had told her the significance of the fact as quickly as her nerves received the pain of it; and the two so overwhelmed her that her overwrought nature had its voice in that dreadful scream. But the words to her thought came quickly; the echo of the scream had not ceased to ring on the air when there came the reaction, and she sank on her knees on the floor in an agony of abasement. Pulling her beautiful hair over her face, as the leper of old his mantle, she wailed out:—

"Unclean! Unclean! Even the Almighty shuns my polluted flesh! I must bear this mark of shame upon my forehead until the Judgment Day." They all paused. I had thrown myself beside her in an agony of helpless grief, and putting my arms around held her tight. For a few minutes our sorrowful hearts beat together, whilst the friends around us turned away their eyes that ran tears silently. Then Van Helsing turned and said gravely; so gravely that I could not help feeling that he was in some way inspired, and was stating things outside himself:—

"It may be that you may have to bear that mark till God Himself see fit, as He most surely shall, on the Judgment Day, to redress all wrongs of the earth and of His children that He has placed thereon. And oh, Madam Mina, my dear, my dear, may we who love you be there to see, when that red scar, the sign of God's knowledge of what has been, shall pass away, and leave your forehead as pure as the heart we know. For so surely as we live, that scar shall pass away when God sees right to lift the burden that is hard upon us. Till then we bear our Cross, as His Son did in obedience to His Will. It may be that we are chosen instruments of His good pleasure, and that we ascend to His bidding as that other through stripes and shame; through tears and blood; through doubts and fears, and all that makes the difference between God and man."

There was hope in his words, and comfort; and they made for resignation. Mina and I both felt so, and simultaneously we each took one of the old man's hands and bent over and kissed it. Then without a word we all knelt down together, and, all holding hands, swore to be true to each other. We men pledged ourselves to raise the veil of sorrow from the head of her whom, each in his own way, we loved; and we prayed for help and guidance in the terrible task which lay before us.

It was then time to start. So I said farewell to Mina, a parting which neither of us shall forget to our dying day; and we set out.

To one thing I have made up my mind: if we find out that Mina must be a vampire in the end, then she shall not go into that unknown and terrible land alone. I suppose it is thus that in old times one vampire meant many; just as their hideous bodies could only rest in sacred earth, so the holiest love was the recruiting sergeant for their ghastly ranks.

We entered Carfax without trouble and found all things the same as on the first occasion. It was hard to believe that amongst so prosaic sur-roundings of neglect and dust and decay there was any ground for such fear as already we knew. Had not our minds been made up, and had there not been terrible memories to spur us on, we could hardly have proceeded with our task. We found no papers, or any sign of use in the house; and in the old chapel the great boxes looked just as we had seen them last. Dr. Van Helsing said to us solemnly as we stood before them:—

"And now, my friends, we have a duty here to do. We must sterilise this earth, so sacred of holy memories, that he has brought from a far distant land for such fell use. He has chosen this earth because it has been holy. Thus we defeat him with his own weapon, for we make it more holy still. It was sanctified to such use of man, now we sanctify it to God." As he spoke he took from his bag a screwdriver and a wrench, and very soon the top of one of the cases was thrown open. The earth smelled musty and close; but we did not somehow seem to mind, for our attention was concentrated on the Professor. Taking from his box a piece of the Sacred Wafer he laid it reverently on the earth, and then shutting down the lid began to screw it home, we aiding him as he worked.

One by one we treated in the same way each of the great boxes, and left them as we had found them to all appearance; but in each was a portion of the Host.

When we closed the door behind us, the Professor said solemnly:—

"So much is already done. If it may be that with all the others we can be so successful, then the sunset of this evening may shine on Madam Mina's forehead all white as ivory and with no stain!"

As we passed across the lawn on our way to the station to catch our train we could see the front of the asylum. I looked eagerly, and in the window of my own room saw Mina. I waved my hand to her, and nodded to tell that our work there was successfully accomplished. She nodded in reply to show that she understood. The last I saw, she was waving her hand in farewell. It was with a heavy heart that we sought the station and just caught the train, which was steaming in as we reached the platform.

I have written this in the train.

Piccadilly, 12:30 o'clock.—Just before we reached Fenchurch Street Lord Godalming said to me:—

"Quincey and I will find a locksmith. You had better not come with us in case there should be any difficulty; for under the circumstances it wouldn't seem so bad for us to break into an empty house. But you are a solicitor and the Incorporated Law Society might tell you that you should have known better." I demurred as to my not sharing any danger even of odium, but he went on: "Besides, it will attract less attention if there are not too many of us. My title will make it all right with the locksmith, and with any policeman that may come along. You had better go with Jack and the Professor and stay in the Green Park, somewhere in sight of the house; and when you see the door opened and the smith has gone away, do you all come across. We shall be on the lookout for you, and shall let you in."

"The advice is good!" said Van Helsing, so we said no more. Godalming and Morris hurried off in a cab, we following in another. At the corner of Arlington Street our contingent got out and strolled into the Green Park. My heart beat as I saw the house on which so much of our hope was centred, looming up grim and silent in its deserted condition amongst its more lively and spruce-looking neighbours. We sat down on a bench within good view, and began to smoke cigars so as to attract as little attention as possible. The minutes seemed to pass with leaden feet as we waited for the coming of the others.

At length we saw a four-wheeler drive up. Out of it, in leisurely fashion, got Lord Godalming and Morris; and down from the box descended a thick-set working man with his rush-woven basket of tools. Morris paid the cabman, who touched his hat and drove away. Together the two ascended the steps, and Lord Godalming pointed out what he wanted done. The workman took off his coat leisurely and hung it on one of the spikes of the rail, saying something to a policeman who just then sauntered along. The policeman nodded acquiescence, and the man kneeling down placed his bag beside him. After searching through it, he took out a selection of tools which he produced to lay beside him in orderly fashion. Then he stood up, looked into the keyhole, blew into it, and turning to his employers, made some remark. Lord Godalming smiled, and the man lifted a good-sized bunch of keys; selecting one of them, he began to probe the lock, as if feeling his way with it. After fumbling about for a bit he tried a second, and then a third. All at once the door opened under a slight push from him, and he and the two others entered the hall. We sat still; my own cigar burnt furiously, but Van Helsing's went cold altogether. We waited patiently as we saw the workman come out and bring in his bag. Then he held the door partly open, steadying it with his knees, whilst he fitted a key to the lock. This he finally handed to Lord Godalming, who took out his purse and gave him something. The man touched his hat, took his bag, put on his coat and departed; not a soul took the slightest notice of the whole transaction.

When the man had fairly gone, we three crossed the street and knocked at the door. It was immediately opened by Quincey Morris, beside whom stood Lord Godalming lighting a cigar.

"The place smells so vilely," said the latter as we came in. It did indeed smell vilely—like the old chapel at Carfax—and with our previous experience it was plain to us that the Count had been using the place pretty freely. We moved to explore the house, all keeping together in case of attack; for we knew we had a strong and wily enemy to deal with, and as yet we did not know whether the Count might not be in the house. In the dining room, which lay at the back of the hall, we found eight boxes of earth. Eight boxes only out of the nine, which we sought! Our work was not over, and would never be until we should have found the missing box. First we opened the shutters of the window which looked out across a narrow stone-flagged yard at the blank face of a stable, pointed to look like the front of a miniature house. There were no windows in it, so we were not afraid of being overlooked. We did not lose any time in examining the chests. With the tools which we had brought with us we opened them, one by one, and treated them as we had treated those others in the old chapel. It was evident to us that the Count was not at present in the house, and we proceeded to search for any of his effects.

After a cursory glance at the rest of the rooms, from basement to attic, we came to the conclusion that the dining-room contained any effects which might belong to the Count; and so we proceeded to minutely examine them. They lay in a sort of orderly disorder on the great dining-room table. There were title deeds of the Piccadilly house in a great bundle; deeds of the purchase of the houses at Mile End and Bermondsey; notepaper, envelopes, and pens and ink. All were covered up in thin wrapping paper to keep them from the dust. There were also a clothes brush, a brush and comb, and a jug and basin—the latter containing dirty water which was reddened as if with blood. Last of all was a little heap of keys of all sorts and sizes, probably those belonging to the other houses. When we had examined this last find, Lord Godalming and Quincey Morris, taking accurate notes of the various addresses of the houses in the East and the South, took with them the keys in a great bunch, and set out to destroy the boxes in these places. The rest of us are, with what patience we can, waiting their return—or the coming of the Count.

CHAPTER 23.

———◆———

DR. SEWARD'S DIARY.

3 October.—The time seemed terribly long whilst we were waiting for the coming of Godalming and Quincey Morris. The Professor tried to keep our minds active by using them all the time. I could see his beneficent purpose, by the side glances which he threw from time to time at Harker. The poor fellow is overwhelmed in a misery that is appalling to see. Last night he was a frank, happy-looking man, with strong, youthful face, full of energy, and with dark brown hair. To-day he is a drawn, haggard old man, whose white hair matches well with the hollow burning eyes and grief-written lines of his face. His energy is still intact; in fact, he is like a living flame. This may yet be his salvation, for, if all go well, it will tide him over the despairing period; he will then, in a kind of way, wake again to the realities of life. Poor fellow, I thought my own trouble was bad enough, but his——! The Professor knows this well enough, and is doing his best to keep his mind active. What he has been saying was, under the circumstances, of absorbing interest. So well as I can remember, here it is:—

"I have studied, over and over again since they came into my hands, all the papers relating to this monster; and the more I have studied, the greater seems the necessity to utterly stamp him out. All through there are signs of his advance; not only of his power, but of his knowledge of it. As I learned from the researches of my friend Arminius of Buda-Pesth, he was in life a most wonderful man. Soldier, statesman, and alchemist—which latter was the highest development of the science-knowledge of his time. He had a mighty brain, a learning beyond compare, and a heart that knew no fear and no remorse. He dared even to attend the Scholomance, and there was no branch of knowledge of his time that he did not essay. Well, in him the brain powers survived the physical death; though it would seem that memory was not all complete. In some faculties of mind he has been, and is, only a child; but he is growing, and some things that were childish at the first are now of man's stature. He is experimenting, and doing it well; and if it had not been that we have crossed his path he would be yet—he may be yet if we fail—the father or furtherer of a new order of beings, whose road must lead through Death, not Life."

Harker groaned and said, "And this is all arrayed against my darling! But how is he experimenting? The knowledge may help us to defeat him!"

"He has all along, since his coming, been trying his power, slowly but surely; that big child-brain of his is working. Well for us, it is, as yet, a child-brain; for had he dared, at the first, to attempt certain things he would long ago have been beyond our power. However, he means to succeed, and a man who has centuries before him can afford to wait and go slow. *Festina lente* may well be his motto."

"I fail to understand," said Harker wearily. "Oh, do be more plain to me! Perhaps grief and trouble are dulling my brain."

The Professor laid his hand tenderly on his shoulder as he spoke:—

"Ah, my child, I will be plain. Do you not see how, of late, this monster has been creeping into knowledge experimentally. How he has been making use of the zoöphagous patient to effect his entry into friend John's home; for your Vampire, though in all afterwards he can come when and how he will, must at the first make entry only when asked thereto by an inmate. But these are not his most important experiments. Do we not see how at the first all these so great boxes were moved by others. He knew not then but that must be so. But all the time that so great child-brain of his was growing, and he began to consider whether he might not himself move the box. So he began to help; and, when he found that this be all right, he try to move them all alone. And so he progress, and he scatter these graves of him; and none but he know where they are hidden. He may have intend to bury them deep in the ground. So that he only use them in the night, or at such time as he can change his form, they do him equal well; and none may know these are his hiding-place! But, my child, do not despair; this knowledge come to him just too late! Already all of his lairs but one be sterilise as for him; and before the sunset this shall be so. Then he have no place where he can move and hide. I delayed this morning that so we might be sure. Is there not more at stake for us than for him? Then why we not be even more careful than him? By my clock it is one hour, and already, if all be well, friend Arthur and Quincey are on their way to us. Today is our day, and we must go sure, if slow, and lose no chance. See! there are five of us when those absent ones return."

Whilst he was speaking we were startled by a knock at the hall-door, the double postman's knock of the telegraph boy. We all moved out to the hall with one impulse, and Van Helsing, holding up his hand to us to keep silence, stepped to the door and opened it. The boy handed in a despatch. The Professor closed the door again, and, after looking at the direction, opened it and read aloud.

"Look out for D. He has just now, 12:45, come from Carfax hurriedly and hastened towards the South. He seems to be going the round and may want to see you: Mina."

There was a pause broken by Jonathan Harker's voice:—

"Now, God be thanked, we shall soon meet!" Van Helsing turned to him quickly and said:—

"God will act in His own way and time. Do not fear, and do not rejoice as yet; for what we wish for at the moment may be our undoings."

"I care for nothing now," he answered hotly, "except to wipe out this brute from the face of creation. I would sell my soul to do it!"

"Oh, hush, hush, my child!" said Van Helsing. "God does not purchase souls in this wise; and the Devil, though he may purchase, does not keep faith. But God is merciful and just, and knows your pain and your devotion to that dear Madam Mina. Think you how her pain would be doubled, did she but hear your wild words. Do not fear any of us, we are all devoted to this cause, and to-day shall see the end. The time is coming for action; to-day this Vampire is limited to the powers of man and till sunset he may not change. It will take him time to arrive here—see, it is twenty minutes past one—and there are yet some times before he can hither come, be he never so quick. What we must hope for is that my Lord Arthur and Quincey arrive first."

About half an hour after we had received Mrs. Harker's telegram, there came a quiet, resolute knock at the hall-door. It was just an ordinary knock, such as is given hourly by thousands of gentlemen, but it made the Professor's heart and mine beat loudly. We looked at each other, and together moved out into the hall; we each held ready to use our various armaments—the spiritual in the left hand, the mortal in the right. Van Helsing pulled back the latch, and, holding the door half open, stood back, having both hands ready for action. The gladness of our hearts must have shown upon our faces when on the step, close to the door, we saw Lord Godalming and Quincey Morris. They came quickly in and closed the door behind them, the former saying, as they moved along the hall:—

"It is all right. We found both places; six boxes in each and we destroyed them all!"

"Destroyed?" asked the Professor.

"For him!" We were silent for a minute, and then Quincey said:—

"There's nothing to do but to wait here. If, however, he doesn't turn up by five o'clock, we must start off; for it won't do to leave Mrs. Harker alone after sunset."

"He will be here before long now," said Van Helsing, who had been consulting his pocket-book. "*Nota bene*, in Madam's telegram he went south from Carfax, that means he went to cross the river, and he could only do so at slack of tide, which should be something before one o'clock. That he went south has a meaning for us. He is as yet only suspicious; and he went from Carfax first to the place where he would suspect interference least. You must have been at Bermondsey only a short time before him. That he is not here already shows that he went to Mile End next. This took him some time; for he would then have to be carried over the river in some way. Believe me, my friends, we shall not have long to wait now. We should have ready some plan of attack, so that we may throw away no chance. Hush, there is no time now. Have all your arms! Be ready!" He held up a warning hand as he spoke, for we all could hear a key softly inserted in the lock of the hall-door.

I could not but admire, even at such a moment, the way in which a dominant spirit asserted itself. In all our hunting parties and adventures in different parts of the world, Quincey Morris had always been the one to arrange the plan of action, and Arthur and I had been accustomed to obey him implicitly. Now, the old habit seemed to be renewed instinctively. With a swift glance around the room, he at once laid out our plan of attack, and, without speaking a word, with a gesture, placed us each in position. Van Helsing, Harker, and I were just behind the door, so that when it was opened the Professor could guard it whilst we two stepped between the incomer and the door. Godalming behind and Quincey in front stood just out of sight ready to move in front of the window. We waited in a suspense that made the seconds pass with nightmare slowness. The slow, careful steps came along the hall; the Count was evidently prepared for some surprise—at least he feared it.

Suddenly with a single bound he leaped into the room, winning a way past us before any of us could raise a hand to stay him. There was something so panther-like in the movement—something so unhuman, that it seemed to sober us all from the shock of his coming. The first to act was Harker, who, with a quick movement, threw himself before the door leading into the room in the front of the house. As the Count saw us, a horrible sort of snarl passed over his face, showing the eye-teeth long and pointed; but the evil smile as quickly passed into a cold stare of lion-like disdain. His expression again changed as, with a single impulse, we all advanced upon him. It was a pity that we had not some better organised plan of attack, for even at the moment I wondered what we were to do. I did not myself know whether our lethal weapons would avail us anything. Harker evidently meant to try the matter, for he had ready his great Kukri knife and made a fierce and sudden cut at him. The blow was a powerful one: only the diabolical quickness of the Count's leap back saved him. A second less and the trenchant blade had shorne through his heart. As it was, the point just cut the cloth of his coat, making a wide gap whence a bundle of bank-notes and a stream of gold fell out. The expression of the Count's face was so hellish, that for a moment I feared for Harker, though I saw him throw the terrible knife aloft again for another stroke. Instinctively I moved forward with a protective impulse, holding the Crucifix and Wafer in my left hand. I felt a mighty power fly along my arm; and it was without surprise that I saw the monster cower back before a similar movement made spontaneously by each one of us. It would be impossible to describe the expression of hate and baffled malignity—of anger and hellish rage—which came over the Count's face. His waxen hue became greenish-yellow by the contrast of his burning eyes, and the red scar on the forehead showed on the pallid skin like a palpitating wound. The next instant, with a sinuous dive he swept under Harker's arm, ere his blow could fall, and, grasping a handful of the money from the floor, dashed across the room, threw himself at the window. Amid the crash and glitter of the falling glass, he tumbled into the flagged area below. Through the sound of the shivering glass I could hear the "ting" of the gold, as some of the sovereigns fell on the flagging.

We ran over and saw him spring unhurt from the ground. He, rushing up the steps, crossed the flagged yard, and pushed open the stable door. There he turned and spoke to us:—

"You think to baffle me, you—with your pale faces all in a row, like sheep in a butcher's. You shall be sorry yet, each one of you! You think you have left me without a place to rest; but I have more. My revenge is just begun! I spread it over centuries, and time is on my side. Your girls that you all love are mine already; and through them you and others shall yet be mine—my creatures, to do my bidding and to be my jackals when I want to feed. Bah!" With a contemptuous sneer, he passed quickly through the door, and we heard the rusty bolt creak as he fastened it behind him. A door beyond opened and shut. The first of us to speak was the Professor, as, realising the difficulty of following him through the stable, we moved toward the hall.

"We have learnt something—much! Notwithstanding his brave words, he fears us; he fears time, he fears want! For if not, why he hurry so? His very tone betray him, or my ears deceive. Why take that money? You follow quick. You are hunters of wild beast, and understand it so. For me, I make sure that nothing here may be of use to him, if so that he return." As he spoke he put the money remaining into his pocket; took the title-deeds in the bundle as Harker had left them, and swept the remaining things into the open fireplace, where he set fire to them with a match.

Godalming and Morris had rushed out into the yard, and Harker had lowered himself from the window to follow the Count. He had, however, bolted the stable door; and by the time they had forced it open there was no sign of him. Van Helsing and I tried to make inquiry at the back of the house; but the mews was deserted and no one had seen him depart.

It was now late in the afternoon, and sunset was not far off. We had to recognise that our game was up; with heavy hearts we agreed with the Professor when he said:—

"Let us go back to Madam Mina—poor, poor dear Madam Mina. All we can do just now is done; and we can there, at least, protect her. But we need not despair. There is but one more earth-box, and we must try to find it; when that is done all may yet be well." I could see that he spoke as bravely as he could to comfort Harker. The poor fellow was quite broken down; now and again he gave a low groan which he could not suppress—he was thinking of his wife.

With sad hearts we came back to my house, where we found Mrs. Harker waiting us, with an appearance of cheerfulness which did honour to her bravery and unselfishness. When she saw our faces, her own became as pale as death: for a second or two her eyes were closed as if she were in secret prayer; and then she said cheerfully:—

"I can never thank you all enough. Oh, my poor darling!" As she spoke, she took her husband's grey head in her hands and kissed it— "Lay your poor head here and rest it. All will yet be well, dear! God will protect us if He so will it in His good intent." The poor fellow groaned. There was no place for words in his sublime misery.

We had a sort of perfunctory supper together, and I think it cheered us all up somewhat. It was, perhaps, the mere animal heat of food to hungry people—for none of us had eaten anything since breakfast—or the sense of companionship may have helped us; but anyhow we were all less miserable, and saw the morrow as not altogether without hope. True to our promise, we told Mrs. Harker everything which had passed; and although she grew snowy white at times when danger had seemed to threaten her husband, and red at others when his devotion to her was manifested, she listened bravely and with calmness. When we came to the part where Harker had rushed at the Count so recklessly, she clung to her husband's arm, and held it tight as though her clinging could protect him from any harm that might come. She said nothing, however, till the narration was all done, and matters had been brought right up to the present time. Then without letting go her husband's hand she stood up amongst us and spoke. Oh, that I could give any idea of the scene; of that sweet, sweet, good, good woman in all the radiant beauty of her youth and animation, with the red scar on her forehead, of which she was conscious, and which we saw with grinding of our teeth—remembering whence and how it came; her loving kindness against our grim hate; her tender faith against all our fears and doubting; and we, knowing that so far as symbols went, she with all her goodness and purity and faith, was outcast from God.

"Jonathan," she said, and the word sounded like music on her lips it was so full of love and tenderness. "Jonathan dear, and you all my true, true friends, I want you to bear something in mind through all this dreadful time. I know that you must fight—that you must destroy even as you destroyed the false Lucy so that the true Lucy might live hereafter; but it is not a work of hate. That poor soul who has wrought all this misery is the saddest case of all. Just think what will be his joy when he, too, is destroyed in his worser part that his better part may have spiritual immortality. You must be pitiful to him, too, though it may not hold your hands from his destruction."

As she spoke I could see her husband's face darken and draw together, as though the passion in him were shrivelling his being to its core. Instinctively the clasp on his wife's hand grew closer, till his knuckles looked white. She did not flinch from the pain which I knew she must have suffered, but looked at him with eyes that were more appealing than ever. As she stopped speaking he leaped to his feet, almost tearing his hand from hers as he spoke:—

"May God give him into my hand just for long enough to destroy that earthly life of him which we are aiming at. If beyond it I could send his soul for ever and ever to burning hell I would do it!"

"Oh, hush! oh, hush! in the name of the good God. Don't say such things, Jonathan, my husband; or you will crush me with fear and horror. Just think, my dear—I have been thinking all this long, long day of it—that . . . perhaps . . . some day . . . I, too, may need such pity; and that some other like you—and with equal cause for anger—may deny it to me! Oh, my husband! my husband, indeed I would have spared you such a thought had there been another way; but I pray that God may not have treasured your wild words, except as the heart-broken wail of a very loving and sorely stricken man. Oh, God, let these poor white hairs go in evidence of what he has suffered, who all his life has done no wrong, and on whom so many sorrows have come."

We men were all in tears now. There was no resisting them, and we wept openly. She wept, too, to see that her sweeter counsels had prevailed. Her husband flung himself on his knees beside her, and putting his arms round her, hid his face in the folds of her dress. Van Helsing beckoned to us and we stole out of the room, leaving the two loving hearts alone with their God.

Before they retired the Professor fixed up the room against any coming of the Vampire, and assured Mrs. Harker that she might rest in peace. She tried to school herself to the belief, and, manifestly for her husband's sake, tried to seem content. It was a brave struggle; and was, I think and believe, not without its reward. Van Helsing had placed at hand a bell which either of them was to sound in case of any emergency. When they had retired, Quincey, Godalming, and I arranged that we should sit up, dividing the night between us, and watch over the safety of the poor stricken lady. The first watch falls to Quincey, so the rest of us shall be off to bed as soon as we can. Godalming has already turned in, for his is the second watch. Now that my work is done I, too, shall go to bed.

JONATHAN HARKER'S JOURNAL.

3-4 October, close to midnight.—I thought yesterday would never end. There was over me a yearning for sleep, in some sort of blind belief that to wake would be to find things changed, and that any change must now be for the better. Before we parted, we discussed what our next step was to be, but we could arrive at no result. All we knew was that one earth-box remained, and that the Count alone knew where it was. If he chooses to lie hidden, he may baffle us for years; and in the meantime!—the thought is too horrible, I dare not think of it even now. This I know: that if ever there was a woman who was all perfection, that one is my poor wronged darling. I love her a thousand times more for her sweet pity of last night, a pity that made my own hate of the monster seem despicable. Surely God will not permit the world to be the poorer by the loss of such a creature. This is hope to me. We are all drifting reefwards now, and faith is our only anchor. Thank God! Mina is sleeping, and sleeping without dreams. I fear what her dreams might be like, with such terrible memories to ground them in. She has not been so calm, within my seeing, since the sunset. Then, for a while, there came over her face a repose which was like spring after the blasts of March. I thought at the time that it was the softness of the red sunset on her face, but somehow now I think it has a deeper meaning. I am not sleepy myself, though I am weary—weary to death. However, I must try to sleep; for there is to-morrow to think of, and there is no rest for me until. . . .

Later.—I must have fallen asleep, for I was awaked by Mina, who was sitting up in bed, with a startled look on her face. I could see easily, for we did not leave the room in darkness; she had placed a warning hand over my mouth, and now she whispered in my ear:—

"Hush! there is someone in the corridor!" I got up softly, and crossing the room, gently opened the door.

Just outside, stretched on a mattress, lay Mr. Morris, wide awake. He raised a warning hand for silence as he whispered to me:—

"Hush! go back to bed; it is all right. One of us will be here all night. We don't mean to take any chances!"

His look and gesture forbade discussion, so I came back and told Mina. She sighed and positively a shadow of a smile stole over her poor, pale face as she put her arms round me and said softly:—

"Oh, thank God for good brave men!" With a sigh she sank back again to sleep. I write this now as I am not sleepy, though I must try again.

4 October, morning.—Once again during the night I was wakened by Mina. This time we had all had a good sleep, for the grey of the coming dawn was making the windows into sharp oblongs, and the gas flame was like a speck rather than a disc of light. She said to me hurriedly:—

"Go, call the Professor. I want to see him at once."

"Why?" I asked.

"I have an idea. I suppose it must have come in the night and matured without my knowing it. He must hypnotise me before the dawn, and then I shall be able to speak. Go quick, dearest; the time is getting close." I went to the door. Dr. Seward was resting on the mattress, and, seeing me, he sprang to his feet.

nd him even if we have to follow him to the jaws of Hell!" She grew
aler as she asked faintly:—

"Why?"

"Because," he answered solemnly, "he can live for centuries, and you
are but mortal woman. Time is now to be dreaded—since once he put
that mark upon your throat."

I was just in time to catch her as she fell forward in a faint.

"Is anything wrong?" he asked, in alarm.

"No," I replied; "but Mina wants to see Dr. Van Helsing at once."

"I will go," he said, and hurried into the Professor's room.

In two or three minutes later Van Helsing was in the room in his
dressing-gown, and Mr. Morris and Lord Godalming were with Dr.
Seward at the door asking questions. When the Professor saw Mina a
smile—a positive smile ousted the anxiety of his face; he rubbed his
hands as he said:—

"Oh, my dear Madam Mina, this is indeed a change. See! friend
Jonathan, we have got our dear Madam Mina, as of old, back to us to-
day!" Then turning to her, he said, cheerfully: "And what am I to do for
you? For at this hour you do not want me for nothings."

"I want you to hypnotise me!" she said. "Do it before the dawn, for I
feel that then I can speak, and speak freely. Be quick, for the time is
short!" Without a word he motioned her to sit up in bed.

Looking fixedly at her, he commenced to make passes in front of
her, from over the top of her head downward, with each hand in turn.
Mina gazed at him fixedly for a few minutes, during which my own
heart beat like a trip hammer, for I felt that some crisis was at hand.
Gradually her eyes closed, and she sat, stock still; only by the gentle
heaving of her bosom could one know that she was alive. The Professor
made a few more passes and then stopped, and I could see that his
forehead was covered with great beads of perspiration. Mina opened
her eyes; but she did not seem the same woman. There was a faraway
look in her eyes, and her voice had a sad dreaminess which was new to
me. Raising his hand to impose silence, the Professor motioned to me
to bring the others in. They came on tip-toe, closing the door behind
them, and stood at the foot of the bed, looking on. Mina appeared not
to see them. The stillness was broken by Van Helsing's voice speaking
in a low level tone which would not break the current of her
thoughts:—

"Where are you?" The answer came in a neutral way:—

"I do not know. Sleep has no place it can call its own." For several
minutes there was silence. Mina sat rigid, and the Professor stood staring

at her fixedly; the rest of us hardly dared to breathe. The room was growing lighter; without taking his eyes from Mina's face, Dr. Van Helsing motioned me to pull up the blind. I did so, and the day seemed just upon us. A red streak shot up, and a rosy light seemed to diffuse itself through the room. On the instant the Professor spoke again:—

"Where are you now?" The answer came dreamily, but with intention; it were as though she were interpreting something. I have heard her use the same tone when reading her shorthand notes.

"I do not know. It is all strange to me!"

"What do you see?"

"I can see nothing; it is all dark."

"What do you hear?" I could detect the strain in the Professor's patient voice.

"The lapping of water. It is gurgling by, and little waves leap. I can hear them on the outside."

"Then you are on a ship?" We all looked at each other, trying to glean something each from the other. We were afraid to think. The answer came quick:—

"Oh, yes!"

"What else do you hear?"

"The sound of men stamping overhead as they run about. There is the creaking of a chain, and the loud tinkle as the check of the capstan falls into the rachet."

"What are you doing?"

"I'm still—oh, so still. It is like death!" The voice faded away into a deep breath as of one sleeping, and the open eyes closed again.

By this time the sun had risen, and we were all in the full light of day. Dr. Van Helsing placed his hands on Mina's shoulders, and laid her head down softly on her pillow. She lay like a sleeping child for a few moments, and then, with a long sigh, awoke and stared in wonder to see all around her. "Have I been talking in my sleep?" was all she said. She seemed, however, to know the situation without telling, though she was eager to know what she had told. The Professor repeated the conversation, and she said:—

"Then there is not a moment to lose: it may not be yet too Morris and Lord Godalming started for the door but the calm voice called them back:—

"Stay, my friends. That ship, wherever it was, was weighi whilst she spoke. There are many ships weighing anchor at the in your so great Port of London. Which of them is it that yo God be thanked that we have once again a clue, though whithe lead us we know not. We have been blind somewhat, blind af manner of men, since when we can look back we see what we have seen looking forward if we had been able to see what we n have seen! Alas, but that sentence is a puddle; is it not? We can k now what was in the Count's mind, when he seize that money, tho Jonathan's so fierce knife put him in the danger that even he dread. meant escape. Hear me, ESCAPE! He saw that with but one earth-b left, and a pack of men following like dogs after a fox, this London wa no place for him. He have take his last earth-box on board a ship, an he leave the land. He think to escape, but no! we follow him. Tally Ho! as friend Arthur would say when he put on his red frock! Our old fox is wily; oh! so wily, and we must follow with wile. I, too, am wily and I think his mind in a little while. In meantime we may rest and in peace, for there are waters between us which he do not want to pass, and which he could not if he would—unless the ship were to touch the land, and then only at full or slack tide. See, and the sun is just rose, and all day to sunset is to us. Let us take bath, and dress, and have breakfast which we all need, and which we can eat comfortably since he be not in the same land with us." Mina looked at him appealingly as she asked:—

"But why need we seek him further, when he is gone away from us?" He took her hand and patted it as he replied:—

"Ask me nothings as yet. When we have breakfast, then I answer all questions." He would say no more, and we separated to dress.

After breakfast Mina repeated her question. He looked at her gravely for a minute and then said sorrowfully:—

"Because my dear, dear Madam Mina, now more than ever must we

CHAPTER 24.

‹——◇——›

DR. SEWARD'S PHONOGRAPH DIARY,
SPOKEN BY VAN HELSING.

This to Jonathan Harker.

You are to stay with your dear Madam Mina. We shall go to make our search—if I can call it so, for it is not search but knowing, and we seek confirmation only. But do you stay and take care of her to-day. This is your best and most holiest office. This day nothing can find him here. Let me tell you that so you will know what we four know already, for I have tell them. He, our enemy, have gone away; he have gone back to his Castle in Transylvania. I know it so well, as if a great hand of fire wrote it on the wall. He have prepare for this in some way, and that last earth-box was ready to ship somewheres. For this he took the money; for this he hurry at the last, lest we catch him before the sun go down. It was his last hope, save that he might hide in the tomb that he think poor Miss Lucy, being as he thought like him, keep open to him. But there was not of time. When that fail he make straight for his last resource—his last earthwork I might say did I wish *double entente*. He is clever, oh, so clever! he know that his game here was finish; and so he decide he go back home. He find ship going by the route he came, and he go in it. We go off now to find what ship, and whither bound; when we have discover that, we come back and tell you all. Then we will comfort you and poor dear Madam Mina with new hope. For it will be hope when you think it over: that all is not lost. This very creature that we pursue, he take hundreds of years to get so far as London; and yet in one day, when we know of the disposal of him we drive him out. He is finite, though he is powerful to do much harm and suffers not as we do. But we are strong, each in our purpose; and we are all more strong together. Take heart afresh, dear husband of Madam Mina. This battle is but begun, and in the end we shall win—so sure as that God sits on high to watch over His children. Therefore be of much comfort till we return.

VAN HELSING.

JONATHAN HARKER'S JOURNAL.

4 October.—When I read to Mina, Van Helsing's message in the phonograph, the poor girl brightened up considerably. Already the certainty that the Count is out of the country has given her comfort, and comfort is strength to her. For my own part, now that his horrible danger is not face to face with us, it seems almost impossible to believe in it. Even my own terrible experiences in Castle Dracula seem like a long-forgotten dream. Here in the crisp autumn air in the bright sunlight——

Alas! how can I disbelieve! In the midst of my thought my eye fell on the red scar on my poor darling's white forehead. Whilst that lasts, there can be no disbelief. And afterwards the very memory of it will keep faith crystal clear. Mina and I fear to be idle, so we have been over all the diaries again and again. Somehow, although the reality seems greater each time, the pain and the fear seem less. There is something of a guiding purpose manifest throughout, which is comforting. Mina says that perhaps we are the instruments of ultimate good. It may be! I shall try to think as she does. We have never spoken to each other yet of the future. It is better to wait till we see the Professor and the others after their investigations.

The day is running by more quickly than I ever thought a day could run for me again. It is now three o'clock.

MINA HARKER'S JOURNAL.

5 October, 5 p.m.—Our meeting for report. Present: Professor Van Helsing, Lord Godalming, Dr. Seward, Mr. Quincey Morris, Jonathan Harker, Mina Harker.

Dr. Van Helsing described what steps were taken during the day to discover on what boat and whither bound Count Dracula made his escape:—

"As I knew that he wanted to get back to Transylvania, I felt sure that he must go by the Danube mouth; or by somewhere in the Black Sea, since by that way he come. It was a dreary blank that was before us. *Omne ignotum pro magnifico*; and so with heavy hearts we start to find what ships leave for the Black Sea last night. He was in sailing ship, since Madam Mina tell of sails being set. These not so important as to go in your list of the shipping in the *Times*, and so we go, by suggestion of Lord Godalming, to your Lloyd's, where are note of all ships that sail, however so small. There we find that only one Black-Sea-bound ship go out with the tide. She is the *Czarina Catherine*, and she sail from Doolittle's Wharf for Varna, and thence on to other parts and up the Danube. 'Soh!' said I, 'this is the ship whereon is the Count.' So off we go to Doolittle's Wharf, and there we find a man in an office. From him we inquire of the goings of the *Czarina Catherine*. He swear much, and he red face and loud of voice, but he good fellow all the same; and when Quincey give him something from his pocket which cracked as he roll it up, and put it in a so small bag which he have hid deep in his clothing, he still better fellow and humble servant to us. He come with us, and ask many men who are rough and hot; these be better fellows too when they have been no more thirsty. They say much of blood and bloom, and of others which I comprehend not, though I guess what they mean; but nevertheless they tell us all things which we want to know.

"They make known to us among them, how last afternoon at about five o'clock comes a man so hurry. A tall man, thin and pale, with high nose and teeth so white, and eyes that seem to be burning. That he be all in black, except that he have a hat of straw which suit not him or the time. That he scatter his money in making quick inquiry as to what ship sails for the Black Sea and for where. Some took him to the office and then to the ship, where he will not go aboard but halt at shore end of gang-plank, and ask that the captain come to him. The captain come, when told that he will be pay well; and though he swear much at the first he agree to term. Then the thin man go and some one tell him where horse and cart can be hired. He go there and soon he come again, himself driving cart on which a great box; this he himself lift down, though it take several to put in on truck for the ship. He give much talk to captain as to how and where his box is to be place; but the captain like it not and swear at him in many tongues, and tell him that if he like he can come and see where it shall be. But he say 'no'; that he come not yet, for that he have much to do. Whereupon the captain tell him that he had better be quick—with blood—for that his ship will leave the place—of blood—before the turn of the tide—with blood. Then the thin man smile and say that of course he must go when he think fit; but he will be surprise if he go quite so soon. The captain swear again, polyglot, and the thin man make him bow, and thank him, and say that he will so far intrude on his kindness as to come aboard before the sailing. Final the captain, more red than ever, and in more tongues, tell him that he doesn't want no Frenchmen—with bloom upon them and also with blood—in his ship—with blood on her also. And so, after asking where there might be close at hand a shop where he might purchase ship forms, he departed.

"No one knew where he went 'or bloomin' well cared,' as they said, for they had something else to think of—well with blood again; for it soon became apparent to all that the *Czarina Catherine* would not sail as was expected. A thin mist began to creep up from the river, and it grew, and grew; till soon a dense fog enveloped the ship and all around her. The captain swore polyglot—very polyglot—polyglot with bloom and blood; but he could do nothing. The water rose and rose; and he began to fear that he would lose the tide altogether. He was in no friendly mood, when just at full tide, the thin man came up the gang-plank again and asked to see where his box has been stowed. Then the captain replied that he wished that he and his box—old and with much bloom and blood—were in hell. But the thin man did not be offended, and went down with the mate and saw where it was place, and came up and stood awhile on deck in fog. He must have come off by himself, for none notice him. Indeed they thought not of him: for soon the fog begin to melt away, and all was clear again. My friends of the thirst and the language that was of bloom and blood laughed, as they told how the captain's swears exceeded even his usual polyglot, and was more than ever full of picturesque, when on questioning other mariners who were on movement up and down on the river that hour, he found that few of them had seen any of fog at all except where it lay round the wharf. However, the ship went out on the ebb tide; and was doubtless by morning far down the river mouth. She was by then, when they told us, well out to sea.

"And so, my dear Madam Mina, it is that we have to rest for a time, for our enemy is on the sea, with the fog at his command, on his way to the Danube mouth. To sail a ship takes time, go she never so quick; and when we start we go on land more quick, and we meet him there. Our best hope is to come on him when in the box between sunrise and sunset; for then he can make no struggle, and we may deal with him as we should. There are days for us, in which we can make ready our plan. We know all about where he go; for we have seen the owner of the ship, who have shown us invoices and all papers that can be. The box we seek is to be landed in Varna, and to be given to an agent, one Ristics who will there present his credentials; and so our merchant friend will have done his part. When he ask if there be any wrong, for that so, he can telegraph and have inquiry made at Varna, we say 'no'; for what is to be done is not for police or of the customs. It must be done by us alone and in our own way."

When Dr. Van Helsing had done speaking, I asked him if he were certain that the Count had remained on board the ship. He replied: "We have the best proof of that: your own evidence, when in the hypnotic trance this morning." I asked him again if it were really necessary that they should pursue the Count, for oh! I dread Jonathan leaving me, and I know that he would surely go if the others went. He answered in growing passion, at first quietly. As he went on, however, he grew more angry and more forceful till in the end we could not but see wherein was at least some of that personal dominance which made him so long a master amongst men:—

"Yes, it is necessary—necessary—necessary! For your sake in the first, and then for the sake of humanity. This monster has done much harm already, in the narrow scope where he find himself, and in the short time when as yet he was only as a body groping his so small measure in darkness and not knowing. All this have I told these others; you, my dear Madam Mina, will learn it in the phonograph of my friend John, or in that of your husband. I have told them how the measure of leaving his own barren land—barren of peoples—and coming to a new land where life of man teems till they are like the multitude of standing corn, was the work of centuries. Were another of the Un-Dead, like him, to try to do what he has done, perhaps not all the centuries of the world that have been, or that will be, could aid him. With this one, all the forces of nature that are occult and deep and strong must have worked together in some wondrous way. The very place, where he have been alive, Un-Dead for all these centuries, is full of strangeness of the geologic and chemical world. There are deep caverns and fissures that reach none know whither. There have been volcanoes, some of whose openings still send out waters of strange properties, and gases that kill or make to vivify. Doubtless, there is something magnetic or electric in some of these combinations of occult forces which work for physical life in strange ways; and in himself were from the first some great qualities. In a hard and war-like time he was celebrate that he have more iron nerve, more subtle brain, more braver heart, than any man. In him some vital principle have in strange way found their utmost; and as his body keep strong and grow and thrive, so his brain grow too. All this without that diabolic aid which is surely to him; for it have to yield to the powers that come from, and are, symbolic of good. And now this is what he is to us. He have infect you—oh, forgive me, my dear, that I must say such; but it is for good of you that I speak. He infect you in such wise, that even if he do no more, you have only to live—to live in your own old, sweet way; and so in time, death, which is of man's common lot, and with God's sanction, shall make you like to him. This must not be! We have sworn together that it must not. Thus are we ministers of God's own wish: that the world, and men for whom His Son die, will not be given over to monsters, whose very existence would defame Him. He have allowed us to redeem one soul already, and we go out as the old knights of the Cross to redeem more. Like them we shall travel towards the sunrise; and like them, if we fall, we fall in good cause." He paused and I said:—

"But will not the Count take his rebuff wisely? Since he has been driven from England, will he not avoid it, as a tiger does the village from which he has been hunted?"

"Aha!" he said, "your simile of the tiger good, for me, and I shall adopt him. Your man-eater, as they of India call the tiger who has once tasted blood of the human, care no more for the other prey, but prowl unceasingly till he get him. This that we hunt from our village is a tiger, too, a man-eater, and he never cease to prowl. Nay, in himself he is not one to retire and stay afar. In his life, his living life, he go over the Turkey frontier and attack his enemy on his own ground; he be beaten back, but did he stay? No! He come again, and again, and again. Look at his persistence and endurance. With the child-brain that was to him he have long since conceive the idea of coming to a great city. What does he do? He find out the place of all the world most of promise for him. Then he deliberately set himself down to prepare for the task. He find in patience just how is his strength, and what are his powers. He study new tongues. He learn new social life; new environment of old ways, the politic, the law, the finance, the science, the habit of a new land and a new people who have come to be since he was. His glimpse

{ 349 }

that he have had, whet his appetite only and enkeen his desire. Nay, it help him to grow as to his brain; for it all prove to him how right he was at the first in his surmises. He have done this alone; all alone! from a ruin tomb in a forgotten land. What more may he not do when the greater world of thought is open to him. He that can smile at death, as we know him; who can flourish in the midst of diseases that kill off whole peoples. Oh, if such an one was to come from God, and not the Devil, what a force for good might he not be in this old world of ours. But we are pledged to set the world free. Our toil must be in silence, and our efforts all in secret; for in this enlightened age, when men believe not even what they see, the doubting of wise men would be his greatest strength. It would be at once his sheath and his armour, and his weapons to destroy us, his enemies, who are willing to peril even our own souls for the safety of one we love—for the good of mankind, and for the honour and glory of God."

After a general discussion it was determined that for to-night nothing be definitely settled; that we should all sleep on the facts, and try to think out the proper conclusions. To-morrow, at breakfast, we are to meet again, and, after making our conclusions known to one another, we shall decide on some definite course of action.

—I feel a wonderful peace and rest to-night. It is as if some haunting presence were removed from me. Perhaps. . . .

My surmise was not finished, could not be; for I caught sight in the mirror of the red mark upon my forehead; and I knew that I was still unclean.

DR. SEWARD'S DIARY.

5 October.—We all rose early, and I think that sleep did much for each and all of us. When we met at early breakfast there was more general cheerfulness than any of us had ever expected to experience again.

It is really wonderful how much resilience there is in human nature. Let any obstructing cause, no matter what, be removed in any way—

even by death—and we fly back to first principles of hope and enjoyment. More than once as we sat around the table, my eyes opened in wonder whether the whole of the past days had not been a dream. It was only when I caught sight of the red blotch on Mrs. Harker's forehead that I was brought back to reality. Even now, when I am gravely revolving the matter, it is almost impossible to realise that the cause of all our trouble is still existent. Even Mrs. Harker seems to lose sight of her trouble for whole spells; it is only now and again, when something recalls it to her mind, that she thinks of her terrible scar. We are to meet here in my study in half an hour and decide on our course of action. I see only one immediate difficulty, I know it by instinct rather than reason: we shall all have to speak frankly; and yet I fear that in some mysterious way poor Mrs. Harker's tongue is tied. I *know* that she forms conclusions of her own, and from all that has been I can guess how brilliant and how true they must be; but she will not, or cannot, give them utterance. I have mentioned this to Van Helsing, and he and I are to talk it over when we are alone. I suppose it is some of that horrid poison which has got into her veins beginning to work. The Count had his own purposes when he gave her what Van Helsing called "the Vampire's baptism of blood." Well, there may be a poison that distils itself out of good things; in an age when the existence of ptomaines is a mystery we should not wonder at anything! One thing I know: that if my instinct be true regarding poor Mrs. Harker's silences, then there is a terrible difficulty—an unknown danger—in the work before us. The same power that compels her silence may compel her speech. I dare not think further; for so I should in my thoughts dishonour a noble woman!

Van Helsing is coming to my study a little before the others. I shall try to open the subject with him.

Later.—When the Professor came in, we talked over the state of things. I could see that he had something on his mind which he wanted to say, but felt some hesitancy about broaching the subject. After beating about the bush a little, he said suddenly:—

"Friend John, there is something that you and I must talk of alone, just at the first at any rate. Later, we may have to take the others into our confidence"; then he stopped, so I waited; he went on:—

"Madam Mina, our poor dear Madam Mina is changing." A cold shiver ran through me to find my worst fears thus endorsed. Van Helsing continued:—

"With the sad experience of Miss Lucy, we must this time be warned before things go too far. Our task is now in reality more difficult than ever, and this new trouble makes every hour of the direst importance. I can see the characteristics of the vampire coming in her face. It is now but very, very slight; but it is to be seen if we have eyes to notice without to prejudge. Her teeth are some sharper, and at times her eyes are more hard. But these are not all, there is to her the silence now often; as so it was with Miss Lucy. She did not speak, even when she wrote that which she wished to be known later. Now my fear is this. If it be that she can, by our hypnotic trance, tell what the Count see and hear, is it not more true that he who have hypnotise her first, and who have drink of her very blood and make her drink of his, should, if he will, compel her mind to disclose to him that which she know?" I nodded acquiescence; he went on:—

"Then, what we must do is to prevent this; we must keep her ignorant of our intent, and so she cannot tell what she know not. This is a painful task! Oh, so painful that it heartbreak me to think of; but it must be. When to-day we meet, I must tell her that for reason which we will not to speak she must not more be of our council, but be simply guarded by us." He wiped his forehead, which had broken out in profuse perspiration at the thought of the pain which he might have to inflict upon the poor soul already so tortured. I knew that it would be some sort of comfort to him if I told him that I also had come to the same conclusion; for at any rate it would take away the pain of doubt. I told him, and the effect was as I expected.

It is now close to the time of our general gathering. Van Helsing has gone away to prepare for the meeting, and his painful part of it. I really believe his purpose is to be able to pray alone.

Later.—At the very outset of our meeting a great personal relief was experienced by both Van Helsing and myself. Mrs. Harker had sent a message by her husband to say that she would not join us at present, as she thought it better that we should be free to discuss our movements without her presence to embarrass us. The Professor and I looked at each other for an instant, and somehow we both seemed relieved. For my own part, I thought that if Mrs. Harker realised the danger herself, it was much pain as well as much danger averted. Under the circumstances we agreed, by a questioning look and answer with finger on lip, to preserve silence in our suspicions, until we should have been able to confer alone again. We went at once into our Plan of Campaign. Van Helsing roughly put the facts before us first:—

"The *Czarina Catherine* left the Thames yesterday morning. It will take her at the quickest speed she has ever made at least three weeks to reach Varna; but we can travel overland to the same place in three days. Now, if we allow for two days less for the ship's voyage, owing to such weather influences as we know that the Count can bring to bear; and if we allow a whole day and night for any delays which may occur to us, then we have a margin of nearly two weeks. Thus, in order to be quite safe, we must leave here on 17th at latest. Then we shall at any rate be in Varna a day before the ship arrives, and able to make such preparations as may be necessary. Of course we shall all go armed—armed against evil things, spiritual as well as physical." Here Quincey Morris added:—

"I understand that the Count comes from a wolf country, and it may be that he shall get there before us. I propose that we add Winchesters to our armament. I have a kind of belief in a Winchester when there is any trouble of that sort around. Do you remember, Art, when we had the pack after us at Tobolsk? What wouldn't we have given then for a repeater apiece!"

"Good!" said Van Helsing, "Winchesters it shall be. Quincey's head is level at all times, but most so when there is to hunt, metaphor be more dishonour to science than wolves be of danger to man. In the meantime we can do nothing here; and as I think that Varna is not familiar to any of us, why not go there more soon? It is as long to wait here as there. To-night and to-morrow we can get ready, and then, if all be well, we four can set out on our journey."

"We four?" said Harker interrogatively, looking from one to another of us.

"Of course!" answered the Professor quickly, "you must remain to take care of your so sweet wife!" Harker was silent for a while and then said in a hollow voice:—

"Let us talk of that part of it in the morning. I want to consult with Mina." I thought that now was the time for Van Helsing to warn him not to disclose our plans to her; but he took no notice. I looked at him significantly and coughed. For answer he put his finger on his lips and turned away.

JONATHAN HARKER'S JOURNAL.

5 October, afternoon.—For some time after our meeting this morning I could not think. The new phases of things leave my mind in a state of wonder which allows no room for active thought. Mina's determination not to take any part in the discussion set me thinking; and as I could not argue the matter with her, I could only guess. I am as far as ever from a solution now. The way the others received it too, puzzled me; the last time we talked of the subject we agreed that there was to be no more concealment of anything amongst us. Mina is sleeping now, calmly and sweetly like a little child. Her lips are curved and her face beams with happiness. Thank God, there are such moments still for her.

Later.—How strange it all is. I sat watching Mina's happy sleep, and came as near to being happy myself as I suppose I shall ever be. As the evening drew on, and the earth took its shadows from the sun sinking lower, the silence of the room grew more and more solemn to me. All at once Mina opened her eyes, and looking at me tenderly, said:—

"Jonathan, I want you to promise me something on your word of honour. A promise made to me, but made holily in God's hearing, and not to be broken though I should go down on my knees and implore you with bitter tears. Quick, you must make it to me at once."

"Mina," I said, "a promise like that, I cannot make at once. I may have no right to make it."

"But, dear one," she said, with such spiritual intensity that her eyes were like pole stars, "it is I who wish it; and it is not for myself. You can ask Dr. Van Helsing if I am not right; if he disagrees you may do as you will. Nay, more, if you all agree, later, you are absolved from the promise."

"I promise!" I said, and for a moment she looked supremely happy; though to me all happiness for her was denied by the red scar on her forehead. She said:—

"Promise me that you will not tell me anything of the plans formed for the campaign against the Count. Not by word, or inference, or implication; not at any time whilst this remains to me!" and she solemnly pointed to the scar. I saw that she was in earnest, and said solemnly:—

"I promise!" and as I said it I felt that from that instant a door had been shut between us.

Later, midnight.—Mina has been bright and cheerful all the evening. So much so that all the rest seemed to take courage, as if infected somewhat with her gaiety; as a result even I myself felt as if the pall of gloom which weighs us down were somewhat lifted. We all retired early. Mina is now sleeping like a little child; it is a wonderful thing that her faculty of sleep remains to her in the midst of her terrible trouble. Thank God for it, for then at least she can forget her care. Perhaps her example may affect me as her gaiety did to-night. I shall try it. Oh! for a dreamless sleep.

6 October, morning.—Another surprise. Mina woke me early, about the same time as yesterday, and asked me to bring Dr. Van Helsing. I thought that it was another occasion for hypnotism, and without question went for the Professor. He had evidently expected some such call, for I found him dressed in his room. His door was ajar, so that he could hear the opening of the door to our room. He came at once; as he passed into the room, he asked Mina if the others might come, too.

"No," she said quite simply, "it will not be necessary. You can tell them just as well. I must go with you on your journey."

Dr. Van Helsing was as startled as I was. After a moment's pause he asked:—

"But why?"

"You must take me with you. I am safer with you, and you shall be safer, too."

"But why, dear Madam Mina? You know that your safety is our solemnest duty. We go into danger, to which you are, or may be, more liable than any of us from—from circumstances—things that have been." He paused, embarrassed.

As she replied, she raised her finger and pointed to her forehead:—

"I know. That is why I must go. I can tell you now, whilst the sun is coming up; I may not be able again. I know that when the Count wills me I must go. I know that if he tells me to come in secret, I must come by wile; by any device to hoodwink—even Jonathan." God saw the look that she turned on me as she spoke, and if there be indeed a Recording Angel that look is noted to her everlasting honour. I could only clasp her hand. I could not speak; my emotion was too great for even the relief of tears. She went on:—

"You men are brave and strong. You are strong in your numbers, for you can defy that which would break down the human endurance of one who had to guard alone. Besides, I may be of service, since you can hypnotise me and so learn that which even I myself do not know." Dr. Van Helsing said very gravely:—

"Madam Mina, you are, as always, most wise. You shall with us come; and together we shall do that which we go forth to achieve." When he had spoken, Mina's long spell of silence made me look at her. She had fallen back on her pillow asleep; she did not even wake when I had pulled up the blind and let in the sunlight which flooded the room. Van Helsing motioned to me to come with him quietly. We went to his room, and within a minute Lord Godalming, Dr. Seward, and Mr. Morris were with us also. He told them what Mina had said, and went on:—

"In the morning we shall leave for Varna. We have now to deal with a new factor: Madam Mina. Oh, but her soul is true. It is to her an agony to tell us so much as she has done; but it is most right, and we are warned in time. There must be no chance lost, and in Varna we must be ready to act the instant when that ship arrives."

"What shall we do exactly?" asked Mr. Morris laconically.

The Professor paused before replying:—

"We shall at the first board that ship; then when we have identified the box, we shall place a branch of the wild rose on it. This we shall fasten, for when it is there none can emerge; so at least says the superstition. And to superstition must we trust at the first; it was man's faith in the early, and it have its root in faith still. Then, when we get the opportunity that we seek, when none are near to see, we shall open the box, and—and all will be well."

"I shall not wait for any opportunity," said Morris. "When I see the box I shall open it and destroy the monster, though there were a thousand men looking on, and if I am to be wiped out for it the next moment!" I grasped his hand instinctively and found it as firm as a piece of steel. I think he understood my look; I hope he did.

"Good boy," said Dr. Van Helsing. "Brave boy. Quincey is all man. God bless him for it. My child, believe me none of us shall lag behind or pause from any fear. I do but say what we may do—what we must do. But, indeed, indeed we cannot say what we shall do. There are so many things which may happen, and their ways and their ends are so various that until the moment we may not say. We shall all be armed, in all ways; and when the time for the end has come, our effort shall not be lack. Now let us to-day put all our affairs in order. Let all things which touch on others dear to us, and who on us depend, be complete; for none of us can tell what, or when, or how, the end may be. As for me, my own affairs are regulate; and as I have nothing else to do, I shall go make arrangements for the travel. I shall have all tickets and so forth for our journey."

There was nothing further to be said, and we parted. I shall now settle up all my affairs of earth, and be ready for whatever may come. . . .

Later.—It is all done; my will is made, and all complete. Mina if she survive is my sole heir. If it should not be so, then the others who have been so good to us shall have remainder.

It is now drawing towards the sunset; Mina's uneasiness calls my attention to it. I am sure that there is something on her mind which the time of exact sunset will reveal. These occasions are becoming harrowing times for us all, for each sunrise and sunset opens up some new danger—some new pain, which, however, may in God's will be means to a good end. I write all these things in the diary since my darling must not hear them now; but if it may be that she can see them again, they shall be ready.

She is calling to me.

CHAPTER 25.

—————◆—————

DR. SEWARD'S DIARY.

11 October, evening.—Jonathan Harker has asked me to note this, as he says he is hardly equal to the task, and he wants an exact record kept.

I think that none of us were surprised when we were asked to see Mrs. Harker a little before the time of sunset. We have of late come to understand that sunrise and sunset are to her times of peculiar freedom; when her old self can be manifest without any controlling force subduing or restraining her, or inciting her to action. This mood or condition begins some half hour or more before actual sunrise or sunset, and lasts till either the sun is high, or whilst the clouds are still aglow with the rays streaming above the horizon. At first there is a sort of negative condition, as if some tie were loosened, and then the absolute freedom quickly follows; when, however, the freedom ceases the change-back or relapse comes quickly, preceded only by a spell of warning silence.

To-night, when we met, she was somewhat constrained, and bore all the signs of an internal struggle. I put it down myself to her making a violent effort at the earliest instant she could do so. A very few minutes, however, gave her complete control of herself; then, motioning her husband to sit beside her on the sofa where she was half reclining, she made the rest of us bring chairs up close. Taking her husband's hand in hers she began:—

"We are all here together in freedom, for perhaps the last time! I know, dear; I know that you will always be with me to the end." This was to her husband whose hand had, as we could see, tightened upon hers. "In the morning we go out upon our task, and God alone knows what may be in store for any of us. You are going to be so good to me as to take me with you. I know that all that brave earnest men can do for a poor weak woman, whose soul perhaps is lost—no, no, not yet, but is at any rate at stake—you will do. But you must remember that I am not as you are. There is a poison in my blood, in my soul, which may destroy me; which must destroy me, unless some relief comes to us. Oh, my friends, you know as well as I do, that my soul is at stake; and though I know there is one way out for me, you must not and I must not take it!" She looked appealingly to us all in turn, beginning and ending with her husband.

"What is that?" asked Van Helsing in a hoarse voice. "What is that way, which we must not—may not—take?"

"That I may die now, either by my own hand or that of another, before the greater evil is entirely wrought. I know, and you know, that were I once dead you could and would set free my immortal spirit, even as you did my poor Lucy's. Were death, or the fear of death, the only thing that stood in the way I would not shrink to die here, now, amidst the friends who love me. But death is not all. I cannot believe that to die in such a case, when there is hope before us and a bitter task to be done, is God's will. Therefore, I, on my part, give up here the certainty of eternal rest, and go out into the dark where may be the blackest things that the world or the nether world holds!" We were all silent, for we knew instinctively that this was only a prelude. The faces of the others were set, and Harker's grew ashen grey; perhaps he guessed better than any of us what was coming. She continued:—

"This is what I can give into the hotch-pot." I could not but note the quaint legal phrase which she used in such a place, and with all seriousness. "What will each of you give? Your lives I know," she went on quickly, "that is easy for brave men. Your lives are God's, and you can give them back to Him; but what will you give to me?" She looked again questioningly, but this time avoided her husband's face. Quincey seemed to understand; he nodded, and her face lit up. "Then I shall tell you plainly what I want, for there must be no doubtful matter in this connection between us now. You must promise me, one and all—even you, my beloved husband—that, should the time come, you will kill me."

"What is that time?" The voice was Quincey's, but it was low and strained.

"When you shall be convinced that I am so changed that it is better that I die that I may live. When I am thus dead in the flesh, then you will, without a moment's delay, drive a stake through me and cut off my head; or do whatever else may be wanting to give me rest!"

Quincey was the first to rise after the pause. He knelt down before her and taking her hand in his said solemnly:—

"I'm only a rough fellow, who hasn't, perhaps, lived as a man should to win such a distinction, but I swear to you by all that I hold sacred and dear that, should the time ever come, I shall not flinch from the duty that you have set us. And I promise you, too, that I shall make all certain, for if I am only doubtful, I shall take it that the time has come!"

"My true friend!" was all she could say amid her fast-falling tears, as, bending over, she kissed his hand.

"I swear the same, my dear Madam Mina!" said Van Helsing.

"And I!" said Lord Godalming, each of them in turn kneeling to her to take the oath. I followed, myself. Then her husband turned to her wan-eyed and with a greenish pallor which subdued the snowy whiteness of his hair, and asked:—

"And must I, too, make such a promise, oh, my wife?"

"You too, my dearest," she said, with infinite yearning of pity in her voice and eyes. "You must not shrink. You are nearest and dearest and all the world to me; our souls are knit into one, for all life and all time. Think, dear, that there have been times when brave men have killed their wives and their womenkind, to keep them from falling into the hands of the enemy. Their hands did not falter any the more because those that they loved implored them to slay them. It is men's duty towards those whom they love, in such time of sore trial! And oh, my dear, if it is to be that I must meet death at any hand, let it be at the hand of him that loves me best. Dr. Van Helsing, I have not forgotten your mercy in poor Lucy's case to him who loved"—she stopped with a flying blush, and changed her phrase—"to him who had best right to give her peace. If that time shall come again, I look to you to make it a happy memory of my husband's life that it was his loving hand which set me free from the awful thrall upon me."

"Again I swear!" came the Professor's resonant voice. Mrs. Harker smiled, positively smiled, as with a sigh of relief she leaned back and said:—

"And now one word of warning, a warning which you must never forget: this time, if it ever come, may come quickly and unexpectedly and in such case you must lose no time in using your opportunity. At such a time I myself might be—nay! if the time ever comes, *shall be*—leagued with your enemy against you."

"One more request"; she became very solemn as she said this, "it is not vital and necessary like the other, but I want you to do one thing for me, if you will." We all acquiesced, but no one spoke; there was no need to speak:—

"I want you to read the Burial Service." She was interrupted by a deep groan from her husband; taking his hand in hers, she held it over her heart, and continued: "You must read it over me some day. Whatever may be the issue of all this fearful state of things, it will be a sweet thought to all or some of us. You, my dearest, will I hope read it, for then it will be in your voice in my memory for ever—come what may!"

"But oh, my dear one," he pleaded, "death is afar off from you."

"Nay," she said, holding up a warning hand. "I am deeper in death at this moment than if the weight of an earthly grave lay heavy upon me!"

"Oh, my wife, must I read it?" he said, before he began.

"It would comfort me, my husband!" was all she said; and he began to read when she had got the book ready.

How can I—how could any one—tell of that strange scene, its solemnity, its gloom, its sadness, its horror; and, withal, its sweetness? Even a sceptic, who can see nothing but a travesty of bitter truth in anything holy or emotional, would have been melted to the heart had he seen that little group of loving and devoted friends kneeling round that stricken and sorrowing lady; or heard the tender passion of her husband's voice, as in tones so broken with emotion that often he had to pause, he read the simple and beautiful service from the Burial of the Dead. I—I cannot go on—words—and—v-voice—f-fail m-me!

She was right in her instinct. Strange as it all was, bizarre as it may hereafter seem even to us who felt its potent influence at the time, it comforted us much; and the silence, which showed Mrs. Harker's coming relapse from her freedom of soul, did not seem so full of despair to any of us as we had dreaded.

JONATHAN HARKER'S JOURNAL.

15 October, Varna.—We left Charing Cross on the morning of the 12th, got to Paris the same night, and took the places secured for us in the Orient Express. We travelled night and day, arriving here at about five o'clock. Lord Godalming went to the Consulate to see if any telegram had arrived for him, whilst the rest of us came on to this hotel—"the Odessus." The journey may have had incidents; I was, however, too eager to get on, to care for them. Until the *Czarina Catherine* comes into port there will be no interest for me in anything in the wide world. Thank God! Mina is well, and looks to be getting stronger; her colour is coming back. She sleeps a great deal; throughout the journey she slept nearly all the time. Before sunrise and sunset, however, she is very wakeful and alert; and it has become a habit for Van Helsing to hypnotise her at such times. At first, some effort was needed, and he had to make many passes; but now, she seems to yield at once, as if by habit, and scarcely any action is needed. He seems to have power at these particular moments to simply will, and her thoughts obey him. He always asks her what she can see and hear. She answers to the first:—

"Nothing; all is dark." And to the second:—

"I can hear the waves lapping against the ship, and the water rushing by. Canvas and cordage strain and masts and yards creak. The wind is high—I can hear it in the shrouds, and the bow throws back the foam." It is evident that the *Czarina Catherine* is still at sea, hastening on her way to Varna. Lord Godalming has just returned. He had four telegrams, one each day since we started, and all to the same effect: that the *Czarina Catherine* had not been reported to Lloyd's from anywhere. He had arranged before leaving London that his agent should send him every day a telegram saying if the ship had been reported. He was to have a message even if she were not reported, so that he might be sure that there was a watch being kept at the other end of the wire.

We had dinner and went to bed early. To-morrow we are to see the Vice-Consul, and to arrange, if we can, about getting on board the ship as soon as she arrives. Van Helsing says that our chance will be to get on the boat between sunrise and sunset. The Count, even if he takes the form of a bat, cannot cross the running water of his own volition, and so cannot leave the ship. As he dare not change to man's form without suspicion—which he evidently wishes to avoid—he must remain in the box. If, then, we can come on board after sunrise, he is at our mercy; for we can open the box and make sure of him, as we did of poor Lucy, before he wakes. What mercy he shall get from us will not count for much. We think that we shall not have much trouble with officials or the seamen. Thank God! this is the country where bribery can do anything, and we are well supplied with money. We have only to make sure that the ship cannot come into port between sunset and sunrise without our being warned, and we shall be safe. Judge Moneybag will settle this case, I think!

16 October.—Mina's report still the same: lapping waves and rushing water, darkness and favouring winds. We are evidently in good time, and when we hear of the *Czarina Catherine* we shall be ready. As she must pass the Dardanelles we are sure to have some report.

17 October.—Everything is pretty well fixed now, I think, to welcome the Count on his return from his tour. Godalming told the shippers that he fancied that the box sent aboard might contain something stolen from a friend of his, and got a half consent that he might open it at his own risk. The owner gave him a paper telling the Captain to give him every facility, in doing whatever he chose on board the ship, and also a similar authorisation to his agent at Varna. We have seen the agent, who was much impressed with Godalming's kindly manner to him, and we are all satisfied that whatever he can do to aid our wishes will be done. We have already arranged what to do in case we get the box open. If the Count is there, Van Helsing and Seward will cut off his head at once and drive a stake through his heart. Morris and Godalming and I shall prevent interference, even if we have to use the arms which we shall have ready. The Professor says that if we can so treat the Count's body, it will soon after fall into dust. In such case there would be no evidence against us, in case any suspicion of murder were aroused. But even if it were not, we should stand or fall by our act, and perhaps some day this very script may be evidence to come between some of us and a rope. For myself, I should take the chance only too thankfully if it were to come. We mean to leave no stone unturned to carry out our intent. We have arranged with certain officials that the instant the *Czarina Catherine* is seen, we are to be informed by a special messenger.

24 October.—A whole week of waiting. Daily telegrams to Godalming, but only the same story: "Not yet reported." Mina's morning and evening hypnotic answer is unvaried: lapping waves, rushing water, and creaking masts.

TELEGRAM, RUFUS SMITH, LLOYD'S, LONDON,
TO LORD GODALMING, CARE OF H. B. M. VICE-CONSUL,
VARNA.

"*24 October.*—*Czarina Catherine* reported this morning from Dardanelles."

DR. SEWARD'S DIARY.

25 October.—How I miss my phonograph! To write diary with a pen is irksome to me; but Van Helsing says I must. We were all wild with excitement yesterday when Godalming got his telegram from Lloyd's. I know now what men feel in battle when the call to action is heard. Mrs. Harker, alone of our party, did not show any signs of emotion. After all, it is not strange that she did not; for we took special care not to let her know anything about it, and we all tried not to show any excitement when we were in her presence. In old days she would, I am sure, have noticed, no matter how we might have tried to conceal it; but in this way she is greatly changed during the past three weeks. The lethargy grows upon her, and though she seems strong and well, and is getting back some of her colour, Van Helsing and I are not satisfied. We talk of her often; we have not, however, said a word to the others. It would break poor Harker's heart—certainly his nerve—if he knew that we had even a suspicion on the subject. Van Helsing examines, he tells me, her teeth very carefully, whilst she is in the hypnotic condition, for he says that so long as they do not begin to sharpen there is no active danger of a change in her. If this change should come, it would be necessary to take steps! . . . . We both know what those steps would have to be, though we do not mention our thoughts to each other. We should neither of us shrink from the task—awful though it be to contemplate. "Euthanasia" is an excellent and a comforting word! I am grateful to whoever invented it.

It is only about 24 hours' sail from the Dardanelles to here, at the rate the *Czarina Catherine* has come from London. She should therefore arrive some time in the morning; but as she cannot possibly get in before then, we made all about to retire early. We shall get up at one o'clock, so as to be ready.

25 October, noon.—No news yet of the ship's arrival. Mrs. Harker's hypnotic report this morning was the same as usual, so it is possible that we may get news at any moment. We men are all in a fever of excitement, except Harker, who is calm; his hands are cold as ice, and an hour ago I found him whetting the edge of the great Ghoorka knife which he now always carries with him. It will be a bad lookout for the Count if the edge of that "Kukri" ever touches his throat, driven by that stern, ice-cold hand!

Van Helsing and I were a little alarmed about Mrs. Harker to-day. About noon she got into a sort of lethargy which we did not like; although we kept silence to the others, we were neither of us happy about it. She had been restless all the morning, so that we were at first glad to know that she was sleeping. When, however, her husband mentioned casually that she was sleeping so soundly that he could not wake her, we went to her room to see for ourselves. She was breathing naturally and looked so well and peaceful that we agreed that the sleep was better for her than anything else. Poor girl, she has so much to forget that it is no wonder that sleep, if it brings oblivion to her, does her good.

Later.—Our opinion was justified, for when after a refreshing sleep of some hours she woke up, she seemed brighter and better than she had been for days. At sunset she made the usual hypnotic report. Wherever he may be in the Black Sea, the Count is hurrying to his destination. To his doom, I trust!

26 October.—Another day and no tidings of the *Czarina Catherine*. She ought to be here by now. That she is still journeying *somewhere* is apparent, for Mrs. Harker's hypnotical report at sunrise was still the same. It is possible that the vessel may be lying by, at times, for fog; some of the steamers which came in last evening reported patches of fog both to north and south of the port. We must continue our watching, as the ship may now be signalled any moment.

27 October, noon.—Most strange; no news yet of the ship we wait for. Mrs. Harker reported last night and this morning as usual: "lapping waves and rushing water," though she added that "the waves were very faint." The telegrams from London have been the same: "no further report." Van Helsing is terribly anxious, and told me just now that he fears the Count is escaping us. He added significantly:—

"I did not like that lethargy of Madam Mina's. Souls and memories can do strange things during trance." I was about to ask him more, but Harker just then came in, and he held up a warning hand. We must try to-night at sunset to make her speak more fully when in her hypnotic state.

TELEGRAM, RUFUS SMITH, LLOYD'S, LONDON, TO LORD GODALMING, CARE OF H. B. M. VICE-CONSUL, VARNA.

"*28 October.*—*Czarina Catherine* reported entering Galatz at one o'clock to-day."

DR. SEWARD'S DIARY.

28 October.—When the telegram came announcing the arrival in Galatz I do not think it was such a shock to any of us as might have been expected. True, we did not know whence, or how, or when, the bolt would come; but I think we all expected that something strange would happen. The delay of arrival at Varna made us individually satisfied that things would not be just as we had expected; we only waited to learn where the change would occur. None the less, however, was it a surprise. I suppose that nature works on such a hopeful basis that we believe against ourselves that things will be as they ought to be, not as we should know that they will be. Transcendentalism is a beacon to the angels, even if it be a will-o'-the-wisp to man. It was an odd experience and we all took it differently. Van Helsing raised his hand over his head for a moment, as though in remonstrance with the Almighty; but he said not a word, and in a few seconds stood up with his face sternly set. Lord Godalming grew very pale, and sat breathing heavily. I was myself half stunned and looked in wonder at one after another. Quincey Morris tightened his belt with that quick movement which I knew so well; in our old wandering days it meant "action." Mrs. Harker grew ghastly white, so that the scar on her forehead seemed to burn, but she folded her hands meekly and looked up in prayer. Harker smiled—actually smiled—the dark, bitter smile of one who is without hope; but at the same time his action belied his words, for his hands instinctively sought the hilt of the great Kukri knife and rested there. "When does the next train start for Galatz?" said Van Helsing to us generally.

"At 6:30 to-morrow morning!" We all started, for the answer came from Mrs. Harker.

"How on earth do you know?" said Art.

"You forget—or perhaps you do not know, though Jonathan does and so does Dr. Van Helsing—that I am the train fiend. At home in Exeter I always used to make up the time-tables, so as to be helpful to my husband. I found it so useful sometimes, that I always make a study of the time-tables now. I knew that if anything were to take us to Castle Dracula we should go by Galatz, or at any rate through Bucharest, so I learned the times very carefully. Unhappily there are not many to learn, as the only train to-morrow leaves as I say."

"Wonderful woman!" murmured the Professor.

"Can't we get a special?" asked Lord Godalming. Van Helsing shook his head: "I fear not. This land is very different from yours or mine; even if we did have a special, it would probably not arrive as soon as our regular train. Moreover, we have something to prepare. We must think. Now let us organise. You, friend Arthur, go to the train and get the tickets and arrange that all be ready for us to go in the morning. Do you, friend Jonathan, go to the agent of the ship and get from him letters to the agent in Galatz, with authority to make search the ship just as it was here. Morris Quincey, you see the Vice-Consul, and get his aid with his fellow in Galatz and all he can do to make our way smooth, so that no times be lost when over the Danube. John will stay with Madam Mina and me, and we shall consult. For so if time be long you may be delayed; and it will not matter when the sun set, since I am here with Madam to make report."

"And I," said Mrs. Harker brightly, and more like her old self than she had been for many a long day, "shall try to be of use in all ways, and shall think and write for you as I used to do. Something is shifting from me in some strange way, and I feel freer than I have been of late!" The three younger men looked happier at the moment as they seemed to realise the significance of her words; but Van Helsing and I, turning to each other, met each a grave and troubled glance. We said nothing at the time, however.

When the three men had gone out to their tasks Van Helsing asked Mrs. Harker to look up the copy of the diaries and find him the part of Harker's journal at the Castle. She went away to get it; when the door was shut upon her he said to me:—

"We mean the same! speak out!"

"There is some change. It is a hope that makes me sick, for it may deceive us."

"Quite so. Do you know why I asked her to get the manuscript?"

"No!" said I, "unless it was to get an opportunity of seeing me alone."

"You are in part right, friend John, but only in part. I want to tell you something. And oh, my friend, I am taking a great—a terrible—risk; but I believe it is right. In the moment when Madam Mina said those words that arrest both our understanding, an inspiration came to me. In the trance of three days ago the Count sent her his spirit to read her mind; or more like he took her to see him in his earth-box in the ship with water rushing, just as it go free at rise and set of sun. He learn then that we are here; for she have more to tell in her open life with eyes to see and ears to hear than he, shut, as he is, in his coffin-box. Now he make his most effort to escape us. At present he want her not.

"He is sure with his so great knowledge that she will come at his call; but he cut her off—take her, as he can do, out of his own power, that so she come not to him. Ah! there I have hope that our man-brains, that have been of man so long and that have not lost the grace of God, will come higher than his child-brain that lie in his tomb for centuries, that grow not yet to our stature, and that do only work selfish and therefore small. Here comes Madam Mina; not a word to her of her trance! She know it not; and it would overwhelm her and make despair just when we want all her hope, all her courage; when most we want all her great brain which is trained like man's brain, but is of sweet woman and have a special power which the Count give her, and which he may not take away altogether—though he think not so. Hush! let me speak, and you shall learn. Oh, John, my friend, we are in awful straits. I fear, as I never feared before. We can only trust the good God. Silence! here she comes!"

I thought that the Professor was going to break down and have hysterics, just as he had when Lucy died, but with a great effort he controlled himself and was at perfect nervous poise when Mrs. Harker tripped into the room, bright and happy-looking, and, in the doing of work, seemingly forgetful of her misery. As she came in, she handed a number of sheets of typewriting to Van Helsing. He looked over them gravely, his face brightening up as he read. Then holding the pages between his finger and thumb he said:—

"Friend John, to you with so much of experience already and you, too, dear Madam Mina, that are young—here is a lesson: do not fear ever to think. A half-thought has been buzzing often in my brain, but I fear to let him loose his wings. Here now, with more knowledge, I go back to where that half-thought come from and I find that he be no half-thought at all; that be a whole thought, though so young that he is not yet strong to use his little wings. Nay, like the 'Ugly Duck' of my friend Hans Andersen, he be no duck-thought at all, but a big swan-thought that sail nobly on big wings, when the time come for him to try them. See I read here what Jonathan have written:—

"'That other of his race who, in a later age, again and again, brought his forces over The Great River into Turkey-land; who, when he was beaten back, came again, and again, and again, though he had to come alone from the bloody field where his troops were being slaughtered, since he knew that he alone could ultimately triumph.'

"What does this tell us? Not much? no! The Count's child-thought see nothing; therefore he speak so free. Your man-thought see nothing;

my man-thought see nothing, till just now. No! But there comes another word from some one who speak without thought because she, too, know not what it mean—what it *might* mean. Just as there are elements which rest, yet when in nature's course they move on their way and they touch—then pouf! and there comes a flash of light, heaven wide, that blind and kill and destroy some; but that show up all earth below for leagues and leagues. Is it not so? Well, I shall explain. To begin, have you ever study the philosophy of crime? 'Yes' and 'No.' You, John, yes; for it is a study of insanity. You, no, Madam Mina; for crime touch you not—not but once. Still, your mind works true, and argues not *a particulari ad universale.* There is this peculiarity in criminals. It is so constant, in all countries and at all times, that even police, who know not much from philosophy, come to know it empirically, that *it is.* That is to be empiric. The criminal always work at one crime—that is the true criminal who seems predestinate to crime, and who will of none other. This criminal has not full man-brain. He is clever and cunning and resourceful; but he be not of man-stature as to brain. He be of child-brain in much. Now this criminal of ours is predestinate to crime also; he, too, have child-brain, and it is of the child to do what he have done. The little bird, the little fish, the little animal learn not by principle, but empirically; and when he learn to do, then there is to the ground to start from to do more. *'Dos pon sto,'* said Archimedes. 'Give me a fulcrum, and I shall move the world!' To do once, is the fulcrum whereby child-brain become man-brain; and until he have the purpose to do more, he continue to do the same again every time, just as he have done before! Oh, my dear, I see that your eyes are opened, and that to you the lightning flash show all the leagues," for Mrs. Harker began to clap her hands and her eyes sparkled. He went on:—

"Now you shall speak. Tell us two dry men of science what you see with those so bright eyes." He took her hand and held it whilst she spoke. His finger and thumb closed on her pulse, as I thought instinctively and unconsciously, as she spoke:—

"The Count is a criminal and of criminal type. Nordau and Lombroso would so classify him, and *quâ* criminal he is of imperfectly formed mind. Thus, in a difficulty he has to seek resource in habit. His past is a clue, and the one page of it that we know—and that from his own lips—tells that once before, when in what Mr. Morris would call a 'tight place,' he went back to his own country from the land he had tried to invade, and thence, without losing purpose, prepared himself for a new effort. He came again better equipped for his work; and won. So he came to London to invade a new land. He was beaten, and when all hope of success was lost, and his existence in danger, he fled back over the sea to his home; just as formerly he had fled back over the Danube from Turkey-land."

"Good, good! oh, you so clever lady!" said Van Helsing, enthusiastically, as he stooped and kissed her hand. A moment later he said to me, as calmly as though we had been having a sick-room consultation:—

"Seventy-two only; and in all this excitement. I have hope." Turning to her again, he said with keen expectation:—

"But go on. Go on! there is more to tell if you will. Be not afraid; John and I know. I do in any case, and shall tell you if you are right. Speak, without fear!"

"I will try to; but you will forgive me if I seem egotistical."

"Nay! fear not, you must be egotist, for it is of you that we think."

"Then, as he is criminal he is selfish; and as his intellect is small and his action is based on selfishness, he confines himself to one purpose. That purpose is remorseless. As he fled back over the Danube, leaving his forces to be cut to pieces, so now he is intent on being safe, careless of all. So his own selfishness frees my soul somewhat from the terrible power which he acquired over me on that dreadful night. I felt it! Oh, I felt it! Thank God, for His great mercy! My soul is freer than it has been since that awful hour; and all that haunts me is a fear lest in some trance or dream he may have used my knowledge for his ends." The Professor stood up:—

"He has so used your mind; and by it he has left us here in Varna, whilst the ship that carried him rushed through enveloping fog up to Galatz, where, doubtless, he had made preparation for escaping from us. But his child-mind only saw so far; and it may be that, as ever is in

God's Providence, the very thing that the evil-doer most reckoned on for his selfish good, turns out to be his chiefest harm. The hunter is taken in his own snare, as the great Psalmist says. For now that he think he is free from every trace of us all, and that he has escaped us with so many hours to him, then his selfish child-brain will whisper him to sleep. He think, too, that as he cut himself off from knowing your mind, there can be no knowledge of him to you; there is where he fail! That terrible baptism of blood which he give you makes you free to go to him in spirit, as you have as yet done in your times of freedom, when the sun rise and set. At such times you go by my volition and not by his; and this power to good of you and others, you have won from your suffering at his hands. This is now all more precious that he know it not, and to guard himself have even cut himself off from his knowledge of our where. We, however, are not selfish, and we believe that God is with us through all this blackness, and these many dark hours. We shall follow him; and we shall not flinch; even if we peril ourselves that we become like him. Friend John, this has been a great hour; and it have done much to advance us on our way. You must be scribe and write him all down, so that when the others return from their work you can give it to them; then they shall know as we do."

And so I have written it whilst we wait their return, and Mrs. Harker has written with her typewriter all since she brought the MS. to us.

CHAPTER 26.

———◇———

DR. SEWARD'S DIARY.

29 October.—This written in the train from Varna to Galatz. Last night we all assembled a little before the time of sunset. Each of us had done his work as well as he could; so far as thought, and endeavour, and opportunity go, we are prepared for the whole of our journey, and for our work when we get to Galatz. When the usual time came round Mrs. Harker prepared herself for her hypnotic effort; and after a longer and more serious effort on the part of Van Helsing than has been usually necessary, she sank into the trance. Usually she speaks on a hint; but this time the Professor had to ask her questions, and to ask them pretty resolutely, before we could learn anything; at last her answer came:—

"I can see nothing; we are still; there are no waves lapping, but only a steady swirl of water softly running against the hawser. I can hear men's voices calling, near and far, and the roll and creak of oars in the rowlocks. A gun is fired somewhere; the echo of it seems far away. There is tramping of feet overhead, and ropes and chains are dragged along. What is this? There is a gleam of light; I can feel the air blowing upon me."

Here she stopped. She had risen, as if impulsively, from where she lay on the sofa, and raised both her hands, palms upward, as if lifting a weight. Van Helsing and I looked at each other with understanding. Quincey raised his eyebrows slightly and looked at her intently, whilst Harker's hand instinctively closed round the hilt of his Kukri. There was a long pause. We all knew that the time when she could speak was passing; but we felt that it was useless to say anything. Suddenly she sat up, and, as she opened her eyes, said sweetly:—

"Would none of you like a cup of tea? You must all be so tired!" We could only make her happy, and so acquiesced. She bustled off to get tea; when she had gone Van Helsing said:—

"You see, my friends. *He* is close to land: he has left his earth-chest. But he has yet to get on shore. In the night he may lie hidden somewhere; but if he be not carried on shore, or if the ship do not touch it, he cannot achieve the land. In such case he can, if it be in the night, change his form and can jump or fly on shore, as he did at Whitby. But if the day come before he get on shore, then, unless he be carried he cannot escape. And if he be carried, then the customs men may discover what the box contain. Thus, in fine, if he escape not on shore to-night, or before dawn, there will be the whole day lost to him. We may then arrive in time; for if he escape not at night we shall come on him in daytime, boxed up and at our mercy; for he dare not be his true self, awake and visible, lest he be discovered."

There was no more to be said, we waited in patience until the dawn; at which time we might learn more from Mrs. Harker.

Early this morning we listened, with breathless anxiety, for her response in her trance. The hypnotic stage was even longer in coming than before; and when it came the time remaining until full sunrise was so short that we began to despair. Van Helsing seemed to throw his whole soul into the effort; at last, in obedience to his will she made reply:—

"All is dark. I hear lapping water, level with me, and some creaking as of wood." She paused, and the red sun shot up. We must wait till to-night.

And so it is that we are travelling towards Galatz in an agony of expectation. We are due to arrive between two and three in the morning; but already, at Bucharest, we are three hours late, so we cannot possibly get in till well after sun-up. Thus we shall have two more hypnotic messages from Mrs. Harker, either or both may possibly throw more light on what is happening.

Later.—Sunset has come and gone. Fortunately it came at a time when there was no distraction; for had it occurred whilst we were at a station, we might not have secured the necessary calm and isolation. Mrs. Harker yielded to the hypnotic influence even less readily than this morning. I am in fear that her power of reading the Count's sensations may die away, just when we want it most. It seems to me that her imagination is beginning to work. Whilst she has been in the trance hitherto she has confined herself to the simplest of facts. If this goes on it may ultimately mislead us. If I thought that the Count's power over her would die away equally with her power of knowledge it would be a happy thought; but I am afraid that it may not be so. When she did speak, her words were enigmatical:—

"Something is going on; I can feel it pass me like a cold wind. I can hear, far off, confused sounds—as of men talking in strange tongues, fierce-falling water, and the howling of wolves." She stopped and a shudder ran through her, increasing in intensity for a few seconds, till, at the end, she shook as though in a palsy. She said no more, even in answer to the Professor's imperative questioning. When she woke from the trance, she was cold, and exhausted, and languid, but her mind was all alert. She could not remember anything, but asked what she had said; when she was told, she pondered over it deeply for a long time and in silence.

30 October, 7 a.m.—We are near Galatz now, and I may not have time to write later. Sunrise this morning was anxiously looked for by us all. Knowing of the increasing difficulty of procuring the hypnotic trance, Van Helsing began his passes earlier than usual. They produced no effect, however, until the regular time, when she yielded with a still greater difficulty, only a minute before the sun rose. The

Professor lost no time in his questioning; her answer came with equal quickness:—

"All is dark. I hear water swirling by, level with my ears, and the creaking of wood on wood. Cattle low far off. There is another sound, a queer one like——" She stopped and grew white, and whiter still.

"Go on; go on! Speak, I command you!" said Van Helsing in an ago-nised voice. At the same time there was despair in his eyes, for the risen sun was reddening even Mrs. Harker's pale face. She opened her eyes, and we all started as she said, sweetly and seemingly with the utmost unconcern:—

"Oh, Professor, why ask me to do what you know I can't? I don't remember anything." Then, seeing the look of amazement on our faces, she said, turning from one to the other with a troubled look:—

"What have I said? What have I done? I know nothing, only that I was lying here, half asleep, and heard you say 'go on! speak, I command you!' It seemed so funny to hear you order me about, as if I were a bad child!"

"Oh, Madam Mina," he said, sadly, "it is proof, if proof be needed, of how I love and honour you, when a word for your good, spoken more earnest than ever, can seem so strange because it is to order her whom I am proud to obey!"

The whistles are sounding; we are nearing Galatz. We are on fire with anxiety and eagerness.

MINA HARKER'S JOURNAL.

30 October.—Mr. Morris took me to the hotel where our rooms had been ordered by telegraph, he being the one who could best be spared, since he does not speak any foreign language. The forces were distrib-uted much as they had been at Varna, except that Lord Godalming went to the Vice-Consul, as his rank might serve as an immediate guarantee of some sort to the official, we being in extreme hurry. Jonathan and the two doctors went to the shipping agent to learn particulars of the arrival of the *Czarina Catherine.*

Later.—Lord Godalming has returned. The Consul is away, and the Vice-Consul sick; so the routine work has been attended to by a clerk. He was very obliging, and offered to do anything in his power.

JONATHAN HARKER'S JOURNAL.

30 October.—At nine o'clock Dr. Van Helsing, Dr. Seward, and I called on Messrs. Mackenzie & Steinkoff, the agents of the London firm of Hapgood. They had received a wire from London, in answer to Lord Godalming's telegraphed request, asking them to show us any civility in their power. They were more than kind and courteous, and took us at once on board the *Czarina Catherine*, which lay at anchor out in the river harbour. There we saw the Captain, Donelson by name, who told us of his voyage. He said that in all his life he had never had so favourable a run.

"Man!" he said, "but it made us afeard, for we expeckit that she should have to pay for it wi' some rare piece o' ill luck, so as to keep up the average. It's no canny to run frae London to the Black Sea wi' a wind ahint ye, as though the Deil himself were blawin' on yer sail for his ain purpose. An' a' the time we could no speer a thing. Gin we were nigh a ship, or a port, or a headland, a fog fell on us and travelled wi' us, till when after it had lifted and we looked out, the deil a thing could we see. We ran by Gibraltar wi'oot bein' able to signal; an' till we came to the Dardanelles and had to wait to get our permit to pass, we never were within hail o' aught. At first I inclined to slack off sail and beat about till the fog was lifted; but whiles, I thocht that if the Deil was minded to get us into the Black Sea quick, he was like to do it whether we would or no. If we had a quick voyage it would be no to our miscredit wi' the owners, or no hurt to our traffic; an' the Old Mon who had served his ain purpose wad be decently grateful to us for no hinderin' him." This mixture of simplicity and cunning, of superstition and commercial reasoning, aroused Van Helsing, who said:—

"Mine friend, that Devil is more clever than he is thought by some;

and he know when he meet his match!" The skipper was not displeased with the compliment, and went on:—

"When we got past the Bosphorus the men began to grumble; some o' them, the Roumanians, came and asked me to heave overboard a big box which had been put on board by a queer lookin' old man just before we had started frae London. I had seen them speer at the fellow, and put out their twa fingers when they saw him, to guard against the evil eye. Man! but the supersteetion of foreigners is pairfectly rideeculous! I sent them aboot their business pretty quick; but as just after a fog closed in on us I felt a wee bit as they did anent something, though I wouldn't say it was agin the big box. Well, on we went, and as the fog didn't let up for five days I joost let the wind carry us; for if the Deil wanted to get somewheres—well, he would fetch it up a'reet. An' if he didn't, well, we'd keep a sharp lookout anyhow. Sure eneuch, we had a fair way and deep water all the time; and two days ago, when the mornin' sun came through the fog, we found ourselves just in the river opposite Galatz. The Roumanians were wild, and wanted me right or wrong to take out the box and fling it in the river. I had to argy wi' them aboot it wi' a handspike; an' when the last o' them rose off the deck wi' his head in his hand, I had convinced them that, evil eye or no evil eye, the property and the trust of my owners were better in my hands than in the river Danube. They had, mind ye, taken the box on the deck ready to fling in and as it was marked Galatz *via* Varna, I thocht I'd let it lie till we discharged in the port an' get rid o't althegither. We didn't do much clearin' that day, an' had to remain the nicht at anchor; but in the mornin', braw an' airly an hour before sun-up, a man came aboard wi' an order, written to him from England, to receive a box marked for one Count Dracula. Sure eneuch the matter was one ready to his hand. He had his papers a' reet, an' glad I was to be rid o' the dam' thing, for I was beginnin' masel' to feel uneasy at it. If the Deil did have any luggage aboord the ship I'm thinkin' it was nane ither than that same!"

"What was the name of the man who took it?" asked Dr. Van Helsing with restrained eagerness.

"I'll be tellin' ye quick!" he answered, and, stepping down to this

cabin, produced a receipt signed "Immanuel Hildesheim." Burgen-
strasse 16 was the address. We found out that this was all the Captain
knew; so with thanks we came away.

We found Hildesheim in his office, a Hebrew of rather the Adelphia
Theatre type, with a nose like a sheep, and a fez. His arguments were
pointed with specie—we doing the punctuation—and with a little bar-
gaining he told us what he knew. This turned out to be simple but
important. He had received a letter from Mr. de Ville of London, telling
him to receive, if possible before sunrise so as to avoid customs, a box
which would arrive at Galatz in the *Czarina Catherine.* This he was to
give in charge to a certain Petrof Skinsky, who dealt with the Slovaks
who traded down the river to the port. He had been paid for his work by
an English bank note, which had been duly cashed for gold at the Danube International Bank. When Skinsky had come to him, he had taken
him to the ship and handed over the box, so as to save porterage. That
was all he knew.

We then sought for Skinsky, but were unable to find him. One of his
neighbours, who did not seem to bear him any affection, said that he
had gone away two days before, no one knew whither. This was cor-
roborated by his landlord, who had received by messenger the key of the
house together with the rent due, in English money. This had been
between ten and eleven o'clock last night. We were at a standstill
again.

Whilst we were talking one came running and breathlessly gasped
out that the body of Skinsky had been found inside the wall of the
churchyard of St. Peter, and that the throat had been torn open as if by
some wild animal. Those we had been speaking with ran off to see the
horror, the man crying out, "This is the work of a Slovak!" We hurried
away lest we should have been in some way drawn into the affair, and so
detained.

As we came home we could arrive at no definite conclusion. We were
all convinced that the box was on its way, by water, to somewhere; but
where that might be we would have to discover. With heavy hearts we
came home to the hotel to Mina.

When we met together, the first thing was to consult as to taking Mina again into our confidence. Things are getting desperate, and it is at least a chance, though a hazardous one. As a preliminary step, I was released from my promise to her.

MINA HARKER'S JOURNAL.

30 October, evening.—They were so tired and worn out and dispirited that there was nothing to be done till they had some rest; so I asked them all to lie down for half an hour whilst I should enter everything up to the moment. I feel so grateful to the man who invented the "Traveller's" typewriter, and to Mr. Morris for getting this one for me. I should have felt quite astray doing the work if I had to write with a pen. . . .

It is all done; poor dear, dear Jonathan, what he must have suffered, what must he be suffering now. He lies on the sofa hardly seeming to breathe, and his whole body appears in collapse. His brows are knit; his face is drawn with pain. Poor fellow, maybe he is thinking, and I can see his face all wrinkled up with the concentration of his thoughts. Oh! If I could only help at all. . . . I shall do what I can.

I have asked Dr. Van Helsing, and he has got me all the papers that I have not yet seen. . . . Whilst they are resting, I shall go over all carefully, and perhaps I may arrive at some conclusion. I shall try to follow the Professor's example, and think without prejudice on the facts before me. . . .

I do believe that under God's providence I have made a discovery. I shall get the maps and look over them. . . .

I am more than ever sure that I am right. My new conclusion is ready, so I shall get our party together and read it. They can judge it; it is well to be accurate, and every minute is precious.

MINA HARKER'S MEMORANDUM—
(Entered in her Journal.)

Ground of inquiry.—Count Dracula's problem is to get back to his own place.

(a) He must be *brought back* by some one. This is evident; for had he power to move himself as he wished he could go either as man, or wolf, or bat, or in some other way. He evidently fears discovery or interference, in the state of helplessness in which he must be—confined as he is between dawn and sunset in his wooden box.

(b) How is he to be taken?—Here a process of exclusions may help us. By road, by rail, by water?

1. *By Road.*—There are endless difficulties, especially in leaving the city.

(x) There are people; and people are curious, and investigate. A hint, a surmise, a doubt as to what might be in the box, would destroy him.

(y) There are, or there may be, customs and octroi officers to pass.

(z) His pursuers might follow. This is his highest fear; and in order to prevent his being betrayed he has repelled, so far as he can, even his victim—me!

2. *By Rail.*—There is no one in charge of the box. It would have to take its chance of being delayed; and delay would be fatal, with enemies on the track. True, he might escape at night; but what would he be, if left in a strange place with no refuge that he could fly to? This is not what he intends; and he does not mean to risk it.

3. *By Water.*—Here is the safest way, in one respect, but with most danger in another. On the water he is powerless except at night; even then he can only summon fog and storm and snow and his wolves. But were he wrecked, the living water would engulf him, helpless; and he would indeed be lost. He could have the vessel drive to land; but if it were unfriendly land, wherein he was not free to move, his position would still be desperate.

We know from the record that he was on the water; so what we have to do is to ascertain *what* water.

The first thing is to realise exactly what he has done as yet; we may, then, get a light on what his later task is to be.

Firstly.—We must differentiate between what he did in London as part of his general plan of action, when he was pressed for moments and had to arrange as best he could.

Secondly.—We must see, as well as we can surmise it from the facts we know of, what he has done here.

As to the first, he evidently intended to arrive at Galatz, and sent invoice to Varna to deceive us lest we should ascertain his means of exit from England; his immediate and sole purpose then was to escape. The proof of this, is the letter of instructions sent to Immanuel Hildesheim to clear and take away the box *before sunrise*. There is also the instruction to Petrof Skinsky. These we must only guess at; but there must have been some letter or message, since Skinsky came to Hildesheim.

That, so far, his plans were successful, we know. The *Czarina Catherine* made a phenomenally quick journey—so much so that Captain Donelson's suspicions were aroused; but his superstition united with his canniness played the Count's game for him, and he ran with his favouring wind through fogs and all till he brought up blindfold at Galatz. That the Count's arrangements were well made, has been proved. Hildesheim cleared the box, took it off, and gave it to Skinsky. Skinsky took it and here we lose the trail. We only know that the box is somewhere on the water, moving along. The customs and the octroi, if there be any, have been avoided.

Now we come to what the Count must have done after his arrival— *on land*, at Galatz.

The box was given to Skinsky before sunrise. At sunrise the Count could appear in his own form. Here, we ask why Skinsky was chosen at all to aid in the work? In my husband's diary, Skinsky is mentioned as dealing with the Slovaks who trade down the river to the port; and the man's remark, that the murder was the work of a Slovak, showed the general feeling against his class. The Count wanted isolation.

My surmise is this: that in London the Count decided to get back to his castle by water, as the most safe and secret way. He was brought from the castle by Szgany, and probably they delivered their cargo to Slovaks who took the boxes to Varna, for there they were shipped for London. Thus the Count had knowledge of the persons who could arrange this service. When the box was on land, before sunrise or after sunset, he came out from his box, met Skinsky and instructed him what to do as to arranging the carriage of the box up some river. When this was done, and he knew that all was in train, he blotted out his traces, as he thought, by murdering his agent.

I have examined the map and find that the river most suitable for the Slovaks to have ascended is either the Pruth or the Sereth. I read in the typescript that in my trance I heard cows low and water swirling level with my ears and the creaking of wood. The Count in his box, then, was on a river in an open boat—propelled probably either by oars or poles, for the banks are near and it is working against stream. There would be no such sound if floating down stream.

Of course it may not be either the Sereth or the Pruth, but we may possibly investigate further. Now of these two, the Pruth is the more easily navigated, but the Sereth is at Fundu, joined by the Bistritza which runs up round the Borgo Pass. The loop it makes is manifestly as close to Dracula's castle as can be got by water.

MINA HARKER'S JOURNAL—*continued.*

When I had done reading, Jonathan took me in his arms and kissed me. The others kept shaking me by both hands, and Dr. Van Helsing said:—

"Our dear Madam Mina is once more our teacher. Her eyes have been where we were blinded. Now we are on the track once again, and this time we may succeed. Our enemy is at his most helpless; and if we can come on him by day, on the water, our task will be over. He has a start, but he is powerless to hasten, as he may not leave his box lest those who carry him may suspect; for them to suspect would be to prompt them to throw him in the stream where he perish. This he knows, and will not. Now men, to our Council of War; for, here and now, we must plan what each and all shall do."

"I shall get a steam launch and follow him," said Lord Godalming.

"And I, horses to follow on the bank lest by chance he land," said Mr. Morris.

"Good!" said the Professor, "both good. But neither must go alone. There must be force to overcome force if need be; the Slovak is strong and rough, and he carries rude arms." All the men smiled, for amongst them they carried a small arsenal. Said Mr. Morris:—

"I have brought some Winchesters; they are pretty handy in a crowd, and there may be wolves. The Count, if you remember, took some other precautions; he made some requisitions on others that Mrs. Harker could not quite hear or understand. We must be ready at all points." Dr. Seward said:—

"I think I had better go with Quincey. We have been accustomed to hunt together, and we two, well armed, will be a match for whatever may come along. You must not be alone, Art. It may be necessary to fight the Slovaks, and a chance thrust—for I don't suppose these fellows carry guns—would undo all our plans. There must be no chances, this time; we shall not rest until the Count's head and body have been separated, and we are sure that he cannot reincarnate." He looked at Jonathan as he spoke, and Jonathan looked at me. I could see that the poor dear was torn about in his mind. Of course he wanted to be with me; but then the boat service would, most likely, be the one which would destroy the . . . the . . . the . . . Vampire. (Why did I hesitate to write the word?) He was silent awhile, and during his silence Dr. Van Helsing spoke:—

"Friend Jonathan, this is to you for twice reasons. First, because you are young and brave and can fight, and all energies may be needed at the last; and again that it is your right to destroy him—that—which has wrought such woe to you and yours. Be not afraid for Madam Mina; she will be my care, if I may. I am old. My legs are not so quick to run as once; and I am not used to ride so long or to pursue as need be, or to fight with lethal weapons. But I can be of other service; I can fight in other way. And I can die, if need be, as well as younger men. Now let me say that what I would is this: while you, my Lord Godalming and friend Jonathan go in your so swift little steamboat up the river, and whilst John and Quincey guard the bank where perchance he might be landed, I will take Madam Mina right into the heart of the enemy's country. Whilst the old fox is tied in his box, floating on the running stream whence he cannot escape to land—where he dares not raise the lid of his coffin-box lest his Slovak carriers should in fear leave him to perish—we shall go in the track where Jonathan went—from Bistritz over the Borgo, and find our way to the Castle of Dracula. Here, Madam Mina's hypnotic power will surely help, and we shall find our way—all dark and unknown otherwise—after the first sunrise when we are near that fateful place. There is much to be done, and other places to be made sanctify, so that that nest of vipers be obliterated." Here Jonathan interrupted him hotly:—

"Do you mean to say, Professor Van Helsing, that you would bring Mina, in her sad case and tainted as she is with that devil's illness, right into the jaws of his deathtrap? Not for the world! Not for Heaven or Hell!" He became almost speechless for a minute, and then went on:—

"Do you know what the place is? Have you seen that awful den of hellish infamy—with the very moonlight alive with grisly shapes, and every speck of dust that whirls in the wind a devouring monster in embryo? Have you felt the Vampire's lips upon your throat?" Here he turned to me, and as his eyes lit on my forehead he threw up his arms with a cry: "Oh, my God, what have we done to have this terror upon us!" and he sank down on the sofa in a collapse of misery. The Professor's voice, as he spoke in clear, sweet tones, which seemed to vibrate in the air, calmed us all:—

"Oh, my friend, it is because I would save Madam Mina from that awful place that I would go. God forbid that I should take her into that place. There is work—wild work—to be done there, that her eyes may not see. We men here, all save Jonathan, have seen with their own eyes what is to be done before that place can be purify. Remember that we are in terrible straits. If the Count escape us this time—and he is strong and subtle and cunning—he may choose to sleep him for a century, and then in time our dear one"—he took my hand—"would come to him to keep him company, and would be as those others that you, Jonathan, saw. You have told us of their gloating lips; you heard their ribald laugh as they clutched the moving bag that the Count threw to them. You shudder; and well may it be. Forgive me that I make you so much pain, but it is necessary. My friend, is it not a dire need for the which I am giving, possibly, my life? If it were that any one went into that place to stay, it is I who have to go to keep them company."

"Do as you will," said Jonathan, with a sob that shook him all over, "we are in the hands of God!"

Later.—Oh, it did me good to see the way that these brave men worked. How can women help loving men when they are so earnest, and so true, and so brave! And, too, it made me think of the wonderful power of money! What can it not do when it is properly applied; and what might it do when basely used. I felt so thankful that Lord Godalming is rich, and that both he and Mr. Morris, who also has plenty of money, are willing to spend it so freely. For if they did not, our little expedition could not start, either so promptly or so well equipped, as it will within another hour. It is not three hours since it was arranged what part each of us was to do; and now Lord Godalming and Jonathan have a lovely steam launch, with steam up ready to start at a moment's notice. Dr. Seward and Mr. Morris have half a dozen good horses, well appointed. We have all the maps and appliances of various kinds that can be had. Professor Van Helsing and I are to leave by the 11:40 train to-night for Veresti, where we are to get a carriage to drive to the Borgo Pass. We are bringing a good deal of ready money, as we are to buy a carriage and horses. We shall drive ourselves, for we have no one whom we can trust in the matter. The Professor knows something of a great many languages, so we shall get on all right. We have all got arms, even for me a large-bore revolver; Jonathan would not be happy unless I was armed like the rest. Alas! I cannot carry one arm that the rest do; the scar on my forehead forbids that. Dear Dr. Van Helsing comforts me by telling me that I am fully armed as there may be wolves; the weather is getting colder every hour, and there are snow flurries which come and go as warnings.

Later.—It took all my courage to say good-bye to my darling. We may never meet again. Courage, Mina! the Professor is looking at you keenly; his look is a warning. There must be no tears now—unless it may be that God will let them fall in gladness.

JONATHAN HARKER'S JOURNAL.

October 30, night.—I am writing this in the light from the furnace door of the steam launch: Lord Godalming is firing up. He is an experienced hand at the work, as he has had for years a launch of his own on the Thames, and another on the Norfolk Broads. Regarding our plans, we finally decided that Mina's guess was correct, and that if any waterway was chosen for the Count's escape back to his Castle, the Sereth and then the Bistritza at its junction, would be the one. We took it, that somewhere about the 47th degree, north latitude, would be the place chosen for crossing the country between the river and the Carpathians. We have no fear in running at good speed up the river at night; there is plenty of water, and the banks are wide enough apart to make steaming, even in the dark, easy enough. Lord Godalming tells me to sleep for a while, as it is enough for the present for one to be on watch. But I cannot sleep—how can I with the terrible danger hanging over my darling, and her going out into that awful place. . . . My only comfort is that we are in the hands of God. Only for that faith it would be easier to die than to live, and so be quit of all the trouble. Mr. Morris and Dr. Seward were off on their long ride before we started; they are to keep up the right bank, far enough off to get on higher lands where they can see a good stretch of river and avoid the following of its curves. They have, for the first stages, two men to ride and lead their spare horses—four in all, so as not to excite curiosity. When they dismiss the men, which shall be shortly, they shall themselves look after the horses. It may be necessary for us to join forces; if so they can mount our whole party. One of the saddles has a movable horn, and can be easily adapted for Mina, if required.

It is a wild adventure we are on. Here, as we are rushing along through the darkness, with the cold from the river seeming to rise up and strike us; with all the mysterious voices of the night around us, it all comes home. We seem to be drifting into unknown places and unknown ways; into a whole world of dark and dreadful things. Godalming is shutting the furnace door. . . .

31 October.—Still hurrying along. The day has come, and Godalming is sleeping. I am on watch. The morning is bitterly cold; the furnace heat is grateful, though we have heavy fur coats. As yet, we have passed only a few open boats, but none of them had on board any box or package of anything like the size of the one we seek. The men were scared every time we turned our electric lamp on them, and fell on their knees and prayed.

1 November, evening.—No news all day; we have found nothing of the kind we seek. We have now passed into the Bistritza; and if we are wrong in our surmise our chance is gone. We have overhauled every boat, big and little. Early this morning, one crew took us for a Government boat, and treated us accordingly. We saw in this a way of smoothing matters, so at Fundu, where the Bistritza runs into the Sereth, we got a Roumanian flag which we now fly conspicuously. With every boat which we have overhauled since then this trick has succeeded; we have had every deference shown to us, and not once any objection to whatever we chose to ask or do. Some of the Slovaks tell us that a big boat passed them, going at more than usual speed as she had a double crew on board. This was before they came to Fundu, so they could not tell us whether the boat turned into the Bistritza or continued on up the Sereth. At Fundu, we could not hear of any such boat, so she must have passed there in the night. I am feeling very sleepy; the cold is perhaps beginning to tell upon me, and nature must have rest some time. Godalming insists that he shall keep the first watch. God bless him for all his goodness to poor dear Mina and me.

2 November, morning.—It is broad daylight. That good fellow would not wake me. He says it would have been a sin to, for I slept peacefully and was forgetting my trouble. It seems brutally selfish to me to have slept so long, and let him watch all night; but he was quite right. I am a new man this morning; and, as I sit here and watch him sleeping, I can do all that is necessary both as to minding the engine, steering, and keeping watch. I can feel that my strength and energy are coming back to me. I wonder where Mina is now, and Van Helsing. They should have got to Veresti about noon on Wednesday. It would take them some time to get the carriage and horses; so if they had started and travelled hard, they would be about now at the Borgo Pass. God guide and help them! I am afraid to think what may happen. If we could only go faster! but we cannot; the engines are throbbing and doing their utmost. I wonder how Dr. Seward and Mr. Morris are getting on. There seem to be endless streams running down the mountains into this river, but as none of them are very large—at present, at all events, though they are terrible doubtless in winter and when the snow melts—the horsemen may not have met much obstruction. I hope that before we get to Strasba we may see them; for if by that time we have not overtaken the Count, it may be necessary to take counsel together what to do next.

DR. SEWARD'S DIARY.

2 November.—Three days on the road. No news, and no time to write it if there had been, for every moment is precious. We have had only the rest needful for the horses; but we are both bearing it wonderfully. Those adventurous days of ours are turning up useful. We must push on: we shall never feel happy till we get the launch in sight again.

3 November.—We heard at Fundu that the launch had gone up the

Bistritza. I wish it wasn't so cold. There are signs of snow coming; and if it falls heavy it will stop us. In such case we must get a sledge and go on, Russian fashion.

4 November.—To-day we heard of the launch having been detained by an accident when trying to force a way up the rapids. The Slovak boats get up all right, by aid of a rope and steering with knowledge. Some went up only a few hours before. Godalming is an amateur fitter himself, and evidently it was he who put the launch in trim again. Finally, they got up the rapids all right, with local help, and are off on the chase afresh. I fear that the boat is not any better for the accident; the peasantry tell us that after she got upon smooth water again, she kept stopping every now and again so long as she was in sight. We must push on harder than ever; our help may be wanted soon.

MINA HARKER'S JOURNAL.

31 October.—Arrived at Veresti at noon. The Professor tells me that this morning at dawn he could hardly hypnotise me at all, and that all I could say was: "dark and quiet." He is off now buying a carriage and horses. He says that he will later on try to buy additional horses, so that we may be able to change them on the way. We have something more than 70 miles before us. The country is lovely, and most interesting; if only we were under different conditions, how delightful it would be to see it all. If Jonathan and I were driving through it alone what a pleasure it would be. To stop and see people, and learn something of their life, and to fill our minds and memories with all the colour and picturesqueness of the whole wild, beautiful country and the quaint people! But, alas!—

Later.—Dr. Van Helsing has returned. He has got the carriage and horses; we are to have some dinner, and to start in an hour. The landlady is putting us up a huge basket of provisions; it seems enough for a company of soldiers. The Professor encourages her, and whispers to me that it may be a week before we can get any good food again. He has been shopping too, and has sent home such a wonderful lot of fur coats and wraps, and all sorts of warm things. There will not be any chance of our being cold.

We shall soon be off. I am afraid to think what may happen to us. We are truly in the hands of God. He alone knows what may be, and I pray Him, with all the strength of my sad and humble soul, that He will watch over my beloved husband; that whatever may happen, Jonathan may know that I loved him and honoured him more than I can say, and that my latest and truest thought will be always for him.

CHAPTER 27.

———◇———

MINA HARKER'S JOURNAL.

1 November.—All day long we have travelled, and at a good speed. The horses seem to know that they are being kindly treated, for they go willingly their full stage at best speed. We have now had so many changes and find the same thing so constantly that we are encouraged to think that the journey will be an easy one. Dr. Van Helsing is laconic; he tells the farmers that he is hurrying to Bistritz, and pays them well to make the exchange of horses. We get hot soup, or coffee, or tea; and off we go. It is a lovely country; full of beauties of all imaginable kinds, and the people are brave, and strong, and simple, and seem full of nice qualities. They are *very, very* superstitious. In the first house where we stopped, when the woman who served us saw the scar on my forehead, she crossed herself and put out two fingers towards me, to keep off the evil eye. I believe they went to the trouble of putting an extra amount of garlic into our food; and I can't abide garlic. Ever since then I have taken care not to take off my hat or veil, and so have escaped their suspicions. We are travelling fast, and as we have no driver with us to carry tales, we go ahead of scandal, but I daresay that fear of the evil eye will follow hard behind us all the way. The Professor seems tireless; all day he would not take any rest, though he made me sleep for a long spell. At sunset time he hypnotised me, and he says that I answered as usual "darkness, lapping water and creaking wood"; so our enemy is still on the river. I am afraid to think of Jonathan, but somehow I have now no fear for him, or for myself. I write this whilst we wait in a farmhouse for the horses to be got ready. Dr. Van Helsing is sleeping. Poor dear, he looks very tired and old and grey, but his mouth is set as firmly as a conqueror's; even in his sleep he is instinct with resolution. When we have well started I must make him rest whilst I drive. I shall tell him that we have days before us, and we must not break down when most of all his strength will be needed. . . . All is ready; we are off shortly.

2 November, morning.—I was successful, and we took turns driving all night; now the day is on us, bright though cold. There is a strange heaviness in the air—I say heaviness for want of a better word; I mean that it oppresses us both. It is very cold, and only our warm furs keep us comfortable. At dawn Van Helsing hypnotised me; he says I answered "darkness, creaking wood and roaring water," so the river is changing as they ascend. I do hope that my darling will not run any chance of danger—more than need be; but we are in God's hands.

2 November, night.—All day long driving. The country gets wilder as we go, and the great spurs of the Carpathians, which at Veresti seemed so far from us and so low on the horizon, now seem to gather round us and tower in front. We both seem in good spirits; I think we make an effort each to cheer the other; in the doing so we cheer ourselves. Dr. Van Helsing says that by morning we shall reach the Borgo Pass. The houses are very few here now, and the Professor says that the last horse we got will have to go on with us, as we may not be able to change. He got two in addition to the two we changed, so that now we have a rude four-in-hand. The dear horses are patient and good, and they give us no trouble. We are not worried with other travellers, and so even I can drive. We shall get to the Pass in daylight; we do not want to arrive before.

So we take it easy, and have each a long rest in turn. Oh, what will to-morrow bring to us? We go to seek the place where my poor darling suffered so much. God grant that we may be guided aright, and that He will deign to watch over my husband and those dear to us both, and who are in such deadly peril. As for me, I am not worthy in His sight. Alas! I am unclean to His eyes, and shall be until He may deign to let me stand forth in His sight as one of those who have not incurred His wrath.

MEMORANDUM BY ABRAHAM VAN HELSING.

4 November.—This to my old and true friend John Seward, M. D., of Purfleet, London, in case I may not see him. It may explain. It is morning, and I write by a fire which all the night I have kept alive—Madam Mina aiding me. It is cold, cold; so cold that the grey heavy sky is full of snow, which when it falls will settle for all winter as the ground is hardening to receive it. It seems to have affected Madam Mina; she has been so heavy of head all day that she was not like herself. She sleeps, and sleeps, and sleeps! She who is usual so alert, have done literally nothing all the day; she even have lost her appetite. She make no entry into her little diary, she who write so faithful at every pause. Something whisper to me that all is not well. However, to-night she is more *vif.* Her long sleep all day have refresh and restore her, for now she is all sweet and bright as ever. At sunset I try to hypnotise her, but alas! with no effect; the power has grown less and less with each day, and to-night it fail me altogether. Well, God's will be done—whatever it may be, and whithersoever it may lead!

Now to the historical; for as Madam Mina write not in her stenography, I must, in my cumbrous old fashion, that so each day of us may not go unrecorded.

We got to the Borgo Pass just after sunrise yesterday morning. When I saw the signs of the dawn I got ready for the hypnotism. We stopped our carriage, and got down so that there might be no disturbance. I made a couch with furs, and Madam Mina, lying down, yield herself as usual, but more slow and more short time than ever, to the hypnotic sleep. As before, came the answer, "darkness and the swirling of water." Then she woke, bright and radiant and we go on our way and soon reach the Pass. At this time and place, she become all on fire with zeal; some new guiding power be in her manifested, for she point to a road and say:—

"This is the way."

"How know you it?" I ask.

"Of course I know it," she answer, and with a pause, add: "Have not my Jonathan travelled it and wrote of his travel?"

At first I think somewhat strange, but soon I see that there be only one such by-road. It is used but little, and very different from the coach road from the Bukovina to Bistritz, which is more wide and hard, and more of use.

So we came down this road; when we meet other ways—not always were we sure that they were roads at all, for they be neglect and light snow have fallen—the horses know and they only. I give rein to them, and they go on so patient. By-and-by we find all the things which Jonathan have note in that wonderful diary of him. Then we go on for long, long hours and hours. At the first, I tell Madam Mina to sleep; she try, and she succeed. She sleep all the time; till at the last, I feel myself to suspicious grow, and attempt to wake her. But she sleep on, and I may not wake her though I try. I do not wish to try too hard lest I harm her; for I know that she have suffer much, and sleep at times be all-in-all to her. I think I drowse myself, for all of sudden I feel guilt, as though I have done something; I find myself bolt up, with the reins in my hand, and the good horses go along jog, jog, just as ever. I look down and find Madam Mina still sleep. It is now not far off sunset time, and over the snow the light of the sun flow in big yellow flood, so that we throw great long shadow on where the mountain rise so steep. For we are going up, and up; and all is oh! so wild and rocky, as though it were the end of the world.

Then I arouse Madam Mina. This time she wake with not much trouble, and then I try to put her to hypnotic sleep. But she sleep not, being as though I were not. Still I try and try, till all at once I find her and myself in dark; so I look round, and find that the sun have gone down. Madam Mina laugh, and I turn and look at her. She is now quite awake, and look so well as I never saw her since that night at Carfax when we first enter the Count's house. I am amaze, and not at ease then; but she is so bright and tender and thoughtful for me that I forget all fear. I light a fire, for we have brought supply of wood with us, and she prepare food while I undo the horses and set them, tethered in shelter, to feed. Then when I return to the fire she have my supper ready. I go to help her; but she smile, and tell me that she have eat already—that she was so hungry that she would not wait. I like it not, and I have grave doubts; but I fear to affright her, and so I am silent of it. She help me and I eat alone; and then we wrap in fur and lie beside the fire, and I tell her to sleep while I watch. But presently I forget all of watching; and when I sudden remember that I watch, I find her lying quiet, but awake, and looking at me with so bright eyes. Once, twice more the same occur, and I get much sleep till before morning. When I wake I try to hypnotise her; but alas! though she shut her eyes obedient, she may not sleep. The sun rise up, and up, and up; and then sleep come to her too late, but so heavy that she will not wake. I have to lift her up, and place her sleeping in the carriage when I have harnessed the horses and made all ready. Madam still sleep, and she look in her sleep more healthy and more redder than before. And I like it not. And I am afraid, afraid, afraid!—I am afraid of all things—even to think but I must go on my way. The stake we play for is life and death, or more than these, and we must not flinch.

5 November, morning.—Let me be accurate in everything, for though you and I have seen some strange things together, you may at the first think that I, Van Helsing, am mad—that the many horrors and the so long strain on nerves has at the last turn my brain.

All yesterday we travel, ever getting closer to the mountains, and moving into a more and more wild and desert land. There are great, frowning precipices and much falling water, and Nature seem to have held sometime her carnival. Madam Mina still sleep and sleep; and though I did have hunger and appeased it, I could not waken her—even for food. I began to fear that the fatal spell of the place was upon her, tainted as she is with that Vampire baptism. "Well," said I to myself, "if it be that she sleep all the day, it shall also be that I do not sleep at night." As we travel on the rough road, for a road of an ancient and imperfect kind there was, I held down my head and slept. Again I waked with a sense of guilt and of time passed, and found Madam Mina still sleeping, and the sun low down. But all was indeed changed; the frowning mountains seemed further away, and we were near the top of a steep-rising hill, on summit of which was such a castle as Jonathan tell of in his diary. At once I exulted and feared; for now, for good or ill, the end was near.

I woke Madam Mina, and again tried to hypnotise her; but alas! unavailing till too late. Then, ere the great dark came upon us—for even after down-sun the heavens reflected the gone sun on the snow, and all was for a time in a great twilight—I took out the horses and fed them in what shelter I could. Then I make a fire; and near it I make Madam Mina, now awake and more charming than ever, sit comfortable amid her rugs. I got ready food; but she would not eat, simply saying that she had not hunger. I did not press her, knowing her unavailingness. But I myself eat, for I must needs now be strong for all. Then, with the fear on me of what might be, I drew a ring so big for her comfort, round where Madam Mina sat; and over the ring I passed some of the Wafer, and I broke it fine so that all was well guarded. She sat still all the time—so still as one dead; and she grew whiter and ever whiter till the snow was not more pale; and no word she said. But when I drew near, she clung to me, and I could know that the poor soul shook her from head to feet with a tremor that was pain to feel. I said to her presently, when she had grown more quiet:—

"Will you not come over to the fire?" for I wished to make a test of what she could. She rose obedient, but when she have made a step she stopped, and stood as one stricken.

"Why not go on?" I asked. She shook her head, and, coming back, sat down in her place. Then, looking at me with open eyes, as of one waked from sleep, she said simply:—"I cannot!" and remained silent. I rejoiced, for I knew that what she could not, none of those that we dreaded could. Though there might be danger to her body, yet her soul was safe!

Presently the horses began to scream, and tore at their tethers till I came to them and quieted them. When they did feel my hands on them, they whinnied low as in joy, and licked at my hands and were quiet for a time. Many times through the night did I come to them, till it arrive to the cold hour when all nature is at lowest; and every time my coming was with quiet of them. In the cold hour the fire began to die, and I was about stepping forth to replenish it, for now the snow came in flying sweeps and with it a chill mist. Even in the dark there was a light of some kind, as there ever is over snow; and it seemed as though the snow flurries and the wreaths of mist took shape as of women with trailing garments. All was in dead, grim silence only that the horses whinnied and cowered, as if in terror of the worst. I began to fear—horrible fears; but then came to me the sense of safety in that ring wherein I stood. I began, too, to think that my imaginings were of the night, and the gloom, and the unrest that I have gone through, and all the terrible anxiety. It was as though my memories of all Jonathan's horrid experience were befooling me; for the snow flakes and the mist began to wheel and circle round, till I could get as though a shadowy glimpse of those women that would have kissed him. And then the horses cowered lower and lower, and moaned in terror as men do in pain. Even the madness of fright was not to them, so that they could break away. I feared for my dear Madam Mina when these weird figures drew near and circled round. I looked at her, but she sat calm, and smiled at me; when I would have stepped to the fire to replenish it, she caught me and held me back, and whispered, like a voice that one hears in a dream, so low it was:—

"No! No! Do not go without. Here you are safe!" I turned to her, and looking in her eyes, said:—

"But you? It is for you that I fear!" whereat she laughed—a laugh, low and unreal, and said:—

"Fear for *me*! Why fear for me? None safer in all the world from them than I am," and as I wondered at the meaning of her words, a puff of wind made the flame leap up, and I see the red scar on her forehead. Then, alas! I knew. Did I not, I would soon have learned, for the wheeling figures of mist and snow came closer, but keeping ever without the Holy circle. Then they began to materialise till—if God have not take away my reason, for I saw it through my eyes—there were before me in actual flesh the same three women that Jonathan saw in the room, when they would have kissed his throat. I knew the swaying round forms, the bright hard eyes, the white teeth, the ruddy colour, the voluptuous lips. They smiled ever at poor dear Madam Mina; and as their laugh came through the silence of the night, they twined their arms and pointed to her, and said in those so sweet tingling tones that Jonathan said were of the intolerable sweetness of the water-glasses:—

"Come, sister. Come to us. Come! Come!" In fear I turned to my poor Madam Mina, and my heart with gladness leaped like flame; for oh! the terror in her sweet eyes, the repulsion, the horror, told a story to my heart that was all of hope. God be thanked she was not, yet, of them. I seized some of the Wafer, advanced on them towards the fire. They drew back before me, and laughed their low horrid laugh. I fed the fire, and feared them not; for I knew that we were safe within our protections. They could not approach me, whilst so armed, nor Madam Mina whilst she remained within the ring, which she could not leave no more than they could enter. The horses had ceased to moan, and lay still on the ground; the snow fell on them softly, and they grew whiter. I knew that there was for the poor beasts no more of terror.

And so we remained till the red of the dawn to fall through the snow-gloom. I was desolate and afraid, and full of woe and terror; but when that beautiful sun began to climb the horizon life was to me again. At the first coming of the dawn the horrid figures melted in the whirling mist and snow; the wreaths of transparent gloom moved away towards the castle and were lost.

Instinctively, with the dawn coming, I turned to Madam Mina, intending to hypnotise her; but she lay in a deep and sudden sleep, from which I could not wake her. I tried to hypnotise through her sleep, but she made no response, none at all; and the day broke. I fear yet to stir. I have made my fire and have seen the horses, they are all dead. To-day I have much to do here, and I keep waiting till the sun is up high; for there may be places where I must go, where that sunlight, though snow and mist obscure it, will be to me a safety.

I will strengthen me with breakfast, and then I will to my terrible work. Madam Mina still sleeps; and, God be thanked! she is calm in her sleep. . . .

JONATHAN HARKER'S JOURNAL.

4 November, evening.—The accident to the launch has been a terrible thing for us. Only for it we should have overtaken the boat long ago; and by now my dear Mina would have been free. I fear to think of her, off on the wolds near that horrible place. We have got horses, and we follow on the track. I note this whilst Godalming is getting ready. We have our arms. The Szgany must look out if they mean to fight. Oh, if only Morris and Seward were with us. We must only hope! If I write no more, good-bye, Mina! God bless and keep you.

DR. SEWARD'S DIARY.

5 November.—With the dawn we saw the body of Szgany before us dashing away from the river with their leiter-wagon. They surrounded it in a cluster, and hurried along as though beset. The snow is falling lightly and there is a strange excitement in the air. It may be our own feelings, but the depression is strange. Far off I hear the howling of wolves; the snow brings them down from the mountains, and there are dangers to all of us, and from all sides. The horses are nearly ready, and we are soon off. We ride to death of some one. God alone knows who, or where, or what, or when, or how it may be. . . .

DR. VAN HELSING'S MEMORANDUM.

5 November, afternoon.—I am at least sane. Thank God for that mercy at all events, though the proving it has been dreadful. When I left Madam Mina sleeping within the Holy circle, I took my way to the castle. The blacksmith hammer which I took in the carriage from Veresti was useful; though the doors were all open I broke them off the rusty hinges, lest some ill-intent or ill-chance should close them, so that being entered I might not get out. Jonathan's bitter experience served me here. By memory of his diary I found my way to the old chapel, for I knew that here my work lay. The air was oppressive; it seemed as if there was some sulphurous fume, which at times made me dizzy. Either there was a roaring in my ears or I heard afar off the howl of wolves. Then I be-thought me of my dear Madam Mina, and I was in terrible plight. The dilemma had me between his horns.

Her, I had not dare to take into this place, but left safe from the Vampire in that Holy circle; and yet even there would be the wolf! I resolve me that my work lay here, and that as to the wolves we must submit, if it were God's will. At any rate it was only death and freedom beyond. So did I choose for her. Had it but been for myself the choice had been easy, the maw of the wolf were better to rest in than the grave of the Vampire! So I make my choice to go on with my work.

I knew that there were at least three graves to find—graves that are inhabit; so I search, and search, and I find one of them. She lay in her Vampire sleep, so full of life and voluptuous beauty that I shudder as though I have come to do murder. Ah, I doubt not that in old time, when such things were, many a man who set forth to do such a task as mine, found at the last his heart fail him, and then his nerve. So he delay, and delay, and delay, till the mere beauty and the fascination of the wanton Un-Dead have hypnotise him; and he remain on and on, till sunset come, and the Vampire sleep be over. Then the beautiful eyes of the fair woman open and look love, and the voluptuous mouth present to a kiss—and man is weak. And there remain one more victim in the

Vampire fold; one more to swell the grim and grisly ranks of the Un-
Dead! . . .

There is some fascination, surely, when I am moved by the mere
presence of such an one, even lying as she lay in a tomb fretted with age
and heavy with the dust of centuries, though there be that horrid odour
such as the lairs of the Count have had. Yes, I was moved—I, Van
Helsing, with all my purpose and with my motive for hate—I was
moved to a yearning for delay which seemed to paralyse my faculties
and to clog my very soul. It may have been that the need of natural
sleep, and the strange oppression of the air were beginning to overcome
me. Certain it was that I was lapsing into sleep, the open-eyed sleep of
one who yields to a sweet fascination, when there came through the
snow-stilled air a long, low wail, so full of woe and pity that it woke me
like the sound of a clarion. For it was the voice of my dear Madam
Mina that I heard.

Then I braced myself again to my horrid task, and found by wrench-
ing away tomb-tops one other of the sisters, the other dark one. I dared
not pause to look on her as I had on her sister, lest once more I should
begin to be enthrall; but I go on searching until, presently, I find in a
high great tomb as if made to one much beloved that other fair sister
which, like Jonathan, I had seen to gather herself out of the atoms of the
mist. She was so fair to look on, so radiantly beautiful, so exquisitely
voluptuous, that the very instinct of man in me, which calls some of my
sex, to love and to protect one of hers, made my head whirl with new
emotion. But God be thanked, that soul-wail of my dear Madam Mina
had not died out of my ears; and, before the spell could be wrought further upon me, I had nerved myself to my wild work. By this time I had
searched all the tombs in the chapel, so far as I could tell; and as there
had been only three of these Un-Dead phantoms around us in the night,
I took it that there were no more of active Un-Dead existent. There was
one great tomb more lordly than all the rest; huge it was, and nobly
proportioned. On it was but one word:

DRACULA

This then was the Un-Dead home of the King-Vampire, to whom so many more were due. Its emptiness spoke eloquent to make certain what I knew. Before I began to restore these women to their dead selves through my awful work, I laid in Dracula's tomb some of the Wafer, and so banished him from it, Un-Dead, for ever.

Then began my terrible task, and I dreaded it. Had it been but one, it had been easy, comparative. But three! To begin twice more after I had been through a deed of horror; for if it was terrible with the sweet Miss Lucy, what would it not be with these strange ones who had survived through centuries, and who had been strengthened by the passing of the years; who would, if they could, have fought for their foul lives. . . .

Oh, my friend John, but it was butcher work; had I not been nerved by thoughts of other dead, and of the living over whom hung such a pall of fear, I could not have gone on. I tremble and tremble even yet, though till all was over, God be thanked, my nerve did stand. Had I not seen the repose in the first place, and the gladness that stole over it just ere the final dissolution came, as realisation that the soul had been won, I could not have gone further with my butchery. I could not have endured the horrid screeching as the stake drove home; the plunging of writhing form, and lips of bloody foam. I should have fled in terror and left my work undone. But it is over! And the poor souls, I can pity them now and weep, as I think of them placid each in her full sleep of death for a short moment ere fading. For, friend John, hardly had my knife severed the head of each, before the whole body began to melt away and crumble into its native dust, as though the death that should have come centuries agone had at last assert himself and say at once and loud "I am here!"

Before I left the castle I so fixed its entrances that never more can the Count enter there Un-Dead.

When I stepped into the circle where Madam Mina slept, she woke from her sleep, and, seeing me, cried out in pain that I had endured too much.

"Come!" she said, "come away from this awful place! Let us go to meet my husband who is, I know, coming towards us." She was looking thin and pale and weak; but her eyes were pure and glowed with fervour.

I was glad to see her paleness and her illness, for my mind was full of the fresh horror of that ruddy vampire sleep.

And so with trust and hope, and yet full of fear, we go eastward to meet our friends—and *him*—whom Madam Mina tell me that she *know* are coming to meet us.

MINA HARKER'S JOURNAL.

6 November.—It was late in the afternoon when the Professor and I took our way towards the east whence I knew Jonathan was coming. We did not go fast, though the way was steeply downhill, for we had to take heavy rugs and wraps with us; we dared not face the possibility of being left without warmth in the cold and the snow. We had to take some of our provisions, too, for we were in a perfect desolation, and, so far as we could see through the snowfall, there was not even the sign of habitation. When we had gone about a mile, I was tired with the heavy walking and sat down to rest. Then we looked back and saw where the clear line of Dracula's castle cut the sky; for we were so deep under the hill whereon it was set that the angle of perspective of the Carpathian mountains was far below it. We saw it in all its grandeur, perched a thousand feet on the summit of a sheer precipice, and with seemingly a great gap between it and the steep of the adjacent mountain on any side. There was something wild and uncanny about the place. We could hear the distant howling of wolves. They were far off, but the sound, even though coming muffled through the deadening snowfall, was full of terror. I knew from the way Dr. Van Helsing was searching about that he was trying to seek some strategic point, where we would be less exposed in case of attack. The rough roadway still led downwards; we could trace it through the drifted snow.

In a little while the Professor signalled to me, so I got up and joined him. He had found a wonderful spot, a sort of natural hollow in a rock, with an entrance like a doorway between two boulders. He took me by the hand and drew me in: "See!" he said, "here you will be in shelter; and if the wolves do come I can meet them one by one." He brought in our furs, and made a snug nest for me, and got out some provisions, and forced them upon me. But I could not eat; to even try to do so was repulsive to me, and, much as I would have liked to please him, I could not bring myself to the attempt. He looked very sad, but did not reproach me. Taking his field-glasses from the case, he stood on the top of the rock, and began to search the horizon. Suddenly he called out:—

"Look! Madam Mina, look! look!" I sprang up and stood beside him on the rock; he handed me his glasses and pointed. The snow was now falling more heavily, and swirled about fiercely, for a high wind was beginning to blow. However, there were times when there were pauses between the snow flurries and I could see a long way round. From the height where we were it was possible to see a great distance; and far off, beyond the white waste of snow, I could see the river lying like a black ribbon in kinks and curls as it wound its way. Straight in front of us and not far off—in fact, so near that I wondered we had not noticed before— came a group of mounted men hurrying along. In the midst of them was a cart, a long leiter-wagon which swept from side to side, like a dog's tail wagging, with each stern inequality of the road. Outlined against the snow as they were, I could see from the men's clothes that they were peasants or gypsies of some kind.

On the cart was a great square chest. My heart leaped as I saw it, for I felt that the end was coming. The evening was now drawing close, and well I knew that at sunset the Thing, which was all then imprisoned there, would take new freedom and could in any of many forms elude all pursuit. In fear I turned to the Professor; to my consternation, however, he was not there. An instant later, I saw him below me. Round the rock he had drawn a circle, such as we had found shelter in last night. When he had completed it he stood beside me again, saying:—

"At least you shall be safe here from *him!*" He took the glasses from me, and at the next lull of the snow swept the whole space below us. "See," he said, "they come quickly; they are flogging the horses, and galloping as hard as they can." He paused and went on in a hollow voice:—

"They are racing for the sunset. We may be too late. God's will be done!" Down came another blinding rush of driving snow, and the whole landscape was blotted out. It soon passed, however, and once more his glasses were fixed on the plain. Then came a sudden cry:—

"Look! Look! Look! See, two horsemen follow fast, coming up from the south. It must be Quincey and John. Take the glass. Look before the snow blots it all out!" I took it and looked. The two men might be Dr. Seward and Mr. Morris. I knew at all events that neither of them was Jonathan. At the same time I *knew* that Jonathan was not far off; looking around I saw on the north side of the coming party two other men, riding at break-neck speed. One of them I knew was Jonathan, and the other I took, of course, to be Lord Godalming. They, too, were pursuing the party with the cart. When I told the Professor he shouted in glee like a schoolboy, and, after looking intently till a snow fall made sight impossible, he laid his Winchester rifle ready for use against the boulder at the opening of our shelter. "They are all converging," he said. "When the time comes we shall have gypsies on all sides." I got out my revolver ready to hand, for whilst we were speaking the howling of wolves came louder and closer. When the snow storm abated a moment we looked again. It was strange to see the snow falling in such heavy flakes close to us, and beyond, the sun shining more and more brightly as it sank down towards the far mountaintops. Sweeping the glass all around us I could see here and there dots moving singly and in twos and threes and larger numbers—the wolves were gathering for their prey.

Every instant seemed an age whilst we waited. The wind came now in fierce bursts, and the snow was driven with fury as it swept upon us in circling eddies, at times we could not see an arm's length before us; but at others, as the hollow-sounding wind swept by us, it seemed to clear the air-space around us so that we could see afar. We had of late been so accustomed to watch for sunrise and sunset, that we knew with fair accuracy when it would be; and we knew that before long the sun would set. It was hard to believe that by our watches it was less than an hour that we waited in that rocky shelter before the various bodies began to converge close upon us. The wind came now with fiercer and more bitter sweeps, and more steadily from the north. It seemingly had driven the snow clouds from us, for, with only occasional bursts, the snow fell. We could distinguish clearly the individuals of each party, the pursued and the pursuers. Strangely enough those pursued did not seem to realise, or at least to care, that they were pursued; they seemed, however, to hasten with redoubled speed as the sun dropped lower and lower on the mountaintops.

Closer and closer they drew. The Professor and I crouched down behind our rock, and held our weapons ready; I could see that he was determined that they should not pass. One and all were quite unaware of our presence.

All at once two voices shouted out to: "Halt!" One was my Jonathan's, raised in a high key of passion; the other Mr. Morris's strong resolute tone of quiet command. The gypsies may not have known the language, but there was no mistaking the tone, in whatever tongue the words were spoken. Instinctively they reined in, and at the instant Lord Godalming and Jonathan dashed up at one side and Dr. Seward and Mr. Morris on the other. The leader of the gypsies, a splendid-looking fellow who sat his horse like a centaur, waved them back, and in a fierce voice gave to his companions some word to proceed. They lashed the horses which sprang forward; but the four men raised their Winchester rifles, and in an unmistakable way commanded them to stop. At the same moment Dr. Van Helsing and I rose behind the rock and pointed our weapons at them. Seeing that they were surrounded the men tightened their reins and drew up. The leader turned to them and gave a word at which every man of the gypsy party drew what weapon he carried, knife or pistol, and held himself in readiness to attack. Issue was joined in an instant.

The leader, with a quick movement of his rein, threw his horse out in front, and pointing first to the sun—now close down on the hill tops—and then to the castle, said something which I did not understand. For answer, all four men of our party threw themselves from their horses and dashed towards the cart. I should have felt terrible fear at seeing Jonathan in such danger, but that the ardour of battle must have been upon me as well as the rest of them; I felt no fear, but only a wild, surging desire to do something. Seeing the quick movement of our parties, the leader of the gypsies gave a command; his men instantly formed round the cart in a sort of undisciplined endeavour, each one shouldering and pushing the other in his eagerness to carry out the order.

In the midst of this I could see that Jonathan on one side of the ring of men, and Quincey on the other, were forcing a way to the cart; it was evident that they were bent on finishing their task before the sun should set. Nothing seemed to stop or even to hinder them. Neither the levelled weapons nor the flashing knives of the gypsies in front, nor the howling of the wolves behind, appeared to even attract their attention. Jonathan's impetuosity, and the manifest singleness of his purpose, seemed to overawe those in front of him; instinctively they cowered aside and let him pass. In an instant he had jumped upon the cart, and, with a strength which seemed incredible, raised the great box, and flung it over the wheel to the ground. In the meantime, Mr. Morris had had to use force to pass through his side of the ring of Szgany. All the time I had been breathlessly watching Jonathan I had, with the tail of my eye, seen him pressing desperately forward, and had seen the knives of the gypsies flash as he won a way through them, and they cut at him. He had parried with his great bowie knife, and at first I thought that he too had come through in safety; but as he sprang beside Jonathan, who had by now jumped from the cart, I could see that with his left hand he was clutching at his side, and that the blood was spurting through his fingers. He did not delay notwithstanding this, for as Jonathan, with desperate energy, attacked one end of the chest, attempting to prize off the lid with his great Kukri knife, he attacked the other frantically with his bowie. Under the efforts of both men the lid began to yield; the nails drew with a quick screeching sound, and the top of the box was thrown back.

By this time the gypsies, seeing themselves covered by the Winchesters, and at the mercy of Lord Godalming and Dr. Seward, had given in and made no further resistance. The sun was almost down on the mountaintops, and the shadows of the whole group fell upon the snow. I saw the Count lying within the box upon the earth, some of which the rude falling from the cart had scattered over him. He was deathly pale, just like a waxen image, and the red eyes glared with the horrible vindictive look which I knew too well.

As I looked, the eyes saw the sinking sun, and the look of hate in them turned to triumph.

But, on the instant, came the sweep and flash of Jonathan's great knife. I shrieked as I saw it shear through the throat; whilst at the same moment Mr. Morris's bowie knife plunged into the heart.

It was like a miracle; but before our very eyes, and almost in the drawing of a breath, the whole body crumbled into dust and passed from our sight.

I shall be glad as long as I live that even in that moment of final dissolution, there was in the face a look of peace, such as I never could have imagined might have rested there.

The Castle of Dracula now stood out against the red sky, and every stone of its broken battlements was articulated against the light of the setting sun.

The gypsies, taking us as in some way the cause of the extraordinary disappearance of the dead man, turned, without a word, and rode away as if for their lives. Those who were unmounted jumped upon their leiter-wagon and shouted to the horsemen not to desert them. The wolves, which had withdrawn to a safe distance, followed in their wake, leaving us alone. Mr. Morris, who had sunk to the ground, leaned on his elbow, holding his hand pressed to his side; the blood still gushed through his fingers. I flew to him, for the Holy circle did not now keep me back; so did the two doctors. Jonathan knelt behind him and the wounded man laid back his head on his shoulder. With a sigh he took, with a feeble effort, my hand in that of his own which was unstained. He must have seen the anguish of my heart in my face, for he smiled at me and said:—

"I am only too happy to have been of any service! Oh, God!" he cried suddenly, struggling up to a sitting posture and pointing to me, "It was worth for this to die! Look! look!"

The sun was now right down upon the mountaintop, and the red gleams fell upon my face, so that it was bathed in rosy light. With one impulse the men sank on their knees and a deep and earnest "Amen" broke from all as their eyes followed the pointing of his finger. The dying man spoke:—

"Now God be thanked that all has not been in vain! See! the snow is not more stainless than her forehead! The curse has passed away!"

And, to our bitter grief, with a smile and in silence, he died, a gallant gentleman.

NOTE

---◇---

Seven years ago we all went through the flames; and the happiness of some of us since then is, we think, well worth the pain we endured. It is an added joy to Mina and to me that our boy's birthday is the same day as that on which Quincey Morris died. His mother holds, I know, the secret belief that some of our brave friend's spirit has passed into him. His bundle of names links all our little band of men together; but we call him Quincey.

In the summer of this year we made a journey to Transylvania, and went over the old ground which was, and is, to us so full of vivid and terrible memories. It was almost impossible to believe that the things which we had seen with our own eyes and heard with our own ears were living truths. Every trace of all that had been was blotted out. The castle stood as before, reared high above a waste of desolation.

When we got home we were talking of the old time—which we could all look back on without despair, for Godalming and Seward are both happily married. I took the papers from the safe where they had been ever since our return so long ago. We were struck with the fact, that in all the mass of material of which the record is composed, there is hardly one authentic document; nothing but a mass of typewriting, except the later notebooks of Mina and Seward and myself, and Van Helsing's memorandum. We could hardly ask any one, even did we wish to, to accept these as proofs of so wild a story. Van Helsing summed it all up as he said, with our boy on his knee:—

"We want no proofs; we ask none to believe us! This boy will some day know what a brave and gallant woman his mother is. Already he knows her sweetness and loving care; later on he will understand how some men so loved her, that they did dare much for her sake."

—JONATHAN HARKER.

THE END

THE TIMES (LONDON) REVIEW

Monday, August 23rd, 1897

Dracula cannot be described as a domestic novel, nor its annals as those of a quiet life. The circumstances described are from the first peculiar. A young solicitor sent for on business by a client in Transylvania goes through some unusual experiences. He finds himself shut up in a half ruined castle with a host who is only seen at night and three beautiful females who have the misfortune of being vampires. Their intentions, which can hardly be described as honourable, are to suck his blood, in order to sustain their own vitality. Count Dracula (the host) is also a vampire but has grown tired of his compatriots, however young and beautiful, and has a great desire for what may literally be called fresh blood. He has therefore sent for the solicitor that through his means he may be introduced to London society. Without understanding the Count's views, Mr. Harker has good reason for having suspicions of his client. Wolves come at his command, and also fogs; he is also too clever by half at climbing. There is a splendid prospect from the castle terrace, which Mr. Harker would have enjoyed but for his conviction that he would never leave the place alive:—

> In the soft moonlight the distant hills became melted and the shadows in the valleys and gorges of velvety blackness. The mere beauty seemed to cheer me; there was peace and comfort in every breath I drew. As I leaned from the window my eye was caught by something moving a storey below me, and somewhat to my left, where I imagined, from the lie of the room that the windows of the Count would look out. The window at which I stood was tall and deep, stone-mullioned, and, though weather-worn, was still complete but it was evidently many a day since the casement had been there. I drew back behind the stonework and looked carefully out.
>
> What I saw was the Count's head coming out from the window. I did not see the face, but I knew the man by the neck and the movement of his back and arms. In any case, I could not mistake the hands, which I had had so many opportunities of studying. I was at first interested and somewhat amused, for it is wonderful how small a matter will interest and amuse a man when he is a prisoner. But my very feelings changed to repulsion and terror when I saw the whole man slowly crawl down the castle wall over that dreadful abyss, face down, with the cloak spreading out around him like great wings.

These scenes and situations, striking as they are, become commonplace compared with Count Dracula's goings on in London. As Falstaff was not only witty himself but the cause of wit in other people, so a vampire, it seems, compels those it has bitten (two little marks on the throat are its token, usually taken by faculty for the scratches of a broach) to become after death vampires also. Nothing can keep them away but garlic, which is, perhaps, why that comestible is so popular in certain countries. One may imagine, therefore, how the thing spread in London after the Count's arrival. The only chance of stopping it was to kill the Count before any of his victims died, and this was a difficult job, for though several centuries old, he was very young and strong, and could become a dog or a bat at pleasure. However, it is undertaken by four resolute and high-principled persons, and how it is managed forms the subject of the story, of which nobody can complain that it is deficient in dramatic situations. We would not however, recommend it to nervous persons for evening reading.

AFTERWORD

A lunatic asylum and an insect-eating madman in England; a macabre castle surrounded by howling wolves in Transylvania; an Un-Dead aristocratic vampire whose canine teeth hang over his lower lip, and who seeks refuge between sunrise and sunset in a coffin filled with graveyard dirt; life-threatening yet strangely attractive sisters; a murderous sleepwalker and her blood-drained child victims; a phantom ship manned by corpses; an invasion of thousands of rats; exorcism amidst the secrets of the crypt; a thrilling chase across Europe; decapitation and stakes through the heart; a body that suddenly crumbles to dust; suggestions of sexual perversion—voyeurism, rape, incest, sadism, masochism, necrophilia and fellatio. These ghoulish ingredients made Bram Stoker's *Dracula* (1897) one of the most famous and popular novels of all time. Not the first nor the last version of the Dracula story, it is the most enduring, and has inspired scores of eerie novels, plays and horror films.

Stoker, an Irish theatrical manager, critic and novelist, was a contemporary of the late-nineteenth-century adventure writers—Robert Louis Stevenson, Rider Haggard, Rudyard Kipling and Arthur Conan Doyle—and *Dracula's* horrific elements have often been compared to Stevenson's *Dr. Jekyll and Mr. Hyde* (1886) as well as to Oscar Wilde's *The Picture of Dorian Gray* (1890). Doyle's trio of Sherlock Holmes, his rather dim friend and assistant Dr. Watson and the evil genius Professor Moriarty clearly influenced Stoker's portrayal of the polymath Professor Abraham Van Helsing of Amsterdam, "a philosopher and a metaphysician, and one of the most advanced scientists of his day"; Jonathan Harker, the mild, dogged English lawyer and passive listener; and the evil Count Dracula of Transylvania, soldier, statesman and alchemist, with "a mighty brain, a learning beyond compare."

Nothing else Stoker wrote came even close to the success of *Dracula*. The plot is preposterous, the characters conventional, the narrative long-winded and repetitive. There is an epidemic of deaths: not only Lucy,

Renfield and Quincey Morris but also, more gratuitously, Lucy's mother, Holmwood's father, Mr. Hawkins, the talkative old sailor in Whitby, the crew of the derelict ship and even a herd of horses in the Carpathians. Stoker constantly tells us how the characters feel—in a world full of "devils," "doom" and "terror," and physiological clichés like hair rises, blood runs cold and everyone shudders with horror—instead of suggesting their fear in what they say and do, as a great novelist, Henry James, does in his ghost story "The Turn of the Screw" (1898). But Stoker had created a mesmerizing character in the figure of Dracula, an ogre in a grown-up fairy tale, and founded his bestseller on a trio of compelling themes: blood, sex and death. His worthy, respectable English characters are pitted against a foreign vampire. Stoker followed the classic recipe for the horror genre, and gave his readers the pleasure of being thoroughly frightened and completely safe.

The setting shifts from Dracula's spooky castle in Romania, to the cozy interiors of English houses, and back again. Dracula, who can only survive by spending the daylight hours in a coffin, smuggles himself and fifty coffins into England, where he sucks blood and creates new disciples. He turns Lucy Westenra, the friend of Harker's fiancée, Mina, into a vampire. She in turn drinks the blood of children, and must be destroyed. Van Helsing, Harker and Dr. Seward, the director of a lunatic asylum, try in vain to protect Mina from Dracula and pursue him back to his castle. This fantastic tale is told by multiple narrators, who reinforce each other's stories. They share their diaries and secret papers and convene executive-style meetings about the current stage of the hunt. Documents, letters, telegrams, invoices, news reports, phonograph recordings and even a translation of the Russian ship's log are used to validate the supernatural elements in the midst of what Van Helsing calls "our scientific, sceptical, matter-of-fact nineteenth century."

Stoker manages his characters and settings with considerable artistry. The opening chapter sets up the dramatic contrast between good and evil, light and darkness. Summoned to complete Count Dracula's purchase of an ancient abbey outside London (conveniently next to Dr. Seward's asylum), Harker travels from England to the remote Carpathian mountains (then part of the Austro-Hungarian Empire and now in north-central Romania), still "one of the wildest and least-known portions of Europe." Parallel events and characters help structure the novel. Harker is threatened in the castle by three weird sisters; Lucy has three suitors; and three of the main characters suffer from mental illness: Van Helsing has a fit of hysterics, Harker has brain fever, Renfield (Dr. Seward's patient and Dracula's disciple) is insane. After the first four exciting chapters, describing Harker's distressing discoveries and conflict with Dracula, the story shifts to England. There, in a parallel yet contrasting plot, the two conventional heroines are in love and about to marry: Lucy to Arthur Holmwood (later Lord Godalming), Mina to Harker. By becoming Dracula's victims, they link the Transylvanian and English episodes. Lucy is a sleepwalker; Mina is hypnotized. After seeing what Dracula has done to Lucy, Mina is well aware of what he's doing to her. Yet Mina prospers as Lucy declines. The heroes first try to save Lucy and then must destroy her. After Lucy's death, her fiancé and two rejected suitors rescue Mina. These chapters are rather dull in comparison to the earlier adventures, and the narrative does not regain its initial impetus until Dracula escapes yet again.

Dracula is a fascinating villain. Formal, punctilious and gracious, exquisitely polite and well educated, he has never been to England but speaks better English than Van Helsing. Dracula moves rapidly yet carefully; Van Helsing, in pursuit, says there's little time to lose and constantly urges haste. Dracula never eats; Van Helsing frequently mentions their need to revive themselves with food. A historical figure, Prince Vlad the Impaler, inspired the legendary Dracula, whose name in Romanian means "dragon" or "devil." Like the reptilian Satan in Milton's *Paradise Lost*, he's a formidable antagonist, by far the most interesting character in the book, who represents the power of evil in the Manichaean struggle against the principle of good. Yet Dracula also engages our sympathy. Lonely, cursed and doomed, devoid of family or religion, unable to love or live a normal life, he must spend all the daylight hours sealed up in a coffin and must quit his container at night to search for human blood. Stoker defines the subhuman Count in animal images. He moves like a lizard and panther; turns into a bat, dog and wolf; and unleashes a plague of rats. (The unfortunate lunatic Renfield feasts on flies, spiders and raw birds.)

Though Dracula is unable to suck Harker's blood (he is repulsed by Harker's crucifix), he virtually steals Harker's identity. When Harker looks in the mirror, he sees himself but does not see Dracula standing behind him. To disguise the fact that he's imprisoned Harker, Dracula goes out dressed in his clothes and the peasants think he's Harker. After Dracula has killed a small child, the mother mistakes Harker for the Count and calls him a monster. In one of the great moments of the book, Harker watches Dracula crawl, face forward and with considerable speed, down the castle wall. Stoker provides a convincing detail as Dracula grasps "the corners of the stones, worn clear of the mortar by the stress of years . . . just as a lizard moves along a wall." Soon afterward, Harker imitates him by escaping along a stone ledge whose mortar has also been washed away.

Dracula not only weakens his victims by stealing their blood, but also infuses them with his own personality. The tragic Lucy Westenra, turned into a vampire by Dracula, also preys on little children and her mode of death foreshadows his own. Dracula, when taken unawares, jumps like a cat; Mina, in a ghastly moment, is compared to a kitten whose nose is forced into a saucer of milk. Dracula reads Bradshaw's railroad guide; Mina has studied the train schedules from London to Eastern Europe. Harker finds a great heap of gold in Dracula's room and the Count, rushing out of another room, leaves "a bundle of banknotes and a stream of gold" behind; Mina rhapsodizes on the "wonderful power of money" she's inherited from her husband's patron, Mr. Hawkins. At the end of the novel, Mina, like Dracula, functions only part of the time. When hypnotized (a state analogous to his daytime sleep), she's able to reveal his malign motives and unexpected movements, and guide the gallant band of heroes as they pursue him from England to Transylvania.

The novel comes full circle, and Harker's first view of the castle at the end of the first chapter recurs at the end of the last: "The Castle of

Dracula now stood out against the red sky, and every stone of its broken battlements was articulated against the light of the setting sun." The red gleams of the sun evoke the central motif of the novel—blood. The characters lose blood in all kinds of ways: through cuts, bites, knife fights and stakes through the heart; and the novel plays on our fears of losing blood. The vampires are monstrous versions of natural bloodsuckers like mosquitoes, bats and leeches. Each of the four heroes—Lucy's fiancé, Arthur Holmwood; Dr. Seward; the American adventurer Quincey Morris (the latter two disappointed suitors for Lucy's hand); and Van Helsing himself—gives Mina a blood transfusion to compensate for Dracula's nocturnal bites. In these early days of experimentation with blood transfusion, before blood types were discovered, this was a sinister, dangerous and potentially fatal process.

In Stoker's hands the vampire theme also leads to an equally disturbing parody of the Christian Communion. The Mass is a symbolic representation of the blood of Christ, taken in the form of wine; the vampire, by contrast, literally drinks the blood of a living human being. More than a dozen biblical quotations and allusions in the novel—including "the blood is the life" (Deuteronomy 12:23) and "Drink ye all of it; For this is my blood of the new testament, which is shed for many for the remission of sins" (Matthew 26:27–28)—emphasize the Christian theme. Men have always been fascinated by the possibility of immortality; and Dracula, supposedly hundreds of years old, has apparently achieved this state. He not only imitates the Mass by drinking human blood, but mocks the Resurrection of Christ from His tomb by emerging each night from his coffin.

In a perverse way, the vampire Dracula and the vampire Lucy are linked by allusions to Christ, which suggest they are tragic victims as well as bloodthirsty predators. Harker, shocked by the appearance of Dracula and echoing Pontius Pilate ("Behold the Man!"—John 19:5), tells Mina, "It is the man himself." Van Helsing, staring at the dead Lucy and echoing Christ's last words on the Cross ("It is finished"—John 19:30), remarks, "It is all over." Vampirism is a kind of disease, where the perpetrators are themselves victims.

Dracula is built upon a series of memorable and sexually suggestive scenes. In Dracula's castle Harker is both threatened and sorely tempted, both excited and disgusted, by three weird vampire sisters—relations or captives of the master. In his diary he recalls his ambivalent feelings. He's awakened from sleep by a vision of the sensual women who are about to kiss and destroy him, and one of them "went on her knees, and bent over me, simply gloating. There was a deliberate voluptuousness which was both thrilling and repulsive, and as she arched her neck she actually licked her lips like an animal. . . . I closed my eyes in a languorous ecstasy and waited—waited with beating heart." Before he can experience the exquisite sexual thrill he can never hope to achieve with his timid and repressed fiancée, Dracula, in a moment of coitus interruptus, breaks into the chamber and claims, with homosexual overtones, that Harker is his property: "How dare you cast eyes on him when I had forbidden it? Back, I tell you all! This man belongs to me!" Harker seems both bewildered and pleased that both men and women are fighting to possess him.

The voracious Lucy, trying to decide which suitor to marry before choosing the man destined to become a lord, reveals her own sexual fantasy. Desiring a male harem, she asks, "Why can't they let a girl marry three men, or as many as want her?" Though all three men do want her, her vampire ventures prevent the possibility of marriage. Instead, before dismembering their beloved, they all have symbolic sex with her by giving her four separate transfusions and ejaculating their blood into her body. As Dr. Seward explains in a thematic passage, "No man knows, till he experiences it, what it is to feel his own life-blood drawn away into the veins of the woman he loves."

In another bizarre scene, Van Helsing and Seward, using medical license to disguise their voyeuristic predilections, revive the blood-drained Lucy by undressing her, placing her in a hot bath and then rubbing her body: "Van Helsing's face almost beamed, and as we lifted her from the bath and rolled her in a hot sheet to dry her he said to me:— 'The first gain is ours!'" The good doctors can scarcely disguise their erotic pleasure as they enact the male fantasy of having absolute power over a beautiful, naked and unconscious woman.

Three chapters later, when they violate her tomb in order to violate her body with a stake, Seward holds a candle from which "the sperm dropped in white patches." He then alludes to their symbolic rape in the bathing scene by naively observing, "It seemed to be as much an affront to the dead as it would have been to have stripped off her clothing in her sleep whilst living." When Van Helsing finally drives the stake into Lucy's heart, she reacts as if she's had an oceanic orgasm: "The Thing in the coffin writhed; and a hideous, blood-curdling screech came from the opened red lips. The body shook and quivered and twisted in wild contortions; the sharp white teeth champed together till the lips were cut, and the mouth was smeared with a crimson foam."

The necessary murder of Lucy by the heroes leads directly to the last great scenes. While Harker sleeps soundly beside Mina, Dracula consummates *his* blood wedding by forcing her to suck his blood. In a sublimely ghoulish metaphor, he refers to Mina as "my bountiful wine-press." "His right hand gripped her by the back of the neck," Stoker writes, "forcing her face down on his bosom. Her white nightdress was smeared with blood, and a thin stream trickled down the man's bare breast which was shown by his torn-open dress. The attitude of the two had a terrible resemblance to a child forcing a kitten's nose into a saucer of milk to compel it to drink." As if this symbolic fellatio were not sufficiently outrageous, Mina also morbidly recalls the incandescent scene. She gasps, "When the blood began to spurt out, he took my hands in one of his, holding them tight, and with the other seized my neck and pressed my mouth to the wound, so that I must either suffocate or swallow some of the— Oh my God! My God! What have I done?" Stoker, who knew exactly what he was doing, achieved his effects by describing these high-voltage scenes with apparent innocence. None of his readers, oddly enough, protested about the sexual implications when the novel first appeared in the decadent *fin-de-siècle* 1890s.

The author of horror fiction always risks moving from the grotesquely terrifying to the comically grotesque. Stoker manages to nail down his incredible events with a series of realistic details and vivid images. Van

Helsing uses a surgical saw to cut out the iron bars on a window and gain entry to a locked house. He desecrates the sacred Host by molding it into strings of putty and using it to seal the cracks of a tomb. But when he removes the putty, Lucy, "a corporeal body as real at that moment as our own, passed in through the interstice where scarce a knife-blade could have gone." As Van Helsing opens the inevitably creaky door to another tomb and motions Seward to precede him, "there was a delicious irony in the offer, in the courtliness [like Dracula's] of giving preference on such a ghastly occasion." When the chorus of wolves howl outside Dracula's castle, "it was almost as if the sound sprang up at the rising of his hand, just as the music of a great orchestra seems to leap under the baton of the conductor." The verb "leap" effectively links the sound of the orchestra to the wolves.

The supernatural arrival of Dracula's ship, sailing from Varna on the Black Sea to Whitby on the northeast coast of England, is another tour de force. In this scene, influenced by Coleridge's "Rime of the Ancient Mariner," the strange schooner, swept by a sudden blast of wind, manages to reach a safe port. The searchlight then reveals that "lashed to the helm was a corpse, with drooping head, which swung horribly to and fro at each motion of the ship," which, "as if by a miracle, had found the harbour, unsteered save by the hand of a dead man!" As soon as the ship touches the shore, a huge dog sprang, from the ship to the strand. The next morning a mastiff, after a savage fight, is found torn to bits. Though there's no explanation for this mysterious landfall, it seems clear that Dracula has broken free to wreak his evil in England.

Stoker also alleviates the horrors with incongruous and often macabre comedy, which ranges from the farcical to the surprisingly subtle. Van Helsing, unfamiliar with English idioms and trying to say "levelheaded," instead says "his head is what you call in plane with the horizon." Using garlic, crucifix and stake against Dracula, Van Helsing crudely puns on one of these weapons by exclaiming, "the stake we play for is life and death." When the fearful wolf escapes from the zoo (as Renfield escapes from the lunatic asylum), the English keeper (analogous to Dr. Seward, keeper of the insane) insouciantly states, "Never mind. . . . I'm used to 'em." The heroes bribe their way through England to get whatever they want (they also forge death certificates, break into houses and ransack tombs). Yet in Transylvania Harker chauvinistically states, "Thank God! this is the country where bribery can do anything." The English laborers constantly complain of their thirsty work and solicit money for beer. The equally thirsty Dracula, parodying their requests, grabs Mina's throat before sipping her blood and remarks, "First, a little refreshment to reward my exertions."

Stoker loves to mingle bizarre with conventionally polite behavior. While visiting Seward's asylum, Mina "came into the room with an easy gracefulness which would at once command the respect of any lunatic." Van Helsing, after dispatching the vampire, punctiliously asks her would-be husband, "May I cut off the head of the dead Miss Lucy?" When they're about to force their way into Mina's boudoir, Quincey hesitates for a moment and superfluously observes, "It is unusual to break into a lady's room!"

After the little band reenacts the execution of Lucy by plunging a knife into Dracula's heart, his whole body crumbles into dust before their eyes and disappears, like the mist whose form he adopted at the start of the novel. In the brief epilogue, which takes place seven years later, Stoker includes a reference to his own life. Harker relates that he and Mina have a seven-year-old son, named after Quincey Morris, who died in the final skirmish with Dracula. Coursing through the veins of the little boy, whose name means "fifth," is the blood of the quintet who helped form the boy: Holmwood, Seward, Morris, Van Helsing—and Dracula. Quincey's age is significant. Throughout his early childhood Stoker suffered from a mysterious, undiagnosed illness, and could not walk on his own till he himself was seven years old.

Two other novels appeared in 1897 with eponymous heroes who, like Dracula, were also consummate outsiders: H. G. Wells' *The Invisible Man* and Joseph Conrad's *The Nigger of the "Narcissus"*. Conrad's *Heart of Darkness* (1899), even closer to Dracula, also described brave men who confront great danger and an idealized woman who cannot bear great strain and is too precious to risk. Kurtz's fiancée in Belgium, like Mina in England, must be protected from harsh reality. The Romanian Prince Vlad the Impaler was depicted in an 1890s print eating a meal while surrounded by the heads of his enemies impaled on spikes. Conrad's Kurtz, whose savage mistress screams from the shore of the river and whose last words are "The horror! The horror!" (a suitable epigraph for *Dracula*), also decorates his fence with the skulls of his African victims. Conrad's novella portrays the pervasive evil that seeps back from the heart of darkness into the supposedly civilized world. In Stoker's fascinating novel, sadistic sexuality escapes from the far reaches of Transylvania to contaminate the victims of Western Europe.

—Jeffrey Meyers

Dear Reader,

I hope you have greatly enjoyed the classic and beloved novel you have just finished. I have always admired it myself. But I have a personal reason for taking such a special interest in *Dracula*: Bram Stoker was my great-granduncle.

I grew up with *Dracula* as part of our family history. We all read the book, and I even wrote a paper for my college English class about my uncle Bram's motivations for writing *Dracula*. In researching that paper I became overwhelmed by the many variations of the story that were available in book and film form. Clearly my ancestor had struck a chord in the popular imagination. But what I found most confounding was that there seemed to be little or no respect for his original work. I became obsessed with the idea of preserving that original vision.

Eventually I met Ian Holt, a young man who had his own fascination with *Dracula*. As a child, Ian was seduced by the hypnotic spell of Tod Browning's 1931 film starring Bela Lugosi. As an adult, Ian spent twenty years researching both the historic Prince Dracula and Bram's *Dracula*, lecturing and giving papers at scholarly gatherings around the world (including Transylvania, Romania, where he once spent the night in Dracula's castle). Ian was mentored in his research by leaders in this field of study, the late, Professor Raymond McNally and Professor Radu Florescu—the historic Prince Dracula's actual descendant. With Ian's scholarship and my familial duty in mind, we undertook to create a sequel to my uncle's famous novel, *Dracula*. The result is *Dracula the Un-Dead*.

In order to plot out our novel, Ian and I explored Bram's notes for *Dracula* that are available in Philadelphia's Rosenbach Museum. For example, in Bram's notes, there was a reference to an Inspector Cotford, though this character does not exist in the published version of *Dracula*. It seems that the original editor cut him out entirely. Using the notes, research of the time period, and our own imaginations, we breathed life into the character of Inspector Cotford for *Dracula the Un-Dead*, and he now plays a pivotal role in our story as he investigates murders, past and present. This is but one example of how we took my uncle's ideas, some mere threads, and expanded them to write our story.

Another basis for our novel was family lore, passed down through the generations. From stories, I learned that Uncle Bram was obsessed with how the actions taken in one's present were preordained by events in one's past. You can see this borne out in the way he changed professions rapidly and often. His past, as a sickly child with a sense that death was always at his heels, led him to constantly search for his true destiny. Again, this legend of Bram synched up with Ian's studied belief that Bram's meticulous nature would not have allowed him to leave out the backstories of his iconic characters. If the past colored everything about the present, then surely Bram would have wanted to make clear issues such as: How did Mina and Lucy meet, and why did they become friends? Why does Renfield just appear in the novel with no explanation of who he is or his connection to Dracula and the rest of the lead characters? How does a Texan from America become lifelong friends with an English lord's son and a middle-class doctor who studied in Holland? Ian and I have finally answered these nagging questions for Bram's readers in *Dracula the Un-Dead*.

Dracula the Un-Dead, which Dutton is publishing, is more than just a sequel. It is a love letter and thank-you to all of *Dracula*'s and Bram's millions of fans around the world. It is true to the classic, merges the vampire mythology of Bram's time into what is commonly accepted now, but stays true to the historical detail of the time period. It is also the first and only book to be endorsed by the Stoker family and marks the first time since Tod Browning's 1931 film that the family has supported any adaptation of Bram's original story. What follows is a short excerpt from our novel. We hope you enjoy it.

—Dacre Stoker

CHAPTER I.

◆

OCEANS OF LOVE, LUCY.

The inscription was the only thing Dr. Jack Seward could focus on as he felt the darkness overtake him. In the darkness was peace, with no harsh light to illuminate the tattered remains of his life. For years, he had devoted himself to fighting back the darkness. Now he simply embraced it.

Only at night could Seward find peace with the memory of Lucy. In his dreams, he still felt her warm embrace. For a fleeting moment, he could go back to London, to a happier era, when he found meaning through his place in the world and his research. This was the life he had wished to share with Lucy.

The early morning din of milk wagons, fishmongers, and other merchant carts rattling hurriedly across the cobblestone streets of Paris intruded on Seward's dream and thrust him back into the harsh present. Seward forced his eyes open. They stung worse than fresh iodine on an open wound. As the cracked ceiling of the stale Parisian flophouse room he had been renting came into focus, he reflected on how much his life had changed. It saddened him to see all the muscle tone he had lost. His bicep sagged, resembling one of those hand-sewn muslin tea bags after it had just been removed from a teapot. The veins on his arm were like rivers on a tattered map. He was a shadow of his former self.

Seward prayed that death would come quickly. He had willed his body to science, to be used in a classroom at his alma mater. He took comfort from the fact that in death he would help to inspire future doctors and scientists.

After a time, he remembered the watch, still nestled in his left hand. He turned it over. Half past six! For an instant, panic overtook him. *Damn it to hell.* He had overslept. Seward staggered to his feet. An empty glass syringe rolled off the table and shattered on the grimy wooden floor. A small, smoked brown bottle of morphine was about to follow the fate of the syringe, but he quickly caught the precious liquid, untying the leather belt from his left bicep with a practiced movement. Normal circulation returned as he rolled down his sleeve and replaced the silver monogrammed cuff link on his frayed dress shirt. He buttoned up his vest and slipped on his jacket. Wallingham & Sons were the finest tailors in London. If his suit had been made by anyone else, it would have disintegrated ten years ago. *Vanity dies hard,* Seward thought to himself with a humorless chuckle.

He had to hurry if he still wanted to make the train. Where was that address? He had put it in a safe place. Now, when he needed it, he could not recall where exactly that was. He overturned the straw-filled mattress, inspected the underside of the wobbly table, and peered under the vegetable crates that served as dining chairs. He sifted through piles of aged newspaper clippings. Their headlines spoke of Seward's current preoccupation: gruesome stories of Jack the Ripper. Autopsy photos of the five known victims. Mutilated women posed, legs open, as if waiting to accept their deranged killer. The Ripper was deemed a butcher of women—but a butcher is more merciful to the animals he slaughters. Seward had reread the autopsy notes countless times. Loose pages of his theories and ideas written on scrap paper, torn cardboard, and unfolded matchboxes fluttered around him like wind-blown leaves.

The sweat flowing from Seward's brow began to sting his bloodshot eyes. *Damn, where had he put it?* The Benefactor had taken enormous risks to get him this information. Seward could not bear the thought of disappointing the only person who still believed in him. Everyone else—the Harkers, the Holmwoods—all thought he had taken leave of his senses. If they could see this room, Seward knew, they would feel justified in that belief. He scanned the crumbling plaster walls, which bore the evidence of his morphine-induced rants, his wild insights handwritten in ink, coal, wine, even his own blood. No madman would be so obvious. He was certain that these writings would one day prove his sanity.

Amidst it all, there was a page torn from a book, stabbed into the wall with a bone-handled bowie knife whose blade was stained with old blood. The page featured a portrait of an elegant, raven-haired beauty. Beneath the picture, an inscription: *Countess Elizabeth Bathory circa 1582.*

Of course, that's where I hid it. He laughed at himself as he pulled the knife out of the wall, seizing the page and turning it over. In his own barely legible handwriting, he found the address of a villa in Marseilles. Seward removed the cross, wooden stake, and garlic wreaths which hung next to Bathory's picture and scooped up a silver knife from the floor. He placed everything into a false bottom in his medical bag and covered it all with standard medical supplies.

The train left the Gare de Lyon exactly on time. Seeing it pull away just as he was paying for his ticket, Seward sprinted across the flood-stained building to reach the chugging behemoth as it left the seventh bay door. He managed to catch the last Pullman car and hoist himself on before it had a chance to pick up speed. His heart surged with pride as he made the daring leap. He had done this sort of thing in his youth with the Texan Quincey P. Morris and his old friend Arthur Holmwood. *Youth was wasted on the young.* Seward smiled to himself as he recalled the reckless days of his innocence . . . and ignorance.

The doctor took a seat in the elaborate dining car as the train lumbered southward. It wasn't moving quickly enough. He glanced down at his pocket watch; only five minutes had passed. Seward lamented that he could no longer pass the time by writing in his journal, as he was unable to afford the luxury of such a thing. They were not scheduled to reach Marseilles for ten more hours. There, he would finally have the evidence to prove his theories and show those who had shunned him that he was not mad; that he had been right all along.

These were going to be the longest ten hours of Seward's life.

"Billets, s'il vous plaît!"

Seward stared wide-eyed at the conductor standing over him with a stern look of impatience.

"Forgive me," Seward said. He handed the conductor his ticket, adjusting his scarf to cover the torn breast pocket.

"You are British?" the conductor asked with a heavy French accent.

"Why, yes."

"A doctor?" The conductor nodded toward the medical bag between Seward's feet.

"Yes."

Seward watched the conductor's gray eyes catalogue the threadbare person in front of him, the ill-fitting suit and well-worn shoes. He was hardly the image of a respectable doctor. "I will see your bag, please."

He handed over the bag, for it was not as if he had much choice in the matter. The conductor methodically pulled out medical bottles, read the labels, and dropped them back in with a clink. Seward knew what the conductor was looking for and hoped he wouldn't dig too deeply.

"Morphine," announced the conductor in a voice so loud that other passengers glanced over. He held up the brown bottle.

"I sometimes have to prescribe it as a sedative."

"I will see your license, please."

Seward searched his pockets. Last month, the International Opium Convention had been signed, prohibiting persons from importing, selling, distributing, and exporting morphine without a medical license. It took him so long to find it that by the time Seward finally produced the license, the conductor was about to pull the cord to stop the train. The conductor examined the paper, frowning, then turned his steely eyes to the travel document. The United Kingdom was the first to use photo identification on their passports. Since that picture had been taken, Seward had lost a tremendous amount of weight. His hair was now much grayer, his beard wild and untrimmed. The man in the train bore little resemblance to the man in the photo.

"Why are you going to Marseilles, doctor?"

"I am treating a patient there."

"What ails this patient?"

"He's suffering from a Narcissistic Personality Disorder."

"*Qu'est-ce que c'est?*"

"It is a psychological instability causing the patient to inflict predatory, autoerotic, antisocial, and parasitic control on those around them. As well as—"

"*Merci.*" The conductor cut Seward off by handing him back his papers and ticket with a deft flick. He turned and addressed only the men at the next table. "*Billets, s'il vous plaît.*"

Jack Seward sighed. Replacing his papers in his jacket, he checked the pocket watch again, a nervous habit. It seemed as if the interrogation had lasted hours, but only another five minutes had passed. He rolled down the fringed window shade to shield his eyes from the daylight and reclined into the plush, burgundy upholstered seat.

Oceans of Love, Lucy.

He held the beloved watch close to his heart and closed his eyes to dream.

It was a quarter century ago. Seward held the same watch up to the light the better to read the inscription. "Oceans of love, Lucy."

She was there. Alive. "You don't like it," she said, and pouted.

He couldn't break his stare away from her green eyes, soft as a summer meadow. Lucy had an odd idiosyncrasy of watching a speaker's mouth as if trying to taste the next word before it passed by his lips. She had such a lust for life. Her smile could bring warmth to the coldest heart. As she sat on the bench in the garden that spring day,

Seward marveled at how the sunlight illuminated the loose strands of red hair that danced in the breeze, haloing her face. The scent of fresh lilacs mixed with the salty sea air of Whitby Harbour. In the years since, whenever he smelled lilacs, he would remember this beautiful, bitter day.

"I can only conclude," Seward said, clearing his throat before his voice had a chance to break, "since you wrote on the gift card 'Dearest Friend' rather than 'Fiancé,' that you have chosen not to accept my proposal of marriage."

Lucy looked away, her eyes moistening. The silence spoke volumes.

"I thought it best that you hear it from me," Lucy finally sighed. "I have consented to wed Arthur."

Arthur had been Jack Seward's friend since they were lads. Seward loved him like a brother, yet always envied how easily everything came to Arthur. He was handsome and rich, and had never in his life known worry or struggle. Or heartbreak.

"I see." Seward's voice sounded like a squeak in his ears.

"I do love you," Lucy whispered. "But . . ."

"But not as much as you love Arthur." Of course he could not compete with the wealthy Arthur Holmwood, nor was he as dashing as Lucy's other suitor, the Texan Quincey P. Morris.

"Forgive me," he went on in a softer tone, suddenly afraid he'd hurt her. "I forgot my place."

Lucy reached out and patted his hand, as one would a beloved pet. "I will always be here."

Back in the present, he stirred in his sleep. If he could just see the beauty in Lucy's eyes . . . The last time he had gazed into them, that terrible night in the mausoleum, he had seen nothing but pain and torment. The memory of Lucy's dying screams still seared Seward's brain.

After leaving the train, Seward walked in a torrential downpour through Marseilles's labyrinth of white buildings and cursed his timing. Of course, his quest brought him to the French Riviera in March, the only rainy month.

He slogged farther inland, glancing back to see Fort Saint-Jean standing like a stone sentinel in the indigo harbor. Then he turned about to study the Provençal city, which had been built around a 2,600-year-old village. Artifacts of the city's Greek and Roman founders were found throughout its streets. Seward lamented that he was in this picturesque haven for such a sinister purpose. Though it would not be the first time malevolence had made its presence felt here: Over the last century, this seaside town had been marred by plague and pirates.

Seward stopped. Looming in front of him was a typical two-story Mediterranean villa with large wooden shutters and wrought-iron bars on the windows. The winter moon peering through the rain clouds cast a spectral glow on the traditional white walls. The roof was covered in red terra-cotta tiles that reminded him of some of the old Spanish houses he had seen when he visited Quincey P. Morris in Texas so many years ago. It created a decidedly foreboding ambience, even unwelcoming, for an ornate villa on the French Riviera. It appeared entirely devoid of life. His heart sank at the thought that he might be too late. Seward looked again at the address.

This was it.

Suddenly, he heard the thunderous approach of a horse and carriage splashing along the cobblestones. He ducked into a vineyard across from the building. There were no grapes on the dripping, weblike branches. A black carriage with ornate gold trim sailed up the hill, pulled by two glistening black mares. The animals drew to a stop without a command. Seward looked up and, to his surprise, saw there was no driver. *How was that possible?*

A strapping figure emerged from the carriage. The mares nipped at each other and squealed, necks arched. Then, again to Seward's amazement, they moved off, in perfect step, with no coachman to direct them. The figure held a walking stick aloft with one black-gloved hand, and dipped into a pocket with the other for a key, then stopped suddenly as if becoming aware of something.

"Damn," Seward muttered to himself.

The person at the door cocked his head, almost as if he heard

Seward's voice through the rain, and turned slowly toward the vineyard. Seward felt waves of panic and adrenaline wash over him but managed to hold his breath. The gloved hand reached up to the brim of the velvet top hat and Seward choked back a gasp as he saw the top hat removed to reveal sensuous locks of black hair cascading onto the figure's shoulders.

His mind reeled. *It is she!* The Benefactor had been right.

Countess Elizabeth Bathory stood at the doorway of the villa, looking exactly as she had in the portrait painted over three hundred years ago.

CHAPTER II.

———◇———

Lightning danced across the sky, illuminating the raindrops like gems on black velvet cloth. Seward knew he should move for cover, but he could do nothing except stare, entranced, at the exotic—and dangerous—beauty before him. Bathory's fair skin contrasted sharply with her midnight hair, and she moved with the silent grace of a predator. Her icy blue eyes searched for any movement in the street as another flash of lightning brightened the grounds before her. When she turned toward the vineyard, he quickly threw himself into the mud to avoid detection.

There, he held his breath, trying not to move and ignoring the cramp in his legs. He desperately longed to glance up, but the lightning flashing on his pale face would reveal him immediately, and so he remained pressed to the ground, his nose a mere inch from the mud. After what seemed like an eternity, he finally allowed himself to look up, half expecting Bathory to be waiting next to him like a cobra ready to strike. But she was nowhere to be seen.

Fighting his rising fear, Seward freed himself from the mud's grasp with a revolting slurp. Too loud. His eyes darted. He needed to move, but he had to wait for the blood to flow back into his legs. He felt like wet burlap, with his oversized clothes weighing heavily on him.

The wind whistled and he turned with a start. Still no one in sight. Setting his resolve, he took a determined step toward the stone building— and felt wet mud soaking his bare foot. Seward looked back to see one of his shoes stuck in the mud. He cursed under his breath and nearly toppled over while balancing to replace it. He continued, stumbling, across the marshy laneway and tripped into a palm tree. Seward was certain he was making a terrible amount of noise but hoped the rain would drown it out. At last he reached the tree adjacent to the villa. He had been good at climbing trees when he was a schoolboy, but five decades later, that was hardly likely to be the case. But there was nothing for it. He took a deep breath and hauled himself up onto the lowest branch.

From the tree, he was able to hoist himself to the roof of the front walkway. The clay shingles were slick with rain. Seward steadied himself by gripping the decorative wrought-iron railing for support and glanced about, terrified that Countess Bathory was laughing in the shadows as he made a fool of himself. He spotted an awning over one of the second-story windows and scurried to its shadow for protection, taking a moment to catch his breath. He listened, and heard nothing except the pounding of rain beating in time with his heart.

He peered into the window and found that it overlooked what must have once been a grand ballroom. Now, devoid of life and full of shadows, it unnerved him. It was like looking into a museum at night. Or worse . . . a tomb.

His thoughts were interrupted by two glowing white figures moving across the ballroom floor. They glided effortlessly and seemed to be carrying something that resembled a crate or chest. Wary of staying in one place too long for fear of being spotted, he gripped the rails, hoisted himself from one balcony to the next, and edged his way to another window.

On this level, the only light came from a few scattered candles and the embers in the fireplace. It was enough for Seward to see that what had seemed like two spirits were in fact beautiful young women dressed in flowing, sheer white gowns. Where was Bathory? Seward still couldn't get over the creeping dread that she was standing behind him.

His heart threatened to burst from his chest at the sound of the French doors flying open. Countess Bathory swept into the ballroom. Seward, relieved, shrank back into the shadows.

Bathory untied her cloak from around her neck and tossed it carelessly over her shoulder, revealing her full statuesque form. She was dressed in an evening jacket, complete with fitted, starched white, wing-collared shirt and black tie. In its severe lines, her tailor had found a way to accentuate her voluptuous feminine figure while projecting a masculine strength.

She strode toward the other two women. "My sweets," she greeted them; and beneath the languorous tone of her voice, Seward detected something infinitely more sinister. He shivered as Bathory kissed each of these "Women in White" on the lips passionately.

"What toy have you brought me?"

The blond woman broke the heavy padlock on the captain's chest with her bare hands, a shockingly casual gesture for one so delicate in appearance. She opened the lid with a flourish, like a waiter proudly presenting the main course. Inside the trunk was a young woman, bound, gagged, and clearly terrified.

Bathory reached into her boot and unsheathed a curved metal blade. Seward immediately recognized the knife: It was a medical amputation lancet.

The young woman's eyes widened at the sight of the blade. In a movement too fast for Seward to see, Bathory sliced the lancet toward the young woman. The gag and the ropes binding her hands fell to the bottom of the chest. Bathory placed the blade's tip under the girl's chin. Seward gripped the handle of his silver throwing knife.

Instead of inflicting a bloody wound, Bathory used the blade to gently guide the girl out of the box. Seward relaxed his grip. The girl touched her face and wrists to feel whether the blade had cut her. There did not appear to be even the slightest scratch.

Seward watched the countess walk around the young woman, appraising her attire. She was dressed in a French teal wool dress, chastely covering her from her neck to her ankles. He felt enraged at the thought of what Bathory's eyes must be seeing—a beautiful package just waiting to be unwrapped.

The girl kept perfectly still. The lancet sliced. Her dress and undergarments fell away like puzzle pieces, leaving her delicate skin unscathed. Despite the young woman's frantic efforts to recover the fabric, more fell away until she was completely revealed.

Bathory's eyes did not blink once as she drank in the sight. Shivering with fear, the girl pulled herself back into the shadows, covering her body. The Women in White laughed.

Seward moved to the next window to get a better view. Once there, he noticed Bathory's eyes narrow. Flickering candlelight reflected from the small gold crucifix around the young woman's neck. Bathory's lancet flashed forward and back so quickly that Seward almost doubted it had moved at all. But there was no mistaking the ting of the cross hitting the marble floor, the broken chain gathering around it in a smooth pile. The young woman gasped in surprise—a small drop of blood glittered like a gem at the base of her throat. The Women in White leapt upon her like wild dogs.

"Mary, Mother of God protect her," Seward prayed, the words coming out as a plaintive whine under his breath. He watched in horror as the Women in White hoisted the naked young woman and hung her upside down by her ankles on a pulley system, suspending her from the ceiling. The dark-haired demon handed Bathory a black leather cat-o'-nine-tails, with curved metal hooks tipping each lash. The countess's red lips curved into a humorless smile, her otherworldly eyes remaining focused on the single drop of blood now sliding down her victim's chest. With a quick flick of her wrist, Bathory stung her flesh with the whip, watching eagerly as the blood began to flow more freely.

Seward turned away from the sight, but he could not shut out the screams. He clutched the cross around his neck; but it gave him no comfort. His instinct was to rush in to save this poor girl—but that would surely be a foolhardy decision. One old man was no match against these three. They would tear him apart.

No matter what you see or feel, nothing must distract you from your duty.

That had been the last message from the Benefactor. Seward finally gathered the nerve to look again though the windowpane into the depraved insanity of the villa.

Bathory was maintaining a steady momentum now as the metal lashes whined through the air. The force of each blow caused her young victim to sway like a pendulum. The blood dripping from the young woman had turned into streams. The Women in White, meanwhile, lay upon the floor beneath her, their mouths open to catch the precious crimson drops that fell like some hellish form of rain.

Seward knew that he was witnessing true madness. When the sun rose, these three creatures would be lying in their coffins, asleep and vulnerable, and it would be his only opportunity to rid the world of their evil. He would drive the silver-plated blade into their hearts, sever their heads, stuff the mouths with garlic, and burn the remains.

Yet he felt tormented by the guilt of standing idle while this innocent girl was tortured. He curled a hand around his blade, squeezing until drops of blood seeped from between his own fingers. If he could not spare this young woman her pain, the least he could do was share it. The girl's screams had finally quieted—but they continued to echo eerily in his head, evoking painful memories of Lucy's second death. A death that Seward himself had helped bring about. Again, the memories came rushing back to him: the anger he had felt at the desecration of his beloved's tomb; the shock of discovering her body still warm and rosy, apparently full of life; the sight of Arthur driving the stake into her heart, as the creature that looked like Lucy cried out in bloodcurdling screams; and the tears he had quietly shed as he stuffed the monster's mouth with garlic and soldered her tomb closed for good. Yet none of these emotions were as shameful as the one he had hidden all these years, even from himself—the secret satisfaction of watching Arthur lose Lucy. If Seward could not have her, at least no one else would. It was a horrible emotion, and every bit of the darkness that had fallen upon his life after this was well deserved. Accepting this final mission was his act of contrition.

He was drawn swiftly back into the present by the sudden silence. In the ballroom below, the young woman had passed out from the pain. He could see her chest still heaving, so she was not yet dead. Bathory threw down her whip, as irritated as a cat when the mouse will not play after its neck is broken. Seward felt hot wetness on his face, and touched his cheek only to realize that he was crying.

"Prepare my bath!" Bathory ordered.

The Women in White propelled the young woman across the pulley system's metal track and thus transported her into another room. Bathory turned to follow, purposefully stepping on the gold cross as she did so, twisting her foot and crushing it beneath her heel. Satisfied, she continued into the adjacent room, stripping off her clothes one by one as she went.

Seward leaned out over the balcony to see if there was another window looking into the adjacent room. The rain pattered to a stop. Its din would no longer hide his footfalls on the clay shingles. Slowly and cautiously, he made his way over to the next window and peered through. The pulley system ended directly above a Roman-style bath. Dozens of candles now illuminated the sight of Bathory slipping delicately out of her trousers. For the first time, Seward had a clear view of her—without a stitch of clothing. She looked nothing like the prostitutes he had encountered in the back rooms of Camden district brothels. The wanton curves of her body, white and smooth as porcelain, would have distracted most observers from ever noticing the calculating cruelty of her eyes—but not Seward. He had seen a gaze like that before.

Yet nothing in the doctor's bleak past could have prepared him for the macabre scene he witnessed next. The young woman, pathetic gurgles issuing from her throat, was suspended above the edge of the empty mosaic bath. Bathory stood at the bottom; arms outstretched, neck arched back, magnificently naked. She turned her palms upward. It was a signal. In that instant, the dark-haired Woman in White used her fingernail to slit the young lady's throat and pushed her to the end of the track just above where Bathory waited. Seward saw Bathory's fanged mouth open wide as she orgasmically bathed in a shower of blood.

Damn them all to hell! His thoughts were inflamed as he reached into the false bottom of his medical bag for a small crossbow, loading it with a silver-tipped arrow. If this rash decision should be his death, so be it. Better to be dead than to allow this perverse evil to continue a second longer.

Seward aimed the crossbow between the wrought-iron bars and prepared to fire on Bathory. That was when he spotted something. His eyes widened in shock. There was a large advertisement poster lying on the desk by the window. The poster seemed to glow eerily as if it were painted by moonlight. The oversized embossed letters stood out:

William Shakespeare's
"The Life and Death of King Richard III"

7 mars, 1912
Théâtre de l'Odéon
rue de Vaugirard 18
Téléf. 811.42
8 heures
Paris

Avec l'acteur roumain
BASARAB
dans le premier rôle

He took an involuntary step back, forgetting the incline of the roof. The tile under his foot cracked and slid down to shatter on the cobblestoned walkway below. He froze.

In the grand ballroom, the blond Woman in White spun at the sound outside. She flew to the door, her soulless eyes scanning the horizon for any sign of life. She saw no one. Remaining in the shadows, she moved around to the side of the house from where she had heard the noise. Again, she saw nothing and was about to return inside the villa when she spotted a broken clay tile on the ground—stained with a drop of fresh blood. Human blood. Its pungent aroma was unmistakable. She tasted it eagerly and immediately spat it out. The blood was polluted with chemicals.

With reptilian agility, she scaled the wall to inspect the villa further. On the rooftop, she spotted a bloodstained silver knife beneath one of the windows. Only an inexperienced vampire hunter would be naïve enough to carry a silver blade.

But the Woman in White knew that her mistress was no longer safe. They had to flee Marseilles tonight. She quickly scurried back into the house.

Seward knew that Bathory and her banshees would not stay in Marseilles this evening. They would assuredly flee to Paris and, once airborne, the dead travel fast. But thanks to the advertisement he had seen, Seward realized he once again had the advantage. He knew their plans. Countess Bathory and her companions would be at the theatre tomorrow night.

He allowed himself a grim smile. *That is where the battle will take place.*